INTERNATIONAL CHEMICAL SERIES

LOUIS P. HAMMETT, PH.D., *Consulting Editor*

CALCULATIONS OF
ANALYTICAL CHEMISTRY

CALCULATIONS OF
ANALYTICAL CHEMISTRY

LEICESTER F. HAMILTON, S. B.

Professor of Analytical Chemistry
Massachusetts Institute of Technology

STEPHEN G. SIMPSON, Ph.D.

Associate Professor of Analytical Chemistry
Massachusetts Institute of Technology

FIFTH EDITION

NEW YORK   TORONTO   LONDON
McGRAW-HILL BOOK COMPANY, INC.
1954

CALCULATIONS OF ANALYTICAL CHEMISTRY

IV

THE MAPLE PRESS COMPANY, YORK, PA.

PREFACE

In this edition, several sections have been expanded and several rewritten. These include topics pertaining to errors, precision measures, titration curves, electrolytic methods, and potentiometric, conducto-metric, and amperometric titrations. In addition, several new topics have been introduced. These include the iodate and bromate processes, colorimetric methods, and illustration of the use of a nomograph.

Altogether, material covering about 25 pages has been added, but since it has seemed desirable not to increase the size of the book mate-rially, problems of a repetitious nature and some of the more lengthy problems without answers have been deleted.

In the sections devoted to redox potentials, signs have been changed to conform to the Lewis convention. This seems to be the convention favored by physical chemists in this country, and, although the opposite convention has some advantages in analytical work, it is felt that the change makes for less confusion with students who continue with chemistry.

As in previous editions, the discussions involving physicochemical principles are kept on as elementary a level as is consistent with an adequate understanding of the related analytical principles, and, as stated in the Preface to the previous edition, the authors feel that the mathematical aspects of general analytical chemistry are adequately covered in the discussions and problems, and that most of the problems are not solved by simple substitution in a formula but require reasoning on the part of the student.

Leicester F. Hamilton
Stephen G. Simpson

CONTENTS

vii

PART II. GRAVIMETRIC ANALYSIS

PART IV. SPECIAL METHODS

PART V. COMMON ANALYTICAL DETERMINATIONS

PART VI. PROBLEMS ON SPECIFIC GROUPS AND DETERMINATIONS

Part I

GENERAL ANALYSIS

CHAPTER 1

MATHEMATICAL OPERATIONS

1. Divisions of Analytical Chemistry. Analytical chemistry is ordinarily divided into qualitative analysis and quantitative analysis. A compound or mixture is analyzed by the methods of qualitative analysis to determine what constituents or components are present; a compound or mixture is analyzed by the methods of quantitative analysis to determine the proportions in which the constituents or components are present.

Calculations in qualitative analysis are limited mostly to those pertaining to equilibrium constants and simple weight and volume relationships. Calculations in quantitative analysis are more extensive and are based on numerical data obtained from careful measurements of masses and volumes of chemical substances.

2. Errors in Quantitative Measurements. In quantitative analysis, as in other fields of science, numerical data and numerical results obtained from them are subject to errors, and independent measurements of the same quantity, even when made under apparently identical conditions, often differ considerably.

Errors can be classed as *determinate errors* and *indeterminate errors.*

Determinate errors are errors that persist in a definite way and to a fixed degree from one determination to another and are of such nature that their magnitudes can be determined and their effects eliminated, or at least largely reduced. They include (1) *instrumental errors*, an example of which is the error caused by the use of a balance with arms of unequal lengths; (2) *personal errors*, an example of which is the error caused by consistently establishing a color change too late; (3) *methodic errors*, an example of which is the error caused by the presence of a foreign substance in a weighed precipitate. Determinate errors can usually be corrected for by proper calibration or by other experimental means.

Indeterminate errors are errors that are more or less beyond the control of the observer and that have signs and magnitudes determined solely by

1

chance.   They may be caused by such factors as fluctuations in temperature and pressure, inability of the observer to estimate correctly fractional parts of marked divisions, and general fatigue of the eye. They are characterized by the fact that positive and negative errors are equally likely to occur.   For this reason, the arithmetical mean of the numerical results of a series of similar observations can usually be taken as the most probable value.

3. Precision and Accuracy.   The *precision* of a numerical value is the degree of agreement between it and other values obtained under substantially the same conditions.   The *accuracy* of a numerical value is the degree of agreement between it and the true value.   Since the true value is never known except within certain limits, the accuracy of a value is never known except within those limits.   A numerical result may have a high degree of precision and yet have a low degree of accuracy, because of the effect of one or more determinate errors that have not been established and corrected for.

The difference between two numerical values can be expressed as the *absolute difference* or as the *relative difference* (the latter usually in parts per thousand).   The absolute difference between the values 2.431 and 2.410 is 0.021; the relative difference is $\dfrac{0.021}{2.4\cdots} \times 1,000 = 8.7$ parts per thousand ($= 8.7$ p.p.t.).

The absolute difference between a numerical result and the true value is the *absolute error* of the result; the relative difference between a numerical result and the true value is the *relative error* of the result.   Thus, in the case just cited, if 2.431 is the true value, the absolute error of the value 2.410 is 0.021 and its relative error is 8.7 parts per thousand.

4. Precision Measures.   In a series of independent determinations of a given quantity, if determinate errors have been effectively eliminated or corrected for, the average, or *mean*, of the numerical values obtained can be taken as the most probable value of the series, and a measure of the degree of precision of this mean value can be considered as a measure of the limiting degree to which the result is likely to differ from the unknown true value.   It is, therefore, a measure of the *reliability* of the result.

Suppose a series of independent measurements or determinations of a given quantity gave the following nine values:

(a)	31.62	(f)	31.53
(b)	31.47	(g)	31.60
(c)	31.64	(h)	31.60
(d)	31.76	(i)	31.71
(e)	31.71		

The mean value (m) is obtained by dividing the sum of the values by the number of determinations (n) made. In the case of a large number of values, it is permissible to express the mean to one more significant figure than is given in the individual values. In the above case the mean is 31.627. The difference between any one of the values and this mean is the deviation (d) of that value from the mean. In the above case, the deviations (regardless of sign) are as follows:

(a)	0.007	(f)	0.097
(b)	0.157	(g)	0.027
(c)	0.013	(h)	0.027
(d)	0.133	(i)	0.083
(e)	0.083		

The *average deviation (a.d.) of a single measurement* is the mean of the deviations of all the individual measurements:

$$a.d. = \frac{d_1 + d_2 + \cdots d_n}{n}$$

In this case it is 0.070 and represents the amount by which an average independent determination of the series is likely to differ from the most probable value.

It is more important, however, to know the precision or reliability of the mean than that of the component determinations. It can be shown that the *average deviation of the mean (A.D.)* is numerically equal to the average deviation of a single determination divided by the square root of the number of determinations made:

$$A.D. = \frac{a.d.}{\sqrt{n}}$$

In the above case, the average deviation of the mean is $0.070/\sqrt{9} = 0.023$.

The *standard deviation* is often used as a precision measure and is considered to be a more reliable measure than the average deviation. The *standard deviation (s.d.) of an average single determination* is found by extracting the square root of the quotient obtained by dividing the sum of the squares of the individual deviations from the mean by one less than the number of determinations made:

$$s.d. = \sqrt{\frac{d_1{}^2 + d_2{}^2 + \cdots d_n{}^2}{n-1}}$$

In the case cited, the standard deviation of an average single determination is $\sqrt{\frac{(0.007)^2 + (0.157)^2 + \cdots}{8}} = 0.091$, and the *standard deviation of the mean (S.D.)* is $0.91/\sqrt{9} = 0.030$. This number serves to give an indication of the reliability of the mean and does not imply that the true value must necessarily fall within the limits of $31.627 - 0.030$ and $31.627 + 0.030$.   Many writers in this field take twice the value of the standard deviation of the mean as an indication of the "reasonable" limits within which the true value is likely to be.   According to this convention, in the case cited (and in the absence of determinate errors) the true value can be expected to fall within the limits of $31.627 - 0.060$ ($= 31.567$) and $31.627 + 0.060$ ($= 31.687$).

In a series of measurements of the same quantity, the *median value* is sometimes taken instead of the mean value to represent the most probable value.   The median or median value of a series of readings is the reading of such magnitude that the number of readings having a greater numerical value is equal to the number having a lesser value.   It is the value half-way in a series arranged in ascending or descending order.   In the series of nine values given in the first part of this section, 31.62 is the median since there are four values greater than 31.62 and four values less than 31.62.   In a series containing an even number of values, the mean of the two "middle values" is taken as the median.

5. Rejection of Measurements.   In a series of similar measurements it sometimes happens that one (or more) of the numerical values stands out as being considerably different from the others, and the temptation is to reject it in establishing the mean value.   Several rules have been proposed for determining whether or not such a rejection is justified from the point of view of mathematical probability.

One rule is as follows: Omit the doubtful value and determine in the usual way the mean and the average deviation (*a.d.*) of the retained values.   The rejection can be considered as mathematically justified if the deviation (*d*) of the suspected value from the mean is at least four times the average deviation of the retained values—that is, if

$$d \geqq 4 \ a.d.$$

Many writers advocate the more rigid requirement of $d \geqq 2\frac{1}{2} \ a.d.$, but this rule will not be used in this book.   In either case, the error of the rejected value is called a *huge error*.

As an example, suppose a tenth value in the series given in the preceding section were 31.34.   The deviation of this suspected low value from the mean is $31.627 - 31.34 = 0.287$.   This is more than four times 0.070, and the rejection is justified.

6. Proper Retention of Significant Figures.   In most chemical analyses relatively few independent readings or determinations are made, so that numerical precision measures are not often used.   In such cases the precision of a numerical value is best indicated by the number of significant figures used in expressing that value.   It is true that this method of expression gives only an approximate idea of the precision of a result, but the importance of the retention of the proper number of significant figures in analytical data cannot be overemphasized. A numerical result expressed by fewer or more significant figures than are warranted by the various factors involved may give to an observer an impression nearly as erroneous as would be given by a result that is inaccurate.

7. Rules Governing the Use of Significant Figures in Chemical Computations. The following definitions and rules are suggested by those given in Goodwin's *Precision of Measurements:*

A *number* is an expression of quantity.

A *figure,* or *digit,* is any one of the characters 0, 1, 2, 3, 4, 5, 6, 7, 8, 9, which, alone or in combination, serve to express numbers.

A *significant figure* is a digit that denotes the amount of the quantity in the place in which it stands. In the case of the number 243, the figures signify that there are two hundreds, four tens, and three units and are therefore all significant. The character 0 is used in two ways. It may be used as a significant figure, or it may be used merely to locate the decimal point. It is a significant figure when it indicates that the quantity in the place in which it stands is known to be nearer zero than to any other value. Thus, the weight of a crucible may be found to be 10.603 grams, in which case all five figures, including the zeros, are significant. If the weight in grams of the crucible were found to be 10.610, meaning that the weight as measured was nearer to 10.610 than to 10.609 or 10.611, both zeros would be significant.

By analysis, the weight of the ash of a quantitative filter paper is found to be 0.00003 gram. Here the zeros are not significant but merely serve to show that the figure 3 belongs in the fifth place to the right of the decimal point. Any other characters except digits would serve the purpose as well. The same is true of the value 356,000 inches, when signifying the distance between two given points as measured by instruments that are accurate to three figures only. The zeros are not significant. In order to avoid confusion, this value should be written 3.56×10^5 inches. If the distance has been measured to the nearest 100 inches, it should be written 3.560×10^5 inches.

Rule I. Retain as many significant figures in a result and in data in general as will give only one uncertain figure. (For very accurate work involving lengthy computations, two uncertain figures may sometimes be retained.) Thus, the value 25.34, representing the reading of an ordinary buret, contains the proper number of significant figures, for the digit 4 is obtained by estimating an ungraduated scale division and is doubtless uncertain. Another observer would perhaps give a slightly different value for the buret reading—*e.g.,* 25.33 or 25.35. All four figures should be retained.

Rule II. In rejecting superfluous and inaccurate figures, increase by 1 the last figure retained if the following rejected figure is 5 or over. Thus, in rejecting the last figure of the number 16.279, the new value becomes 16.28.

Rule III. In adding or subtracting a number of quantities, extend the significant figures in each term and in the sum or difference only to the point corresponding to that uncertain figure occurring farthest to the left relative to the decimal point.

For example, the sum of the three terms 0.0121, 25.64, and 1.05782, on the assumption that the last figure in each is uncertain, is

$$
\begin{array}{r}
0.01 \\
25.64 \\
\underline{1.06} \\
26.71
\end{array}
$$

Rule IV. In multiplication or division, the percentage precision of the product or quotient cannot be greater than the percentage precision of the least precise factor entering into the computation. Hence, in computations involving multiplication or division, or both, retain as many significant figures in each factor and in the numerical result as are contained in the factor having the largest percentage deviation. In most cases, as many significant figures may be retained in each factor and in the result as are contained in the factor having the least number of significant figures.

For example, the product of the three terms 0.0121, 25.64, and 1.05782, on the assumption that the last figure in each is uncertain, is

$$0.0121 \times 25.6 \times 1.06 = 0.328$$

for, if the first term is assumed to have a possible variation of 1 in the last place, it has an actual deviation of 1 unit in every 121 units, and its percentage deviation would be $\frac{1}{121} \times 100 = 0.8$. Similarly, the possible percentage deviation of the second term would be

$$\frac{1}{2,564} \times 100 = 0.04$$

and that of the third term would be $\frac{1}{105,782} \times 100 = 0.0009$. The first term, having the largest percentage deviation, therefore governs the number of significant figures that may be properly retained in the product, for the product cannot have a precision greater than 0.8 per cent. That is, the product may vary by 0.8 part in every hundred or by nearly 3 parts in every 328. The last figure in the product as expressed with three significant figures above is therefore doubtful, and the proper number of significant figures has been retained.

Rule V. Computations involving a precision not greater than one-fourth of 1 per cent should be made with a 10-inch slide rule. For greater precision, logarithm tables should be used. If the old-style method of multiplication or division must be resorted to, reject all superfluous figures at each stage of the operation.

Rule VI. In carrying out the operations of multiplication or division by the use of logarithms, retain as many figures in the mantissa of the logarithm of each factor as are properly contained in the factors themselves under Rule IV. Thus, in the solution of the example given under Rule IV, the logarithms of the factors are expressed as follows:

$$\begin{aligned}
\log 0.0121 &= 8.083 - 10 \\
\log 25.64 &= 1.409 \\
\log 1.05782 &= \underline{0.024} \\
& 9.516 - 10 = \log 0.328
\end{aligned}$$

8. Conventions Regarding the Solution of Numerical Problems. In the calculation of numerical results from chemical data that have been obtained under known conditions and by known methods, little difficulty should be experienced in forming an approximate estimate of the precision of the various factors and of the results obtained. In the case of numerical problems that are unaccompanied by any data to show the conditions under which the various measurements were made or the precision of the values given, the retention of the proper number of significant figures in the final computed results may be a matter of considerable judgment. In such cases the rules listed above are subject to modification, but in any case the need for a certain amount of common sense and judgment in using them in no way detracts from their value.

In the solution of problems in this book, it may be assumed that the given data conform to Rule I, above. In problems containing such expressions as "a two-gram sample," "a 25-ml. pipetful," or "a tenth-normal solution," it may be assumed that the weight of the sample, the volume of the pipet, and the normality of the solution are known to a precision at least as great as that of the other factors involved in the problem.

It should also be remembered that the atomic weights of the elements are known only to a limited number of significant figures and, in the absence of further data, it may be assumed that the values ordinarily given in atomic-weight tables conform to Rule I above, in that the last figure in each is doubtful. It follows, therefore, that the same attention should be paid to the precision of the atomic and molecular weights involved in computations as to that of any other data.

It often happens that independent calculations from given data give results which disagree by only one or two units in the last significant figure retained. This is usually due to the fact that figures have been rejected at different stages of the operations involved; but this is usually of no importance, since, when properly expressed, the last significant figure in the result is doubtful anyway.

Analytical determinations are usually done in duplicate. In most of the problems in this book, however, data apparently covering only one determination are given. It may be assumed that such values represent mean values obtained from duplicate determinations.

Problems

1.1. How many significant figures are implied in the value 2.20×10^{-9}? In the value 5,000,002? In the value 2.010×10^5?

Ans. Three. Seven. Four.

1.2. Calculate the molecular weight of $OsCl_4$ to as high a degree of precision as is warranted by the atomic weights involved.

Ans. 332.0.

1.3. Express the velocity of light, 186,000 miles per second, in such a way as to indicate that it has been measured to the nearest 100 miles per second.

Ans. 1.860×10^5 miles per second.

1.4. Samples were sent to seven different chemists to be analyzed for percentage of protein. The values reported were 43.18, 42.96, 42.88, 43.21, 43.01, 43.10, 43.08. What is the mean value, the average deviation of a single value from the mean, and the deviation of the mean? If the correct percentage is 43.15, what is the relative error of the mean in parts per thousand?

Ans. 43.060, 0.094, 0.036. 2.1.

1.5. An ore actually contains 33.79 per cent Fe_2O_3. Duplicate determinations give 33.80 and 34.02 per cent, and the mean of these is reported. By how many parts per thousand do the duplicate results differ from each other? What is the mean value? What is the absolute error? What is the relative error in parts per thousand?

Ans. 6.5. 33.91 per cent. 0.12 per cent. 3.5.

1.6. Two analysts, working independently, analyze a sample of steel and report the following results:

ANALYST A:	ANALYST B:
Sulfur = 0.042 per cent	Sulfur = 0.04199 per cent
0.041 per cent	0.04101 per cent

By how many parts per thousand do the check values agree in each case? Each man uses a 3.5-gram sample weighed to the nearest tenth of a gram. Is analyst B justified in his report? Do his figures necessarily indicate greater ability as an analyst?

Ans. 24 parts, 24 parts. No. No.

1.7. What is the lower of two values if the higher value is 168.1 and the relative difference between them is 6.5 p.p.t.?

Ans. 167.0.

1.8. The following six independent results were obtained for the normality of a solution: 0.2562, 0.2566, 0.2565, 0.2560, 0.2568, and 0.2566. A seventh value, lower than the others, was justifiably rejected according to the rule for determining a huge error. (*a*) What is the highest value that the rejected result could have? (*b*) What is the average deviation of the retained results? (*c*) What is the standard deviation of the mean of the retained results? (*d*) What is the median value?

Ans. (*a*) 0.2555. (*b*) 0.00023. (*c*) 0.00012. (*d*) 0.25655.

1.9. Eleven analysts, using the same method, reported the percentages of protein in a certain cereal product. The values reported were as follows: 22.62, 22.73, 22.75, 22.78, 22.79, 22.83, 22.84, 22.87, 22.92, 22.94, and these were examined with a view of establishing the most probable value. (*a*) According to the criterion given in the text, is the rejection of the first value (22.62) justifiable on the basis that it involves a huge error? (*b*) What are the two deviation measures that establish this decision? (*c*) What is the mean value of the 11 results? (*d*) What is the average deviation of the mean? (*e*) What is the standard deviation of the mean? (*f*) What is the median value? (*g*) What is the relative difference between the lowest and highest reported values? (*h*) Assuming the mean to be the true value, what is the relative error of the lowest reported value?

Ans. (*a*) No. (*b*) 0.212 and 0.056. (*c*) 22.813. (*d*) 0.020. (*e*) 0.028. (*f*) 22.83. (*g*) 14 p.p.t. (*h*) 8.5 p.p.t.

1.10. It is necessary to solve the following:

$$(1.276 \times 0.00047) + (1.7 \times 10^{-4}) - (0.0021764 \times 0.0121)$$

each term being uncertain in the last significant figure. Should you use arithmetic, logarithms, or a slide rule in the multiplications? What is the final answer?

Ans. Slide rule. 7.5×10^{-4}.

1.11. A value which has been found by duplicate analyses to be 0.1129 and 0.1133, respectively, is to be multiplied by 1.36 ml. as measured by an ordinary buret, and the product is to be subtracted from the value 0.93742 which has been very accurately measured. Express the result by the proper number of significant figures.

Ans. 0.784.

1.12. If in the analysis of a given substance a variation of 0.30 per cent is allowable, to how many milligrams should a 10-gram sample be weighed?

1.13. How many significant figures are implied in the value 16×10^3? In the value 16.00×10^3? In the value 1.60×10^{-2}?

1.14. In the following multiplication the last figure in each of the three factors is uncertain. How many figures in the product as given should be rejected as superfluous? Express the product in such a way as to indicate the correct number of significant figures.

$$2.0000 \times 0.30 \times 500 = 300.00$$

1.15. Calculate the molecular weight of $Hf(NO_3)_4$ to as high a degree of precision as is warranted by the atomic weights involved.

1.16. A book on astronomy gives the polar diameter of the earth as 7,900.0 miles. To what precision of measurement does this number imply? If the measurement had been made only to the nearest 10 miles, how should the value be expressed to indicate this fact?

1.17. Assuming each term to be uncertain in the last figure given, solve the following and express the answer to the correct number of significant figures:

$$(1.586 \div 29.10) + [162.22(3.221 \times 10^{-4})] - 0.00018$$

1.18. A sample of pure anhydrous $BaCl_2$ containing 65.97 per cent Ba is given for analysis. One analyst obtains 65.68, 65.79, and 65.99 for triplicate determinations and reports the mean value. By how many parts per thousand does each result differ from the mean? What is the absolute error of the mean, and what is the relative error (parts per thousand) of the mean?

1.19. The percentage of carbon in a sample of steel is found to be 0.42 per cent. The calculations involve only multiplication and division. To how many decimal places would you weigh out a 1-gram sample in order to duplicate the result?

1.20. A sample of limonite was analyzed by 12 students at different times during the college year. The values obtained for the percentage of iron were: 34.62, 34.42, 34.60, 34.48, 33.71, 34.50, 34.50, 34.22, 34.41, 35.00, 34.65, 34.44. What is the mean value, the mean deviation of a single result, and the deviation of the mean? If the correct percentage is 34.75 what is the absolute error of the mean and what is its relative error in parts per thousand? What is the median value?

1.21. A sample of material was sent to two chemists. Each used the same method and reported the results of four analyses, as follows:

CHEMIST A	CHEMIST B
30.15	30.251
30.15	30.007
30.14	30.101
30.16	30.241

Calculate in each case the mean value and its deviation measure. Other conditions being equal, which mean value is the more reliable?

1.22. The relative difference between two values is 12 p.p.t. What is the absolute difference, and what is the higher value if the lower one is 233.6?

1.23. The following four independent results were obtained for a certain instrumental reading: 3.685, 3.689, 3.681, and 3.692. A fifth reading, higher than the others, was justifiably rejected according to the rule for determining a huge error. (*a*) What is the lowest value that the rejected reading could have? (*b*) What is the average deviation of the mean of the retained results? (*c*) What is the standard deviation of the mean of the retained results? (*d*) What is the median value?

1.24. A student obtained the following values for the normality of a solution: 0.6143, 0.6153, 0.6148, 0.6142, 0.6146, 0.6154. (*a*) What is the mean value? (*b*) What is the average deviation of a single determination? (*c*) What is the average deviation of the mean? (*d*) What is the standard deviation of the mean? (*e*) What is the median value? (*f*) Another value obtained for the normality was 0.6164, but this was rejected on the basis that it involved a huge error. Was this rejection justified? (*g*) If the true value for the normality is 0.6145, what is the relative error of the rejected value?

9. Rules Governing the Use of Logarithms.
In calculations of quantitative analysis involving multiplication and division where four-significant-figure accuracy is required, four-place logarithms should be used; in calculations where two- or three-significant-figure accuracy is sufficient,

a slide rule should be used. Grammar-school methods of multiplication and long division should not be employed.

Although the theory and use of logarithms are ordinarily covered in preparatory and high schools, the following outline is given as a review of the essential points in this phase of mathematics.

1. The logarithm of a number is the exponent of the power to which some fixed number, called the *base*, must be raised to equal the given number. Thus, suppose

$$a^x = n$$

then x is the logarithm of n to the base a and may be written

$$x = \log_a n$$

2. The base in the common system of logarithms is 10, and the term *log*, without subscript, is commonly used to denote a logarithm in this system. Hence,

10^0	$= 1,$	$\log 1$	$= 0$
10^1	$= 10,$	$\log 10$	$= 1$
10^2	$= 100,$	$\log 100$	$= 2$
10^3	$= 1000,$	$\log 1000$	$= 3$
10^{-1}	$= 0.1,$	$\log 0.1$	$= -1$
10^{-2}	$= 0.01,$	$\log 0.01$	$= -2$
10^{-3}	$= 0.001,$	$\log 0.001$	$= -3$

etc.

It is evident that the logarithms of all numbers between

1 and 10	will be	0 plus a fraction
10 and 100	will be	1 plus a fraction
100 and 1000	will be	2 plus a fraction
1 and 0.1	will be	-1 plus a fraction
0.1 and 0.01	will be	-2 plus a fraction

etc.

3. If a number is not an exact power of 10, its common logarithm can be expressed only approximately as a number with a continuing decimal fraction. Thus,

$$36 = 10^{1.5563\cdots}$$

or

$$\log 36 = 1.5563 \cdot \cdot \cdot$$

The integral part of the logarithm is called the *characteristic;* the decimal part is called the *mantissa*. In the case just cited, the characteristic is 1; the mantissa is .5563. Only the mantissa of a logarithm is given in a table of logarithms (see next section); the characteristic is found by means of the next two rules.

4. The characteristic of the logarithm of a number greater than 1 is 1 less than the number of digits to the left of the decimal point. For example, the characteristic of log 786.5 is 2; the characteristic of log 7.865 is 0.

5. The characteristic of the logarithm of a decimal number between 0 and 1 is negative and is equal in numerical value to the number of the place occupied by the first significant figure of the decimal. For example, the characteristic of log 0.007865 is -3.

6. The mantissa of a logarithm is always positive; the characteristic may be either positive or negative. For example,

$$\log 36.55 = +1 + .5629 = 1.5629$$
$$\log 0.08431 = -2 + .9259$$

This last logarithm is more conventionally written as $\bar{2}.9259$ with the understanding that only the 2 is negative. Another common method of expressing this logarithm is $8.9259 - 10$.

7. The mantissas of the common logarithms of numbers having the same sequence of figures are equal. For example,

$$\log 2.383 = 0.3772$$
$$\log 23.83 = 1.3772$$
$$\log 0.002383 = \bar{3}.3772 \text{ (or } 7.3772 - 10)$$

8. The *cologarithm* of a number is the logarithm of the reciprocal of that number. It is found by subtracting the logarithm of the number from zero. For example,

$$\log 7.130 = 0.8531$$
$$\text{colog } 7.130 = 0.0000 - 0.8531$$
$$= \bar{1}.1469$$

or

$$\begin{array}{r} 10.0000 - 10 \\ 0.8531 \\ \hline \end{array}$$
$$\text{colog } 7.130 = \overline{9.1469} - 10$$

9. The *antilogarithm* of A is the number that has A for a logarithm. For example,

$$\log 7.130 = 0.8531$$
$$\text{antilog } 0.8531 = 7.130$$

10. The logarithm of a product is equal to the sum of the logarithms of its factors. For example,

$$\log (7.180 \times 586.3) = \log 7.180 + \log 586.3$$
$$= 0.8531 + 2.7681$$
$$= 3.6212$$

11. The logarithm of a fraction is equal to the logarithm of the numerator minus the logarithm of the denominator; it is also equal to the logarithm of the numerator plus the cologarithm of the denominator. For example,

$$\log \frac{7.180}{586.3} = \log 7.180 - \log 586.3$$
$$= 0.8531 - 2.7681$$
$$= \bar{2}.0850 \text{ (or } 8.0850 - 10)$$

or

$$\log \frac{7.180}{586.3} = \log 7.180 + \text{colog } 586.3$$
$$= 0.8531 + \bar{3}.2319 \text{ (or } 7.2319 - 10)$$
$$= \bar{2}.0850 \text{ (or } 8.0850 - 10)$$

The use of cologarithms is particularly advantageous when the multiplication and division of several factors are involved in the same mathematical process. This is shown in the example at the end of Sec. 10.

12. The logarithm of any power of a quantity is equal to the logarithm of the quantity multiplied by the exponent of the power. For example,

$$\log 71.80^3 = 3 \times \log 71.80$$
$$= 3 \times 1.8531$$
$$= 5.5593$$

13. The logarithm of any root of a quantity is equal to the logarithm of the quantity divided by the index of the root. For example,

$$\log \sqrt[2]{5.002} = \tfrac{1}{2} \times \log 5.002$$
$$= \tfrac{1}{2} \times 0.6992$$
$$= 0.3496$$

10. Method of Using Logarithm Tables. The precision of ordinary chemical analytical work is seldom great enough to permit the retention of more than four significant figures in the numerical data obtained and in the calculations made from such data. Hence a four-place logarithm table such as is given in the back of this book is entirely adequate.

To use the logarithm table in finding a mantissa proceed as follows: First find the first two digits of the number in the column headed "natural numbers," then go to the right until the column is reached which has the third digit of the number as a heading. To the number thus found add the number which is in the same horizontal line at the right-hand side of the table and in the column of proportional parts headed by the fourth significant figure of the number. Thus the number representing the mantissa of log 236.8 is 3729 + 15 = 3744, and the logarithm is 2.3744.

Antilogarithms may be looked up in the antilogarithm table in the same way.   Only the mantissa is used in looking up the number; the characteristic is used merely to locate the decimal point.   Thus the sequence of digits in the number having a logarithm of 1.8815 is

$$7603 + 9 = 7612$$

and the actual number is 76.12 as determined by the given characteristic of the logarithm.

In actual calculations from analytical data the essential purpose of the characteristic in a logarithm is to locate the position of the decimal point in the final numerical value obtained.   Since in most cases a very rough mental calculation is all that is needed to establish the position of the decimal point, the use of characteristics can be dispensed with.   The retention of characteristics is, however, helpful in serving as a check on the other method.

Calculations of quantitative chemical analysis in which logarithms are of value seldom involve operations other than those of multiplication and division.

EXAMPLE.   Calculate by logarithms: $\dfrac{9.827 \times 50.62}{0.005164 \times 136.59}$.

SOLUTION:

Method A (without using cologarithms)

$$\log 9.827 = 0.9924$$
$$\log 50.62 = 1.7044$$
$$\text{Sum} = \overline{2.6968}$$

$$
\begin{array}{rcll}
\log 0.005164 &=& \overline{3}.7129 & \text{or} \quad 7.7129 - 10 \\
\log 136.59 &=& 2.1354 & \phantom{\text{or} \quad} 2.1354 \\ \hline
\text{Sum} &=& \overline{1}.8483 & \phantom{\text{or} \quad} 9.8483 - 10
\end{array}
$$

$$
\begin{array}{rcll}
\log \text{numerator} &=& 2.6968 & \text{or} \quad 12.6968 - 10 \\
\log \text{denominator} &=& \overline{1}.8483 & \phantom{\text{or} \quad} \ 9.8483 - 10 \\ \hline
\text{Difference} &=& 2.8485 & \phantom{\text{or} \quad} 2.8485
\end{array}
$$

$$\text{antilog} = 705.5. \quad Ans.$$

Method B (using cologarithms)

$$
\begin{array}{rcll}
\log 9.827 &=& 0.9924 & \text{or} \quad 0.9924 \\
\log 50.62 &=& 1.7044 & \phantom{\text{or} \quad} 1.7044 \\
\text{colog } 0.005164 &=& 2.2871 & \phantom{\text{or} \quad} 2.2871 \\
\text{colog } 136.59 &=& \overline{3}.8646 & \phantom{\text{or} \quad} 7.8646 - 10 \\ \hline
\text{Sum} &=& 2.8485 & \phantom{\text{or} \quad} 12.8485 - 10
\end{array}
$$

$$\text{antilog} = 705.5. \quad Ans.$$

As previously mentioned, much time is saved by omitting all characteristics in the solution of the above problem and merely writing down the mantissas of each logarithm or cologarithm. The location of the decimal point is then determined by a simple mental calculation on the original expression. Thus, inspection shows that the two factors in the numerator of the above expression give a result approximating 500 and that the factors in the denominator give a result approximating 0.7. The answer must therefore be in the neighborhood of 700, which establishes the position of the decimal point.

11. Use of the Slide Rule. The slide rule is essentially a logarithm table, mechanically applied. On the scales used for multiplication and division the numbers are stamped on the rule in positions proportionate to their logarithms. Multiplication by means of the rule is merely a mechanical addition of two logarithms; division is a mechanical subtraction of two logarithms. Manuals covering the proper use of a slide rule are readily obtainable and are usually provided by the manufacturer of the rule.

The student of quantitative analysis should be proficient in the use of a slide rule, particularly in the processes of multiplication and division. The slide rule saves a great deal of time in making minor calculations and is an excellent means of checking calculations made by logarithms. Although the precision of the ordinary 10-inch slide rule is limited to three significant figures, it is suggested that slide-rule accuracy be permitted in solving quiz problems and home problems, even though the data given may thoeretically require four-significant-figure accuracy. The purpose of the problems is more to make sure that the methods of calculation are understood than to give practice in fundamental mathematical operations.

Most laboratory calculations, however, require four-significant-figure accuracy, and four-place logarithms are necessary.

12. Nomographs. A nomograph is a device by means of which the numerical result of a given calculation can be read directly from a previously drawn scale or series of scales. It is roughly comparable to a slide rule in fixed position, but has the advantage of being equally applicable to formulas and equations containing additive and subtractive terms. The scales are drawn on a plain surface and are so constructed that a straight edge, applied one or more times, connects the points corresponding to the given numerical data to the point corresponding to the desired numerical answer. Since a separate nomograph is needed for each formula to be solved, nomographs are of practical use only when the same type of calculation is made repeatedly. A typical nomograph is shown in Fig. 2, and its use is discussed in Sec. 61.

The subject of the theory and construction of nomographs constitutes a branch of mathematics known as *nomography*.[1]

Problems

1.25. Using four-place logarithms determine the following: (*a*) log 387.6, (*b*) log 0.0009289, (*c*) colog 52.61, (*d*) colog 0.06003, (*e*) antilog 2.4474, (*f*) antilog $\overline{4}.1733$, (*g*) antilog 7.2068 − 10.

Ans.   (*a*) 2.5884, (*b*) $\overline{4}.9679$ or 6.9679 − 10, (*c*) $\overline{2}.2789$ or 8.2789 − 10, (*d*) 1.2216, (*e*) 280.2, (*f*) 0.0001490, (*g*) 0.001610.

1.26. Using four-place logarithms calculate the following: (*a*) 226.3 × 0.00002591, (*b*) 0.05811 ÷ 64.53, (*c*) fourth power of 0.3382, (*d*) cube root of 0.09508.   Check these to three significant figures with a slide rule.

Ans.   (*a*) 0.005864, (*b*) 0.0009005, (*c*) 0.01308, (*d*) 0.4564.

1.27. Using four-place logarithms find the value of the following.   Locate the position of the decimal point by mental arithmetic and also by the proper use of characteristics.   Also check the answer to three significant figures with a slide rule.

$$\frac{0.0046191 \times 287.7}{51.42 \times 0.84428}$$

Ans.   0.03061.

1.28. Using four-place logarithms determine the following: (*a*) log 67.84, (*b*) log 0.005903, (*c*) colog 0.9566, (*d*) colog 718.1, (*e*) antilog 3.6482, (*f*) antilog $\overline{2}.0696$, (*g*) antilog 6.0088 − 10.

1.29. Using four-place logarithms calculate the following: (*a*) 33.81 × 0.0009915, (*b*) 0.1869 ÷ 362.4, (*c*) cube of 0.09279, (*d*) square root of 0.5546.   Check these to three significant figures with a slide rule.

1.30. Using four-place logarithms find the numerical value of the following expression.   Locate the position of the decimal point by the proper use of characteristics and check by mental arithmetic.   Also check the answer to three significant figures by means of a slide rule.

$$\frac{5987.9 \times 0.006602}{1.864 \times 0.4617 \times 1053.3}$$

---

[1] For further information the student is referred to such books as *Elements of Nomography*, by Douglass and Adams (McGraw-Hill); *Nomography*, by Levens (Wiley), *A First Course in Nomography*, by Brodetsky (Bell); and *The Nomogram*, by Allcock and Jones (Pitman).

CHAPTER 2

CHEMICAL EQUATIONS

13. Purpose of Chemical Equations. When the nature and composition of the initial and final products of a chemical reaction are known, the facts can be symbolized in the form of a chemical equation. When properly written, the equation indicates (1) the nature of the atoms and the composition of the molecules taking part in the reaction, (2) the relative number of atoms and molecules of the substances taking part in the reaction, (3) the proportions by weight of the interacting and resulting substances, and (4) the proportions by volume of all gases involved. These four principles applied to reactions which go to completion serve as the foundation of quantitative chemical analysis. Before the calculation of a chemical analysis can be made, it is important to understand the chemistry involved and to be able to express the reactions in the form of balanced equations.

14. Types of Chemical Equations. The determination of the nature of the products formed by a given reaction requires a knowledge of general chemistry which, it is assumed, has already been acquired from previous study, but the ability to write and balance equations correctly and quickly is acquired only by considerable practice. The following discussion is given to help the student attain this proficiency, especially with regard to equations involving oxidation and reduction, which usually give the most trouble to the beginner.

With equations expressing the reactions of (1) combination, (2) decomposition, and (3) metathesis, it is seldom that much difficulty is experienced in bringing about equality between the atoms and molecules of the reacting substances and those of the products, for little more is involved than purely mechanical adjustment of the terms and an elementary knowledge of valence. As examples of the above types of chemical change in the order given, the following equations may be cited:

$$(1) \ 2H_2 + O_2 \rightarrow 2H_2O$$
$$(2) \ 2HgO \rightarrow 2Hg + O_2$$
$$(3) \ FeCl_3 + 3NH_4OH \rightarrow Fe(OH)_3 + 3NH_4Cl$$

Equations expressing reactions of oxidation and reduction, although usually somewhat more complicated, offer little additional difficulty,

17

provided that the principles underlying these types of chemical change are understood.

The above equations are molecular equations. For reactions taking place in aqueous solution (such as the third case above) equations are usually better written in the ionic form. To do so correctly requires a knowledge of the relative degrees of ionization of solutes and the correct application of a few simple rules.

15. Ionization of Acids, Bases, and Salts. Although the theory of ionization should be familiar to the student from his previous study of general chemistry, the following facts should be kept in mind because they are particularly important in connection with writing equations:

"Strong" acids include such familiar acids as HCl, HBr, HI, H_2SO_4, HNO_3, $HClO_3$, $HBrO_3$, HIO_3, $HClO_4$, and $HMnO_4$. These acids in solution are completely ionized, although at ordinary concentrations nter-ionic effects may give conductivities corresponding to an apparent degree of ionization a little less than 100 per cent. In ionic equations (see below) strong acids are written in the form of ions.

"Strong" bases include $NaOH$, KOH, $Ba(OH)_2$, $Sr(OH)_2$, and $Ca(OH)_2$. These bases in solution are completely ionized and in ionic equations are written as ions.

Salts, with few exceptions, are completely dissociated in solution, and in ionic equations are written as ions. Two common exceptions are lead acetate and mercuric chloride.

Many acids and bases are ionized in solution to only a slight degree at ordinary concentrations. Table IX in the Appendix lists most of such acids and bases ordinarily encountered in analytical chemistry, and the student should familiarize himself with the names of these substances and have at least a general idea of the magnitude of the degree of ionization in the case of the more common ones.

Certain acids contain more than one hydrogen replaceable by a metal (*polybasic acids*). It will be noted that these acids ionize in steps, and the degree of ionization of the first hydrogen is invariably greater than that of the others. Phosphoric acid, for example, is about 30 per cent ionized in tenth-molar solution to give H^+ and $H_2PO_4^-$ ions, but the concentration of $HPO_4^=$ ions is much less, and that of $PO_4^{\equiv}$ ions is very small. Sulfuric acid at moderately low concentrations is completely ionized into H^+ and HSO_4^- ions, but the bisulfate ion is only moderately ionized further to give H^+ ions and $SO_4^=$ ions.

16. Ionic Equations Not Involving Oxidation. Most of the reactions of analytical chemistry are reactions between ions in solution. For this reason, although the molecular type of equation is serviceable as a basis for quantitative analytical calculations, the so-called ionic equation is usually easier to write and is generally preferable.

In writing ionic equations, the following basic rules should be observed:

1. *Include in the equation only those constituents actually taking part in the chemical reaction.*

EXAMPLE I. The addition of a solution of sodium hydroxide to a solution of ferric nitrate results in a precipitation of ferric hydroxide. The ionic equation is as follows:

$$Fe^{+++} + 3OH^- \rightarrow \underline{Fe(OH)_3}^*$$

The sodium ions from the sodium hydroxide and the nitrate ions from the ferric nitrate do not enter into the reaction and hence are not represented in the equation.

2. *In cases where a reactant or product exists in equilibrium with its constituent ions, express in the equation that form present in greatest amount.*

It follows that weak acids, weak bases, and the slightly ionized salts should be written in the molecular form. Substances of this type most often encountered in analytical chemistry are the following: H_2O, $HC_2H_3O_2$, NH_4OH, H_2S, H_2CO_3, HNO_2, HF, HCN, $Pb(C_2H_3O_2)_2$, $HgCl_2$, H_3PO_4, $H_2C_2O_4$, and H_2SO_3 (see Table IX, Appendix). The last three of these are borderline cases since at concentrations ordinarily encountered in analytical work they are ionized to a moderate degree to give hydrogen ions and $H_2PO_4^-$, $HC_2O_4^-$, and HSO_3^- ions, respectively. The salts lead acetate and mercuric chloride may be dissociated somewhat into complex ions [*e.g.*, $Pb(C_2H_3O_2)^+$ in the former case] but are relatively little ionized to give the metal ions. They are therefore usually written in the molecular form.

EXAMPLE II. The addition of an aqueous solution of ammonium hydroxide to a solution of ferric nitrate results in a precipitation of ferric hydroxide. The ionic equation is as follows:

$$Fe^{+++} + 3NH_4OH \rightarrow \underline{Fe(OH)_3} + 3NH_4^+$$

In this case, although ammonium hydroxide is ionized into ammonium ions and hydroxyl ions, the ionization is comparatively slight and only the undissociated ammonium hydroxide molecules are expressed in the equation.[1]

---

* It is desirable to underline formulas of precipitates. The use of downward-pointing arrows is equally satisfactory. If desired, formulas of gases may be overlined or denoted by upward-pointing arrows.

[1] As a matter of fact, it is not entirely certain that an appreciable concentration of NH_4OH exists at all. The equilibrium existing in an aqueous solution of ammonia can be expressed as follows:

$$NH_3 + H_2O \rightleftarrows [NH_4OH \ (?)] \rightleftarrows NH_4^+ + OH^-$$

Here again, the concentration of OH^- is relatively low, and the equation for the above reaction can therefore be written

$$Fe^{+++} + 3NH_3 + 3H_2O \rightarrow \underline{Fe(OH)_3} + 3NH_4^+$$

EXAMPLE III.   The addition of a solution of hydrogen sulfide to an acid solution of copper sulfate gives a precipitate of copper sulfide:

$$Cu^{++} + H_2S \rightarrow \underline{CuS} + 2H^+$$

The fact that the original solution is acid does not require that hydrogen ions be on the left-hand side of the equation.   The equation merely indicates that the solution becomes more acid.

EXAMPLE IV.   When a solution containing lead nitrate is treated with sulfuric acid, a white precipitate of lead sulfate is obtained.   This precipitate dissolves in a solution of ammonium acetate, and the addition of a solution of potassium chromate then causes a yellow precipitate to appear.   The ionic equations for these reactions are

$$Pb^{++} + HSO_4^- \rightarrow \underline{PbSO_4} + H^+$$
$$\underline{PbSO_4} + 2C_2H_3O_2^- \rightarrow Pb(C_2H_3O_2)_2 + SO_4^=$$
$$Pb(C_2H_3O_2)_2 + CrO_4^= \rightarrow \underline{PbCrO_4} + 2C_2H_3O_2^-$$

EXAMPLE V.   Silver chloride dissolves in an aqueous solution of ammonia.   The equation is written as follows (see Example II and footnote above):

$$\underline{AgCl} + 2NH_4OH \rightarrow Ag(NH_3)_2^+ + Cl^- + 2H_2O$$

or

$$\underline{AgCl} + 2NH_3 \rightarrow Ag(NH_3)_2^+ + Cl^-$$

The silver ammino ion, like most complex ions, is only very slightly dissociated into its constituents: $Ag(NH_3)_2^+ \rightarrow Ag^+ + 2NH_3$.

EXAMPLE VI.   A nitric acid solution of ammonium molybdate $[(NH_4)_2$-$MoO_4]$ added to a solution of phosphoric acid results in the precipitation of ammonium phosphomolybdate.

$$12MoO_4^= + H_3PO_4 + 3NH_4^+ + 21H^+ \rightarrow$$
$$\underline{(NH_4)_3PO_4.12MoO_3.H_2O} + 11H_2O$$

Note here that for every 12 molybdate ions only 3 of the corresponding 24 ammonium ions present enter into the reaction.   The nitrate ions of course take no part in the reaction.

17. Oxidation Number.   Although the term "valence" usually refers to the degree of combining power of an atom or radical, it is likely to be applied somewhat differently in the various branches of chemistry. For this reason, in inorganic chemistry the term "oxidation number" is to be preferred in expressing state of oxidation.

It is assumed that the student is already familiar with the general aspects of the periodic table and with the combining power of the elements he has thus far studied. It will be recalled that (1) the oxidation number of all free elements is zero, (2) the oxidation number of hydrogen in its compounds is $+1$ (except in the case of the relatively rare hydrides), (3) the oxidation number of sodium and potassium in their compounds is $+1$, and (4) the oxidation number of oxygen in its compounds is -2 (with few exceptions).

Since the algebraic sum of the oxidation numbers of the elements of a given compound is zero, the oxidation number of any element in a compound can usually be readily calculated from those of the other elements making up the compound. Thus, the oxidation number of Cl in $HClO_3$ is $+5$, since $+1 + 5 + [3 \times (-2)] = 0$. In this case the oxidation number of the ClO_3 *radical* is -1, since it is combined with the $+1$ hydrogen. The oxidation number of S_2 in $Na_2S_2O_7$ is $+12$ since $Na_2 = +2$ and 7 oxygen atoms $= -14$. Each sulfur atom therefore has an oxidation number of $+6$.

The oxidation number of an ion is the same as the charge it bears. Thus, the oxidation number of the nitrate ion (NO_3^-) is -1, that of the sulfate ion ($SO_4^=$) is -2, and that of the phosphate ion ($PO_4^\equiv$) is -3.

A few cases may give trouble. Thus, in the compound HCNO the sum of the oxidation numbers of the carbon and nitrogen atoms is obviously $+1$, but this would be true if $C = +4$ and $N = -3$, or $C = +3$ and $N = -2$, or $C = +2$ and $N = -1$, etc. However, since the oxidation number of carbon is so often $+4$ (*e.g.*, CO_2) and that of nitrogen is so often -3 (*e.g.*, NH_3), these would be the most likely oxidation numbers to take.

A compound like Fe_3O_4 shows an apparent fractional oxidation number for the metal constituent,—in this case $2\frac{2}{3}$. Actually two of the iron atoms have an oxidation number of $+3$, and one iron atom has an oxidation number of $+2$. This is called a *mixed oxide* ($FeO.Fe_2O_3$). A similar case is the salt $Na_2S_4O_6$; the *average* oxidation number of each sulfur atom is $2\frac{1}{2}$.

In so-called per-oxy acids and salts of these acids, one (or more) of the oxygen atoms has an oxidation number of zero. For example, in hydrogen peroxide, H_2O_2, the oxidation number of one oxygen atom is -2; that of the other is 0. Sulfur forms analogous per-sulfur acids.

18. Ionic Oxidation and Reduction Equations. In the case of equations involving oxidation and reduction the two rules given in Sec. 16 should also be observed. It will be found convenient in most cases to write equations systematically according to the following steps:

a. Write the formula of the oxidizing agent and of the reducing agent on the left-hand side of the equation. These should conform to Rules 1 and 2.

b. Write the formulas of the resulting principal products on the right-hand side of the equation. These should likewise conform to Rules 1 and 2.

c. *Under the formula of the oxidizing substance, write the number expressing the total change in oxidation number of all of its constituent elements. Under the formula of the reducing substance, write the number expressing the total change in oxidation number of its constituent elements.*

d. *Use the number under the formula of the oxidizing agent in the equation as the coefficient for the reducing substance; use the number under the formula of the reducing agent in the equation as the coefficient for the oxidizing substance.*

e. *Insert coefficients for the principal products to conform to the preceding step.*

f. *If possible, divide all the coefficients by the greatest common divisor, or, it necessary, clear of fractions by multiplying all the coefficients by the necessary factor.*

g. *If the reaction takes place in acid solution, introduce the formulas H_2O and H^+ (or H_3O^+) in amounts necessary to balance the atoms of oxygen and hydrogen on the two sides of the chemical equation. If the reaction takes place in basic solution, introduce the formulas H_2O and OH^- in amounts necessary to balance the atoms of oxygen and hydrogen.*

h. *Check the equation by determining the total net ionic charge on each of the two sides of the equation. They should be the same.*

EXAMPLE I.   When a solution of chlorine water is added to a sulfuric acid solution of ferrous sulfate, the iron is oxidized.   The step-by-step formulation of the equation for this reaction is as follows:

STEP	RESULT
a, b	$Fe^{++} + Cl_2 \rightarrow Fe^{+++} + Cl^-$
c	$Fe^{++} + Cl_2 \rightarrow Fe^{+++} + Cl^-$
	1 2
d, e	$2Fe^{++} + Cl_2 \rightarrow 2Fe^{+++} + 2Cl^-$
f	None
g	None
h	$4+ = 4+$

EXAMPLE II.   When a dilute nitric acid solution of stannous chloride is treated with a solution of potassium dichromate, tin is oxidized (from 2 to 4) and chromium is reduced (from 6 to 3).   Neglecting the partial formation of complex ions (*e.g.*, $SnCl_6^=$) the development of the equation is as follows:

STEP	RESULT
a, b	$Sn^{++} + Cr_2O_7^= \rightarrow Sn^{++++} + Cr^{+++}$
c	$Sn^{++} + Cr_2O_7^= \rightarrow Sn^{++++} + Cr^{+++}$
	2 3+3
d, e	$6Sn^{++} + 2Cr_2O_7^= \rightarrow 6Sn^{++++} + 4Cr^{+++}$
f	$3Sn^{++} + Cr_2O_7^= \rightarrow 3Sn^{++++} + 2Cr^{+++}$
g	$3Sn^{++} + Cr_2O_7^= + 14H^+ \rightarrow 3Sn^{++++} + 2Cr^{+++} + 7H_2O$
h	$18+ = 18+$

Note that in writing this equation in the molecular form one would be at a loss to express the products correctly. The question would arise whether to write stannic chloride and chromic nitrate or stannic nitrate and chromic chloride. As a matter of fact, none of these is formed since the salts are completely ionized in dilute solution.

EXAMPLE III. When hydrogen sulfide is bubbled into a dilute sulfuric acid solution of potassium permanganate, the latter is reduced (to manganous salt) and a white precipitate of free sulfur is obtained.

STEP	RESULT
a, b	$MnO_4^- + H_2S \rightarrow Mn^{++} + S$
c	$MnO_4^- + H_2S \rightarrow Mn^{++} + S$
	$\quad 5 \qquad\qquad 2$
d, e	$2MnO_4^- + 5H_2S \rightarrow 2Mn^{++} + 5\underline{S}$
f	None
g	$2MnO_4^- + 5H_2S + 6H^+ \rightarrow 2Mn^{++} + 5\underline{S} + 8H_2O$
h	$4+ = 4+$

EXAMPLE IV. In the presence of sulfuric acid an excess of potassium permanganate solution will oxidize a chromic salt to dichromate.

STEP	RESULT
a, b	$Cr^{+++} + MnO_4^- \rightarrow Cr_2O_7^= + Mn^{++}$
c	$Cr^{+++} + MnO_4^- \rightarrow Cr_2O_7^= + Mn^{++}$
	$\quad 3 \qquad\qquad 5$
d, e	$5Cr^{+++} + 3MnO_4^- \rightarrow 2\frac{1}{2}Cr_2O_7^= + 3Mn^{++}$
f	$10Cr^{+++} + 6MnO_4^- \rightarrow 5Cr_2O_7^= + 6Mn^{++}$
g	$10Cr^{+++} + 6MnO_4^- + 11H_2O \rightarrow 5Cr_2O_7^= + 6Mn^{++} + 22H^+$
h	$24+ = 24+$

EXAMPLE V. When metallic aluminum is added to a solution of a nitrate in caustic alkali, the latter is reduced and ammonia gas is evolved.

STEP	RESULT
a, b	$\underline{Al} + NO_3^- \rightarrow AlO_2^- + NH_3$
c	$\underline{Al} + NO_3^- \rightarrow AlO_2^- + NH_3$
	$\quad \underline{3} \qquad\quad 8$
d, e	$8\underline{Al} + 3NO_3^- \rightarrow 8AlO_2^- + 3NH_3$
f	None
g	$8\underline{Al} + 3NO_3^- + 5OH^- + 2H_2O \rightarrow 8AlO_2^- + 3NH_3$
h	$8- = 8-$

EXAMPLE VI. Solid cuprous sufide is oxidized by hot concentrated nitric acid forming a cupric salt, sulfate, and NO₂ gas.

STEP	RESULT
a, b	$\underline{Cu_2S} + NO_3^- \rightarrow Cu^{++} + SO_4^= + NO_2$
c	$\underline{Cu_2S} + NO_3^- \rightarrow Cu^{++} + SO_4^= + NO_2$
	$\overline{1+1+8} \qquad 1$
d, e	$\underline{Cu_2S} + 10NO_3^- \rightarrow 2Cu^{++} + SO_4^= + 10NO_2$
f	None
g	$\underline{Cu_2S} + 10NO_3^- + 12H^+ \rightarrow 2Cu^{++} + SO_4^= + 10NO_2 + 6H_2O$
h	$2+ = 2+$

Another method of writing oxidation-reduction equations is shown in Sec. 47.

Problems

2.1. What is the oxidation number of each of the elements (other than hydrogen and oxygen) in each of the following: (a) N_2O_3; (b) $SbS_3^=$; (c) $H_4P_2O_5$; (d) $K_2Pt(NO_2)_4$; (e) S_8; (f) $Co(NH_3)_6^{+++}$; (g) $Cu_3[Fe(CN)_6]_2$; (h) $NaCHO_2$?

Ans. (a) +3; (b) +3, −2; (c) +3; (d) +1, +2, +3; (e) 0; (f) +3, −3; (g) +2, +3, +2, −3; (h) +1, +2.

2.2. What is the oxidation number of each of the elements (other than hydrogen and oxygen) in each of the following: (a) MnO_2; (b) $Al_2(SO_4)_3$; (c) $NaCu(CN)_2$; (d) $(VO)_3(PO_4)_2$; (e) $Fe(ClO_3)_3$; (f) $HAsO_4^=$; (g) $CdS_2O_6.6H_2O$; (h) $(UO_2)(ClO_4)_2.-4H_2O$?

Ans. (a) +4; (b) +3, +6; (c) +1, +1, +2, −3; (d) +4, +5; (e) +3, +5; (f) +5; (g) +2, +5; (h) +6, +7.

2.3. What is the oxidation number of each element (other than hydrogen and oxygen) in the following: (a) N_2; (b) N_2O; (c) $Na_2Cr_2O_7$; (d) K_2MnO_4; (e) $Bi_2O_2SO_4$; (f) $K_3Co(NO_2)_6$; (g) AlO_2^-; (h) $Cu(NH_3)_4^{++}$; (i) SbS_3^-; (j) VO^{+++}; (k) $HC_2O_4^-$; (l) $Na_2S_4O_6$?

2.4. What is the oxidation number of each element (other than hydrogen and oxygen) in the following: (a) Mn_2O_7; (b) $Mg_2P_2O_7$; (c) $SbOCl$; (d) S_8; (e) $KH(IO_3)_2$; (f) $Ca_3(IO_6)_2$; (g) LiH; (h) CrO_2^{++}; (i) $B_4O_7^=$; (j) $HPO_4^=$; (k) FeS_2; (l) $HgI.HgNH_2I$?

2.5. What is the oxidation number of each element (other than hydrogen and oxygen) in the following: (a) Li_2PtCl_6; (b) $MgNH_4AsO_4$; (c) $K_2H_2Sb_2O_7$; (d) $(UO_2)_3(PO_4)_2$; (e) $Fe_3[Fe(CN)_6]_2$; (f) NH_2OH; (g) NH_4CNS; (h) HN_3; (i) Pb_3O_4; (j) VO_2^+; (k) $Na_2S_2O_8$; (l) $Co(NH_3)_6Cl_3$?

2.6. The following unbalanced equations do not involve oxidation and reduction. Convert them to complete, balanced ionic equations. Introduce H_2O and other constituents if necessary. Substances are in solution unless underlined.

(a) $AlCl_3 + NaOH \rightarrow NaAlO_2 + NaCl$

(b) $Fe_2(SO_4)_3 + NH_4OH \rightarrow \underline{Fe(OH)_3} + (NH_4)_2SO_4$

(c) $CuSO_4 + NH_4OH \rightarrow [Cu(NH_3)_4]SO_4$

(d) $K_2[Cd(CN)_4]$ (neutral solution) $+ H_2S \rightarrow \underline{CdS}$

(e) $\underline{Pb(OH)_2} + KOH \rightarrow K_2PbO_2$

(f) $H_3PO_4 + (NH_4)_2MoO_4 + HNO_3 \rightarrow \underline{(NH_4)_3PO_4.12MoO_3} + H_2O$

(g) $Na_3AsS_4 + H_2SO_4 \rightarrow \underline{As_2S_5} + H_2S + Na_2SO_4$

(h) $Bi_2O_2SO_4$ (acid solution) $+ H_2S \rightarrow \underline{Bi_2S_3}$

(i) $(NH_4)_2U_2O_7 + HCl \rightarrow UO_2Cl_2$

(j) $\underline{HC_2H_3O_2} + \underline{PbO} \rightarrow Pb(C_2H_3O_2)_2$

(k) $Pb(C_2H_3O_2)_2 + K_2CrO_4 \rightarrow \underline{PbCrO_4} + KC_2H_3O_2$

(l) $Hg(NO_3)_2 + KI \rightarrow K_2HgI_4$

(m) $UO_2SO_4 + KOH \rightarrow K_2U_2O_7$

(n) $\underline{Bi(OH)_3} + SnO_2^-$ (alkaline solution) $\rightarrow \underline{Bi} + SnO_3^-$

2.7. Balance the following oxidation-reduction equations:

(a) $Fe^{++} + ClO_3^- + H^+ \rightarrow Fe^{+++} + Cl^- + H_2O$

(b) $Mo^{+++} + Ce^{++++} + H_2O \rightarrow MoO_4^= + Ce^{+++} + H^+$

(c) $MnO_4^- + Cl^- + H^+ \rightarrow Mn^{++} + Cl_2 + H_2O$

(d) $Sn^{++} + BrO_3^- + Cl^- + H^+ \rightarrow SnCl_6^= + Br^- + H_2O$

(e) $IO_3^- + I^- + H^+ \rightarrow I_2 + H_2O$

(f) $MnO_4^- + S_2O_3^= + H^+ \rightarrow Mn^{++} + S_4O_6^= + H_2O$

(g) $Cr_2O_7^= + H_2S + H^+ \rightarrow Cr^{+++} + \underline{S} + H_2O$

(h) $\underline{Zn} + OH^- \rightarrow ZnO_2^= + H_2$

(i) $\underline{H_3AsO_4} + Zn + H^+ \rightarrow AsH_3 + Zn^{++} + H_2O$

(j) $NO_2^- + \underline{Al} + OH^- + H_2O \rightarrow NH_3 + AlO_2^-$

(k) $Cr^{+++} + \underline{NO_2^-} + OH^- \rightarrow CrO_4^= + NO + H_2O$

(l) $\underline{Fe_3P} + NO_3^- + H^+ \rightarrow Fe^{+++} + H_2PO_4^- + NO + H_2O$

(m) $\underline{FeS_2} + NO_3^- + H^+ \rightarrow Fe^{+++} + SO_4^= + NO_2 + H_2O$

(n) $\underline{Na_2FeO_4} + H_2O \rightarrow \underline{Fe(OH)_3} + O_2 + Na^+ + OH^-$

2.8. The following unbalanced oxidation-reduction equations represent reactions taking place in acid solution. Convert them to balanced ionic equations, introducing H^+ and H_2O wherever necessary.

(a) $Cr_2O_7^= + NO_2^- \rightarrow Cr^{+++} + NO_3^-$

(b) $Cr^{+++} + S_2O_8^= \rightarrow Cr_2O_7^= + SO_4^=$

(c) $MnO_4^- + H_2O_2 \rightarrow Mn^{++} + O_2$

(d) $Mn^{++} + BiO_2 \rightarrow MnO_4^- + BiO^+$

(e) $VO^{++} + \underline{MnO_4^-} \rightarrow HVO_3 + Mn^{++}$

(f) $UO_2^{++} + Zn \rightarrow U^{++++} + Zn^{++}$

(g) $Cr^{+++} + \underline{MnO_4^-} \rightarrow Cr_2O_7^= + Mn^{++}$

(h) $MnO_4^- + H_2C_2O_4 \rightarrow CO_2 + Mn^{++}$

(i) $S_2O_3^= + I_2 \rightarrow S_4O_6^= + I^-$

(j) $UO_5^- + H^+ \rightarrow UO_2^{++} + O_2$

(k) $\underline{Hg_2Cl_2} + IO_3^- + Cl^- \rightarrow HgCl_2 + ICl$

(l) $AlCl_3 + Na_2S_2O_3 \rightarrow \underline{Al(OH)_3} + \underline{S} + SO_2$

2.9. The following molecular equations involve oxidation and reduction, and the reactions take place in the presence of acid. Convert the equations to balanced ionic equations. Introduce H^+, H_2O, and other simple constituents wherever necessary.

(a) $FeCl_3 + H_2SO_3 \rightarrow FeCl_2 + H_2SO_4$

(b) $K_2Cr_2O_7 + HI + HCl \rightarrow CrCl_3 + KCl + I_2$

(c) $Zn + HNO_3 \text{ (very dilute)} \rightarrow Zn(NO_3)_2 + NH_4NO_3$

(d) $\underline{Fe_2Si} + HNO_3 \rightarrow Fe(NO_3)_3 + H_2SiO_3 + NO$

(e) $\underline{Co(NH_3)_6Cl_3} + HCl \rightarrow CoCl_2 + Cl_2 + \underline{NH_4Cl}$

(f) $H_3PO_3 + HgCl_2 \rightarrow Hg_2Cl_2 + H_3PO_4 + HCl$

(g) $K_2Na[Co(NO_2)_6] + \underline{KMnO_4} \rightarrow KNO_3 + NaNO_3 + Co(NO_3)_2 + Mn(NO_3)_2$

(h) $\underline{Sn} + HNO_3 \rightarrow \underline{H_2SnO_3} + NO$

(i) $\underline{Ag_3AsO_4} + Zn + H_2SO_4 \rightarrow AsH_3 + \underline{Ag} + ZnSO_4$

(j) $\underline{Se_2Cl_2} + H_2O \rightarrow H_2SeO_3 + Se$

(k) $Ce(IO_3)_4 + H_2C_2O_4 \rightarrow Ce_2(\underline{C_2O_4})_3 + I_2 + CO_2$

2.10. Write balanced ionic equations for the following reactions taking place in acid solution (unless otherwise specified). Introduce hydrogen ions, hydroxyl ions, and water wherever necessary. (a) Dichromate reduced by sulfurous acid to give chromic salt and sulfate; (b) chromic salt oxidized by free chlorine to give dichromate and chloride; (c) chromite ions oxidized in alkaline solution with hydrogen peroxide to chromate; (d) manganous salt and chlorate to give a precipitate of manganese dioxide and chlorine dioxide gas; (e) cobaltous chloride in alkaline solution with hydrogen peroxide to give a precipitate of cobaltic oxide; (*f*) nitrate plus metallic aluminum in the presence of NaOH to give aluminate plus hydrogen gas plus ammonia gas; (*g*) dichromate plus hydrogen peroxide to give chromic salt plus oxygen gas; (*h*) cupric sulfate plus potassium iodide to give a precipitate of cuprous iodide and free iodine; (*i*) cobaltic oxide plus acid to give cobaltous salt and oxygen gas; (*j*) manganous salt plus potassium permanganate in slightly alkaline solution to give a precipitate of manganese dioxide.

2.11. Complete and balance the following molecular equations which represent fusions and reactions taking place in concentrated solution. Introduce water and other constituents wherever necessary.

(*a*) $Cu + H_2SO_4$ (concentrated) $\rightarrow CuSO_4 + SO_2$

(*b*) $Fe(CrO_2)_2 + Na_2CO_3 + O_2 \rightarrow Fe_2O_3 + Na_2CrO_4 + CO_2$

(*c*) $Cr_2(SO_4)_3 + Na_2O_2 \rightarrow Na_2CrO_4$

(*d*) $TiO_2 + K_2S_2O_7 \rightarrow Ti(SO_4)_2$

(*e*) $KAlSi_3O_8 + CaCO_3 + NH_4Cl \rightarrow CaSiO_3 + Ca(AlO_2)_2 + KCl + CO_2 + NH_3 + H_2O$

(*f*) $FeS_2 + Na_2O_2 \rightarrow Na_2FeO_4 + Na_2SO_4$

CHAPTER 3

CALCULATIONS BASED ON FORMULAS AND EQUATIONS

19. Mathematical Significance of a Chemical Formula. The law of definite proportions states that in any pure compound the proportions by weight of the constituent elements are always the same. A chemical formula therefore is not only a shorthand method of naming a compound and of indicating the constituent elements of the compound, but it also shows the relative masses of the elements present.

Thus the formula Na_2SO_4 (molecular weight = 142.06) indicates that for every 142.06 grams of pure anhydrous sodium sulfate there are $2 \times 23.00 = 46.00$ grams of sodium, 32.06 grams of sulfur, and $4 \times 16.00 = 64.00$ grams of oxygen. The percentage of sodium in pure anhydrous sodium sulfate is therefore $\dfrac{2 \times 23.00}{142.06} \times 100 = 32.38$ per cent.

20. Formula Weights. A *gram-molecular weight* of a substance is its molecular weight expressed in grams. Thus, a gram-molecular weight (or *gram-mole*, or simply *mole*) of Na_2SO_4 is 142.06 grams. A mole of nitrogen gas (N_2) is 28.016 grams of the element.

A *formula weight* (F.W.) is that weight in grams corresponding to the formula of the substance as ordinarily written. In most cases it is identical to the gram-molecular weight, but occasionally the true molecular weight of a compound is a multiple of the weight expressed by the formula as ordinarily written in a chemical equation. In practically all the reactions of analytical chemistry, however, it can be assumed that the value of the formula weight and that of the mole are the same.

The *gram-atom* or *gram-atomic weight* is the atomic weight of the element expressed in grams (*e.g.*, 40.08 grams of calcium; 14.008 grams of nitrogen). A *gram-ion* is the atomic or formula weight of an ion expressed in grams (*e.g.*, 40.08 grams of Ca^{++}; 62.008 grams of NO_3^-).

A *millimole* is one thousandth of a mole; a *milligram-atom* is one thousandth of a gram-atom.

A formula weight of hydrated ferric sulfate, $Fe_2(SO_4)_3.9H_2O$, for example, is 562.0 grams of the salt. It contains 2 gram-atoms of iron (= 117.0 grams), 21 gram-atoms of oxygen (= 336 grams), 9 formula weights (9 F.W.) of water, 3,000 milligram-atoms of sulfur, and in solution would give 3 gram-ions of sulfate.

21. Mathematical Significance of a Chemical Equation. A chemical equation not only represents the chemical changes taking place in a

27

given reaction but also expresses the relative quantities of the substances involved. Thus, the molecular equation

$$H_2SO_4 + BaCl_2 \rightarrow BaSO_4 + 2HCl$$

not only states that sulfuric acid reacts with barium chloride to give barium sulfate and hydrochloric acid, but it also expresses the fact that every 98.08 parts by weight of sulfuric acid react with 208.27 parts of barium chloride to give 233.42 parts of barium sulfate and 2×36.47 = 72.94 parts of hydrogen chloride, these numerical values being the molecular weights of the respective compounds. These are relative weights and are independent of the units chosen. If a weight of any one of the above four substances is known, the weight of any or all of the other three can be calculated by simple proportion. This is the basis of analytical computations.

EXAMPLE I.   A sample of pure lead weighing 0.500 gram is dissolved in nitric acid according to the equation

$$3Pb + 8HNO_3 \rightarrow 3Pb(NO_3)_2 + 2NO + 4H_2O$$

How many grams of pure HNO_3 are theoretically required?   How many grams of $Pb(NO_3)_2$ could be obtained by evaporating the resulting solution to dryness?   How many grams of NO gas are formed in the above reaction?

SOLUTION:

Atomic weight of lead = 207
Molecular weight of HNO_3 = 63.0
Molecular weight of $Pb(NO_3)_2$ = 331
Molecular weight of NO = 30.0
(3×207) grams of Pb react with (8×63.0) grams of HNO_3
(3×207) grams of Pb would form (3×331) grams of $Pb(NO_3)_2$ and (2×30.0) grams of NO
Hence 0.500 gram of Pb would require

$$0.500 \times \frac{8 \times 63.0}{3 \times 207} = 0.405 \text{ gram of } HNO_3$$

and would form

$$0.500 \times \frac{3 \times 331}{3 \times 207} = 0.799 \text{ gram of } Pb(NO_3)_2 \quad Ans.$$

and

$$0.500 \times \frac{2 \times 30.0}{3 \times 207} = 0.0483 \text{ gram of NO}$$

EXAMPLE II.   How many grams of H_2S would theoretically be required to precipitate the lead as lead sulfide from the above solution?   How many milliliters of H_2S under standard temperature and pressure would theoretically be required for the precipitation? (A gram-molecular weight of a gas under standard conditions occupies 22.4 liters. See Sec. 126.)

SOLUTION:

$Pb^{++} + H_2S \rightarrow PbS + 2H^+$
Atomic weight of lead = 207
Molecular weight of H_2S = 34.1
207 grams of Pb^{++} require 34.1 grams of H_2S
Hence 0.500 gram of Pb^{++} requires

$$0.500 \times \frac{34.1}{207} = 0.0822 \text{ gram of } H_2S. \quad Ans.$$

34.1 grams of H_2S occupy 22,400 ml. under standard conditions

Volume of $H_2S = \dfrac{0.0822}{34.1} \times 22,400 = 54.1$ ml. *Ans.*

EXAMPLE III. In the reaction expressed by the equation:

$$2Ag_2CO_3 \rightarrow 4Ag + \overline{O_2} + 2\overline{CO_2}$$

(*a*) how many gram-atoms of silver can be obtained from 1 F.W. of silver carbonate, (*b*) how many gram-atoms of silver can be obtained from 1.00 gram of silver carbonate, (*c*) how many grams of silver carbonate are required to give 3.00 grams of oxygen gas, (*d*) how many moles of gas ($CO_2 + O_2$) are produced from 50.0 grams of silver carbonate, and (*e*) how many milliliters of gas ($CO_2 + O_2$) are produced from 1 millimole of silver carbonate?

SOLUTION:

(*a*) 2 F.W. $Ag_2CO_3 \rightarrow$ 4 gram-atoms Ag
   1 F.W. $Ag_2CO_3 \rightarrow$ 2 gram-atoms Ag. *Ans.*
(*b*) Molecular weight Ag_2CO_3 = 276

$$1.00 \text{ gram } Ag_2CO_3 = \frac{1.00}{Ag_2CO_3} = \frac{1.00}{276} = 0.00363 \text{ F.W. } Ag_2CO_3$$

   $0.00363 \times 2 = 0.00726$ gram-atom Ag. *Ans.*
(*c*) 2 moles Ag_2CO_3 (= 2×276 = 552 grams) give 1 mole O_2 (= 32 grams)

$$3.00 \text{ grams } O_2 = 3.00 \times \frac{552}{32} = 51.7 \text{ grams } Ag_2CO_3. \quad Ans.$$

(*d*) 2 moles Ag_2CO_3 (= 552 grams) $\rightarrow$ 3 moles ($O_2 + CO_2$)

$$50.0 \text{ grams } Ag_2CO_3 = \frac{50.0}{552} \times 3 = 0.272 \text{ mole gas.} \quad Ans.$$

(e) 1 mole $Ag_2CO_3 \rightarrow 1\frac{1}{2}$ moles gas

1 mole gas (standard temperature and pressure) = 22,400 ml.

$$1 \text{ millimole } Ag_2CO_3 = 1\frac{1}{2} \times \frac{22,400}{1,000}$$

$$= 33.8 \text{ ml. of gas.}\quad Ans.$$

EXAMPLE IV.   In the reaction expressed by the equation

$$MnO_2 + 2NaCl + 3H_2SO_4 \rightarrow MnSO_4 + 2NaHSO_4 + Cl_2 + 2H_2O$$

or

$$MnO_2 + 2Cl^- + 6H^+ \rightarrow Mn^{++} + \overline{Cl_2} + 2H_2O$$

(a) how many gram-ions of Mn^{++} can be obtained from 1 millimole of MnO_2, (b) how many grams of $MnSO_4$ can be obtained from 5.00 grams of MnO_2, (c) how many millimoles of MnO_2 are required to give 100 ml. Cl_2 (standard conditions), and (d) if 1.00 gram of MnO_2, 1.00 gram of NaCl, and 5.00 grams of H_2SO_4 are used, which is the limiting reagent, and how many milliliters of Cl_2 (standard conditions) are evolved?

SOLUTION:

(a) 1 mole $MnO_2 \rightarrow$ 1 gram-ion Mn^{++}

1 millimole $MnO_2 \rightarrow 0.001$ gram-ion Mn^{++}.   Ans.

(b) 1 mole MnO_2 (= 86.9 grams) $\rightarrow$ 1 mole $MnSO_4$ (= 151 grams)

$$5.00 \text{ grams } MnO_2 = 5.00 \times \frac{151}{86.9}$$

$$= 8.69 \text{ grams } MnSO_4.\quad Ans.$$

(c) $100 \text{ ml. } Cl_2 = \dfrac{100}{22.4} = 4.47$ millimoles Cl_2

1 millimole $Cl_2 = 1$ millimole MnO_2

100 ml. $Cl_2 = 4.47$ millimoles MnO_2.   Ans.

(d) $1.00 \text{ gram } MnO_2 = \dfrac{1.00}{MnO_2} = \dfrac{1.00}{86.9} = 0.0115$ mole

$1.00 \text{ gram NaCl} = \dfrac{1.00}{NaCl} = \dfrac{1.00}{58.5} = 0.0171$ mole

$5.00 \text{ grams } H_2SO_4 = \dfrac{5.00}{H_2SO_4} = \dfrac{5.00}{98.1} = 0.0510$ mole

According to the equation these substances react in the molar ratio of 1:2:3, or 0.0115:0.0230:0.0345.   The NaCl is therefore the limiting reagent and the other two are in excess.

$$2 \text{ moles NaCl} \rightarrow 1 \text{ mole } Cl_2 = 22,400 \text{ ml. } Cl_2$$

$$0.0171 \text{ mole NaCl} \rightarrow \frac{0.0171}{2} \times 22,400$$

$$= 192 \text{ ml. } Cl_2.\quad Ans.$$

Problems

3.1. How many grams of potassium and of carbon are contained in (*a*) 0.211 gram of $K_4Fe(CN)_6.3H_2O$; (*b*) 1 F.W. of $KHC_4H_4O_6$?

Ans. (*a*) 0.0782 gram, 0.0360 gram; (*b*) 39.1 grams, 48.0 grams.

3.2. A certain weight of lead phosphate, $Pb_3(PO_4)_2$, contains 0.100 gram of lead. How many grams of phosphorus are present? What is the weight of the lead phosphate? What is the percentage of oxygen present?

Ans. 0.00997 gram. 0.131 gram. 15.8 per cent.

3.3. How many grams of oxygen are present in 1.00 gram of $Fe(NO_3)_3.6H_2O$? What is the percentage by weight of sulfur in $K_2SO_4.Al_2(SO_4)_3.24H_2O$?

Ans. 0.686 gram. 13.5 per cent.

3.4. Ignition of anhydrous magnesium ammonium phosphate forms magnesium pyrophosphate according to the equation: $2MgNH_4PO_4 \rightarrow Mg_2P_2O_7 + 2NH_3 + H_2O$. Calculate: (*a*) number of formula weights of $Mg_2P_2O_7$ produced from 1.00 F.W. of $MgNH_4PO_4$, (*b*) number of grams of NH_3 produced at the same time, (*c*) number of milliliters of NH_3 (standard conditions) accompanying the formation of 1 millimole of $Mg_2P_2O_7$.

Ans. (*a*) 0.500, (*b*) 17.0 grams, (*c*) 44.8 ml.

3.5. Calculate the number of pounds of materials theoretically necessary for the preparation of 1.00 pound of (*a*) KOH from CaO and K_2CO_3, (*b*) $BaSO_4$ from $Na_2SO_4.$-$10H_2O$ and $BaCl_2.2H_2O$.

Ans. (*a*) CaO = 0.500 pound, K_2CO_3 = 1.23 pounds.
(*b*) $Na_2SO_4.10H_2O$ = 1.38 pounds, $BaCl_2.2H_2O$ = 1.04 pounds.

3.6. Balance the following equation and also write it as a balanced ionic equation: $Al_2(SO_4)_3 + BaCl_2 \rightarrow AlCl_3 + \underline{BaSO_4}$. Calculate from it the following: (*a*) number of gram-ions of Al^{+++} contained in 1 gram-mole of $Al_2(SO_4)_3$, (*b*) number of gram-ions of Ba^{++} reacting with 1.00 gram of Al^{+++}, (*c*) number of grams of $BaSO_4$ obtainable from 2.00 grams of $Al_2(SO_4)_3.18H_2O$, (*d*) number of grams of $BaSO_4$ produced by mixing solutions containing 3.00 grams of $Al_2(SO_4)_3$ and 4.00 grams of $BaCl_2$.

Ans. (*a*) 2, (*b*) 0.0556, (*c*) 2.10 grams, (*d*) 4.48 grams.

3.7. From the reaction: $4FeS_2 + 11O_2 \rightarrow 2Fe_2O_3 + 8SO_2$, calculate the following: (*a*) number of moles of FeS_2 required to form 1 F.W. of Fe_2O_3, (*b*) number of grams of oxygen required to react with 2.00 moles of FeS_2, (*c*) number of millimoles of SO_2 equivalent to 0.320 gram of O_2, (*d*) volume of SO_2 (standard conditions) accompanying the formation of 0.160 gram of Fe_2O_3.

Ans. (*a*) 2, (*b*) 176 grams, (*c*) 7.27, (*d*) 89.6 ml.

3.8. Complete and balance the following ionic equation for a reaction taking place in the presence of acid: $Fe^{++} + MnO_4^- \rightarrow Fe^{+++} + Mn^{++}$. Calculate from it the following: (*a*) number of gram-ions of Mn^{++} produced from 1 gram-ion of Fe^{++}, (*b*) number of millimoles of $Fe_2(SO_4)_3.9H_2O$ obtainable if 1 millimole of $KMnO_4$ is reduced, (*c*) decrease in the number of gram-ions of H^+ accompanying the formation of 1.00 gram of Fe^{+++}, (*d*) number of grams of $Fe_2(SO_4)_3$ obtainable by mixing solutions containing 1.00 gram of $FeSO_4.7H_2O$, 0.100 gram of $KMnO_4$ and 1.00 gram of H_2SO_4.

Ans. (*a*) $\frac{1}{5}$, (*b*) $2\frac{1}{2}$, (*c*) 0.0286, (*d*) 0.633 gram.

3.9. How many grams of the element chlorine are in the anhydrous chromic chloride, $CrCl_3$, that could be obtained from 100 mg. of $K_2Cr_2O_7$ after reduction by H_2S in the presence of $HCl:Cr_2O_7^- + 3H_2S + 8H^+ \rightarrow 2Cr^{+++} + 3S + 7H_2O$? How many grams and how many milliliters (standard conditions) of H_2S would be required?

Ans.   0.0723 gram, 0.0347 gram, 22.8 ml.

3.10. How many grams of chromium are present in 0.250 gram of $K_2Cr_2O_7$? What is the percentage of potassium in this compound?

3.11. What weight of alum, $K_2SO_4.Al_2SO_4.24H_2O$, contains 0.200 gram of aluminum? What is the percentage of oxygen in the compound?

3.12. What weight of sulfur is present in an amount of $Na_2S_2O_3$ that contains (*a*) 318 mg. of sodium, (*b*) 1.00 gram-atom of oxygen?

3.13. What is the percentage of oxygen in $K_2SO_4.Cr_2(SO_4)_3.24H_2O$?

3.14. Ignition of bismuth basic carbonate takes place according to the following equation: $2BiOHCO_3 \rightarrow Bi_2O_3 + 2CO_2 + H_2O$. Calculate the following: (*a*) number of formula weights of $\overline{Bi_2O_3}$ produced from 1 F.W. of the carbonate, (*b*) number of millimoles of CO_2 accompanying the formation of 1.00 gram of Bi_2O_3, (*c*) volume of CO_2 (standard conditions) formed from 0.0200 gram of $BiOHCO_3$, (*d*) volume of gas (CO_2 + water vapor) accompanying the formation of 1.00 millimole of Bi_2O_3.

3.15. Convert the following to balanced molecular and ionic equations: $FeCl_3 + AgNO_3 \rightarrow Fe(NO_3)_3 + \underline{AgCl}$. Calculate from them the following: (*a*) number of formula weights of AgCl obtainable from 1 F.W. of $FeCl_3$, (*b*) number of gram-ions of Fe^{+++} produced per millimole of AgCl, (*c*) number of grams of $Fe(NO_3)_3.6H_2O$ obtainable if 1.00 gram-molecular weight of $AgNO_3$ is used up, (*d*) number of grams of AgCl obtained by mixing solutions containing 0.700 gram of $FeCl_3$ and 0.600 gram of $AgNO_3$. How many grams of which reactant are left over?

3.16. Convert the following to a balanced molecular equation: $\underline{Fe(CrO_2)_2} + Na_2CO_3 + NaNO_3 \rightarrow Na_2FeO_4 + Na_2CrO_4 + \overline{N_2} + \overline{CO_2}$. From it calculate the number of millimoles and the number of milliliters of gas (standard conditions) that are formed from that weight of $Fe(CrO_2)_2$ containing (*a*) 1.00 gram-atom of Cr, (*b*) 1.00 gram of Cr.

3.17. Balance the following equation: $MnO_4^- + Fe^{++} + H^+ \rightarrow Mn^{++} + Fe^{+++} + H_2O$ and calculate from it the number of grams of $FeSO_4.7H_2O$ required to reduce that weight of $KMnO_4$ that contains 0.250 gram of Mn.

3.18. Balance the following equation: $Cr_2O_7^- + Fe^{++} + H^+ \rightarrow Cr^{+++} + Fe^{+++} + H_2O$. If 1.00 gram-molecular weight of K_2CrO_4 is dissolved in water and the solution acidified ($2CrO_4^- + 2H^+ \rightarrow Cr_2O_7^- + H_2O$), how many grams of $FeSO_4.(NH_4)_2SO_4.6H_2O$ would be required to reduce the chromium in the resulting solution?

3.19. When used for the oxidizing effect of its nitrate, which is the more economical reagent, potassium nitrate at 65 cents per pound or sodium nitrate at 50 cents per pound? How much is saved per pound of the more economical reagent?

CHAPTER 4

CONCENTRATION OF SOLUTIONS

22. Methods of Expressing Concentration. Solution reagents used in analytical chemistry are usually either (1) laboratory reagents the concentrations of which need be known only approximately, or (2) titration reagents the concentrations of which must be known to a high degree of precision. In analytical work the following methods of expressing concentrations are most commonly used.

23. Grams per Unit Volume. By this method a concentration is expressed in terms of the number of grams (or milligrams) of solute in each liter (or milliliter) of solution. A 5-gram-per-liter solution of sodium chloride is prepared by dissolving 5 grams of the salt in water and diluting to one liter (*not* by adding one liter of water to the salt).

This method is simple and direct but it is not a convenient method from a stoichiometric point of view, since solutions of the same concentration bear no simple relation to each other so far as volumes involved in chemical reactions are concerned.

24. Percentage Composition. This method is on a percentage-by-weight basis and expresses concentration in terms of grams of solute per 100 grams of solution. A 5 per cent solution of sodium chloride is made by dissolving 5 grams of the salt in 95 grams of water, which of course gives 100 grams of solution.

25. Specific Gravity. The specific gravity of the solution of a single solute is a measure of the concentration of the solute in the solution. Although occasionally used in analytical chemistry, it is a cumbersome method, since it necessitates consulting a table in order to determine the percentage-by-weight composition. Tables of specific gravities of common reagents are found in the handbooks and other reference books of chemistry. Tables covering common acids and bases are also in the Appendix of this text. Here it will be found, for example, that hydrochloric acid of specific gravity 1.12 contains 23.8 grams of hydrogen chloride in 100 grams of solution.

26. Volume Ratios. Occasionally in analytical work the concentration of a mineral acid or of ammonium hydroxide is given in terms of the volume ratio of the common concentrated reagent and water. Thus HCl (1:3) signifies a solution of hydrochloric acid made by mixing one volume of common concentrated hydrochloric (sp. gr. about 1.20) with three volumes of water. This method of expressing concentrations is cumbersome, particularly in work where subsequent calculations involving the solutions are to be made.

27. Molar and Formal Solutions. A *molar solution* is one containing a gram-mole of substance dissolved in a liter of *solution*. This is usually identical to a *formal solution* which contains a formula weight of substance in a liter of solution (see Sec. 20). A gram-molecular weight of substance dissolved in a liter of *water* does not constitute a molar solution, for the resulting solution does not occupy a volume of exactly a liter.[1] A liter of molar (M) sulfuric acid solution contains 98.08 grams of H_2SO_4; a liter of half-molar ($\frac{1}{2}M$, or $M/2$) sulfuric acid solution contains 49.04 grams of H_2SO_4. In this particular case 98.08 grams of H_2SO_4 does not mean 98.08 grams of the ordinary *concentrated* sulfuric acid, but of hydrogen sulfate. The concentrated acid contains about 96 per cent of the latter.

Since 1 mole of hydrochloric acid reacts with 1 mole of sodium hydroxide, a certain volume of sodium hydroxide solution will be exactly neutralized by an equal volume of hydrochloric acid of the same molar concentration, or twice the volume of hydrochloric acid of one-half the molar concentration of the sodium hydroxide. One molecule of hydrogen sulfate will react with 2 molecules of sodium hydroxide.

$$H_2SO_4 + 2NaOH \rightarrow Na_2SO_4 + 2H_2O$$

To neutralize a certain volume of sodium hydroxide solution, only one-half that volume of sulfuric acid of the same molar concentration would be required. Volumetric calculations are therefore greatly simplified when concentrations are expressed in terms of moles of substance per unit volume of solution; for, when so expressed, the volumes of reacting solutions of the same molar concentration, although not necessarily equal, bear simple numerical relationships to each other.

EXAMPLE. What volume of 0.6380 M potassium hydroxide solution will neutralize 430.0 ml. of 0.4000 M sulfuric acid?

SOLUTION:

1 mole $H_2SO_4 \backsim$ 2 moles KOH

430.0 ml. of 0.4000 molar solution contains

$$\frac{430.0}{1,000} \times 0.4000 = 0.1720 \text{ mole } H_2SO_4$$

0.1720 mole $H_2SO_4 \backsim$ 0.3440 mole KOH

1 ml. KOH contains 0.0006380 mole KOH

$$\text{Volume required} = \frac{0.3440}{0.0006380} = 539.3 \text{ ml.} \quad \textit{Ans.}$$

---

[1] Solutions containing a gram-molecular weight of substance dissolved in 1,000 grams of water are useful in computations involving certain physicochemical phenomena. Such solutions are often referred to as *molal* solutions, but this standard is not used in general analytical work.

28. Equivalent Weight and Normal Solution. The *equivalent weight* of an element or compound is that weight equivalent in reactive power to one atomic weight of hydrogen. The *milliequivalent weight* is one thousandth of the equivalent weight. The *gram-equivalent* weight is the equivalent weight expressed in grams; the *gram-milliequivalent weight* is the milliequivalent weight expressed in grams.[1] The application of gram-equivalent weights to various types of chemical reactions will be taken up in detail in Part III, but simple cases, applying particularly to qualitative analysis, will be considered briefly here.

The gram-equivalent weight of an acid, base, or salt involved in a simple metathesis such as a neutralization or precipitation is that weight in grams of the substance equivalent in neutralizing or precipitating power to 1 gram-ion of hydrogen (*i.e.*, 1.008 grams of H^+).

A *normal solution* contains 1 gram-equivalent weight of solute in 1 liter of solution, or 1 gram-milliequivalent weight in 1 milliliter of solution. The *normality* of a solution is its relation to a normal solution. A half-normal solution therefore contains in a unit volume one-half the weight of solute contained in its normal solution, and this weight may be expressed as $\frac{1}{2}$ N, or $N/2$. The concentration of a normal solution is expressed simply as N.

Since the concentrations of solutions used in precise volumetric analysis are usually found experimentally, the concentrations cannot often be expressed by whole numbers or by simple fractions. They are more likely to be expressed as decimal fractions, *e.g.*, 0.1372 N.

29. Simple Calculations Involving Equivalents, Milliequivalents, and Normality. The use of equivalents, milliequivalents, and normality is so extensive in analytical chemistry and the terms are so fundamental that a clear understanding of them is essential at this time. More detailed discussions applying particularly to quantitative analysis will be given in Part III.

Let us consider here only the simplest reactions between common acids, bases, and salts, and as an example let us take sulfuric acid. The molecular weight of H_2SO_4 is 98.08. A mole, or gram-molecular weight, of H_2SO_4 is 98.08 grams, and a molar solution of the acid therefore contains this amount of pure hydrogen sulfate in a liter of solution. Since 98.08 grams of H_2SO_4 has a neutralizing power equivalent to 2 gram-atoms (2.016 grams) of hydrogen as an ion, the gram-equivalent of H_2SO_4 as an acid is 98.08/2 = 49.04 grams, which is equivalent in neutralizing power

---

[1] The equivalent weight of a substance, like the atomic or molecular weight, is merely a number without a unit of weight; the gram-equivalent weight is a definite number of grams. However, when the connotation is clear, the terms "equivalent weight" and "milliequivalent weight" are frequently used to signify gram-equivalent weight and gram-milliequivalent weight, respectively.

to 1 gram-atom (1.008 grams) of hydrogen as an ion. The gram-milliequivalent weight is 0.04904 gram. A normal solution of sulfuric acid
therefore contains 49.04 grams of H_2SO_4 in a liter of solution, or 0.04904
gram of H_2SO_4 in a millimeter of solution. A 1-molar solution of sulfuric
acid is 2 normal; a 1-normal solution of sulfuric acid is $\frac{1}{2}$ molar.

Sodium hydroxide is a base with a molecular weight of 40.00. The
gram-equivalent weight of NaOH is 40.00 grams, since this amount is

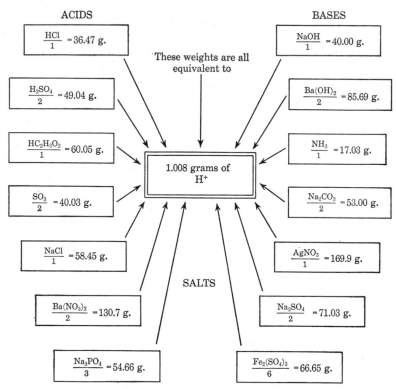

FIG. 1. Gram-equivalent weights of some acids, bases, and salts.

neutralized by 1.008 grams of H^+. A normal solution of NaOH contains
40.00 grams in a liter of solution and is likewise 1 molar.

The gram-equivalent weight of a simple salt is determined in the same
way as that of an acid or base, namely by reference to 1.008 grams of H^+
as a standard. In the case of the salt of a metal, the equivalent weight is
ordinarily the molecular weight of the salt divided by the total oxidation
number represented by the atoms of metal in the formula.

The equivalent weights of a few acids, bases, and salts are shown in
Fig. 1. *Since each of these amounts is equivalent to the same standard, they
are mutually equivalent to one another.*

In each case the specified amount when dissolved in one liter of solution will produce a one-normal solution.

It follows that 1 liter of 1 N HCl will neutralize 1 liter of 1 N NaOH, or 1 liter of 1 N Ba(OH)$_2$, or 1 liter of *any* one-normal base. One liter of 1 N H$_2$SO$_4$ will also neutralize 1 liter of any one-normal base. More generally, a certain volume of any acid will neutralize the same volume of any base of the same normality.

Similarly, 1 liter of 1 N AgNO$_3$ will precipitate the chloride from 1 liter of 1 N NaCl or 1 liter of 1 N BaCl$_2$, and the latter will just precipitate the sulfate from 1 liter of 1 N Na$_2$SO$_4$ or 1 liter of 1 N Fe$_2$(SO$_4$)$_3$.

We found that when two solutions of equal *molarity* react, the volumes are in simple ratio to each other. But when two solutions of equal *normality* react, the volumes of the solutions are *equal*.

Since volumes of reagents in analytical chemistry are usually measured in milliliters rather than in liters, it is more convenient to consider a normal solution as containing 1 gram-milliequivalent weight per milliliter. Hence the number of gram-milliequivalent weights present in a solution can be found from the simple relationship:

Number of milliliters $\times$ normality =
$$\text{number of gram-milliequivalent weights}$$

or
$$ml. \times N = number\ of\ me.\ wts.$$
(See footnote, Sec. 28)

Thus, 2.00 ml. of 6.00 N HCl contain 12.0 milliequivalent weights, or $12.0 \times \dfrac{\text{HCl}}{1,000} = 0.438$ gram of hydrogen chloride. This will exactly neutralize 12.0 milliequivalents of any base, for example, 4.00 ml. of 3.00 N NaOH, or 4.00 ml. of 3.00 N Na$_2$CO$_3$, or 80.0 ml. of 0.150 N Ba(OH)$_2$, etc.

It follows that when solutions A and B mutually interact to a complete reaction,
$$ml._A \times N_A = ml._B \times N_B$$

EXAMPLE I. What is the approximate molarity and normality of a 13.0 per cent solution of H$_2$SO$_4$? To what volume should 100 ml. of the acid be diluted in order to prepare a 1.50 N solution?

SOLUTION: From specific gravity table in the Appendix, the specific gravity of the acid is 1.090.

1 liter weighs 1,090 grams
1 liter contains 1,090 $\times$ 0.130 = 142 grams H$_2$SO$_4$
1 mole H$_2$SO$_4$ = 98.08 grams
Molarity of solution = 142/98.08 = 1.45 M. *Ans.*

1 gram-equivalent $H_2SO_4 = H_2SO_4/2 = 49.04$ grams
Normality of solution $= 142/49.04 = 2.90\ N$.   *Ans.*
100 ml. contain 290 milliequivalents H_2SO_4
After dilution x ml. of 1.50 N contain 290 milliequivalents

$$x \times 1.50 = 290$$
$$x = 193\ \text{ml.}\quad Ans.$$

EXAMPLE II.   A solution contains 3.30 grams of $Na_2CO_3.10H_2O$ in each 15.0 ml.   What is its normality?   What is its molarity?   With how many milliliters of 3.10 N acetic acid, $HC_2H_3O_2$, will 25.0 ml. of the carbonate react according to the equation: $2H^+ + CO_3^= \rightarrow H_2O + CO_2$? With how many milliliters of 3.10 N H_2SO_4 will 25.0 ml. of the carbonate react?

SOLUTION:

Molecular wt. $Na_2CO_3.10H_2O = 286$

Equivalent wt. $Na_2CO_3.10H_2O = \dfrac{286}{2} = 143$

Milliequivalent weight $= 0.143$

Solution contains $\dfrac{3.30}{15.0} = 0.220$ gram per ml.

1 normal solution would contain 0.143 gram per ml.

Normality $= \dfrac{0.220}{0.143} = 1.54\ N$.   *Ans.*

Molarity $= \dfrac{0.220}{0.286} = 0.77\ M$.   *Ans.*

$$x \times 3.10 = 25.0 \times 1.54$$
$$x = 12.4\ \text{ml.}\ HC_2H_3O_2.\quad Ans.$$
$$= 12.4\ \text{ml.}\ H_2SO_4.\quad Ans.$$

EXAMPLE III.   (*a*) A 0.100 M solution of aluminum sulfate, $Al_2(SO_4)_3$, would be of what normality as an aluminum salt?   (*b*) What normality as a sulfate?   (*c*) How many milliequivalents of the salt are contained in each milliliter?   (*d*) What volume of 6.00 N NH_4OH would be required to react with the aluminum in 35.0 ml. of the salt solution according to the equation: $Al^{+++} + 3NH_4OH \rightarrow Al(OH)_3 + 3NH_4^+$?   (*e*) What volume of 6.00 N $BaCl_2.2H_2O$ solution would be required to precipitate the sulfate from 35.0 ml. of the solution?   (*f*) How many grams of $BaCl_2.2H_2O$ are contained in each milliliter of the above solution?

SOLUTION:

(*a*) 1 mole $Al_2(SO_4)_3 = 6$ equivalents (2 $Al^{+++} \leftrightarrows 6H^+$)
      0.100 molar $= 0.600$ normal as Al salt.   *Ans.*
(*b*) $= 0.600$ normal as sulfate.   *Ans.*

(c) 0.600 milliequivalent per milliliter. *Ans.*

(d) $ml._A \times N_A = ml._B \times N_B$

$$x \times 6.00 = 35.0 \times 0.600$$

$$x = 3.50 \text{ ml.} \textit{Ans.}$$

(e) $ml._A \times N_A = ml._B \times N_B$

$$x \times 6.00 = 35.0 \times 0.600$$

$$x = 3.50 \text{ ml.} \textit{Ans.}$$

(f) $6.00 \times \dfrac{\text{BaCl}_2.2\text{H}_2\text{O}}{2,000} = 0.732 \text{ gram.} \textit{Ans.}$

Problems

4.1. What fraction of the molecular weight represents the milliequivalent weight in the case of each of the following acids, bases, and salts (assuming complete replacement of the hydrogen in the acids): (a) H_2SiF_6, (b) H_3AsO_4, (c) $H_4P_2O_7$, (d) ThO_2, (e) $(NH_4)_2SO_4$, (f) $Zn_3(AsO_3)_2$?

Ans. (a) 1/2,000, (b) 1/3,000, (c) 1/4,000, (d) 1/4,000, (e) 1/2,000, (f) 1/6,000.

4.2. How many grams of K_2SO_4 are contained in 50.0 ml. of 0.200 N solution? How many millimoles of K_2SO_4 are present?

Ans. 0.872 gram. 5.00 millimoles.

4.3. A solution of H_2SO_4 has a specific gravity of 1.150. What is the normality of the solution?

Ans. 4.90 N.

4.4. What is the normality of a solution of NH_4OH having a specific gravity of 0.900? How many milliters of 13.0 N H_2SO_4 would be neutralized by 15.0 ml. of the NH_4OH? To what volume should 250 ml. of the 13.0 N H_2SO_4 be diluted to make a solution that is 5.00 molar?

Ans. 15.0 N. 17.3 ml. 325 ml.

4.5. A 30 per cent solution of H_3PO_4 has a specific gravity of 1.180. What is its normality as an acid assuming partial neutralization to form HPO_4^-? What is its molar concentration?

Ans. 7.22 N. 3.61 M.

4.6. How many grams of $SrCl_2.6H_2O$ are required to prepare 500 ml. of 0.550 N solution? What is the molarity of the solution? How many milliliters of 1.00 N $AgNO_3$ would be required to precipitate the chloride from 20.0 ml. of the strontium chloride solution?

Ans. 36.6 grams. 0.275 M. 11.0 ml.

4.7. How much water must be added to 50.0 ml. of a 0.400 N solution of $Cr_2(SO_4)_3$.-$18H_2O$ in order to make it 0.0500 molar? How many milliliters of 0.200 N NH_4OH would be required to precipitate all the chromium as $Cr(OH)_3$ from 20.0 ml. of the original undiluted solution?

Ans. 16.7 ml. 40.0 ml.

4.8. A piece of aluminum weighing 2.70 grams is treated with 75.0 ml. of H_2SO_4 (sp. gr. 1.18 containing 24.7 per cent H_2SO_4 by weight). After the metal is completely dissolved $(2Al + 6H^+ \rightarrow 2Al^{+++} + 3H_2)$ the solution is diluted to 400 ml. Calculate (a) normality of the resulting solution in free sulfuric acid, (b) normality of the solution with respect to the aluminum salt it contains, (c) total volume of 6.00 N NH_4OH required to neutralize the acid and precipitate all the aluminum as $Al(OH)_3$ from 50.0 ml. of the solution.

Ans.   (a) 0.365 N, (b) 0.750 N, (c) 9.30 ml.

4.9. What is the gram-equivalent weight of each of the following acids, bases, and salts (assuming complete replacement of the hydrogen in the acids): (a) $H_2C_2O_4.2H_2O$, (b) H_3PO_4, (c) CaO, (d) Fe_2O_3, (e) $SnCl_4$, (f) $Ca_3(PO_4)_2$?

4.10. How many milliliters of 2.30 M H_2SO_4 would be neutralized by 15.8 ml. of 3.20 M NaOH?   How many milliliters of 4.60 N $H_2C_2O_4.2H_2O$ solution would be neutralized by 10.0 ml. of 5.10 N NaOH?   By 10.0 ml. of 5.10 N $Ba(OH)_2$?   How many milliliters of 4.60 N $HC_2H_3O_2$ would be neutralized by 10.0 ml of 5.10 N NaOH?

4.11. To what volume must 25.0 ml. of HCl (sp. gr. 1.100) be diluted in order to make a solution of HCl with a specific gravity of 1.04?   How many milliliters of 0.500 N $Ba(OH)_2$ would be required to neutralize 40.0 ml. of the resulting diluted solution?

4.12. A 12.0 per cent solution of $H_2C_2O_4.2H_2O$ has a specific gravity of 1.04.   What is the normality of the solution as an acid?   How many milliliters of 3.00 molar KOH would be neutralized by 18.0 ml. of the acid?

4.13. How many milliliters of 0.500 N $BaCl_2$ solution would be required to precipitate all the sulfate from 10.0 millimoles of $FeSO_4.(NH_4)_2SO_4.6H_2O$?   How many milliliters of 0.100 N $AgNO_3$ would be required to precipitate the chloride from 8.30 ml. of the barium chloride solution?

4.14. What is the approximate normality of a solution of nitric acid marked "HNO_3 1:4"?

4.15. A solution of H_3PO_4 contains 0.500 millimole per milliliter.   What is the normality of the solution as a phosphate?   How many milliliters of 1.20 N KOH would be required to form KH_2PO_4 with 5.00 ml. of the phosphoric acid?   To what volume must 25.0 ml. of the original acid be diluted in order to make the solution 1.10 N as a phosphate?

4.16. How many grams of $FeCl_3$ are contained in 25.0 ml. of 0.520 N ferric chloride solution?   How many millimoles of $FeCl_3.6H_2O$ could be obtained by evaporating the solution to dryness?   How many milliliters of 0.200 N NH_4OH are required to react with 25.0 ml. of the ferric chloride solution to precipitate $Fe(OH)_3$?

CHAPTER 5

EQUILIBRIUM CONSTANTS

30. Law of Mass Action. In simple terms the law of mass action may be expressed as follows: *The rate of reaction between two or more interacting substances in a mixture is proportional to the product of the prevailing active concentrations of the substances.*

A great many of the reactions of analytical chemistry are reversible reactions. This means that the products of a given reaction interact, at least to some extent, to give the initial substances. Consider a general reversible reaction between substances A and B at a given temperature to give substances C and D according to the following equation:

$$A + B \rightleftarrows C + D$$

At the start of the reaction, only substances A and B are present. These react at a certain rate to give C and D and, as the latter are produced, the concentrations of A and B decrease. According to the law of mass action, the rate of the reaction between A and B at any given moment is proportional to the prevailing concentrations of A and B at that moment. In symbols this may be expressed as follows:

$$\text{Rate of reaction between A and B} = k'[A][B]$$

where [A] and [B] are the prevailing molar concentrations of A and B, respectively, and k' is a constant at a given temperature. As the concentrations of substances C and D increase, these substances in turn react at a constantly increasing rate to produce A and B. The rate of this reaction at any moment is proportional to the product of the prevailing concentrations of C and D.

$$\text{Rate of reaction between C and D} = k''[C][D]$$

When equilibrium has been established, these two rates are equal. Hence,

$$\frac{[C][D]}{[A][B]} = \frac{k'}{k''} = K$$

In the reaction $A + 2B \rightleftarrows C + D$ (*i.e.*, $A + B + B \rightleftarrows C + D$), the rate of reaction between A and B is proportional to the concentration of A and to the *square* of the concentration of B. Hence, at equilibrium,

$$\frac{[C][D]}{[A][B]^2} = K$$

41

More generally, in the reaction $w\text{A} + x\text{B} + \cdot \cdot \cdot \rightleftarrows y\text{C} + z\text{D} + \cdot \cdot \cdot$, the equilibrium constant is expressed as follows:

$$\frac{[\text{C}]^y[\text{D}]^z \cdot \cdot \cdot}{[\text{A}]^w[\text{B}]^x \cdot \cdot \cdot} = \text{K}$$

For the value K to be approximately a true constant, concentrations must be relatively small (see Sec. 36). Furthermore, although in computations involving chemical equilibria, concentrations are better expressed in terms of the number of moles of substance per kilogram of *solvent*, for dilute solutions this is practically the same as the number of moles of substance per liter of solution; and as the latter is consistent with the definition of a molar solution as used in analytical computations, it will be employed here in formulating mass-action expressions as well. In mass-action expressions molar concentrations will be represented as above by enclosing in brackets the symbol of the element, compound, or radical in question.

In general, if a solid substance is involved in a chemical equilibrium, its concentration is not included in the formulation of the mass-action constant, since the concentration of the solid is itself essentially a constant. The same is true of water in an equilibrium involving dilute aqueous solutions. Thus, the mass-action constant for the dissociation equilibrium

$$\text{NH}_4\text{OH} \rightleftarrows \text{NH}_3 + \text{H}_2\text{O}$$

is simply

$$\frac{[\text{NH}_3]}{[\text{NH}_4\text{OH}]} = \text{K}$$

31. Ion Product Constant of Water. Water dissociates slightly into hydrogen ions[1] and hydroxyl ions as follows:

$$\text{H}_2\text{O} \rightleftarrows \text{H}^+ + \text{OH}^-$$

The mass-action expression for this dissociation is simply

$$[\text{H}^+][\text{OH}^-] = \text{K}_w$$

since the concentration of undissociated H_2O in dilute aqueous solutions is essentially a constant and, as stated above, is omitted from mass-action expressions. In any aqueous solution, therefore, the product of the molar hydrogen-ion concentration and the molar hydroxyl-ion con-

---

[1] Experiments indicate that the hydrogen ion is hydrated. It is therefore often expressed as H_3O^+. This ion is called the *hydronium ion* and is formed by the union of a proton with a molecule of the solvent. Since the use of this symbol complicates equations and offers no particular advantages in analytical computations, the more simple symbol (H^+) is used in this text.

centration is a constant at a given temperature. This constant is called the *ion product constant* of water and at 25°C. has a value of 1.0×10^{-14}.

$$[H^+][OH^-] = K_w = 1.0 \times 10^{-14} \text{ (at 25°C.)}$$
$$= 1.2 \times 10^{-15} \text{ (at 0°C.)}$$
$$= 5.8 \times 10^{-13} \text{ (at 100°C.)}$$

In pure water the hydrogen-ion and the hydroxyl-ion concentrations are equal; at 25°C. each has a value of 1.0×10^{-7} molar.

32. pH Value. It is often convenient to express hydrogen-ion concentrations in terms of the *pH value*. The pH value as used in analytical chemistry is simply the common logarithm of the reciprocal of the molar hydrogen-ion concentration.

$$pH = \log \frac{1}{[H^+]} = - \log [H^+] = \text{colog} [H^+]$$

Similarly the pOH value, although less often used, is the logarithm of the reciprocal of the hydroxyl-ion concentration. The pH value of pure water at 25°C. is 7.0. The pH value of acid solutions is less than 7.0; the pH value of alkaline solutions is greater than 7.0. In general, at 25°C.,

$$pH + pOH = 14.0$$

EXAMPLE I. What is the pH value and what is the hydroxyl-ion concentration of a solution that is 0.0010 M in HCl (effective ionization = 100 per cent)?

SOLUTION:

$$[H^+] = 0.0010 = 1.0 \times 10^{-3}$$
$$pH = \log \frac{1}{1.0 \times 10^{-3}} = 3.0. \quad Ans.$$
$$pOH = 14.0 - 3.0 = 11.0$$
$$[OH^-] = 1.0 \times 10^{-11}. \quad Ans.$$

EXAMPLE II. The hydrogen-ion concentration in a certan dilute solution of sulfuric acid is 2.0×10^{-5}. What is the pH value? What is the pOH value?

SOLUTION:

$$pH = \log \frac{1}{2.0 \times 10^{-5}} = \log \frac{1}{0.20 \times 10^{-4}} = \log (5.0 \times 10^4)$$
$$= \log 10^4 + \log 5.0 = 4.00 + 0.70 = 4.70. \quad Ans.$$
$$pOH = 14.0 - 4.70 = 9.30. \quad Ans.$$

EXAMPLE III. The pH value of a certain solution is 5.92. What is the pOH value, the hydrogen-ion concentration, and the hydroxyl-ion concentration?

SOLUTION:

$$pH + pOH = 14.0$$
$$pOH = 14.0 - 5.92 = 8.08. \quad Ans.$$
$$[H^+] = 10^{-5.92} = 10^{+0.08} \times 10^{-6} = 1.20 \times 10^{-6}. \quad Ans.$$
$$[H^+][OH^-] = 1.0 \times 10^{-14}$$
$$[OH^-] = \frac{1.0 \times 10^{-14}}{1.20 \times 10^{-6}} = 8.3 \times 10^{-9}. \quad Ans.$$

Problems

(Temperatures are 25°C.)

5.1. (*a*) What is the pH value of a solution in which the hydrogen-ion concentration is 2.8×10^{-3}? Is the solution acid or alkaline? (*b*) What is the hydrogen-ion concentration of a solution with a pOH value of 4.17? Is the solution acid or alkaline?

Ans. (*a*) 2.55, acid. (*b*) 1.5×10^{-10}, alkaline.

5.2. What is the pH value of 0.010 molar HCl (100 per cent ionized)? Of 0.30 molar NaOH (90 per cent effective ionization)? Of a solution of HCl in which the hydrogen-ion concentration is 8.0 molar?

Ans. 2.0. 13.43. −0.90.

5.3. What is the hydrogen-ion concentration of a solution in which pH = −0.55?

Ans. 3.6 molar.

5.4. (*a*) Given pH = 10.46. Calculate $[H^+]$, $[OH^-]$, and pOH. (*b*) Given $[OH^-]$ = 5.6×10^{-2}. Calculate $[H^+]$, pH, and pOH.

Ans. (*a*) 3.5×10^{-11}, 2.9×10^{-4}, 3.54. (*b*) 1.8×10^{-13}, 12.75, 1.25.

5.5. (*a*) What is the pOH value of a solution in which the hydrogen-ion concentration is 5.3×10^{-4}? Is the solution acid or alkaline? (*b*) What is the hydroxyl-ion concentration of a solution in which the pH value is 9.27? Is the solution acid or alkaline?

5.6. What is the pH value of 0.050 molar HNO_3 (100 per cent ionized)? Of 0.80 molar KOH (effective ionization = 85 per cent)? Of a solution of HCl in which the hyrogen-ion concentration is 5.0 molar?

5.7. What is the hydroxyl-ion concentration of a solution in which pOH = −0.27?

5.8. (*a*) Given pOH = 5.80. Calculate $[H^+]$, $[OH^-]$, and pH. (*b*) Given $[H]^+$ = 3.1×10^{-9}. Calculate $[OH^-]$, pH, and pOH.

33. Ionization Constant. The law of mass action can be applied to the equilibrium in dilute solution between the molecules of a weak acid or weak base and its ions. Thus, acetic acid, $HC_2H_3O_2$, is partially ionized in solution as follows:

$$HC_2H_3O_2 \rightleftarrows H^+ + C_2H_3O_2^-$$

Therefore,

$$\frac{[H^+][C_2H_3O_2^-]}{[HC_2H_3O_2]} = K_{HC_2H_3O_2}$$

That is, in a solution containing acetic acid, the total molar concentration of hydrogen ions (from whatever source) multiplied by the total molar concentration of acetate ions (from whatever source) divided by the molar concentration of un-ionized acetic acid, is a constant at a given temperature. This value is called the ionization constant of acetic acid. Its value at 25°C is 1.86×10^{-5}.

A similar mass-action expression can be set up for the ionization of a solution of ammonia in water. Here ammonium hydroxide molecules are presumably formed which, in turn, dissociate partially into ammonium ions and hydroxyl ions.

$$NH_4OH \rightleftarrows NH_4^+ + OH^-$$

The ionization constant is therefore usually written

$$\frac{[NH_4^+][OH^-]}{[NH_4OH]} = K_{NH_4OH}$$

Since ammonium hydroxide molecules (if they exist at all) are in equilibrium with ammonia and water, the equilibrium is more generally expressed as

$$NH_3 + H_2O \rightleftarrows (NH_4OH) \rightleftarrows NH_4^+ + OH^-$$

and the ionization constant can be written

$$\frac{[NH_4^+][OH^-]}{[NH_3]} = K_{NH_4OH}$$

In either case the *total* concentration of NH_3, either dissolved as such or combined as NH_4OH, is used in the denominator of the fraction, so the numerical value of the constant is the same in the two cases. At 25°C. it is 1.75×10^{-5}.

The ionization constants of a few weak acids and bases are given in the Appendix.

EXAMPLE I. What is the ionization constant of acetic acid at a certain temperature if in tenth-molar solution it is 1.3 per cent ionized?

$$HC_2H_3O_2 \rightleftarrows H^+ + C_2H_3O_2^-$$

SOLUTION: If 0.10 mole of $HC_2H_3O_2$ were completely ionized, it would give 0.10 mole (or 0.10 gram-ion) of H^+ and 0.10 mole (or 0.10 gram-ion) of $C_2H_3O_2^-$. Being only 1.3 per cent ionized, it gives 0.10×0.013 = 0.0013 mole of H^+ and 0.0013 mole of $C_2H_3O_2^-$, leaving 0.0987 mole of undissociated $HC_2H_3O_2$ molecules. The molar concentrations are therefore as follows:

$$[H^+] = 0.0013$$
$$[C_2H_3O_2^-] = 0.0013$$
$$[HC_2H_3O_2] = 0.0987$$

Substituting these in the above expression for the ionization constant of acetic acid, we get

$$\frac{(0.0013)(0.0013)}{0.0987} = K$$

$$K = 1.7 \times 10^{-5}. \quad Ans.$$

EXAMPLE II.   At 25°C. the ionization constant of acetic acid is 1.86 $\times 10^{-5}$. What is the molar concentration of hydrogen ions in a 0.20-molar solution of acetic acid at 25°C.?

SOLUTION:

Let x = molar concentration of H^+

Then

x = molar concentration of $C_2H_3O_2^-$

and

$0.20 - x$ = molar concentration of undissociated $HC_2H_3O_2$

$$\frac{[H^+][C_2H_3O_2^-]}{[HC_2H_3O_2]} = K = 1.86 \times 10^{-5}$$

$$\frac{(x)(x)}{(0.20 - x)} = 1.86 \times 10^{-5}$$

Solving,

$$x = 1.9 \times 10^{-3} \text{ mole per liter.} \quad Ans.$$

Numerical values in mass-action expressions need not be expressed to more than two or, at the most, three significant figures. Therefore simplifying assumptions can often be made. In the above fractional equation, the value of x is so small compared with the value 0.20 from which it is subtracted, that it is well within the limit of precision to write

$$\frac{(x)(x)}{0.20} = 1.86 \times 10^{-5}$$

and thus avoid solving a quadratic equation.[1]

34. Common Ion Effect. Buffered Solution. Suppose into a dilute solution of acetic acid is dissolved a considerable quantity of sodium acetate, *i.e.*, a highly ionized salt of acetic acid. The total acetate-ion concentration is greatly increased, but since the equilibrium constant $\frac{[H^+][C_2H_3O_2^-]}{HC_2H_3O_2} = K_{HC_2H_3O_2}$ must be maintained, the greater part of the hydrogen ions present must unite with acetate ions to form more of the undissociated acetic acid molecules. In other words, the equilibrium

---

[1] In cases where such simplifying assumptions cannot be made, the formula for solving the general quadratic equation $ax^2 + bx + c = 0$ is

$$x = \frac{-b \pm \sqrt{b^2 - 4ac}}{2a}$$

reaction $HC_2H_3O_2 \rightleftarrows H^+ + C_2H_3O_2^-$ must go to the left to a degree sufficient to reestablish the numerical value of the constant. The solution therefore becomes much less acidic, with a hydrogen-ion concentration only slightly greater than that of pure water.

A similar case is one in which an ammonium salt is added to a solution of ammonium hydroxide. The common ion, NH_4^+, represses the ionization $NH_3 + H_2O \rightleftarrows (NH_4OH) \rightleftarrows NH_4^+ + OH^-$ to a very great extent, for in order to maintain the equilibrium constant $\dfrac{[NH_4^+][OH^-]}{[NH_3]} = K$, the hydroxyl-ion concentration must be greatly decreased. The resulting solution is only slightly more basic than pure water.

In each of the above two cases the solution is said to be *buffered* by the common ion added. The acetic acid-sodium acetate combination, for example, has a low hydrogen-ion concentration which is little affected even by the addition of small amounts of a strong acid, for the additional hydrogen ions merely unite with the acetate ions (still present in excess) to give more acetic acid, the ionization of which is repressed by the acetate. Similarly, the basicity of a buffered ammonium hydroxide solution is not much affected even by the addition of small amounts of a strong base like sodium hydroxide.

Buffered solutions are much used both in qualitative and quantitative analysis to effect certain separations of elements where a carefully controlled hydrogen-ion or hydroxyl-ion concentration is essential. Problems covering some of these separations are included in this book.

EXAMPLE. What is the hydrogen-ion concentration in 500 ml. of a 0.10-molar solution of acetic acid at 25°C. if the solution contains an additional 2.0 grams of acetate ions added in the form of sodium acetate? $(K_{HC_2H_3O_2} = 1.86 \times 10^{-5}.)$

SOLUTION:

$$2.0 \text{ grams } C_2H_3O_2^- \text{ per 500 ml.} = 0.068 \text{ mole per liter}$$
$$\text{Let } x = \text{concentration of } H^+ \text{ ions}$$

Then
$$x + 0.068 = \text{concentration of } C_2H_3O_2^- \text{ ions}$$

and
$$0.10 - x = \text{concentration of un-ionized } HC_2H_3O_2$$

Therefore,
$$\frac{(x)(x + 0.068)}{(0.10 - x)} = 1.86 \times 10^{-5}$$

or approximately (since x is small),

$$\frac{(x)(0.068)}{(0.10)} = 1.86 \times 10^{-5}$$

Solving,

$$x = 2.6 \times 10^{-5} \text{ mole per liter.} \quad Ans.$$

35. Ionization of Polybasic Acids. Polybasic acids like H_2S, H_2CO_3, H_3PO_4, etc., ionize in steps, and a mass-action expression can be written for each step. Thus, H_2S ionizes to form H^+ and HS^-, in which case the ionization constant is

$$\frac{[H^+][HS^-]}{[H_2S]} = K_1 = 9.1 \times 10^{-8}$$

The HS^- ions are further ionized into H^+ and $S^=$, in which case

$$\frac{[H^+][S^=]}{[HS^-]} = K_2 = 1.2 \times 10^{-15}$$

Multiplying the two equations one by the other gives

$$\frac{[H^+]^2[S^=]}{[H_2S]} = K = 1.1 \times 10^{-22}$$

A *saturated* solution of H_2S is about 0.10 molar, and $[H_2S] = 0.10$. Therefore in cases where metallic elements are precipitated by saturating their solutions with H_2S, $[H^+]^2[S^=] = 1.1 \times 10^{-23}$.

It is seen that the primary ionization of H_2S is much greater than the secondary ionization and that the ionization cannot be correctly expressed by the equation $H_2S \rightleftarrows 2H^+ + S^=$. The concentration of H^+ ions in a solution of H_2S is not twice that of the $S^=$ ions. The primary ionization of any polybasic acid is much greater than the secondary ionization.

EXAMPLE I. What is the approximate hydrogen-ion concentration in a solution of hydrogen sulfide which is 0.07 molar in H_2S?

SOLUTION: In solving this problem, the expression $\frac{[H^+]^2[S^=]}{[H_2S]} = 1.1 \times 10^{-22}$ cannot be used since neither $[H^+]$ nor $[S^=]$ is known and there is no simple relation between them. On the other hand, although H_2S is ionized in two steps, the first ionization is so much greater than the second ionization that, for the purpose of obtaining an approximate answer, the latter may be considered negligible. In other words, practically all of the hydrogen ions may be considered to come from the ionization of H_2S into H^+ and HS^-. Therefore $[H^+]$ and $[HS^-]$ are practically equal in value and

$$\frac{[H^+][HS^-]}{[H_2S]} = 9.1 \times 10^{-8}$$

or

$$\frac{(x)(x)}{0.07} = 9.1 \times 10^{-8}$$

$$x = 8 \times 10^{-5} \text{ mole per liter.} \quad Ans.$$

EXAMPLE II. What is the concentration of $S^=$ ions in 200 ml. of a solution that is 0.050 molar in H_2S and that by the addition of HCl contains a total of 0.12 equivalent of H^+ ions?

SOLUTION:

$$\text{Let } x = \text{molar concentration of } S^= \text{ ions}$$
$$0.050 - x = \text{approx. } 0.050 = \text{concentration of undissociated } H_2S$$
$$0.12 \times 5 = 0.60 = \text{concentration of } H^+ \text{ ions}$$
$$\frac{(0.60)^2(x)}{(0.050)} = K = 1.1 \times 10^{-22}$$
$$x = 1.5 \times 10^{-23} \text{ mole per liter. } Ans.$$

36. Activity and Activity Coefficients. In analytical chemistry mass-action calculations are usually applied to equilibria involving electrolytes in solution. As solutions of electrolytes are made progressively more concentrated, the quantitative effect on such properties as conductivity and freezing-point lowering becomes progressively less than that calculated solely from the net change in molar concentration. This is likewise true of mass-action equilibria. This phenomenon was formerly explained by assuming that electrolytes are less completely ionized in more concentrated solutions; that the degree of ionization approaches 100 per cent only as dilution approaches infinity. A more satisfactory explanation is based on the assumption that most salts and the so-called strong acids and bases are practically completely ionized in all aqueous solutions but that the effective concentration, or *activity*, of the ions is decreased because of forces of attraction between the positive and negative ions. These forces become less at higher dilutions since the ions are farther apart.

In mass-action expressions, therefore, activities or effective concentrations, rather than molar concentrations should be used for accurate results. The activity (a) of an ion or molecule can be found by multiplying its molar concentration (c) by an activity coefficient (f).

$$a = fc$$

An *activity coefficient* is therefore a factor which converts a molar concentration to a value which expresses quantitatively the true mass-action effect. Thus, the ionization constant of acetic acid is correctly expressed as

$$\frac{f_1[H^+] \times f_2[C_2H_3O_2^-]}{f_3[HC_2H_3O_2]} = K$$

where f_1, f_2, and f_3 are the activity coefficients of the hydrogen ion, the acetate ion, and the acetic acid molecule, respectively.

Activity coefficients vary with temperature and, in general, decrease with increasing concentration. The activity coefficient of 0.01 M HCl is 0.92, that of 0.05 M HCl is 0.86, and that of 0.10 M HCl is 0.82. In general, too, under the same conditions of concentration and temperature, the activity coefficients of electrolytes of the valence type A^+B^- are greater than those of the types $(A^+)_2B^=$ and $A^{++}(B^-)_2$ and are still greater than those of the type $A^{++}B^=$. For example, the activity coefficient of 0.01 M BaCl$_2$ is 0.72; that of 0.01 M MgSO$_4$ is 0.40. The activity of a given electrolyte is also influenced by the presence of other electrolytes in the solution.

In general, it is difficult to determine experimentally or otherwise the numerical values of activity coefficients under any but the simplest conditions, but in the case of relatively dilute solutions (*e.g.*, 0.01 formal or less) and particularly where univalent ions are involved, activity coefficients are not far from unity, and so no great error is introduced when molar concentrations are used in place of activities. Since concentrations in most analytical operations are relatively low and since a high degree of precision is seldom required in analytical computations involving mass-action constants, activity coefficients can be omitted without much error. They are therefore not included in the calculations in this book.

37. Dissociation Constants of Complex Ions. A complex ion is one that is in equilibrium with its constituents. These constituents are ordinarily a simple positive ion and either a neutral molecule or a negative ion. The mass-action principle can be applied to dilute solutions of such ions. Thus the copper ammino (or copper ammonio) ion, $Cu(NH_3)_4^{++}$, ionizes slightly as follows:

$$Cu(NH_3)_4^{++} \rightleftarrows Cu^{++} + 4NH_3$$

Its dissociation constant is therefore expressed as follows:

$$\frac{[Cu^{++}][NH_3]^4}{[Cu(NH_3)_4^{++}]} = K \; (= 4.6 \times 10^{-14})$$

This means that in a dilute solution containing the complex ion, the total molar concentration of the simple cupric ions present, multiplied by the fourth power of the total molar concentration of ammonia (NH$_3$ + NH$_4$OH), divided by the molar concentration of the undissociated complex ion, is a constant at a given temperature.

Complex ions of this type frequently encountered in analytical chemistry are $Ag(NH_3)_2^+$, $Cu(NH_3)_4^{++}$, $Cd(NH_3)_4^{++}$, $Ni(NH_3)_4^{++}$, $Co(NH_3)_6^{+++}$, and $Zn(NH_3)_4^{++}$.

Important cyanide complexes include $Fe(CN)_6^{\equiv}$, $Fe(CN)_6^=$, $Ag(CN)_2^-$, $Cd(CN)_4^=$, $Cu(CN)_3^=$, $Hg(CN)_4^=$, $Co(CN)_6^{\equiv}$, and $Ni(CN)_4^=$. Halide complexes like $SnCl_6^=$ and $HgI_4^=$ and oxalate complexes like $Mg(C_2O_4)_2^=$ are also common.

EXAMPLE I. What is the molar concentration of mercuric ions and of cyanide ions in a tenth-molar solution of $K_2Hg(CN)_4$? (Dissociation constant of $Hg(CN)_4^= = 4.0 \times 10^{-42}$.)

SOLUTION:

$$\frac{[Hg^{++}][CN^-]^4}{[Hg(CN)_4^=]} = 4.0 \times 10^{-42}$$

Let $x =$ concentration of Hg^{++} in the dissociation:

$$Hg(CN)_4^= \rightleftarrows Hg^{++} + 4CN^-$$

Then

$$4x = \text{concentration of } CN^-$$

$$0.10 - x = 0.10 \text{ (approximately)} = \text{concentration of } Hg(CN)_4^=$$

$$\frac{(x)(4x)^4}{0.10} = 4.0 \times 10^{-42}$$

$$x = 1.1 \times 10^{-9} \text{ molar } Hg^{++}. \quad Ans.$$
$$4x = 4.4 \times 10^{-9} \text{ molar } CN^-. \quad Ans.$$

EXAMPLE II. What is the dissociation constant of $Ag(NH_3)_2^+$ if a solution of 0.020 formula weight of AgCl, in sufficient excess NH_4OH to give a total ammonia concentration of 2.0 molar and a total volume of one liter, has a silver-ion concentration of only 0.000037 mg. per liter?

SOLUTION:

$$\frac{[Ag^+][NH_3]^2}{[Ag(NH_3)_2^+]} = K$$

$$[Ag^+] = \frac{0.000037 \times 10^{-3}}{108} = 3.4 \times 10^{-10} \text{ mole per liter}$$

$$[NH_3] = 2.0$$
$$[Ag(NH_3)_2^+] = 0.020 \text{ (approximately)}$$
$$\frac{(3.4 \times 10^{-10})(2.0)^2}{0.020} = K$$

$$= 6.8 \times 10^{-8}. \quad Ans.$$

Problems

(See Appendix for ionization constants and dissociation constants. Temperatures are 25°C. unless otherwise specified.)

5.9. A certain organic acid has one replaceable hydrogen and in 0.010 molar aqueous solution is 0.18 per cent ionized. What is the ionization constant of the acid?

Ans. 3.2×10^{-8}.

5.10. Lactic acid is a monobasic acid with an ionization constant of 1.6×10^{-4}. What is the lactate-ion concentration in a 0.50 N solution of the acid?

Ans. 8.9×10^{-3} molar.

5.11. What is the molar concentration of each of the three constituents of acetic acid in 0.050 N solution?

Ans. $H^+ = 0.00096$, $C_2H_3O_2^- = 0.00096$, $HC_2H_3O_2 = 0.049$.

5.12. What is the concentration of a solution of NH_4OH if it is 3.0 per cent ionized? If it is 0.50 per cent ionized?

Ans.   0.020 molar.   0.72 molar.

5.13. Formic acid is a monobasic acid that is 3.2 per cent ionized in 0.20-molar solution.   What is the ionization constant of formic acid, and what is its percentage ionization in 0.050 molar solution?

Ans. 2.1×10^{-4}, 6.4 per cent.

5.14. What is the hydrogen-ion concentration in a 0.10-normal solution of acetic acid containing sufficient dissolved sodium acetate to give a total acetate-ion concentration of 0.85 mole per liter?

Ans. 2.2×10^{-6} molar.

5.15. What is the hydrogen-ion concentration and the pOH value of a 0.010-molar solution of hypochlorous acid at 25°C.?

Ans. 2×10^{-5} molar, 9.30.

5.16. What is the pH value of a 0.30-normal solution of NH_4OH?   What is the pH value of a 0.30-normal solution of NH_4OH containing sufficient dissolved NH_4Cl to give an ammonium-ion concentration of 1.2 moles per liter?

Ans.   11.36.   8.63.

5.17. Approximately how many grams of acetate ions should be dissolved in a liter of 0.10 M acetic acid in order to cut down the hydrogen-ion concentration one hundredfold?

Ans.   8 grams.

5.18. To what volume should 100 ml. of any weak 0.30 molar monobasic acid or mono-acidic base be diluted in order to triple its percentage ionization?

Ans.   900 ml.

5.19. What is the approximate concentration of sulfide ions and of hydrosulfide ions (HS^-) in a 0.070-molar solution of hydrogen sulfide?   (*Hint:* Assume that practically all the hydrogen ions come from the primary ionization.)

Ans. 1.2×10^{-15} molar, 8×10^{-5} molar.

5.20. Calculate the concentration of sulfide ions in a solution which is 0.080 molar in H_2S and contains sufficient HCl to give a pH value of 3.40.

Ans. 5.5×10^{-17} molar.

5.21. What is the approximate molar concentration of silver ions and of cyanide ions in a tenth-molar solution of $KAg(CN)_2$?   [Dissociation constant of $Ag(CN)_2^-$ $= 1.0 \times 10^{-21}$.]

Ans. 3×10^{-8} molar, 6×10^{-8} molar.

5.22. What are the approximate molar concentrations of Na^+, Cd^+, CN^-, and $Cd(CN)_4^-$ in a solution made by dissolving 0.020 F.W. of $Na_2Cd(CN)_4$ in water and diluting to one liter?

Ans. $[Na^+] = 0.040$ molar, $[Cd^{++}] = 6.4 \times 10^{-5}$ molar, $[CN^-] = 2.5 \times 10^{-4}$ molar, $[Cd(CN)_4^-] = 0.020$ molar.

5.23. If 100 mg. of AgCl are dissolved in excess ammonium hydroxide to give a volume of 500 ml. of solution, and the total concentration of ammonia is 0.30 molar, what is the silver-ion concentration? Dissociation constant of $Ag(NH_3)_2^+ = 6.8 \times 10^{-8}$.

Ans. 1.06×10^{-9} molar.

5.24. What is the concentration of Cd^{++} ions in a solution 0.040 molar in $Cd(NH_3)_4^{++}$ and 1.5 molar in NH_3?

Ans. 2.0×10^{-9} molar.

5.25. A certain organic amine acts as a mono-acidic base in aqueous solution. A 0.05-molar solution is found to give a hydroxyl-ion concentration of 7.5×10^{-5} molar. What is the ionization constant of the base? What is its pH value?

5.26. Lactic acid ($HC_3H_5O_2$) is a monobasic acid with an ionization constant at 25°C. of 1.6×10^{-4}. In a tenth-molar solution how many grams of lactic acid are present in the un-ionized form?

5.27. What is the molar concentration of the three constituents of benzoic acid in 0.080 M solution at 25°C.? What is the pH value?

5.28. What molarity acetic acid is 2.0 per cent ionized at 25°C.?

5.29. Ethylamine is a derivative of ammonia and in aqueous solution is basic like ammonia. At a certain temperature ethylamine in 0.30-molar solution gives a hydroxyl-ion concentration of 1.3×10^{-2} molar. What is the ionization constant of ethylamine at that temperature, and what is its percentage of ionization in 0.20-molar solution?

5.30. Calculate the cyanide-ion concentration and the percentage ionization of a 0.030-molar solution of hydrocyanic acid.

5.31. Calculate the hydrogen-ion concentration of a solution at 25°C. containing 25 ml. of 4 N acetic acid in a total volume of 1,200 ml. Calculate the hydrogen-ion concentration in the same solution after adding 15 grams of sodium acetate (assuming the effective ionization of the salt to be 85 per cent). What is the pH value in each case?

5.32. To what volume should 50 ml. of any weak 0.20-molar monobasic acid be diluted in order to double its percentage ionization?

5.33. In a 0.20-molar solution of ammonium hydroxide, what percentage of the base is un-ionized? What is its pH value?

5.34. Approximately how many grams of NH_4^+ ions should be dissolved into a liter of 0.20 M NH_4OH in order to cut down the concentration of hydroxyl ions to one-fiftieth its previous value?

5.35. What is the pH value of a 0.25-normal solution of acetic acid? What is the pH value of a 0.25-normal solution of acetic acid containing sufficient dissolved sodium acetate to give an acetate-ion concentration of 2.0 moles per liter?

5.36. What are the approximate concentrations of HCO_3^- and of CO_3^- in a 0.0010-molar solution of carbonic acid? (*Hint:* Assume that practically all of the hydrogen ions come from the primary ionization of the acid.)

5.37. What is the sulfide-ion concentration of a solution 0.090 molar in H_2S and containing sufficient HCl to give a pH value of 4.50?

5.38. What are the approximate molar concentrations of K^+, Hg^{++}, HgI_4^- and I^- in a solution made by dissolving 0.010 F.W. of K_2HgI_4 in water and diluting to one liter? (Dissociation constant of $HgI_4^- = 5.0 \times 10^{-31}$.)

5.39. What is the approximate molar concentration of cyanide ion in a solution 0.010 molar in $K_4Fe(CN)_6$?

5.40. If 50 milligrams of AgCl are dissolved in excess NH_4OH ($AgCl + 2NH_4OH \rightarrow Ag(NH_3)_2^+ + Cl^- + 2H_2O$) and the resulting solution is 0.50 formal in NH_3 and has a volume of 500 ml., what is the concentration of Ag^+ ions in formula weights per liter?

5.41. What is the molar cyanide-ion concentration of an aqueous solution containing 0.020 F.W. of $K_2Ni(CN)_4$ per 500 ml.? What is the concentration of Ni^{++} in such a solution if sufficient additional KCN is present to give a total cyanide concentration of 0.10 molar?

5.42. If 0.10 F.W. of $Hg(NO_3)_2$ is treated with excess Na_2S solution in the presence of NaOH, the precipitate of HgS that first forms dissolves to give $HgS_2^=$ ions. If the dissociation constant of $HgS_2^=$ is 2×10^{-55} and the sulfide-ion concentration of the solution is 2.0 molar, what is the concentration of Hg^{++}?

38. Solubility Product.

A very important equilibrium constant applies to a saturated solution of a slightly soluble, completely ionized salt. Most of the precipitates encountered in analytical chemistry belong to this category.

Consider the simple case of a saturated solution of silver chloride in equilibrium with some of the undissolved salt. What little silver chloride is in solution is completely ionized, and the equilibrium can be written

$$AgCl(solid) \rightleftarrows Ag^+ + Cl^-$$

The mass-action equilibrium constant is expressed simply as

$$[Ag^+][Cl^-] = K_{AgCl}$$

or more accurately as

$$f_1[Ag^+] \times f_2[Cl^-] = K_{AgCl}$$

where f_1 and f_2 are the respective activity coefficients of the two ions (see Sec. 36). These coefficients are only slightly less than 1.00 in value.

This constant, applying as it does to a saturated solution of a slightly soluble salt, is called a *solubility product* ($K_{S.P.}$). The numerical value of the solubility product of silver chloride at 25°C. is 1.0×10^{-10}. This means that in a solution saturated with silver chloride at this temperature the total molar concentration of silver ions in the solution multiplied by the total molar concentration of chloride ions equals 1.0×10^{-10}. Conversely, when the product of the total concentration of silver ions and the total concentration of chloride ions in any solution exceeds this value, a precipitate of silver chloride is obtained under conditions of stable equilibrium.

Lead chloride ionizes as follows:

$$PbCl_2 \rightleftarrows Pb^{++} + 2Cl^-$$

Its solubility product is therefore

$$[Pb^{++}][Cl^-]^2 = K_{PbCl_2}$$

Here the square of the total chloride-ion concentration must be used. In terms of activities, the solubility product is

$$f_1[Pb^{++}] \times f_2^2[Cl^-]^2 = K_{PbCl_2}$$

In most mass-action calculations two significant figures are all that are warranted by the precision of the data and of the constant itself. The precision is much less in calculations involving the solubilities and solubility products of the more insoluble hydroxides and sulfides. These values are usually known only very approximately, for the composition of a precipitate of this type may be quite variable. In addition, in the case of insoluble salts of weak polybasic acids like H_2S and H_3PO_4, conditions are somewhat complicated by hydrolysis effects. Thus, sulfide ions are in equilibrium with bisulfide ions (HS^-), and phosphate ions hydrolyze to give $HPO_4^=$ and $H_2PO_4^-$ ions. Numerical values obtained in simple calculations that neglect such side reactions can be considered as only approximate. They are nevertheless valuable in showing relative magnitudes of effects.

EXAMPLE I. What is the solubility product of Ag_3PO_4 if the solubility of the salt is 6.5×10^{-3} gram per liter? Neglect hydrolysis effects.

SOLUTION: 6.5×10^{-3} gram per liter $= (6.5 \times 10^{-3})/418.7 = 1.6 \times 10^{-5}$ mole per liter. The salt is 100 per cent ionized as follows:

$$Ag_3PO_4 \rightarrow 3Ag^+ + PO_4^=$$

Therefore,

$$[Ag^+] = 3 \times 1.6 \times 10^{-5}$$
$$[PO_4^=] = 1.6 \times 10^{-5}$$
$$(3 \times 1.6 \times 10^{-5})^3(1.6 \times 10^{-5}) = 1.8 \times 10^{-18}. \quad Ans.$$

EXAMPLE II. The solubility product of CaF_2 is 3.2×10^{-11}. How many grams of Ca^{++} are present in 500 ml. of a saturated solution of CaF_2? How many grams of $CaCl_2$ can be dissolved in 500 ml. of a solution containing 9.5 grams of fluoride ions?

SOLUTION:

Let x = molar concentration of Ca^{++}

Then

$$2x = \text{molar concentration of } F^-$$
$$(x)(2x)^2 = 3.2 \times 10^{-11}$$
$$x = 2.0 \times 10^{-4} \text{ mole per liter}$$
$$2.0 \times 10^{-4} \times 40 \times \frac{1}{2} = 0.0040 \text{ gram } Ca^{++} \text{ per 500 ml.} \quad Ans.$$

$$9.5 \text{ grams } F^- \text{ per 500 ml.} = 1 \text{ mole } F^- \text{ per liter}$$
$$(x)(1)^2 = 3.2 \times 10^{-11}$$
$$x = 3.2 \times 10^{-11} \text{ mole } Ca^{++} \text{ per liter}$$
$$3.2 \times 10^{-11} \times 111 = 2.9 \times 10^{-9} \text{ gram } CaCl_2 \text{ per liter}$$
$$= 1.45 \times 10^{-9} \text{ gram } CaCl_2 \text{ per 500 ml.} \quad Ans.$$

EXAMPLE III.   What is the hydroxyl-ion concentration in a solution of sodium hydroxide having a pH value of 11.6?   How many grams of magnesium could remain dissolved in 500 ml. of such a solution [solubility product of $Mg(OH)_2 = 3.4 \times 10^{-11}$]?

SOLUTION:

$$[H^+] = 10^{-11.6} = 10^{(-12+0.4)} \text{ or } 10^{\overline{12}.4}$$
$$= 2.52 \times 10^{-12} \text{ (since antilog } 0.4 = 2.52)$$
$$[OH^-] = \frac{1.0 \times 10^{-14}}{2.52 \times 10^{-12}} = 3.98 \times 10^{-3}. \quad Ans.$$
$$pOH = 14 - 11.6 = 2.4$$
$$[OH^-] = 10^{-2.4} = 10^{0.6} \times 10^{-3} = 3.98 \times 10^{-3}. \quad Ans.$$
$$[Mg^{++}][OH^-]^2 = 3.4 \times 10^{-11}$$
$$[Mg^{++}] = \frac{3.4 \times 10^{-11}}{(3.98 \times 10^{-3})^2} = 2.1 \times 10^{-6} \text{ mole per liter} =$$
$$2.55 \times 10^{-5} \text{ gram per 500 ml.} \quad Ans.$$

39. Fractional Precipitation.   Ordinarily when a precipitating agent is added slowly to a solution containing two ions capable of being precipitated by the agent, the substance with the lesser solubility will precipitate first.   The point at which the second substance will precipitate can be determined from the solubility products of the two precipitates.

Suppose to a solution 0.10 molar in Ba^{++} and 0.10 molar in Sr^{++} is added gradually and in very minute quantities a solution of Na_2SO_4. Insoluble $BaSO_4$ (solubility product $K_{BaSO_4} = 1.1 \times 10^{-10}$) precipitates first, then $SrSO_4$ ($K_{SrSO_4} = 2.8 \times 10^{-7}$) begins to precipitate.   The ratio of the two solubility products is as follows:

$$\frac{[Ba^{++}][SO_4^=]}{[Sr^{++}][SO_4^=]} = \frac{1.1 \times 10^{-10}}{2.8 \times 10^{-7}}$$

Therefore

$$\frac{[Ba^{++}]}{[Sr^{++}]} = 0.00039$$

At the point where $SrSO_4$ just *begins* to precipitate (and the concentration of Sr^{++} is still 0.10 M) the barium-ion concentration will have been reduced to 0.000039 molar, since

$$\frac{[Ba^{++}]}{0.10} = 0.00039$$

Separation of the two cations is therefore nearly complete at this point.

In qualitative analysis the preparation of a solution of a water-insoluble salt for the anion tests is usually made by metathesis of the solid with a solution of Na_2CO_3. The extent of metathesis can be determined, roughly at least, from the solubility product of the original salt and that of the insoluble compound of the metal formed by the metathesis.

EXAMPLE. If lead iodide (PbI_2) is boiled with a solution of sodium carbonate which is 2.0 molar in carbonate ions, the insoluble lead iodide is converted to the more insoluble lead carbonate ($\underline{PbI_2 + CO_3^= \rightarrow 2I^- + PbCO_3}$). Assuming that sufficient PbI_2 is present to give equilibrium conditions between the two insoluble substances and that the solubility products of PbI_2 and $PbCO_3$ at the temperature of the solution are 2.4×10^{-8} and 5.6×10^{-14}, respectively, what would be the concentration of iodide ion in the resulting solution?

SOLUTION:

$$\frac{[Pb^{++}][I^-]^2}{[Pb^{++}][CO_3^=]} = \frac{2.4 \times 10^{-8}}{5.6 \times 10^{-14}}$$

$$\frac{[I^-]^2}{2.0} = 4.3 \times 10^5$$

$$[I^-] = 930 \text{ moles per liter. } Ans.$$

This concentration is of course impossible to attain, not only because of the limited solubility of the NaI formed, but also because the PbI_2 is completely metathesized before the equilibrium condition is reached. The result merely shows that PbI_2 is readily and completely metathesized by Na_2CO_3 solution.

Problems

(Temperatures are 25°C. unless otherwise specified. A table of solubility products is given in the Appendix.)

5.43. A saturated solution of barium fluoride, BaF_2, is 7.5×10^{-3} molar. What is the solubility product of barium fluoride?

Ans. 1.7×10^{-6}.

5.44. If 0.11 mg. of silver bromide dissolves in one liter of water, what is the solubility product of silver bromide?

Ans. 3.5×10^{-13}

5.45. If the solubility product of calcium iodate, $Ca(IO_3)_2$, is 6.4×10^{-9}, how many milligrams will dissolve in 500 ml. of water? How many milligrams of Ca^{++} can remain dissolved in 500 ml. of a solution that is 0.20 molar in IO_3^- ions?

Ans. 228 mg.   0.0032 mg.

5.46. From the solubility product of PbI_2 (see Appendix) and assuming no complex ions to be formed, calculate how many grams of lead ions and of iodide ions are contained in each milliliter of a saturated solution of lead iodide. What is the molarity, and what is the normality of the solution?

Ans. 3.7×10^{-4}, 4.6×10^{-4} gram. 1.8×10^{-9} molar, 3.6×10^{-9} normal.

5.47. A saturated solution of K_2PtCl_6 contains 11 mg. of the salt in each milliliter. What is the solubility product of the salt? How many milligrams of Pt can remain dissolved (as $PtCl_6^-$) in each milliliter of a solution that contains 3.9 grams of K^+ per liter?

Ans. 4.6×10^{-5}.   0.90 mg.

5.48. Mercurous bromide, Hg_2Br_2, dissociates into Hg_2^{++} and $2Br^-$.   Its solubility at 25°C. is 0.039 mg. per liter.   What is its solubility product at that temperature?

Ans. 1.4×10^{-21}.

5.49. What is the solubility product of $Pb(IO_3)_2$ if a saturated solution of the salt contains 1.0×10^{-2} gram of iodate ions per liter?

Ans. 9.3×10^{-14}.

5.50. Excess CaF_2 is boiled with a solution of Na_2CO_3 that is 2.0 molar in carbonate ions, and a very small amount of $CaCO_3$ and fluoride ions is formed.   If the solubility product of $CaCO_3$ is A and the molar solubility of CaF_2 is B, what (in terms of A and B) is the molar concentration of fluoride ions in the resulting solution after equilibrium has been reached?

Ans. $\sqrt[2]{\dfrac{8B^3}{A}}$.

5.51. The concentration of a saturated solution of Ag_2SO_4 is 0.052 normal.   What is the solubility product of Ag_2SO_4?

Ans. 7.0×10^{-5}.

5.52. If A moles of Ag_3PO_4 dissolve in 500 ml. of water, express the solubility product of Ag_3PO_4 in terms of A, and the normality of a saturated solution of Ag_3PO_4 in terms of A.   Neglect hydrolysis effects.

Ans. $432A^4$, $6A$.

5.53. If the solubility product of $Ca_3(PO_4)_2$ is A, express in terms of A the solubility of $Ca_3(PO_4)_2$ in moles per liter.   Also express in terms of A the normality of a saturated solution of the salt.   Neglect hydrolysis effects.

Ans. $\sqrt[5]{\dfrac{A}{108}}$, $6\sqrt[5]{\dfrac{A}{108}}$ $(= \sqrt[5]{72A})$.

5.54. How many milligrams of Mn^{++} can remain dissolved in 100 ml. of a solution of pH 8.6 without precipitating $Mn(OH)_2$?

Ans.   13.5 mg.

5.55. From the solubility product of $Fe(OH)_3$, calculate the weight of Fe^{+++} in milligrams which must be present in one liter of solution in order to cause precipitation of the hydroxide when the hydroxyl-ion concentration is 8.0×10^{-5} mole per liter.

Ans. 1.2×10^{-19} mg.

5.56. Given $K_{S.P.}$ $MgCO_3 = 2.6 \times 10^{-5}$; $K_{S.P.}$ $CaCO_3 = 1.7 \times 10^{-8}$.   In a solution 0.20 molar in Ca^{++} and 0.20 molar in Mg^{++} and with a volume of 250 ml., which cation would precipitate first on the slow addition of Na_2CO_3?   How many milligrams of this cation would still remain in solution when the other cation just starts to precipitate?

Ans.   About 1.3 mg.

5.57. What are the solubility products of BaF_2 and of $BaSO_4$ at a certain temperature if the solubilities at that temperature are 1.3 grams per liter and 2.5×10^{-3} gram per liter, respectively?   A solution has a volume of 100 ml. and contains 0.010

mole of Na_2SO_4 and 0.020 mole of NaF. If $BaCl_2$ is slowly added, which anion will precipitate first? How many milligrams of this ion will still remain in solution when the other ion just begins to precipitate?

Ans. 1.6×10^{-6}, 1.1×10^{-10}. Sulfate. 0.027 mg.

5.58. A saturated solution of magnesium fluoride, MgF_2, is 1.2×10^{-3} molar. What is the solubility product of magnesium fluoride?

5.59. What are the solubility products of $CaSO_4$ and of CaF_2 if the solubilities are 1.1 mg. per milliliter and 0.016 mg. per milliliter, respectively? How many milligrams of calcium ions can remain in 100 ml. of a solution that is 0.50 molar in fluoride ions?

5.60. If the solubility products of BaC_2O_4 and of $Ba(IO_3)_2$ are 1.7×10^{-7} and 6.0×10^{-10}, respectively, what is the solubility of each salt in milligrams per liter?

5.61. Mercurous iodide, Hg_2I_2, dissociates into Hg_2^{++} and $2I^-$. Its solubility product is 1.2×10^{-28}. How many milligrams of the salt dissolve in 250 ml.?

5.62. The normality of a saturated solution of cerous iodate, $Ce(IO_3)_3$, is 5.7×10^{-3}. What is the solubility product of the salt? How many milligrams of cerous ions can remain dissolved in 500 ml. of a solution that is 0.30 molar in iodate ions?

5.63. If A grams of $Ba_3(AsO_4)_2$ dissolve in 500 ml., express the solubility product of $Ba_3(AsO_4)_2$ in terms of A.

5.64. If the solubility product of $Ag_2Cr_2O_7$ is 2.7×10^{-11}, how many milligrams of silver will be present in solution when excess salt is shaken with 250 ml. of water until equilibrium is reached?

5.65. If a saturated solution of $Pb_3(PO_4)_2$ is A normal, what is the solubility product of $Pb_3(PO_4)_2$?

5.66. If the solubility product of Ag_2CrO_4 is A, what (in terms of A) is the normality of a saturated solution of Ag_2CrO_4? How many grams of chromium can remain dissolved (as CrO_4^-) in 500 ml. of a solution that is B molar in silver ions?

5.67. Mercurous chloride, Hg_2Cl_2, ionizes as follows: $Hg_2Cl_2 \rightarrow Hg_2^{++} + 2Cl^-$. If its solubility product is 1.1×10^{-18}, how many grams of mercurous mercury can remain dissolved in 2.00 ml. of a solution that contains one gram-milliequivalent weight of chloride ions?

5.68. How many grams of $FeCl_3$ could be present in 200 ml. of an acid solution with a pH value of 3.0 without causing a precipitation of $Fe(OH)_3$?

5.69. Show by calculation from the solubility product of Ag_2SO_4 whether or not this compound would be suitable as a final precipitate in the detection or determination of silver. What would the concentration of sulfate ions theoretically have to be in solution so that not more than 30 mg. of silver would remain unprecipitated in 500 ml. of solution?

5.70. What is the ratio of the concentrations of Br^- and Cl^- in a solution in which sufficient $AgNO_3$ has been added to cause precipitation of both halides? Solubility products: $AgBr = 5.0 \times 10^{-13}$; $AgCl = 1.0 \times 10^{-10}$.

5.71. Calculate the number of milligrams of $BaSO_4$ converted to $BaCO_3$ by 20 ml. of a solution of Na_2CO_3 which is 2.0 normal in carbonate ions, under equilibrium conditions, at a temperature at which the solubility products are 1.0×10^{-10} and 8.0×10^{-9} for $BaSO_4$ and $BaCO_3$, respectively.

5.72. From the appropriate solubility products show which cation would precipitate first on the slow addition of K_2CrO_4 to 500 ml. of a solution 0.10 molar in Sr^{++}

and 0.10 molar in Ba^{++}. How many milligrams of this cation would still remain in solution when the other cation just starts to precipitate?

5.73. What are the solubility products of $CaSO_4$ and of CaF_2 if the solubilities are 1.1 grams per liter and 0.016 gram per liter, respectively? A solution has a volume of 250 ml. and contains 0.020 mole of Na_2SO_4 and 0.030 mole of NaF. If $CaCl_2$ is slowly added, which anion will precipitate first? How many milligrams of this ion will still remain in solution when the other ion just begins to precipitate?

5.74. The solubility of $SrCO_3$ is A mg. per milliliter; the solubility product of SrF_2 is B. Assuming that when solid SrF_2 is boiled with a solution of Na_2CO_3 that is C molar in carbonate ions, a very small amount of the SrF_2 is metathesized, calculate in terms of A, B, and C the molar concentration of fluoride ions in the resulting solution after equilibrium is reached.

40. Application of Buffered Solutions in Analytical Separations.

Buffered solutions are frequently used in both qualitative and quantitative analysis to effect certain separations of elements. A familiar case is one in which a solution is buffered, usually either with $NH_4OH + NH_4Cl$ or with $HC_2H_3O_2 + NH_4C_2H_3O_2$, and the pH value thus brought to such a value that the solubility product of the hydroxide of an element (or the hydroxides of a group of elements) is greatly exceeded but the solubility products of other hydroxides are not reached.

The composition of many insoluble hydroxides is somewhat variable, and they are perhaps more properly called "hydrous oxides." Their solubility products are not known accurately and numerical values obtained from them should therefore be considered as showing only relative orders of magnitude.

EXAMPLE. The solubility product of $Mg(OH)_2$ at a certain temperature is 3.4×10^{-11}; that of $Fe(OH)_3$ is 1.1×10^{-36}. At that temperature (a) how many grams of Mg^{++} and of Fe^{+++} can remain dissolved in 100 ml. of $M/10$ solution of NH_4OH (ionization constant $= 1.75 \times 10^{-5}$); (b) how many grams of Mg^{++} and of Fe^{+++} can remain dissolved in 100 ml. of $M/10$ NH_4OH containing a sufficient amount of dissolved NH_4Cl to make the ammonium-ion concentration 2.0 molar?

SOLUTION:

(a) $NH_4OH \rightleftarrows NH_4^+ + OH^-$

$$\frac{[NH_4^+][OH^-]}{[NH_4OH]} = 1.75 \times 10^{-5}$$

Let x = concentration of OH^- = concentration of NH_4^+

Then

$0.10 - x$ = concentration of undissociated NH_4OH

$$\frac{(x)(x)}{0.10 - x} = 1.75 \times 10^{-5}$$

$$\frac{(x)(x)}{0.10} = 1.75 \times 10^{-5} \text{ (since } x \text{ is small compared to 0.10)}$$

$$x = 1.3 \times 10^{-3} \text{ mole per liter}$$

$$[Mg^{++}][OH^-]^2 = 3.4 \times 10^{-11}$$

$$[Mg^{++}](1.3 \times 10^{-3})^2 = 3.4 \times 10^{-11}$$

$$[Mg^{++}] = 2.0 \times 10^{-5} \text{ mole per liter}$$

$$= 2.0 \times 10^{-5} \times \tfrac{1}{10} \times 24.3$$

$$= 4.9 \times 10^{-5} \text{ gram per 100 ml.} \quad Ans.$$

$$[Fe^{+++}][OH^-]^3 = 1.1 \times 10^{-36}$$

$$[Fe^{+++}](1.3 \times 10^{-3})^3 = 1.1 \times 10^{-36}$$

$$[Fe^{+++}] = \frac{1.1 \times 10^{-36}}{(1.3 \times 10^{-3})^3} \times \frac{1}{10} \times 55.8$$

$$= 2.8 \times 10^{-27} \text{ gram per 100 ml.} \quad Ans.$$

(b) $\dfrac{[NH_4^+][OH^-]}{[NH_4OH]} = 1.75 \times 10^{-5}$

$$\frac{(2.0)(x)}{0.10} = 1.75 \times 10^{-5}$$

$$x = 8.8 \times 10^{-7}$$

$$[Mg^{++}](8.8 \times 10^{-7})^2 = 3.4 \times 10^{-11}$$

$$[Mg^{++}] = \frac{3.4 \times 10^{-11}}{(8.8 \times 10^{-7})^2} \times \frac{1}{10} \times 24.3$$

$$= 106 \text{ grams per 100 ml.} \quad Ans.$$

$$[Fe^{+++}](8.8 \times 10^{-7})^3 \; 1.1 \times 10^{-36}$$

$$[Fe^{+++}] = \frac{1.1 \times 10^{-36}}{(8.8 \times 10^{-7})^3} = \frac{1}{10} \times 55.8$$

$$= 9.0 \times 10^{-18} \text{ gram per 100 ml.} \quad Ans.$$

41. Control of Acidity in Hydrogen Sulfide Precipitations. The separation of certain elements by precipitation from acid solution with H_2S is effectively used in analytical chemistry, particularly in qualitative analysis. Probably the most important factor influencing the effectiveness of the separation is the sulfide-ion concentration and its control by the regulation of the hydrogen-ion concentration. The concentration of the sulfide ion can be regulated to such a point that the solubility products of certain sulfides are greatly exceeded while the solubility products of other sulfides are not reached. The quantitative effect of the presence of acid on the ionization of H_2S and the calculation of the sulfide-ion concentration have been illustrated in Examples I and II of Sec. 35 and should be reviewed at this time.

Solubility products of sulfides are not known precisely, and hydrolysis effects and rates of precipitation influence the quantitative aspect of the separation of sulfides. Therefore, in the following example and problems of a similar nature, the calculated values may not agree well with corresponding values determined experimentally, but they do show relative orders of magnitude and are useful only in this connection.

EXAMPLE.   How many grams of Zn^{++} and how many grams of Cd^{++} can remain dissolved in 200 ml. of the solution of $H_2S + HCl$ mentioned in Example II of Sec. 35 (solubility product of $ZnS = 1.2 \times 10^{-23}$; solubility product of $CdS = 3.6 \times 10^{-29}$)?

SOLUTION:

$$[S^=] = 1.5 \times 10^{-23} \text{ (as calculated)}$$
$$[Zn^{++}][S^=] = 1.2 \times 10^{-23}$$
$$[Zn^{++}] = \frac{1.2 \times 10^{-23}}{1.5 \times 10^{-23}} = 0.80 \text{ mole per liter}$$
$$= 0.80 \times 65 \times \tfrac{1}{5} = 10 \text{ grams per 200 ml.} \quad Ans.$$
$$[Cd^{++}][S^=] = 3.6 \times 10^{-29}$$
$$[Cd^{++}] = \frac{3.6 \times 10^{-29}}{1.5 \times 10^{-23}}$$
$$= 2.4 \times 10^{-6} \text{ mole per liter}$$
$$= 2.4 \times 10^{-6} \times 112 \times \tfrac{1}{5}$$
$$= 5.4 \times 10^{-5} \text{ gram per 200 ml.} \quad Ans.$$

42. Separations by Means of Complex-ion Formation. Certain separations in analytical chemistry are effected by making use of the equilibrium that exists between a complex ion and its constituents. The following cases illustrate the two general ways in which this is applied.

1. When an ammoniacal solution of silver nitrate containing a carefully controlled excess of ammonia is added to a mixture of iodide and chloride, only silver iodide is precipitated, since most of the silver in the solution is as the ammino complex, $Ag(NH_3)_2{}^+$, and the concentration of Ag^+ is too small to exceed the solubility product of AgCl but is great enough to exceed the solubility product of the more insoluble AgI.

2. When potassium cyanide is added to an ammoniacal solution of copper and cadmium salts, the two ions $Cu(CN)_3{}^=$ and $Cd(CN)_4{}^=$ are formed. When hydrogen sulfide is passed into the solution, only cadmium sulfide is precipitated, since the degree of dissociation of the copper complex is much less than that of the cadmium complex. A sufficiently high concentration of Cd^{++} is present to exceed the solubility product of CdS, but the concentration of Cu^+ is too low to exceed the solubility product of Cu_2S.

EXAMPLE I.   How many grams of silver bromide will dissolve in one liter of NH_4OH if the resulting solution is 2.0 molar in NH_3?

SOLUTION:

$$[Ag^+][Br^-] = 5.0 \times 10^{-13} \text{ (see Appendix)}$$
$$\frac{[Ag^+][NH_3]^2}{[Ag(NH_3)_2{}^+]} = 6.8 \times 10^{-8} \text{ (see Appendix)}$$

Let x = moles of AgBr dissolved = $[Br^-]$ = $[Ag(NH_3)_2{}^+]$

$$\frac{5.0 \times 10^{-13}}{x} = [Ag^+]$$

$$\frac{(5.0 \times 10^{-13}/x)(2.0)^2}{x} = 6.8 \times 10^{-8}$$

Solving,

$$x = 5.4 \times 10^{-3} \text{ molar}$$
$$5.4 \times 10^{-3} \times AgBr = 1.0 \text{ gram. } Ans.$$

EXAMPLE II. A solution 0.10 molar in Cu^{++} and 0.10 molar in Cd^{++} is treated with NH_4OH and KCN, forming $Cu(CN)_3{}^=$ and $Cd(CN)_4{}^=$. The solution is 0.020 molar in excess CN^- ions. If H_2S is passed into the solution to give a sulfide-ion concentration of 0.010 molar, will Cu_2S or CdS precipitate?

SOLUTION:

$$\frac{[Cu^+][CN^-]^3}{[Cu(CN)_3{}^=]} = 5.0 \times 10^{-28} \text{ (see Appendix)}$$

$$\frac{[Cu^+](0.020)^3}{0.10} = 5.0 \times 10^{-28}$$

$$[Cu^+] = 6.2 \times 10^{-24}$$

Therefore,

$$[Cu^+]^2[S^=] = (6.2 \times 10^{-24})^2(0.01)$$
$$= 3.8 \times 10^{-49}$$

The solubility product of Cu_2S ($= 1.0 \times 10^{-46}$) is greater than this value. Hence Cu_2S will not precipitate. *Ans.*

$$\frac{[Cd^{++}][CN^-]^4}{[Cd(CN)_4{}^=]} = 1.4 \times 10^{-17}$$

$$\frac{[Cd^{++}](0.020)^4}{0.10} = 1.4 \times 10^{-17}$$

$$[Cd^{++}] = 8.7 \times 10^{-12}$$

Therefore,

$$[Cd^{++}][S^=] = (8.7 \times 10^{-12})(0.01)$$
$$= 8.7 \times 10^{-14}$$

The solubility product of CdS ($= 3.6 \times 10^{-29}$) is less than this value. Hence CdS will precipitate. *Ans.*

Problems

(See Appendix for solubility products and ionization constants.)

5.75. How many grams of Mg^{++} could remain dissolved [*i.e.*, unprecipitated as $Mg(OH)_2$] in a liter of 0.20 M NH_4OH, and how many grams of Mg^{++} could remain dissolved in a liter of 0.20 M NH_4OH containing enough dissolved NH_4Cl to make the ammonium-ion concentration 1.0 molar? [$K_{S.P.}$ $Mg(OH)_2 = 3.4 \times 10^{-11}$.]

Ans. 2.4×10^{-4} gram, 68 grams.

5.76. How many milligrams of Fe^{+++} could remain dissolved [*i.e.*, unprecipitated as $Fe(OH)_3$] in 100 ml. of a solution 2.0 normal in acetic acid and containing a sufficient amount of sodium acetate to make the acetate-ion concentration 0.15 molar? [$K_{S.P.}$ $Fe(OH)_3 = 1.1 \times 10^{-36}$.]

Ans. 0.095 mg.

5.77. Calculate from appropriate equilibrium constants the number of grams of zinc and of cadmium that can remain dissolved in 1,500 ml. of a solution that contains 0.050 mole of dissolved H_2S and is 0.30 N in hydrogen ions.

Ans. 29.0 grams, 1.5×10^{-4} gram.

5.78. By saturating with hydrogen sulfide 350 ml. of a solution that is 0.010 molar in a certain trivalent element and 1.0 molar in hydrogen ions, all but 12 millimoles of the element precipitates as sulfide. What is the approximate solubility product of the sulfide of the element? (Solubility of $H_2S = 0.10$ molar.)

Ans. 1.5×10^{-72}.

5.79. How many formula weights of chloride ion must be introduced into a liter of a tenth-molar solution of $NaAg(CN)_2$ in order for AgCl to start to precipitate? [Dissociation constant of $Ag(CN)_2^- = 1.0 \times 10^{-21}$; solubility product of AgCl = 1.0 $\times 10^{-10}$.]

Ans. 0.0033 F.W.

5.80. How many formula weights of silver iodide will dissolve in one liter of NH_4OH which is 6.0 molar in NH_3? [Dissociation constant of $Ag(NH_3)_2^+ = 6.8 \times 10^{-8}$; solubility product of AgI = 1.0×10^{-16}.] (*Hint:* In the resulting solution [$Ag(NH_3)_2^+$] = [I^-].)

Ans. 2.4×10^{-4} F.W.

5.81. A solution 0.080 molar in $AgNO_3$ is treated with $Na_2S_2O_3$ which converts practically all of the Ag^+ into $Ag(S_2O_3)_2^-$. If the solution contains sufficient excess thiosulfate to make the $S_2O_3^-$ 0.20 molar, how many grams of I^- per liter could be present without causing a precipitation of AgI?

Ans. 0.16 gram.

5.82. What is the maximum molar concentration of sulfide ion in a solution 0.20 molar in $Cd(NH_3)_4Cl_2$ and 2.0 molar in NH_3 without forming a precipitate of cadmium sulfide?

Ans. 1.2×10^{-20}.

5.83. What must be the maximum pH value of a solution in order that 0.500 gram of Mg^{++} in 100 ml. will remain unprecipitated as $Mg(OH)_2$? [Solubility product $Mg(OH)_2 = 3.4 \times 10^{-11}$.] How many grams of Fe^{+++} could remain dissolved in such a solution?

5.84. How many milligrams of Mn^{++} could remain unprecipitated as $Mn(OH)_2$ in 500 ml. of 0.10 M NH_4OH, and how many milligrams of Mn^{++} could remain dissolved in 500 ml. of 0.10 M NH_4OH containing sufficient dissolved NH_4Cl to make the ammonium-ion concentration 2.0 molar?

5.85. How many milligrams of Fe^{+++} could remain unprecipitated as $Fe(OH)_3$ in 250 ml. of a solution 1.5 molar in acetic acid buffered by that amount of dissolved sodium acetate that makes the acetate-ion concentration 0.20 molar?

5.86. If the solubility product of Bi_2S_3 is 1.6×10^{-72}, find the weight of bismuth ions that must be present in a liter of solution to cause precipitation of Bi_2S_3 in a solution which is 0.10 molar in H_2S and contains 0.010 mole of H^+ per liter.

5.87. What is the maximum pH value that 100 ml. of a solution containing 0.0050 gram of $PbCl_2$ can have so that on saturating the solution with H_2S no lead sulfide will precipitate? (Saturated solution of H_2S = 0.10 molar.)

5.88. A solution of 1.2 grams of $ZnSO_4.7H_2O$ in 500 ml. of dilute acid is saturated with H_2S. The resulting solution is found to be 0.10 molar in H_2S and 0.050 molar in H^+ ions. What fraction of the zinc has been precipitated as ZnS? What maximum pH value should the solution have in order for no precipitate to form if the concentrations of zinc salt and H_2S are as above?

5.89. If 50 ml. of 0.010 molar $AgNO_3$ and 50 ml. of 3.0 molar NH_4OH are mixed, what is the resulting concentration of Ag^+ ions? How many moles of Cl^- would have to be introduced before precipitation of AgCl would take place? [Ionization constant of $Ag(NH_3)_2^+ = 6.8 \times 10^{-8}$; solubility product of $AgCl = 1.0 \times 10^{-10}$.]

5.90. If a solution is 0.050 molar in K_2HgI_4 and 1.5 molar in I^-, show by calculation whether or not a precipitation of HgS would be expected if the solution is made 1.0×10^{-15} molar in sulfide ions.

5.91. How many grams of S^- can be present in a liter of a solution containing 0.10 F.W. of $Cd(NH_3)_4Cl_2$ and 1.5 mole of NH_3 without forming a precipitate of CdS?

5.92. A solution containing 0.10 F.W. of $MgCl_2$ and 0.20 F.W. of $CaCl_2$ would require a total of how many milliliters of $N/2$ $H_2C_2O_2$ solution in order to form the complex ion $Mg(C_2O_4)_2^-$ and precipitate the calcium as $CaC_2O_4.H_2O$?

5.93. How many grams of silver bromide will dissolve in one liter of NH_4OH which is 1.5 molar in NH_3? [Dissociation constant of $Ag(NH_3)_2^+ = 6.8 \times 10^{-8}$; solubility product of $AgBr = 5.0 \times 10^{-13}$.] (*Hint:* In the resulting solution $[Ag(NH_3)_2^+]$ = $[Br^-]$.)

43. Distribution Ratio.

Occasionally in analytical chemistry the greater part of a solute is removed from aqueous solution by shaking the solution with an organic solvent in which the solute is much more soluble. In qualitative analysis the removal of liberated bromine and iodine by means of carbon tetrachloride in the test for bromide and iodide occurs in many schemes of analysis. In quantitative analysis ferric chloride is often extracted in greater part from hydrochloric acid solution by means of ethyl ether or isopropyl ether. This is of value in the analysis of certain constituents in iron alloys where a high concentration of ferric ions in the solution is undesirable. Certain hydrolytic separations (*e.g.*, titanium from iron) are more readily carried out if a preliminary extraction of the iron is made.

The *distribution law* states that when a solute is in simultaneous equilibrium with two mutually insoluble solvents the ratio of the concentrations of the solute in the two solvents is a constant at a given temperature regardless of the volumes of solvents used or of the quantity of solute present:

$$\frac{\text{Concentration of } x \text{ in solvent } A}{\text{Concentration of } x \text{ in solvent } B} = K$$

The ratio K is called a distribution ratio and is determined experimentally for each solute and each pair of mutually insoluble liquids. The value is a true constant only in the case of perfect solutions and perfectly immiscible solvents, but it is very nearly a constant at a given temperature for the dilute solutions ordinarily encountered in analytical chemistry. The law applies only to a particular species of molecule; that is, the solute must be in the same condition in the two phases. The law does not hold, for example, if the solute is ionized in one solvent and not ionized in the other, or if it is as associated molecules in one solvent and not in the other.

EXAMPLE. An aqueous potassium iodide solution has a volume of 100 ml. and contains 0.120 gram of dissolved iodine. Assuming that the distribution ratio of iodine between carbon tetrachloride and an aqueous solution of potassium iodide is 85 at 25°C., how many grams of iodine will remain in the aqueous phase if the above solution is shaken with 25 ml. of carbon tetrachloride?

SOLUTION:

Let x = grams iodine remaining in H_2O phase
Then
$0.120 - x$ = grams iodine in CCl_4 phase

Concentration of iodine in CCl_4 phase = $\dfrac{0.120 - x}{25}$ grams per ml.

Concentration in H_2O phase = $\dfrac{x}{100}$ grams per ml.

$$\frac{(0.120 - x)/25}{x/100} = 85$$

Solving,

$$x = 0.00539 \text{ gram.} \quad Ans.$$

Problems

5.94. If 0.568 gram of iodine is dissolved in 50 ml. of carbon tetrachloride and the solution is shaken at a certain temperature with 500 ml. of water, it is found that the aqueous layer contains 0.0592 gram of iodine. Calculate the distribution ratio of iodine at that temperature between the two solvents, in both of which it exists as I_2 molecules.

Ans. 86.0

5.95. At 20°C. the distribution ratio of a certain organic acid between water and ether is 0.400. A solution of 5.00 grams of the acid in 100 ml. of water is shaken successively with three 20-ml. portions of water-saturated ether. Calculate the number of grams of acid left in the water. Also calculate the number of grams of acid that would have been left in the water if the solution had been shaken with a single 60-ml. portion of ether.

Ans. 1.48 grams. 2.00 grams.

5.96. If 90 ml. of an aqueous solution containing 1.00 millimole of bromine are shaken at 25°C. with 30 ml. of a certain organic solvent, 0.128 gram of the bromine is extracted from the aqueous layer. What is the distribution ratio? What percentage of the bromine would have been extracted by two successive extractions with 15-ml. portions of the solvent? Assume bromine to be as diatomic molecules in both solvents.

Ans. 12.0. 88.89 per cent.

5.97. The distribution ratio of bromine between carbon tetrachloride and water is 29.0 at 25°C. If a certain aqueous solution of bromine is shaken with one-half its volume of carbon tetrachloride, what percentage of the bromine is removed from the aqueous phase?

5.98. If a 0.0010-molar solution of bromine in solvent A is shaken with one-tenth of its volume of solvent B, 78.0 per cent of the bromine remains in A. If at the same temperature a solution of 0.0300 gram of bromine in 50 ml. of solvent B is shaken with 20 ml. of solvent A, how many grams of bromine remain in B? Assume A and B to be immiscible and bromine to be as diatomic molecules in both solvents.

5.99. In certain methods of analysis iron is removed from hydrochloric acid solution by repeated extraction with either ordinary ether or with isopropyl ether. If 36 ml. of an aqueous solution of $FeCl_3$ + HCl are shaken with 18 ml. of ether (previously saturated with HCl), 94 per cent of the iron is removed from the aqueous layer. What is the distribution ratio of iron between the two solvents and what per cent of the iron would have been removed if the initial solution had been extracted with two separate 9-ml. portions of ether?

CHAPTER 6

REDOX POTENTIALS

44. Relation of the Electric Current to Oxidation-Reduction ("Redox") Reactions. Experiment shows that at ordinary concentrations free chlorine or bromine will oxidize ferrous ions ($2Fe^{++} + Cl_2 \rightarrow 2Fe^{+++} + 2Cl^-$), but free iodine will not. Conversely, iodide ions will reduce ferric ions ($2Fe^{+++} + 2I^- \rightarrow 2Fe^{++} + I_2$) but chloride or bromine will not. Hydrogen ions at ordinary concentrations will oxidize metallic zinc ($Zn + 2H^+ \rightarrow Zn^{++} + H_2$) but will not oxidize metallic copper.

To be able to predict whether or not a given pair of oxidizing and reducing agents will or will not mutually interact to an appreciable extent is of considerable importance, particularly in qualitative analysis, and tables showing relative tendencies for substances to be oxidized or reduced, if used properly, are of great value.

In the light of the modern concept of the structure of atoms, oxidation and reduction may be defined in terms of transfer of electrons. An element is oxidized when it loses electrons; an element is reduced when it gains electrons.

Redox reactions can be brought about by the application of an electric current; conversely, an electric current can be obtained from oxidation-reduction processes. The electrolysis of a solution of sodium chloride is an example of the first class. At the anode, negative chloride ions are oxidized to free chlorine gas; at the cathode, positive hydrogen ions from the water are reduced to free hydrogen gas. The voltaic cell is an example of the second class.

45. Standard Electrode Potentials. Suppose we have on the end of a platinum wire a platinum foil covered with platinum black. Suppose further that the foil is immersed in a solution of sulfuric acid that is one molar in hydrogen ions and that pure hydrogen gas at one atmosphere pressure continually bubbles over the foil. Such a setup is called a *normal hydrogen electrode*. It may be represented graphically, thus:

$$H_2(1 \text{ atm.}), 2H^+(1 \text{ molar}) \mid Pt$$

The platinum is chemically inert, but an equilibrium exists between the hydrogen gas and the hydrogen ions, thus: $H_2 \rightleftarrows 2H^+ + 2\epsilon$, the symbol ϵ representing an electron. Suppose now we have a strip of metallic zinc immersed in a solution of zinc sulfate that is one molar in zinc ions.

68

Equilibrium exists between the metal and its ions, thus: $Zn \rightleftarrows Zn^{++} + 2\epsilon$. If the two electrodes are connected by means of a wire and the two solutions are connected by means of a capillary tube containing a solution of an electrolyte (*e.g.*, K_2SO_4), a current will flow through the wire and solution. Its initial potential will be 0.76 volt.

In this system, the flow of electrons in the wire is from the zinc electrode to the hydrogen electrode. In the solution, the negative ions ($SO_4^=$) of the electrolyte pass from the solution containing the sulfuric acid to that containing the zinc sulfate, and the charges on these transported ions just balance the charges gained or lost at the electrodes. At the same time, metallic zinc is oxidized and hydrogen ions are reduced, the net reaction being represented by the equation $\underline{Zn} + 2H^+ \rightarrow Zn^{++} + H_2$. We therefore have a voltaic cell made up of two *half cells*, and the entire system may be represented thus:

$$Zn \mid Zn^{++}(1 \text{ molar}) \parallel H^+(1 \text{ molar}), H_2(1 \text{ atmosphere}) \mid Pt$$

In representing cells in this way, a single line represents a junction between an electrode and a solution. A double line denotes a junction between two solutions, and it is assumed that the small potential difference between the solutions has been corrected for in formulating the total e.m.f. of the cell.

It should also be noted that oxidation always takes place at the anode; reduction always takes place at the cathode. The passage of electrons through the wire is from anode to cathode.

In similar fashion, a copper electrode dipping in a solution of copper sulfate that is one molar in copper ions can be connected to a normal hydrogen electrode. A current having a potential of 0.34 volt will be generated. The passage of electrons in the wire is from the hydrogen electrode to the copper electrode.

If now we connect the above copper half cell with the above zinc half cell, we obtain a voltaic cell that is represented thus:

$$Cu \mid Cu^{++}(1 \text{ molar}) \parallel Zn^{++}(1 \text{ molar}) \mid Zn$$

It will be found that a current with a potential of 1.10 volts will be generated. The passage of electrons in the wire is from the zinc to the copper. At the same time metallic zinc is oxidized to zinc ions, and the copper ions are reduced to metallic copper, the net reaction being

$$\underline{Zn} + Cu^{++} \rightarrow \underline{Cu} + Zn^{++}$$

It is difficult to determine absolute potential differences between electrodes and solutions; but since we are usually concerned only with *differences* of potential, we can refer electrode potentials to some common standard. The normal hydrogen electrode is arbitrarily given the value of zero, and other electrode potentials are referred to it. The *molar electrode potential* or *standard electrode potential* of zinc (*i.e.*, the potential relative to the hydrogen potential between metallic zinc and a one-molar solution of zinc ions) is $+0.76$ volt; the standard potential of copper is -0.34 volt. Giving the zinc potential a positive sign and the copper potential a negative sign is again purely arbitrary. Some chemists use the opposite convention.

In this book, standard potentials will be denoted by the symbol E^0, and a table of such potentials is given in the Appendix. When applied to an active metallic electrode, the numerical value refers to the potential at 25°C. between a metal and a one-molar solution of its ions relative to the potential between hydrogen gas at one atmosphere pressure and a one-molar solution of hydrogen ions.

The e.m.f. of a cell is the difference between the potentials of its two half cells, or $E = E_1 - E_2$. In the case of the above-mentioned cell, $E = E_1 - E_2 = E_{Zn}^0 - E_{Cu}^0 = +0.76 - (-0.34) = 1.10$ volts.

Electrode potentials are not limited to those between elements and their ions. They also apply to potentials between ions at two states of oxidation. Thus, as shown in the potential table in the Appendix, the standard potential between ferrous and ferric ions ($Fe^{++} = Fe^{+++} + \epsilon$) is -0.771 volt, indicating that a current having a potential of 0.771 volt would flow through the following cell:

$$Pt \mid Fe^{++}(1\ M),\ Fe^{+++}(1\ M) \parallel H^+(1\ M),\ H_2(1\ atm.) \mid Pt$$

The negative sign indicates that electrons would pass through the wire from right to left as written above (*i.e.*, from the hydrogen electrode to the ferrous-ferric half cell). Ferric ions would be reduced to ferrous ions; hydrogen gas would be oxidized to hydrogen ions.

Similarly, the standard potential between chromic ions and dichromate ions in the presence of acid ($2Cr^{+++} + 7H_2O = Cr_2O_7^= + 14H^+ + 6\epsilon$) is -1.36 volts. The numerical value 1.36 represents the voltage of the following cell:

$$Pt \left| \begin{array}{l} Cr^{+++}(1\ M) \\ Cr_2O_7^=(1\ M) \\ H^+(1\ M) \end{array} \right\| \left. \begin{array}{l} H^+(1\ M),\ H_2(1\ atm.) \end{array} \right| Pt$$

The negative sign indicates a behavior similar to that of the preceding case. Dichromate ions are reduced during the operation of the cell.

The e.m.f. of the following cell

$$Pt \left| \begin{array}{l} Fe^{++}(1\ M) \\ Fe^{+++}(1\ M) \end{array} \right\| \left. \begin{array}{l} Cr^{+++}(1\ M) \\ Cr_2O_7^=(1\ M) \\ H^+(1\ M) \end{array} \right| Pt$$

would be the algebraic difference between the two half cells comprising it, or $-0.771 - (-1.36) = +0.59$ volt. The positive sign indicates that the passage of electrons through the wire is from left to right as written above. The ferrous ions are oxidized and the dichromate ions are reduced during the process. The over-all reaction would be

$$6Fe^{++} + Cr_2O_7^= + 14H^+ \rightarrow 6Fe^{+++} + 2Cr^{+++} + 7H_2O$$

46. Rules for Writing Equations for Half-cell Reactions. In writing and balancing equations for half-cell reactions the following steps should be followed:

1. Write the reduced form of the element that changes its oxidation number on the left-hand side of the equation; write the oxidized form on the right-hand side. If necessary, balance the number of atoms of the element by inserting the proper coefficients.

2. On the right-hand side of the equation introduce that number of electrons equal to the total change in oxidation number of the element.

3. If necessary, introduce sufficient hydrogen ions (if the reaction takes place in acid solution) or hydroxyl ions (if the reaction takes place in basic solution) to balance the electrical charges. Remember that each electron symbol represents a negative charge.

4. If necessary, introduce water molecules into the equation to balance the hydrogen and oxygen atoms.

EXAMPLE. Write balanced half-cell reactions for the following changes: (a) $VO^{++} \rightarrow VO_3^-$ (acid solution); (b) $Cr^{+++} \rightarrow Cr_2O_7^=$ (acid solution); (c) $Mn^{++} \rightarrow \underline{MnO_2}$ (basic solution).

Following the above four steps, the results in each case are as follows:

(a) 1. $VO^{++} \rightarrow VO_3^-$
    2. $VO^{++} \rightarrow VO_3^- + \epsilon$ (change $= 5 - 4 = 1$)
    3. $VO^{++} \rightarrow VO_3^- + 4H^+ + \epsilon$
    4. $VO^{++} + 2H_2O \rightarrow VO_3^- + 4H^+ + \epsilon$

(b) 1. $2Cr^{+++} \rightarrow Cr_2O_7^=$
    2. $2Cr^{+++} \rightarrow Cr_2O_7^= + 6\epsilon$ [change $= (6 - 3) \times 2 = 6$]
    3. $2Cr^{+++} \rightarrow Cr_2O_7^= + 14H^+ + 6\epsilon$
    4. $2Cr^{+++} + 7H_2O \rightarrow Cr_2O_7^= + 14H^+ + 6\epsilon$

(c) 1. $Mn^{++} \rightarrow \underline{MnO_2}$
    2. $Mn^{++} \rightarrow \underline{MnO_2} + 2\epsilon$
    3. $Mn^{++} + \underline{4OH^-} \rightarrow MnO_2 + 2\epsilon$
    4. $Mn^{++} + 4OH^- \rightarrow \underline{MnO_2} + 2H_2O + 2\epsilon$

47. Oxidation-Reduction Equations in Terms of Half-cell Reactions. In order to write an ordinary redox equation in terms of half-cell reactions the appropriate couples are merely written one below the other and sub-tracted in algebraic fashion. Since electron symbols should not appear in the net equation, it is frequently necessary to multiply one or both half-cell equations by a factor in order that the electrons may "cancel" out. This is illustrated in the following examples. Obviously the potential of the half-cell reaction is not affected by such multiplication.

The oxidation of ferrous ions by chlorine can be written:

$$Fe^{++} = Fe^{+++} + \epsilon \qquad (E_1^0 = -0.771)$$

or

$$
\begin{array}{ll}
(1) & 2Fe^{++} = 2Fe^{+++} + 2\epsilon \\
(2) & 2Cl^- = Cl_2 + 2\epsilon \qquad (E_2^0 = -1.358) \\
\hline
(1)-(2) & 2Fe^{++} + Cl_2 = 2Fe^{+++} + 2Cl^-
\end{array}
$$

The oxidation of ferrous ions by dichromate in the presence of acid can be written:

$$
\begin{array}{ll}
(1) & 6Fe^{++} = 6Fe^{+++} + 6\epsilon \qquad (E_1^0 = -0.771) \\
(2) & 2Cr^{+++} + 7H_2O = Cr_2O_7^= + 14H^+ + 6\epsilon \qquad (E_2^0 = -1.36) \\
\hline
(1)-(2) & 6Fe^{++} + Cr_2O_7^= + 14H^+ = 6Fe^{+++} + 2Cr^{+++} + 7H_2O
\end{array}
$$

The oxidation of stannous ions in the presence of acid by permanganate can be written:

$$
\begin{array}{ll}
(1) & 5Sn^{++} = 5Sn^{++++} + 10\epsilon \qquad (E_1^0 = -0.15) \\
(2) & 2Mn^{++} + 8H_2O = 2MnO_4^- + 16H^+ + 10\epsilon \qquad (E_2^0 = -1.52) \\
\hline
(1)-(2) & 5Sn^{++} + 2MnO_4^- + 16H^+ = 5Sn^{++++} + 2Mn^{++} + 8H_2O
\end{array}
$$

If concentrations are all 1 molar, the net potentials of the above three illustrations are the algebraic differences between the standard potentials corresponding to the two half-cell reactions, namely,

$$
\begin{aligned}
E &= E_1^0 - E_2^0 = (-0.771) - (-1.358) = +0.587 \text{ volt} \\
E &= E_1^0 - E_2^0 = (-0.771) - (-1.36) \ \ = +0.59 \text{ volt} \\
E &= E_1^0 - E_2^0 = (-0.15) \ \ - (-1.52) \ \ = +1.37 \text{ volts}
\end{aligned}
$$

In cases like the above, if the algebraic difference between the electrode potentials, as written, is positive, the net reaction can be expected to go as written (i.e., from left to right). If the algebraic difference is negative, the reaction will not go as written but can be expected to go from right to left. Thus,

$$
\begin{array}{ll}
(1) & 2Fe^{++} = 2Fe^{+++} + 2\epsilon \qquad (-0.771) \\
(2) & 2I^- = I_2 + 2\epsilon \qquad\quad (-0.535) \\
\hline
(1)-(2) & 2Fe^{++} + I_2 = 2Fe^{+++} + 2I^-
\end{array}
$$

$$[(-0.771) - (-0.535) = -0.236 \text{ volt}]$$

This reaction at 1 molar concentrations will therefore not take place from left to right as written, but will go in the opposite direction ($2Fe^{+++} + 2I^- \rightarrow 2Fe^{++} + I_2$).

The behavior of metals with acids can be treated in the same way. Metallic zinc dissolves in 1 M HCl:

$$
\begin{array}{lll}
(1) & Zn = Zn^{++} + 2\epsilon & (+0.762) \\
(2) & \overline{H_2 = 2H^+ + 2\epsilon} & (0.00) \\
(1)-(2) & Zn + 2H^+ \rightarrow Zn^{++} + H_2 & (+0.762 \text{ volt})
\end{array}
$$

Metallic copper does not dissolve in HCl:

$$
\begin{array}{lll}
(1) & Cu = Cu^{++} + 2\epsilon & (-0.344) \\
(2) & \overline{H_2 = 2H^+ + 2\epsilon} & (0.00) \\
(1)-(2) & Cu + 2H^+ \leftarrow Cu^{++} + H_2 & (-0.344 \text{ volt})
\end{array}
$$

Both zinc and copper dissolve in 1 M HNO$_3$. In this acid two oxidizing agents are present, namely, H$^+$ and NO$_3^-$, but the nitrate ion has the greater oxidizing effect:

$$
\begin{array}{lll}
(1) & 3Cu = 3Cu^{++} + 6\epsilon & (-0.344) \\
(2) & 2NO + 4H_2O = 2NO_3^- + 8H^+ + 6\epsilon & (-0.96) \\
(1)-(2) & 3Cu + 2NO_3^- + 8H^+ \rightarrow 3Cu^{++} + 2NO + 4H_2O & \\
& [(-0.344) - (-0.96) = +0.62 \text{ volt}]
\end{array}
$$

The potential table therefore shows relative tendencies for substances to lose or gain electrons. Substances at the top left of the table lose their electrons most readily and gain them least readily. They are therefore the strongest reducing agents. Similarly, the oxidizing agents at the bottom of the table are the strongest; those at the top are the weakest.

Such predictions as given above must be applied cautiously. In a few cases reactions that should proceed according to the relative positions in the potential series do so at such a slow rate that they are almost negligible. More important still, as shown in the next section, the concentration of each component of an oxidation-reduction equilibrium affects the value of the potential. A substance may be present that is capable of forming a complex ion with one of the components of the half-cell equilibrium and thus reduces the concentration of that component to a point where it no longer reacts. Thus, the potential of the equilibrium $Sn^{++} \rightleftarrows Sn^{++++} + 2\epsilon$ is greatly affected by the presence of chloride ions which form $SnCl_6^=$ ions with the stannic tin. In a few cases precipitation effects interfere in the same way. For example, according to the table, iodide ions should reduce silver ions to metallic silver ($2Ag^+ + 2I^- \rightarrow$

$2Ag + I_2$). Actually, a precipitation of silver iodide takes place instead ($\overline{Ag^+} + I^- \rightarrow \underline{AgI}$) and the concentration of Ag^+ in the residual solution is made too small to be affected by excess iodide. In the case of a few metals, passivity effects may occur. Pure aluminum should dissolve readily in nitric acid ($Al + NO_3^- + 4H^+ \rightarrow Al^{+++} + NO + 2H_2O$). Actually it does not do so, probably because of the formation of a protective coating of oxide on the surface of the metal.

48. Relation between Electrode Potential and Concentration. When the prevailing concentrations are not 1 molar, the electrode potentials are no longer molar electrode potentials but can be calculated from them. From considerations of free energy it can be shown that at 25°C. electrode potentials can be calculated from the following formula:

$$E = E^0 - \frac{0.0591}{n} \log Q^1$$

where E^0 = molar electrode potential

n = number of faradays involved in the change

log = common logarithm

Q = ratio obtained by dividing the prevailing molar concentrations of the oxidation products of the reaction by the prevailing molar concentrations of the reacting substances, each concentration being raised to a power equal to the coefficient of the substance in the equation representing the reaction taking place in the half cell. In expressing Q, reactions should be written as oxidations, and, as in the case of mass-action expressions, concentrations of water and of solid substances are omitted. Gases are expressed in terms of partial pressures (in atmospheres)

In calculations of electrode potentials, as in the case of calculations of equilibrium constants, activities rather than concentrations should be used for precise results (see Sec. 36). Values for standard electrode potentials should therefore be for unit activity rather than for molar concentration. Analytical calculations in this particular field, however, do not require a precision greater than one or two significant figures, and the use of activities and activity coefficients (which are not always easily determined) can be dispensed with.

---

[1] As stated in Sec. 45, in some tables of electrode potentials the signs are opposite to those given in this book; this is, the numerical values of those potentials listed above hydrogen are minus, and those below hydrogen are plus. If this alternative system is used, the given formula becomes $E = E^0 + \frac{0.0591}{n} \log Q$. The consistent use of either system leads to correct results.

EXAMPLE I.   Find the e.m.f. at 25°C. of the cell

$$\text{Pt} \left| \begin{array}{l} \text{Ce}^{+++}(0.10 \text{ molar}) \\ \text{Ce}^{++++}(0.00010 \text{ molar}) \end{array} \right| \left| \begin{array}{l} \text{Fe}^{++}(0.010 \text{ molar}) \\ \text{Fe}^{+++}(1.0 \text{ molar}) \end{array} \right| \text{Pt}$$

SOLUTION:

$$\begin{aligned}
(1) \quad \text{Ce}^{+++} = \text{Ce}^{++++} + \epsilon \quad E_1 &= E_1{}^0 - \frac{0.0591}{1} \log \frac{[\text{Ce}^{++++}]}{[\text{Ce}^{+++}]} \\
&= -1.61 - 0.0591 \log 10^{-3} \\
&= -1.43
\end{aligned}$$

$$\begin{aligned}
(2) \quad \text{Fe}^{++} = \text{Fe}^{+++} + \epsilon \quad E_2 &= E_2{}^0 - \frac{0.0591}{1} \log \frac{[\text{Fe}^{+++}]}{[\text{Fe}^{++}]} \\
&= -0.771 - 0.0591 \log 100 \\
&= -0.889
\end{aligned}$$

Subtracting (2) from (1):

$$\text{Ce}^{+++} + \text{Fe}^{+++} = \text{Ce}^{++++} + \text{Fe}^{++} \quad E$$
$$= E_1 - E_2 = -1.43 - (-0.889) = -0.54$$
$$\text{e.m.f.} = 0.54 \text{ volt.} \quad Ans.$$

The negative sign of the derived value shows that the corresponding derived equation proceeds from *right* to *left*. The ceric ions are reduced and the ferrous ions are oxidized ($\text{Ce}^{++++} + \text{Fe}^{++} \rightarrow \text{Ce}^{+++} + \text{Fe}^{+++}$) until concentrations are such that equilibrium conditions are reached and no current flows.

In this example the concentrations given are those of the simple cations. Calculations become more complicated in cases where secondary equilibria exist between the cations and complex ions, such as $\text{FeCl}_4{}^-$, $\text{Ce}(\text{SO}_4)_3{}^=$, etc.

EXAMPLE II.   What is the potential of the half cell represented by the following equilibrium: $2\text{Cr}^{+++}(0.20 \text{ } M) + 7\text{H}_2\text{O} = \text{Cr}_2\text{O}_7{}^=(0.30 \text{ } M) + 14\text{H}^+(2.0 \text{ } M) + 6\epsilon$?

SOLUTION:

$$\begin{aligned}
E &= E^0 - \frac{0.0591}{n} \log \frac{[\text{Cr}_2\text{O}_7{}^=][\text{H}^+]^{14}}{[\text{Cr}^{+++}]^2} \\
&= -1.36 - \frac{0.0591}{6} \log \frac{(0.30)(2.0)^{14}}{(0.20)^2} \\
&= -1.41 \text{ volts.} \quad Ans.
\end{aligned}$$

EXAMPLE III.   What is the e.m.f. of the following cell:

$$\text{Zn} \left| \text{Zn}^{++}(1.0 \times 10^{-6} \text{ molar}) \right| \left| \text{Cu}^{++}(0.010 \text{ molar}) \right| \text{Cu}$$

SOLUTION:

$$E_1 = E_{Zn}{}^0 - \frac{0.0591}{n} \log [Zn^{++}]$$

$$= +0.76 - \frac{0.0591}{2} \log (1.0 \times 10^{-6})$$

$$= +0.94$$

$$E_2 = E_{Cu}{}^0 - \frac{0.0591}{n} \log [Cu^{++}]$$

$$= -0.34 - \frac{0.0591}{2} \log (0.010)$$

$$= -0.28$$

$$E = E_1 - E_2 = 1.22 \text{ volts.} \quad Ans.$$

EXAMPLE IV.   Calculate the e.m.f. of the following cell:

$$Cu \mid Cu^{++}(0.010 \text{ molar}) \parallel Cu^{++}(2.0 \text{ molar}) \mid Cu$$

This type of cell, made up of the same half-cell equilibrium (Cu = $Cu^{++} + 2\epsilon$, in this case) but with the ions at two different concentrations, is known as a *concentration cell*.

SOLUTION:

$$E_1 = -0.344 - \frac{0.0591}{2} \log 0.010$$

$$E_2 = -0.344 - \frac{0.0591}{2} \log 2.0$$

$$E = E_1 - E_2 = -\frac{0.0591}{2} (\log 0.010 - \log 2.0)$$

$$= 0.068 \text{ volt.} \quad Ans.$$

49. Calculation of the Extent to Which an Oxidation-Reduction Reaction Takes Place.   All reversible reactions proceed in one direction or the other until equilibrium conditions are reached, at which point the two rates of reaction are equal.

During the progress of an oxidation-reduction reaction in a cell, the concentrations of the reacting substances are steadily decreasing and those of the products are increasing.   The voltage of the cell decreases steadily until equilibrium is reached, at which point no current flows. The potentials of the two half cells making up the cell are therefore equal at this point of equilibrium.   In order to calculate the extent to which an oxidation-reduction reaction takes place, it is only necessary to express the reaction as two half-cell reactions and to express an equality between the two electrode potentials.

EXAMPLE I. When excess metallic aluminum is added to a solution 0.30 M in cupric ions, what is the theoretical concentration of Cu^{++} after equilibrium is reached $(2Al + 3Cu^{++} \rightleftarrows 2Al^{+++} + 3Cu)$?

SOLUTION: Experiment shows that the reaction is practically complete.

$$[Al^{+++}] = 0.20 \ M \ (3 \text{ moles of } Cu^{++} \text{ give 2 moles of } Al^{+++})$$
$$[Cu^{++}] = x \ M$$
$$+1.67 - \frac{0.0591}{3} \log 0.20 = -0.344 - \frac{0.0591}{2} \log x$$
$$\log x = -69$$
$$x = 1 \times 10^{-69} \text{ mole.} \quad Ans.$$

EXAMPLE II. A solution is prepared so as to be initially 0.060 molar in Fe^{++}, 0.10 molar in $Cr_2O_7^=$ and 2.0 molar in H^+. After the reaction, what would be the approximate concentration of the Fe^{++} remaining $(6 \ Fe^{++} + Cr_2O_7^= + 14H^+ \rightleftarrows 6Fe^{+++} + 2Cr^{+++} + 7H_2O)$?

SOLUTION: Experiment shows that the reaction is practically complete. Since, according to the equation, 0.060 mole of Fe^{++} would react with 0.010 mole of $Cr_2O_7^=$ and 0.14 mole of H^+, the latter two are initially present in excess and the concentration of Fe^{++} is the limiting factor. At equilibrium, $[Fe^{+++}] = 0.060$; $[Fe^{++}] = x$; $[Cr^{+++}] = 0.020$; $[Cr_2O_7^=] = 0.10 - 0.010 = 0.090$; $[H^+] = 2.0 - 0.14 = 1.86$. The two half-cell equilibria are

$$6Fe^{++}(x \ M) = 6Fe^{+++}(0.060 \ M) + 6\epsilon$$
$$2Cr^{+++}(0.020 \ M) + 7H_2O = Cr_2O_7^=(0.090 \ M) + 14H^+(1.86 \ M) + 6\epsilon$$
$$-0.771 - \frac{0.0591}{1} \log \frac{[Fe^{+++}]}{[Fe^{++}]} = -1.36 - \frac{0.0591}{6} \log \frac{[Cr_2O_7^=][H^+]^{14}}{[Cr^{+++}]^2}$$
$$-0.771 - \frac{0.0591}{1} \log \frac{0.060}{x} = -1.36 - \frac{0.0591}{6} \log \frac{(0.090)(1.86)^{14}}{(0.020)^2}$$
$$x = 6 \times 10^{-13}. \quad Ans.$$

50. Calculation of Equilibrium Constant from Electrode Potentials. A mass-action constant (Sec. 30) applies to a reaction under conditions of equilibrium. At this point the electrode potentials of the half-cell equilibria are equal and the over-all potential is zero. This gives a method of calculating the numerical value of the mass-action equilibrium constant of an oxidation-reduction equation from the respective specific electrode potentials.

EXAMPLE. Calculate the numerical value of the equilibrium constant of the reaction $2Fe^{++} + I_2 \rightleftarrows 2Fe^{+++} + 2I^-$ (which at moderate concentrations proceeds only very slightly from left to right as written).

SOLUTION:

$$(1) \quad 2Fe^{++} = 2Fe^{+++} + 2\epsilon$$

$$(2) \quad 2I^- = I_2 + 2\epsilon$$

$$\underline{(1)-(2) \quad 2Fe^{++} + I_2 = 2Fe^{+++} + 2I^-}$$

$$\frac{[Fe^{+++}]^2[I^-]^2}{[Fe^{++}]^2[I_2]} = K \text{ (mass-action constant)}$$

$$E_1 = E_2 \text{ (at equilibrium)}$$

$$-0.771 - \frac{0.0591}{2} \log \frac{[Fe^{+++}]^2}{[Fe^{++}]^2} = -0.535 - \frac{0.0591}{2} \log \frac{[I_2]}{[I^-]^2}$$

$$\frac{0.0591}{2} \log \frac{[Fe^{+++}]^2[I^-]^2}{[Fe^{++}]^2[I_2]} = -0.236$$

$$\frac{0.0591}{2} \log K = -0.236$$

$$\log K = -8.0$$

$$K = 1.0 \times 10^{-8}. \quad Ans.$$

Problems

(See Table VII, Appendix, for the necessary standard potentials.   Temperatures are 25°C.)

6.1. Calculate the potentials of the half cells:

(a) $Hg = Hg^{++}(0.0010 \ M) + 2\epsilon$

(b) $Co = Co^{++}(0.24 \ M) + 2\epsilon$

(c) $Pb^{++}(0.050 \ M) + 2H_2O = \underline{PbO_2} + 4H^+(0.010 \ M) + 2\epsilon$

(d) $H_2O_2(0.0020 \ M) = O_2 (2 \text{ atm.}) + 2H^+(1.5 \ M) + 2\epsilon$

Ans.   (a) -0.765 volt.   (b) $+0.295$ volt.   (c) -1.270 volts.   (d) -0.781 volt.

6.2. Balance the following equation and express it as the difference between two half-cell reactions:

$$PbO_2 + Br^- + H^+ \rightarrow Pb^{++} + Br_2 + H_2O.$$

Ans. $\underline{PbO_2} + 2Br^- + 4H^+ \rightarrow Pb^{++} + Br_2 + 2H_2O; (2Br^- = Br_2 + 2\epsilon) - (Pb^{++} + 2H_2O = \underline{PbO_2} + 4H^+ + 2\epsilon).$

6.3. Write the equation showing the net reaction indicated by each of the following pairs of half-cell reactions.   Show from the respective electrode potentials in which direction each reaction will go, assuming all ion concentrations to be 1 molar.   (a) $Ag = Ag^+ + \epsilon, \quad Cu = Cu^{++} + 2\epsilon;$ (b) $H_2O_2 = O_2 + 2H^+ + 2\epsilon, \quad Mn^{++} + 2H_2O = \underline{MnO_2} + 4H^+ + 2\epsilon.$

Ans.   (a) $Cu + 2Ag^+ \rightarrow Cu^{++} + 2\underline{Ag};$ (b) $\underline{MnO_2} + H_2O_2 + 2H^+ \rightarrow Mn^{++} + O_2 + 2H_2O.$

6.4. Write complete and balanced equations for the half-cell reactions indicated by the following changes taking place in acid solution: (a) $\underline{Sb} \rightarrow SbO^+$, (b) $HNO_2 \rightarrow NO_3^-$, (c) $\underline{As} \rightarrow HAsO_2$, (d) $BiO^+ \rightarrow \underline{Bi_2O_4}$, (e) $Br_2 \rightarrow BrO_3^-$.

Ans.   (a) $\underline{Sb} + H_2O = SbO^+ + 2H^+ + 3\epsilon$,   (b) $HNO_2 + H_2O = NO_3^- + 3H^+ + 2\epsilon$,   (c) $\underline{As} + 2H_2O = HAsO_2 + 3H^+ + 3\epsilon$,   (d) $2BiO^+ + 2H_2O = \underline{Bi_2O_4} + 4H^+ + 2\epsilon$,   (e) $Br_2 + 6H_2O = 2BrO_3^- + 12H^+ + 10\epsilon.$

6.5. Write complete and balanced equations for the half-cell reactions indicated by the following changes taking place in basic solution: (a) $\underline{Zn} \rightarrow ZnO_2^-$, (b) HCHO $\rightarrow HCO_2^-$, (c) $HSnO_2^- \rightarrow Sn(OH)_6^=$, (d) $PH_3 \rightarrow \underline{P}$, (e) $\underline{Ag} \rightarrow \underline{Ag_2O}$.

Ans. (a) $\underline{Zn} + 4OH^- = ZnO_2^= + 2H_2O + 2\epsilon$, (b) HCHO $+ 3OH^- = HCO_2^- + 2H_2O + 2\epsilon$, (c) $HSnO_2^- + 3OH^- + H_2O = Sn(OH)_6^= + 2\epsilon$, (d) $PH_3 + 3OH^- = \underline{P} + 3H_2O + 3\epsilon$, (e) $2\underline{Ag} + 2OH^- = \underline{Ag_2O} + H_2O + 2\epsilon$.

6.6. What is the e.m.f. of the following concentration cell?

$$Ag \mid Ag^+(0.40 \text{ molar}) \parallel Ag^+(0.0010 \text{ molar}) \mid Ag$$

In what direction is the flow of electrons through the wire connecting the electrodes as written?

Ans. 0.16 volt. Right to left.

6.7. What e.m.f. can be obtained at 25°C. from the following cell?

$$Zn \mid Zn^{++}(0.010 \text{ molar}) \parallel Ag^+(0.30 \text{ molar}) \mid Ag$$

In what direction is the flow of electrons through the wire connecting the electrodes? Write an equation for the reaction at each electrode and for the net reaction. What would the concentration of Ag^+ have to be for no current to flow?

Ans. 1.590 volts. Left to right. $\underline{Zn} \rightarrow Zn^{++} + 2\epsilon$, $2Ag^+ + 2\epsilon \rightarrow 2\underline{Ag}$, $\underline{Zn} + 2Ag^+ \rightarrow Zn^{++} + 2\underline{Ag}$. 2.5×10^{-28} molar.

6.8. Calculate the e.m.f. obtainable from each of the following cells. In each case indicate the direction of the flow of electrons in the wire connecting the electrodes, and write an equation for the net reaction.

(a) $Cd \mid Cd^{++}(1.0 \ M) \parallel Cu^{++}(1.0 \ M) \mid Cu$

(b) $Hg \mid Hg^{++}(0.10 \ M) \parallel Hg^{++}(0.0071 \ M) \mid Hg$

(c) $Pt \begin{vmatrix} Fe^{++}(0.10 \ M) \\ Fe^{+++}(0.30 \ M) \end{vmatrix} \begin{vmatrix} Cr^{+++}(0.010 \ M) \\ Cr_2O_7^=(0.20 \ M) \\ H^+(1.0 \ M) \end{vmatrix} Pt$

(d) $Pt \begin{vmatrix} Mn^{++}(0.10 \ M) \\ MnO_4^-(0.060 \ M) \\ H^+(0.20 \ M) \end{vmatrix} \begin{vmatrix} Sn^{++}(0.050 \ M) \\ Sn^{++++}(0.020 \ M) \end{vmatrix} Pt$

(e) $Ag \begin{vmatrix} \underline{Ag^+Cl} \text{ (satd.)} \end{vmatrix} \begin{vmatrix} Fe^{++} \ (0.10 \ M) \\ Fe^{+++}(0.20 \ M) \end{vmatrix} Pt$

Ans. (a) 0.746 volt, left to right. (b) 0.0340 volt, right to left. (c) 0.59 volt, left to right. (d) 1.31 volts, right to left. (e) 0.565 volt, left to right.

6.9. What must be the value of x for the following reaction to be at equilibrium at 25°C.?

$$Cu + 2Ag^+(x \text{ molar}) \rightleftarrows Cu^{++}(0.10 \text{ molar}) + 2\underline{Ag}$$

Ans. 6×10^{-9} molar.

6.10. The standard potential between elementary arsenic and the arsenite ion (AsO_2^-) in alkaline solution is +0.68 volt. Calculate the potential of this system when the concentrations of arsenite and of hydroxyl ions are each 0.10 molar.

Ans. +0.62 volt.

6.11. By how many volts would the potential between iodate (IO_3^-) and periodate $(H_3IO_6^=)$ in alkaline solution differ from the standard potential if the concentrations of the iodate, periodate, and hydroxyl ions are each 0.20 molar?

Ans. 0.062 volt.

6.12. When excess metallic zinc is added to a solution 0.010 molar in Ag^+, what is the theoretical concentration of Ag^+ after equilibrium is reached? The reaction is practically complete as follows: $Zn + 2Ag^+ \rightarrow Zn^{++} + 2Ag$.

Ans. 2.8×10^{-28}.

6.13. Equal volumes of a solution 0.10 molar in Fe^{++} and a solution 0.30 molar in Ce^{++++} are mixed. After the reaction is practically complete ($Fe^{++} + Ce^{++++} \rightarrow Fe^{+++} + Ce^{+++}$) and equilibrium has been attained, what is the resulting concentration of Fe^{++}?

Ans. 1.4×10^{-16} molar.

6.14. Calculate the approximate equilibrium constant for each of the following:
    (a) $Zn + Cu^{++} \rightleftarrows Zn^{++} + Cu$
    (b) $Fe^{+++} + Ag \rightleftarrows Fe^{++} + Ag^+$
    (c) $2Ce^{+++} + I_2 \rightleftarrows 2Ce^{++++} + 2I^-$
    (d) $6Fe^{++} + Cr_2O_7^- + 14H^+ \rightleftarrows 6Fe^{+++} + 2Cr^{+++} + 7H_2O$
    (e) $2Fe^{+++} + 2Br^- \rightleftarrows 2Fe^{++} + Br_2$

Ans.   (a) 10^{37}. (b) 0.32. (c) 1.6×10^{-36}. (d) 10^{60}. (e) 10^{-10}.

6.15. Write complete and balanced equations for the half-cell reactions indicated by the following changes taking place in acid solution: (a) $P \rightarrow H_3PO_4$, (b) $MnO_2 \rightarrow MnO_4^-$, (c) $U^{++++} \rightarrow UO_2^{++}$, (d) $SbO^+ \rightarrow Sb_2O_5$, (e) $Cl_2 \rightarrow HClO_2$, (f) $S_2O_3^- \rightarrow H_2SO_3$.

6.16. Write complete and balanced equations for the half-cell reactions indicated by the following changes taking place in basic solution: (a) $P \rightarrow PO_3^=$, (b) $Pb^{++} \rightarrow PbO_2$, (c) $SO_3^- \rightarrow SO_4^-$, (d) $CrO_2^- \rightarrow CrO_4^-$, (e) $N_2O_4 \rightarrow NO_3^-$, (f) $Ag_2O \rightarrow AgO$.

6.17. Calculate the potentials of the following half cells:
    (a) $Ag = Ag^+(0.010\ M) + \epsilon$
    (b) $Co = Co^{++}(0.063\ M) + 2\epsilon$
    (c) $Mn^{++}(0.030\ M) + 4H_2O = MnO_4^-(0.020\ M) + 8H^+(0.10\ M) + 5\epsilon$
    (d) $2Cr^{+++}(0.010\ M) + 7H_2O = Cr_2O_7^-(0.020\ M) + 14H^+(0.030\ M) + 6\epsilon$

6.18. Balance the following equations and express each as the difference between two half-cell reactions: (a) $Fe + H^+ \rightarrow Fe^{++} + H_2$, (b) $Fe^{++} + MnO_4^- + H^+ \rightarrow Fe^{+++} + Mn^{++} + H_2O$, (c) $Fe + NO_3^- + H^+ \rightarrow Fe^{+++} + NO + H_2O$, (d) $Cl_2 + H_2O \rightarrow HOCl + H^+ + Cl^-$, (e) $PbS + H_2O_2 \rightarrow PbSO_4 + H_2O$.

6.19. Balance the following equations and express each as the difference between two half-cell reactions: (a) $Fe^{++} + H_2O_2 + H^+ \rightarrow Fe^{+++} + H_2O$, (b) $MnO_4^- + H_2O_2 + H^+ \rightarrow Mn^{++} + O_2 + H_2O$, (c) $Cr^{+++} + MnO_4^- + H_2O \rightarrow Cr_2O_7^- + Mn^{++} + H^+$, (d) $I_2 + H_2O_2 \rightarrow H^+ + IO_3^- + H_2O$, (e) $H_2SO_3 + H_2S \rightarrow S + H_2O$.

6.20. Write the following as balanced ionic equations and express each as the difference between two half-cell reactions: (a) $SnSO_4 + K_2Cr_2O_7 + H_2SO_4 \rightarrow Sn(SO_4)_2 + K_2SO_4 + Cr_2(SO_4)_3 + H_2O$, (b) $As + HNO_3 + H_2O \rightarrow H_3AsO_4 + NO$, (c) $Br_2 + NH_4OH \rightarrow NH_4Br + N_2 + H_2O$, (d) $KI + KIO_3 + HCl \rightarrow I_2 + H_2O + KCl$.

6.21. Write an equation showing the net reaction indicated by each of the following pairs of half-cell reactions. Show from the respective electrode potentials in which direction each reaction should go, assuming all ion concentrations to be 1 molar. (a) $Hg = Hg^{++} + 2\epsilon$, $Zn = Zn^{++} + 2\epsilon$; (b) $H_2O_2 = O_2 + 2H^+ + 2\epsilon$, $Fe^{++} = Fe^{+++}$

$+ \epsilon$; (c) $Pb^{++} + 2H_2O = PbO_2 + 4H^+ + 2\epsilon$, $2Cl^- = Cl_2 + 2\epsilon$; (d) $2Cl^- = Cl_2 + 2\epsilon$, $2Br^- = Br_2 + 2\epsilon$.

6.22. Solve the preceding problem with respect to the following half-cell reactions: (a) $Sn^{++} = Sn^{++++} + 2\epsilon$, $2I^- = I_2 + 2\epsilon$; (b) $2Cr^{+++} + 7H_2O = Cr_2O_7^= + 14H^+ + 6\epsilon$, $Fe(CN)_6^{\equiv} = Fe(CN)_6^= + \epsilon$; (c) $Mn^{++} + 2H_2O = MnO_2 + 4H^+ + 2\epsilon$, $Fe^{++} = Fe^{+++} + \epsilon$; (d) $Ag = Ag^+ + \epsilon$, $NO + 2H_2O = NO_3^- + 4H^+ + 3\epsilon$.

6.23. The following reactions take place at ordinary concentrations as written:

$$V^{++} + TiO^{++} + 2H^+ \rightarrow V^{+++} + Ti^{+++} + H_2O$$
$$Bi + 3Fe^{+++} + H_2O \rightarrow BiO^+ + 3Fe^{++} + 2H^+$$
$$Zn + 2Cr^{+++} \rightarrow Zn^{++} + 2Cr^{++}$$
$$6Br^- + Cr_2O_7^= + 14H^+ \rightarrow 3Br_2 + 2Cr^{+++} + 7H_2O$$
$$3Ti^{+++} + BiO^+ + 2H_2O \rightarrow 3TiO^{++} + Bi + 4H^+$$
$$2Fe^{++} + NO_3^- + 3H^+ \rightarrow 2Fe^{+++} + HNO_2 + H_2O$$
$$Mg + Zn^{++} \rightarrow Mg^{++} + Zn$$
$$Cr^{++} + V^{+++} \rightarrow Cr^{+++} + V^{++}$$
$$HNO_2 + Br_2 + H_2O \rightarrow NO_3^- + 2Br^- + 3H^+$$

Convert each of these reactions into two half-cell reactions, placing the reduced form on the left and the oxidized form and electrons on the right. Rearrange the 9 half-cell reactions in tabular form in such a manner that the strongest reducing agent is at the top left and the strongest oxidizing agent is at the bottom right. From the tabulation predict which of the following do not react at ordinary concentrations and write balanced ionic equations for those that do: (a) $Zn^{++} + V^{++}$, (b) $Fe^{++} + TiO^{++}$, (c) $Cr^{++} + NO_3^- + H^+$, (d) $Bi + Br_2$, (e) $Cr_2O_7^= + TiO^{++} + H^+$.

6.24. Which of the following reactions should take place as indicated when ion concentrations are 1 molar? (a) $2Cl^- + I_2 \rightarrow Cl_2 + 2I^-$, (b) $2Fe(CN)_6^= + H_2O_2 \rightarrow 2Fe(CN)_6^{\equiv} + O_2 + 2H^+$, (c) $2Fe^{++} + PbO_2 + 4H^+ \rightarrow 2Fe^{+++} + Pb^{++} + 2H_2O$, (d) $2Bi + 6H^+ \rightarrow 2Bi^{+++} + 3H_2$, (e) $10Cr^{+++} + 6MnO_4^- + 11H_2O \rightarrow 5Cr_2O_7^= + 6Mn^{++} + 22H^+$.

6.25. The standard potential between elementary rhenium and the perrhenate ion (ReO_4^-) in alkaline solution is $+0.81$ volt. Calculate the potential of this system when the concentration of perrhenate and of hydroxyl ions are each 0.10 molar.

6.26. By how many volts would the potential between hypoiodite (IO^-) and iodate (IO_3^-) in alkaline solution differ from the standard potential if the concentrations of the hypoiodite, iodate, and hydroxyl ions are each 0.30 molar?

6.27. Calculate the e.m.f. of each of the following cells. In each case indicate the direction of the passage of electrons in the wire connecting the electrodes, and write an equation for the net reaction.

(a) $Ag \mid Ag^+(1.0\ M) \parallel Cd^{++}(1.0\ M) \mid Cd$

(b) $Cu \mid Cu^{++}(0.010\ M) \parallel Cu^{++}(0.090\ M) \mid Cu$

(c) $Pt \left| \begin{matrix} Cr^{+++}(0.050\ M) \\ Cr_2O_7^=(0.10\ M) \\ H^+(2.0\ M) \end{matrix} \right\| \left. \begin{matrix} Fe^{++}(0.090\ M) \\ Fe^{+++}(0.015\ M) \end{matrix} \right| Pt$

(d) $Pt \left| \begin{matrix} Sn^{++}(0.020\ M) \\ Sn^{++++}(0.080\ M) \end{matrix} \right\| \left. \begin{matrix} Mn^{++}(0.050\ M) \\ MnO_4^-(0.10\ M) \\ H^+(0.40\ M) \end{matrix} \right| Pt$

(e) $Pt \left| \begin{matrix} Fe^{++}(0.25\ M) \\ Fe^{+++}(0.050\ M) \end{matrix} \right\| AgCl\ (satd.) \mid Ag$

6.28. What is the e.m.f. of the following concentration cell?

$$\text{Cu} \mid \text{Cu}^{++}(1.0 \times 10^{-5} \text{ molar}) \parallel \text{Cu}^{++}(0.080 \text{ molar}) \mid \text{Cu}$$

In what direction is the flow of electrons through the wire?

6.29. What e.m.f. can be obtained at 25°C. from the following cell?

$$\text{Ag} \mid \text{Ag}^{+}(0.30 \text{ molar}) \parallel \text{Cd}^{++}(1.0 \times 10^{-3} \text{ molar}) \mid \text{Cd}$$

In what direction is the flow of electrons through the wire connecting the electrodes? Write the equation for the reaction at each electrode and for the net reaction. What would the concentration of Ag^+ have to be for no current to flow?

6.30. What must be the value of x in order that the following reaction shall be at equilibrium: $\text{Zn} + 2\text{Ag}^{+}(x \text{ molar}) \rightleftarrows \text{Zn}^{++}(1.0 \times 10^{-3} \text{ molar}) + 2\text{Ag}$?

6.31. When excess metallic aluminum is added to a solution 0.10 molar in Cu^{++}, what is the theoretical concentration of Cu^{++} after equilibrium is reached? The reaction is practically complete as follows: $2\text{Al} + 3\text{Cu}^{++} \rightarrow 2\text{Al}^{+++} + 3\text{Cu}$.

6.32. Equal volumes of a solution 0.40 molar in Fe^{++} and a solution 0.10 molar in Ce^{++++} are mixed. After the reaction is practically complete ($Fe^{++} + Ce^{++++} \rightarrow Fe^{+++} + Ce^{+++}$) and equilibrium has been attained, what is the resulting concentration of Ce^{++++}?

6.33. Calculate the equilibrium constant for each of the following:

    (a) $\text{Cu}^{++} + 2\text{Ag} \rightleftarrows \text{Cu} + 2\text{Ag}^{+}$

    (b) $3\text{Cu}^{++} + 2\text{Al} \rightleftarrows 3\text{Cu} + 2\text{Al}^{+++}$

    (c) $\text{Fe}^{++} + \text{Ce}^{++++} \rightleftarrows \text{Fe}^{+++} + \text{Ce}^{+++}$

    (d) $2\text{Br}^{-} + \text{I}_2 \rightleftarrows \text{Br}_2 + 2\text{I}^{-}$

    (e) $10\text{I}^{-} + 2\text{MnO}_4^{-} + 16\text{H}^{+} \rightleftarrows 5\text{I}_2 + 2\text{Mn}^{++} + 8\text{H}_2\text{O}$

Part II

GRAVIMETRIC ANALYSIS

CHAPTER 7

THE CHEMICAL BALANCE

51. Sensitivity of the Chemical Balance. The determination of the weight of a body is a fundamental measurement of analytical chemistry and is made with an equal-arm balance of high degree of precision. An equal-arm balance consists essentially of a rigid beam supported horizontally at its center on a knife-edge and so constructed that the center of gravity of the swinging portion is below the point of support.

The *sensitivity* of a chemical balance is the tangent of the angle through which the equilibrium position of the pointer is displaced by a small excess load (usually 1 mg.) on the balance pan. This angle is usually so small that it is sufficiently accurate to define the sensitivity of a balance as the number of scale divisions through which the equilibrium position of the pointer of the balance is displaced by an excess load of 1 mg.

The sensitivity varies directly with the length of the balance beam, inversely with the weight of the beam, and inversely with the distance between the center of gravity of the swinging portion and the point of support. That is,

$$\tan \alpha = \frac{l}{bd} k$$

where α = the angle through which the pointer is moved
b = the weight of the beam
l = the length of the beam
d = the distance between the center of gravity and the point of support
k = a constant

The sensitivity of a balance decreases slightly with increasing load.

52. Method of Swings. In most analytical work, it is sufficiently accurate to make weighings by the *method of short swings*. The pointer of the balance is allowed to swing only one or two scale divisions to the right or left of the zero point of the scale, and the reading of the weights is taken when the extreme positions of the pointer to the right and left of the zero point are equal. The balance is, of course, previously adjusted so that with no load on the pans the extreme positions of the pointer are likewise equal.

For more precise work the *method of long swings* is used. The equilibrium position of the pointer is first determined by allowing the beam of the empty balance to swing so that the pointer passes over six to eight divisions on the scale. Extreme positions of the pointer in an odd number of consecutive swings are recorded; for example, three readings are taken to the right of the zero point of the scale, and two readings are taken to the left of the zero point. The two sets of readings are averaged, and the equilibrium position of the pointer is taken as the algebraic mean of the two values. As an illustration, assume that the pointer of a balance swings as indicated below:

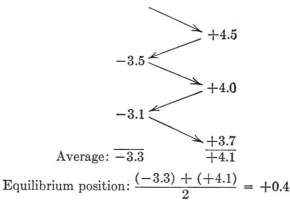

$$\text{Equilibrium position:} \frac{(-3.3) + (+4.1)}{2} = +0.4$$

The weight of an object can then be determined by placing it on the left-hand pan and (1) adjusting the weights and rider, or weights and chain, so that the equilibrium position is the same as that obtained with the empty balance, or (2) calculating the weight from the sensitivity of the balance and the equilibrium position corresponding to an approximate weighing of the object. For example, suppose the equilibrium position of the pointer under zero load is +0.4 as determined above. Suppose that, when an object is balanced with 20.1260 grams, the equilibrium position is found to be +1.6 and the sensitivity of the balance under a 20-gram load is 4.0 (*i.e.*, a 1-mg. increment shifts the equilibrium position by 4.0 scale divisions); then the necessary shift of 1.2 divisions to the left to bring the equilibrium position to +0.4 is accomplished by increasing the weight on the right-hand side of the balance by 1.2/4.0 = 0.3 mg. The weight of the object is, therefore, 20.1263 grams.

53. Conversion of Weight in Air to Weight in Vacuo. Archimedes' principle states that any substance immersed in a fluid weighs less by an amount equal to the weight of fluid displaced. Consequently, a substance weighed in the ordinary manner is buoyed up to a slight extent by the surrounding air, and for accurate determinations, especially those involving the weighing of objects of large volume, a correction for this buoyant effect must be applied. Since the usual method of weighing consists in balancing the substance to be weighed against standard weights, the surrounding air likewise exerts a buoyant effect upon the weights. If the volume occupied by the weights used is equal to the volume occupied by the substance, the buoyant effects will be equal, and the weight of the substance in vacuo will be the same as its weight in air. If the volume occupied by the substance is greater than the volume occupied by the weights, the substance will weigh more in vacuo than in air; and if the weights have the greater volume, the substance will weigh less in vacuo than in air. In any case, the difference between the weight in air and the weight in vacuo will be equal to the difference between the weight of the air displaced by the substance and the weight of the air displaced by the weights used. The weight in vacuo W^0 may be expressed by the equation

$$W^0 = W + (V - V')a$$

where W = the weight of the substance in air
V = the volume occupied by the substance
V' = the volume occupied by the weights used
a = the weight of a unit volume of air

Since in practice, the volume occupied by the substance and the volume occupied by the weights are usually unknown, the formula is better written by expressing the values V and V' in terms of weight and density. If d is the density of the substance and d' the density of the weights, the volume occupied by the substance will be W^0/d, and the volume occupied by the weights used will be W/d'. The formula may now be written

$$W^0 = W + \left(\frac{W^0}{d} - \frac{W}{d'}\right) a$$

Since the value following the plus sign in this expression is small compared with the value W to which it is added and since W and W^0 are nearly equal, W may be substituted for the W^0 in the parentheses without appreciably affecting the accuracy of the formula. The formula now becomes

$$W^0 = W + \left(\frac{W}{d} - \frac{W}{d'}\right) a$$

or

$$W^0 = W + W \left(\frac{a}{d} - \frac{a}{d'}\right)$$

Although the value of a varies slightly with the temperature and barometric pressure, the approximate value of 0.0012 gram for the weight of one milliliter of air may be used except in cases where extreme accuracy is required or where the atmospheric conditions are highly abnormal. The densities of a few common substances are shown in Table I. A consideration of the precision of the various terms shows that the values of a, d, and d' need be known only approximately and that in most cases the computation may be performed with sufficient accuracy by means of a slide rule.

TABLE I. DENSITIES OF A FEW COMMON SUBSTANCES

Aluminum	2.7	Mercury	13.6
Brass	8.4	Nickel	8.7
Brass (balance weights)	8.0	Platinum	21.4
Copper	8.9	Porcelain	2.4
Glass	2.6	Quartz	2.7
Gold	19.3	Silver	10.5
Lead	11.3	Steel	7.8

EXAMPLE.   A platinum crucible weighs 25.6142 grams in air against brass analytical weights.   What is its weight in vacuo?

SOLUTION:

$$\text{Density of platinum} = 21.4 = d$$
$$\text{Density of brass weights} = 8.0 = d'$$
$$\text{Weight of 1 ml. of air} = 0.0012 \text{ gram} = a$$

Substituting in the above formula,

$$W^0 = 25.6142 + \left(\frac{25.6142}{21.4} - \frac{25.6142}{8.0} \right) 0.0012$$

$$= 25.6142 + \left(\frac{26}{21} - \frac{26}{8.0} \right) 0.0012$$

$$= 25.6142 - 0.0024$$

$$= 25.6118 \text{ grams.} \textit{Ans.}$$

54. Calibration of Weights. In an ordinary quantitative chemical analysis, if the same set of weights is used throughout, it is immaterial whether or not the masses of the weights are exactly as marked so long as they are in correct *relative* proportion. The mass of the 5-gram weight should be exactly one-half that of the 10-gram weight, and the others should be similarly in proportion. In order to establish this relationship and to determine what correction factors must be applied to the individual weights of a given set, the weights must be calibrated.

There are several ways of calibrating weights. One of the simplest is to assume temporarily that one of the smaller weights, say the 10-mg. weight, is correct and to determine the value of the other weights in relation to it. In order to allow for the possible fact that the arms of the balance may be slightly unequal in length, weighings should be made by the *method of substitution*, which practically eliminates any error from this source.

Ordinarily the masses of objects A and B are compared by placing them on opposite pans of a balance, but by the method of substitution, object A is placed on the left-hand pan and is balanced against a tare (which may be a weight from an auxiliary set) on the right-hand pan. A is removed and B is placed on the left-hand pan. If it exactly balances against the same tare, it has the same mass as A. If there is a slight difference, the change in position of the rider or chain necessary to reestablish equilibrium can be taken as a measure of the difference in mass.

TABLE II. TYPICAL CALIBRATION CORRECTIONS

Face value of weight, grams	True value, based on 0.010-gram standard	Fractional part of 10-gram standard	Necessary correction, mg.
0.010 (initial standard)	0.0100	0.0101	−0.1
0.010′	0.0101	0.0101	0
0.020	0.0199	0.0202	−0.3
0.050	0.0506	0.0506	0
0.100	0.1012	0.1011	+0.1
0.100′	0.1014	0.1015	−0.1
0.200	0.2023	0.2023	0
0.500	0.5056	0.5056	0
1	1.0110	1.0113	−0.3
2	2.0225	2.0226	−0.1
2	2.0228	2.0226	+0.2
5	5.0562	5.0564	−0.2
10 (final standard)	10.1128	10.1128	0
10′	10.1130	10.1128	+0.2
20	20.2262	20.2256	+0.6
50	50.5635	50.5640	−0.5

The relative mass of the other 10-mg. weight (which can be marked 10′) in the set is determined by comparing with the 10-mg. weight; the relative mass of the 20-mg. weight is similarly determined by balancing against the combined 10-mg. and 10′-mg. weights. This process is continued up through the entire set of weights, the combined values of the smaller weights being used to establish the values of the larger weights. In this way values similar to those listed in the second column of Table II are obtained. Because of the small standard taken, it will usually be found that the larger weights have large correction factors.   It is therefore convenient to convert the values to a larger standard, say one of the 10-gram weights of the set (or an auxiliary 10-gram weight from a set checked by the Bureau of Standards, which has been included in the above series of weighings).   In the case cited in the table, the new 10-gram standard has a value of 10.1128 grams (relative to the original small standard).   The 5-gram weight should have a value of exactly one half of this, or 5.0564 grams.   Actually its value is 5.0562 grams; hence it is 0.0002 gram too light.   Therefore 0.2 mg. must be *subtracted* from a weighing in which its face value is used.

In weighing a given object, instead of applying a correction for each weight used, it is less tedious to construct a table showing *cumulative* corrections.   By means of such a table the total correction is found from the sum of the face values of the weights on the pan.   In this case it is necessary when weighing an object to adopt the convention of using the smallest number of weights possible, to use an "unprimed" weight (*e.g.*, 0.100 gram) in preference to a "primed" weight (*e.g.*, 0.100′ gram), and to construct the table accordingly.   In the table given, a total weight of 0.18 gram would show a net correction of −0.3 mg., which is the algebraic sum of the individual corrections of the weights having the face values 100, 50, 20, and 10 mg. (*i.e.*, +0.1 + 0.0 − 0.3 − 0.1 = −0.3).

Problems

7.1. The addition of a small weight to a certain balance displaces the pointer through an angle of 6°.   Through what angle would a weight 1½ times as great displace it?

Ans.   8° 57′.

7.2. A crucible weighing approximately 10 grams is being weighed.   The pointer of the empty balance has an equilibrium position at +0.2 on the scale, and the sensitivity of the balance under a 10-gram load is known to be 3.6 divisions.   With the rider at 4.8 (mg.) on the beam, the equilibrium point of the balance is found to be at +2.7 on the scale.   To what point on the beam should the rider be moved to make the correct final reading?

Ans.   5.5.

7.3. When the pointer of a balance (having a 10-gram load on each pan) is set in motion, it swings on the scale as follows: right to +7.6; left to −6.4; right to +7.0; left to −5.8; right to +6.2.   With an additional 1-mg. weight on the right-hand pan, the pointer swings as follows: right to +1.0; left to −8.2; right to +0.4; left to −7.6; right to −0.3.   What is the sensitivity (in scale divisions) of the balance under a 10-gram load?

Ans.   4.2 divisions.

7.4. The balance of the preceding problem is used to weigh a certain crucible and is adjusted so that the equilibrium position of the pointer is at zero when the balance is empty.   With the crucible on the left-hand pan, with weights totaling to 10.12 grams on the right-hand pan, and with the rider at 3.0 mg. on the right-hand beam, the equilibrium position of the pointer is found to be at −1.7 on the scale division. What is the weight of the crucible to the nearest tenth of a milligram?

Ans. 10.1226 grams.

7.5. A sample of an alloy having a volume of 2 ml. is weighed in air with brass weights and is found to weigh 16.0000 grams. What is its weight in vacuo?

Ans. 16.0000 grams.

7.6. Find the weight in vacuo of a piece of gold that weighs 35.0000 grams in air against brass weights.

Ans. 34.9968 grams.

7.7. A substance weighing 12.3456 grams in air has a volume of 2 ml. and a density equal to three times that of the weights used. What does it weigh in vacuo?

Ans. 12.3408 grams.

7.8. A quartz crucible weighing 16.0053 grams in a vacuum would weigh how many grams in air against brass weights?

Ans. 16.0005 grams.

7.9. A sample of brass weighs 12.8150 grams in air against platinum weights. What is its weight in vacuo?

Ans. 12.8162 grams.

7.10. If a piece of gold in vacuo weighs thirty-five times as much as a 1-gram brass weight in vacuo, what would the brass weigh in air against gold weights? What would the piece of gold weigh in air against brass weights?

Ans. 0.99991 gram. 35.0031 grams.

7.11. In calibrating a given set of weights the 10-mg. weight is temporarily taken as a standard and assumed to be 0.0100 gram. On this basis the 2-gram weight is found to be 2.0169 grams and a 10-gram weight (certified by the Bureau of Standards to be correct to within less than 0.05 mg.) is found to be 10.0856 grams. What correction should be applied for the 2-gram weight in any weighing in which its face value is taken as its true weight?

Ans. −0.2 mg.

7.12. A weight of 1 mg. on the right-hand pan of a certain balance displaces the equilibrium position of the pointer by 6.0 mm. The pointer is 24.6 cm. long. What is the tangent of the angle through which the pointer has moved? If the beam weighs 32.0 grams and is 16.0 cm. long, what is the distance between the middle knife-edge and the center of gravity of the moving parts?

7.13. When the pointer of a balance (having a 20-gram scale on each pan) is set in motion, it swings on the scale as follows: right to +6.2; left to −6.1; right to +5.7; left to −5.5; right to +5.3. With an additional 1-mg. weight on the right-hand pan, the pointer swings as follows: right to +3.1; left to −9.2; right to +2.6; left to −8.7; right to +2.2. What is the sensitivity (in scale divisions) of the balance under a 20-gram load?

7.14. The balance mentioned in the preceding problem is adjusted so that the equilibrium position of the pointer of the empty balance is at zero and is used to weigh a certain crucible. With the crucible on the left-hand pan, with weights adding to

19.87 grams on the right-hand pan, and with the rider at 8.0 mg. on the right-hand beam, the equilibrium position of the pointer is found to be at +1.2 on the scale division. What is the weight of the crucible to the nearest tenth of a milligram?

7.15. What would be the weight of a piece of gold in vacuo if in air against brass weights it weighs 14.2963 grams?

7.16. In vacuo, a quartz dish weighs 22.9632 grams. Calculate the weight in air against brass weights.

7.17. In determining an atomic weight, a final product which has a density of 6.32 is weighed in air against gold weights. What percentage error would be made by failing to convert this weight (10.0583 grams) to the weight in vacuo?

7.18. Find to the nearest tenth of a milligram the weight in vacuo of a piece of silver which weighs 20.0113 grams in air against brass weights.

7.19. Find the weights in vacuo of two crucibles, one of gold and one of aluminum, each weighing 15.0000 grams in air against brass weights. What would the gold crucible weigh in air against aluminum weights?

7.20. What is the density of a solid which weighs approximately 20 grams in air against brass weights and the weight of which increases by exactly 0.01 per cent in vacuo? What is the density of a similar substance the weight of which decreases by 0.01 per cent in vacuo?

7.21. From the correction values given in Table II construct a table of cumulative corrections for weighings ranging from 0.01 to 0.99 gram and construct another table of cumulative corrections for weighings ranging from 1.00 gram to 99.99 grams. (*Hint:* To save space use a tabulation similar to that used in logarithm tables.)

7.22. Assuming that the 20-gram weight in a given set has a value of 20.2364 grams in relation to the 10-mg. weight as a standard, what should be the value of a 500-mg. weight to have a zero correction if the 20-gram weight is taken as the final standard and assumed to be 20.0000 grams? If the 500-mg. weight actually has a value of 0.5063 on the basis of the smaller standard, what correction should be applied for this weight in any weighing in which its face value is taken as its true weight?

CHAPTER 8

CALCULATIONS OF GRAVIMETRIC ANALYSIS

55. Law of Definite Proportions Applied to Calculations of Gravimetric Analysis. Gravimetric analysis is based on the law of definite proportions, which states that in any pure compound the proportions by weight of the constituent elements are always the same, and on the law of constancy of composition, which states that masses of the elements taking part in a given chemical change always exhibit a definite and invariable ratio to each other. It consists in determining the proportionate amount of an element, radical, or compound present in a sample by eliminating all interfering substances and converting the desired constituent or component into a weighable compound of definite, known composition. Having then determined the weight of this isolated compound, the weight of the desired component present in the sample can be calculated (see also Chap. 3).

EXAMPLE I. A sample of impure sodium chloride is dissolved in water, and the chloride is precipitated with silver nitrate:

$$NaCl + AgNO_3 \rightarrow AgCl + NaNO_3$$

or

$$Cl^- + Ag^+ \rightarrow \underline{AgCl}$$

furnishing 1.000 gram of silver chloride. What is the weight of chlorine in the original sample?

SOLUTION: Since silver chloride always contains silver and chlorine in the respective ratio of their atomic weights, or in the ratio of 107.88 : 35.46, in every 143.34 (107.88 + 35.46) grams of silver chloride there are 35.46 grams of chlorine. In 1.000 gram of silver chloride there is

$$1.000 \times \frac{Cl}{AgCl} = 1.000 \times \frac{35.46}{143.34} = 0.2474 \text{ gram of chlorine.} \quad Ans.$$

EXAMPLE II. The iron in a sample of $FeCO_3$ containing inert impurities is converted by solution, oxidation, precipitation, and ignition into Fe_2O_3 weighing 1.000 gram. What is the weight of iron expressed as $FeCO_3$, as Fe, and as FeO in the original sample?

SOLUTION: The reactions may be expressed by the following molecular equations:

$$FeCO_3 + 2HCl \rightarrow FeCl_2 + CO_2 + H_2O$$
$$2FeCO_3 + 4HCl \rightarrow 2FeCl_2 + 2CO_2 + 2H_2O$$
$$2FeCl_2 + Br_2 + 2HCl \rightarrow 2FeCl_3 + 2HBr$$
$$2FeCl_3 + 6NH_4OH \rightarrow 2Fe(OH)_3 + 6NH_4Cl$$
$$2Fe(OH)_3 \rightarrow Fe_2O_3 + 3H_2O$$

From these equations it is seen that one molecular weight in grams (one *mole*) of $FeCO_3$ will furnish one molecular weight in grams of $FeCl_2$, or 2 moles of $FeCO_3$ will furnish 2 moles of $FeCl_2$. Two moles of $FeCl_2$ will give 2 moles of $FeCl_3$, which in turn will precipitate 2 moles of $Fe(OH)_3$; and this last compound on ignition will give *one* mole of Fe_2O_3. Hence, every 2 moles (231.72 grams) of $FeCO_3$ will eventually furnish one mole (159.70) grams of Fe_2O_3, and it will do so independently of the nature of the process or composition of the reagents used to bring about the conversion. Indeed, the above reactions are better written in the ionic form, thus:

$$FeCO_3 + 2H^+ \rightarrow Fe^{++} + CO_2 + H_2O$$
$$\overline{Fe^{++} + \tfrac{1}{2}Br_2 \rightarrow Fe^{+++}} + Br^-$$
$$Fe^{+++} + 3NH_4OH \rightarrow \underline{Fe(OH)_3} + 3NH_4^+$$
$$2\underline{Fe(OH)_3} \rightarrow \underline{Fe_2O_3} + 3H_2O$$

and for purposes of calculations all the intermediate steps may be omitted and the fundamental change expressed by the hypothetical equation

$$2FeCO_3 + O \rightarrow Fe_2O_3 + 2CO_2$$

In general, it is unnecessary to determine the weights of intermediate products in a reaction that takes place in steps, and for purposes of calculation only the initial and final substances need be considered.

Since two moles (231.72 grams) of $FeCO_3$ will furnish one mole (159.70 grams) of Fe_2O_3, by simple proportion, 1.0000 gram of Fe_2O_3 will be obtained from $1.0000 \times \dfrac{2FeCO_3}{Fe_2O_3} = 1.0000 \times \dfrac{231.72}{159.70} = 1.4510$ grams of $FeCO_3$. Since each mole of $FeCO_3$ contains one gram-atomic weight (55.85 grams) of Fe and represents the equivalent of one mole (71.85 grams) of $FeO (FeCO_3 \rightarrow FeO + CO_2)$, the corresponding weights of Fe and FeO would be

$$1.0000 \times \frac{2Fe}{Fe_2O_3} = 1.0000 \times \frac{2 \times 55.85}{159.70} = 0.6994 \text{ gram of Fe}$$

and

$$1.0000 \times \frac{2FeO}{Fe_2O_3} = 1.0000 \times \frac{2 \times 71.85}{159.70} = 0.8998 \text{ gram of FeO,}$$

respectively. *Ans.*

EXAMPLE III. What weight of Fe_3O_4 will furnish 0.5430 gram of Fe_2O_3?

SOLUTION: Whatever equations may be written to represent the conversion of the Fe_3O_4 to the Fe_2O_3 it will be found that from every 2 moles of Fe_3O_4 there are obtained 3 moles of Fe_2O_3, and the hypothetical equation may be written

$$2Fe_3O_4 + O \rightarrow 3Fe_2O_3$$

Hence,

$$0.5430 \times \frac{2Fe_3O_4}{3Fe_2O_3} = 0.5430 \times \frac{463.1}{479.1} = 0.5249 \text{ gram } Fe_3O_4. \quad Ans.$$

56. Gravimetric Factors. A gravimetric factor (or *chemical factor*) may be defined as the weight of desired substance equivalent to a unit weight of given substance. Thus, in the above three examples, the numbers obtained from the ratios $Cl/AgCl$, $2FeCO_3/Fe_2O_3$, $2Fe/Fe_2O_3$, $2FeO/Fe_2O_3$, and $2Fe_3O_4/3Fe_2O_3$ are gravimetric factors since they represent the respective weights of Cl, $FeCO_3$, Fe, FeO, and Fe_3O_4 equivalent to one unit weight of AgCl or of Fe_2O_3 as the case may be.

A weight of one substance is said to be *equivalent* to that of another substance when the two will mutually enter into direct or indirect reaction in exact respective proportion to those weights. In the example cited above, 231.72 grams of $FeCO_3$ produce 159.70 grams of Fe_2O_3. Hence, 231.72 grams of $FeCO_3$ are equivalent to 159.70 grams of Fe_2O_3. The equivalent weights of elements and compounds may be expressed by mutual proportions as in the case just given, or they may be referred to a common standard for which purpose the atomic weight of hydrogen (1.008) is usually taken (see Sec. 28).

Notice that in expressing a gravimetric factor the atomic or molecular weight of the substance *sought* is placed in the numerator, the atomic or molecular weight of the substance *weighed* is placed in the denominator, and the coefficients are adjusted *in accordance with the reactions involved*. When the principal element or radical desired occurs in both numerator and denominator, usually the number of atomic weights of this element or radical will be the same in both numerator and denominator, although there are instances when this is not true. For example, in the reaction

$$2CuCl \rightarrow CuCl_2 + Cu$$

the weight of free copper liberated from one gram of cuprous chloride is $1.000 \times (Cu/2CuCl) = 0.3210$ gram, and 0.3210 is the gravimetric factor in this particular case.

That the principal element does not always occur in both numerator and denominator is shown in the determination of bromine by precipitation as silver bromide and conversion to silver chloride with a current of chlorine.

$$2AgBr + Cl_2 \rightarrow 2AgCl + Br_2$$

Here the weight of bromine represented by one gram of silver chloride is

$$\frac{Br_2}{2AgCl} = \frac{2 \times 79.92}{2 \times 143.34} = 0.5578 \text{ gram.}$$

57. Calculation of Percentages. Since the gravimetric factor represents the weight of desired element or compound equivalent to one unit weight of the element or compound weighed, from any weight of the latter the weight of the former can be calculated. The percentage of that substance present in the sample may be found by dividing by the weight of sample and multiplying by 100.

EXAMPLE I.   If 2.000 grams of impure sodium chloride are dissolved in water and, with an excess of silver nitrate, 4.6280 grams of silver chloride are precipitated, what is the percentage of chlorine in the sample?

SOLUTION: The gravimetric factor of Cl in AgCl is 0.2474, indicating that 1.000 gram of AgCl contains 0.2474 gram of Cl.   In 4.6280 grams of AgCl there are therefore $4.6280 \times 0.2474 = 1.145$ grams of Cl.   Since this amount represents the chlorine present in 2.000 grams of the material, the percentage weight of chlorine must be

$$\frac{1.145}{2.000} \times 100 = 57.25 \text{ per cent.}   \textit{Ans.}$$

EXAMPLE II.   A half-gram sample of impure magnetite (Fe_3O_4) is converted by chemical reactions to Fe_2O_3, weighing 0.4110 gram.   What is the percentage of Fe_3O_4 in the magnetite?

SOLUTION: The gravimetric factor in this case is $2Fe_3O_4/3Fe_2O_3 = 0.9666$ which represents the weight of Fe_3O_4 equivalent to 1.000 gram of Fe_2O_3.   The weight of Fe_3O_4 equivalent to 0.4110 gram of Fe_2O_3 must be $0.4110 \times 0.9666 = 0.3973$ gram, and the percentage of Fe_3O_4 in the sample must be $\frac{0.3973}{0.5000} \times 100 = 79.46$ per cent.   *Ans.*

Problems

8.1. Calculate the gravimetric factors for converting (a) $BaSO_4$ to Ba, (b) Cb_2O_5 to Cb, (c) $Mg_2P_2O_7$ to MgO, (d) $KClO_4$ to K_2O, (e) Fe_3O_4 to Fe_2O_3.

Ans.   (a) 0.5885, (b) 0.6990, (c) 0.3621, (d) 0.3399, (e) 1.035.

8.2. Calculate the gravimetric factors of the following:

WEIGHED	SOUGHT
(a) $(NH_4)_2PtCl_6$	NH_3
(b) MoS_3	MoO_3
(c) U_3O_8	U
(d) B_2O_3	$Na_2B_4O_7.10H_2O$
(e) $(NH_4)_3PO_4.12MoO_3$	P_2O_5

Ans. (a) 0.07671, (b) 0.7492, (c) 0.8480, (d) 2.738, (e) 0.03783.

8.3. What is the weight of sulfur in 5.672 grams of barium sulfate?

Ans. 0.7790 gram.

8.4. How many grams of $Na_2SO_4.10H_2O$ are equivalent to the Na in the NaCl required to precipitate AgCl from 2.000 grams of $AgNO_3$?

Ans. 1.896 gram.

8.5. A sample of impure ferrous ammonium sulfate weighs 0.5013 gram and furnishes 0.0968 gram of Fe_2O_3. What is the percentage of $Fe(NH_4)_2(SO_4)_2.6H_2O$?

Ans. 94.82 per cent.

8.6. A sample of limestone weighing 1.2456 grams furnishes 0.0228 gram of Fe_2O_3, 1.3101 grams of $CaSO_4$, and 0.0551 gram of $Mg_2P_2O_7$. Calculate the percentage of (a) Fe, (b) CaO, (c) MgO in the limestone. What weight of CO_2 could be in combination with the calcium?

Ans. (a) 1.28 per cent, (b) 43.32 per cent, (c) 1.60 per cent. 0.4237 gram.

8.7. What weight of pyrite containing 36.40 per cent of sulfur must have been taken for analysis in order to give a precipitate of barium sulfate weighing 1.0206 grams?

Ans. 0.3850 gram.

8.8. What is the percentage composition of a brass containing only copper, lead, and zinc if a half-gram sample furnishes 0.0023 gram of $PbSO_4$ and 0.4108 gram of $ZnNH_4PO_4$? What weight of $Zn_2P_2O_7$ could be obtained by igniting the zinc ammonium phosphate?

Ans. Cu = 69.59 per cent, Pb = 0.32 per cent, Zn = 30.09 per cent. 0.3510 gram.

8.9. What is the percentage of fluorine in a sample of soluble fluoride weighing 1.205 grams if it yields a precipitate of CaF_2 weighing 0.4953 gram?

Ans. 20.01 per cent.

8.10. The nitrogen in a half-gram sample of organic material is converted to NH_4HSO_4 by digestion with concentrated H_2SO_4. If the NH_4^+ ions are precipitated as $(NH_4)_2PtCl_6$ and the precipitate is ignited to Pt, what is the percentage of nitrogen in the sample if the metallic platinum weighs 0.1756 gram?

Ans. 5.044 per cent.

8.11. A sample of pyrite, FeS_2, contains only silica and other inert impurities and weighs 0.5080 gram. After decomposing and dissolving the sample, a precipitate of 1.561 gram of $BaSO_4$ is subsequently obtained. Calculate the percentage of sulfur in the sample. If the iron in the solution had been precipitated as $Fe(OH)_3$ and ignited to Fe_2O_3, what weight of ignited precipitate would have been obtained?

Ans. 42.20 per cent. 0.2671 gram.

8.12. A sample of alum, $K_2SO_4.Al_2(SO_4)_3.24H_2O$, containing only inert impurities weighs 1.421 grams. It gives a precipitate of $Al(OH)_3$ which, after ignition to Al_2O_3, weighs 0.1410 gram. What is the percentage of S in the alum? What is the percentage purity of the alum?

Ans. 12.49 per cent. 92.43 per cent.

8.13. Calculate the gravimetric factors for converting (a) Fe_2O_3 to Fe; (b) AgCl to $KClO_4$; (c) $Cu_3(AsO_3)_2.2As_2O_3.Cu(C_2H_3O_2)_2$ (mol. wt. = 1,014) to As_2O_3; (d) $BaSO_4$ to HSCN; (e) $K_2Al_2(SO_4)_4.24H_2O$ to H_2SO_4.

8.14. Calculate the gravimetric factors of the following:

WEIGHED	SOUGHT
(a) $Mg_2P_2O_7$	P
(b) K_2PtCl_6	KCl
(c) Mn_3O_4	Mn_2O_3
(d) $Cu_2(SCN)_2$	HSCN
(e) KBF_4	$Na_2B_4O_7.10H_2O$

8.15. What weight of AgBr could be obtained from 4.7527 grams of $Ag_2Cr_2O_7$?

8.16. How many pounds of phosphorus are contained in 1.000 ton of $Ca_3(PO_4)_2$?

8.17. A manufacturer using potassium cyanide in a process involving its use as cyanide only, substituted sodium cyanide at 45 cents a pound for a chemically equivalent quantity of potassium cyanide at $2 a pound. How much did he save per pound of KCN?

8.18. An ammonium salt is converted into $(NH_4)_2PtCl_6$ and the latter ignited until only the Pt remains in the crucible. If the residue weighs 0.1000 gram, what weight of NH_3 was present in the original salt?

8.19. What weight of water could be obtained by strongly igniting 2.000 grams of datolite $[CaB(OH)SiO_4]$ (mol. wt. = 160.0)?

8.20. Find the percentage composition of the following in terms of the oxides of the metallic elements: (a) $FeSO_4.7H_2O$, (b) $K_2SO_4.Al_2(SO_4)_3.24H_2O$, (c) $3Ca_3(PO_4)_2.CaCO_3$ (mol. wt. = 503.7).

8.21. An alloy is of the following composition: Cu = 65.40 per cent; Pb = 0.24 per cent; Fe = 0.56 per cent; Zn = 33.80 per cent.

A sample weighing 0.8060 gram is dissolved in HNO_3 and electrolyzed. Copper is deposited on the cathode; PbO_2 is deposited on the anode. When NH_4OH is added to the residual solution, $Fe(OH)_3$ is precipitated and the precipitate is ignited to Fe_2O_3. The zinc in the filtrate is precipitated as $ZnNH_4PO_4$ and ignited to $Zn_2P_2O_7$. What weights of Cu, PbO_2, Fe_2O_3 and $Zn_2P_2O_7$ were obtained?

8.22. How many grams of KNO_3 are equivalent to the potassium in that weight of K_3PO_4 which contains the same amount of combined P_2O_5 that is contained in 1.100 grams of $Ca_3(PO_4)_2$?

8.23. The antimony in a sample of alloy weighing 0.2500 gram is converted to Sb_2O_5 and this substance is ignited to Sb_2O_4. If the latter weighs 0.1305 gram, what is the percentage of Sb in the alloy?

8.24. A sample of Pb_3O_4, containing only inert matter, weighs 0.1753 gram and, after dissolving, subsequently yields a precipitate of $PbSO_4$ weighing 0.2121 gram. What is the purity of the sample expressed in terms of percentage of Pb? In terms of percentage of Pb_3O_4?

8.25. A sample of $FeSO_4.(NH_4)_2SO_4.6H_2O$ containing only inert impurities weighs 1.658 grams. After dissolving, oxidizing, and precipitating the iron, the $Fe(OH)_3$ ignites to Fe_2O_3 and weighs 0.3174 gram. Calculate the percentage of sulfur in the sample. What is the percentage of impurities in the sample?

58. Calculation of Atomic Weights.

Determinations of atomic-weight values at the present time are chiefly revisions of those already established, in order that their accuracy may be in keeping with improved apparatus and methods. In such cases, the formulas of the compounds involved are well established and the required calculations are thereby made very simple. The experimental procedure usually followed is to prepare from the element a known compound of high degree of purity. This compound is weighed, and the percentages of its constituents are determined gravimetrically. The mathematical computations involved are exactly similar to those of an ordinary gravimetric analysis, except that the atomic weight of the desired element is the only unknown factor.

EXAMPLE. Carefully purified sodium chloride weighing 2.56823 grams furnishes 6.2971 grams of silver chloride. Assuming the atomic weights of the chlorine and silver to be established as 35.457 and 107.880, respectively, calculate the atomic weight of sodium.

SOLUTION:

$$\text{Weight of NaCl} = \text{weight of AgCl} \times \frac{\text{NaCl}}{\text{AgCl}}$$

$$2.56823 = 6.2971 \times \frac{\text{NaCl}}{\text{AgCl}}$$

$$2.56823 = 6.2971 \times \frac{\text{Na} + 35.457}{107.880 + 35.457}$$

Solving,

$$\text{Na} = 23.003. \quad Ans.$$

Problems

8.26. If silver phosphate is found by careful analysis to contain 77.300 per cent silver, what is the calculated atomic weight of phosphorus (Ag = 107.88)?

Ans. 31.04.

8.27. From an average of 13 experiments, Baxter finds the ratio of silver bromide to silver chloride to be 1.310171. If the atomic weight of silver is taken as 107.880 and that of chlorine as 35.457, what is the atomic weight of bromine?

Ans. 79.915.

8.28. In determining the atomic weight of manganese, Berzelius in 1828 obtained 0.7225 gram of Mn_2O_3 from 0.5075 gram of Mn. Von Hauer in 1857 obtained 13.719 grams of Mn_3O_4 from 12.7608 grams of MnO. In 1906 Baxter and Hines obtained an average of 11.43300 grams of AgBr from 6.53738 grams of $MnBr_2$. What are the three values as determined? (Br = 79.916.)

Ans. 56.66, 55.024, 54.932.

8.29. In determining the atomic weight of arsenic, Baxter and Coffin converted several samples of Ag_3AsO_4 into AgCl and found the average value for the factor $3AgCl/Ag_3AsO_4$ to be 0.929550. Using the factor Ag/AgCl as found by Richards and Wells to be 0.752632, calculate the percentage of Ag in Ag_3AsO_4. Taking the atomic weight of silver as 107.880, calculate to five figures the atomic weight of arsenic.

Ans. 69.9609 per cent. 74.961.

8.30. In determining the atomic weight of aluminum, Richards and Krepelka prepared pure samples of $AlBr_3$ and experimentally determined the weight of silver required to precipitate the halogen. Results of four experiments were as follows:

WT. AlBr$_3$		WT. Ag
Sample 1..........	5.03798	6.11324
Sample 2..........	5.40576	6.55955
Sample 3..........	3.41815	4.14786
Sample 4..........	1.98012	2.40285

If the atomic weight of silver is taken as 107.880 and that of bromine is taken as 79.916, what is the mean value obtained for the atomic weight of aluminum?

8.31. The ratio of the weight of silicon tetrachloride to the weight of an equivalent amount of silver has been found to be 0.393802 ± 0.000008.   Assuming Cl = 35.457 and Ag = 107.880, calculate the atomic weight of silicon.

8.32. Classen and Strauch have determined the weights of bismuth oxide obtainable from several samples of pure bismuth triphenyl.   In one such determination, 5.34160 grams of $Bi(C_6N_5)_3$ gave 2.82761 grams of Bi_2O_3.   Calculate the atomic weight of bismuth as shown from these figures.   C = 12.010; H = 1.0080.

8.33. From the ratios $NaNO_3/NaCl$ = 1.45422, AgCl/Ag = 1.328668, and $NaCl/Ag$ = 0.541854 and assuming N = 14.008, calculate the atomic weights of silver, sodium, and chlorine.

59. Calculations Involving a Factor Weight Sample.   It is sometimes

desirable in industrial work, where large numbers of samples of similar material are analyzed, to regulate the weight of sample so that the weight of the final product obtained multiplied by a simple factor will exactly equal the percentage of the desired constituent.   This makes it possible to have the sample weighed out directly against a tare, perhaps by someone inexperienced in exact weighing, and at the same time to eliminate both the tedious calculations necessary for each analysis and the possibility of mathematical errors.

The calculation of a desired constituent in a chemical analysis involving a direct gravimetric determination is carried out by means of the following formula:

$$\frac{Grams\ of\ product \times gravimetric\ factor}{Grams\ of\ sample} \times 100 = per\ cent$$

Since for a specific determination the gravimetric factor is a constant, the expression contains only three variable factors, *viz.*, the weight of product, the weight of sample, and the percentage of desired constituent. If any two are known, the third can be calculated; or, since the expression involves only multiplication and division, if the numerical *ratio* between the weight of product and the weight of sample, or between the weight of product and the percentage of desired constituent, is known, the remaining term can be determined.   Thus, if the weight of product is numerically equal to the percentage of desired constituent, these values cancel, and the weight of sample becomes equal to one hundred times the gravimetric factor.   If the weight of product is numerically equal to the weight of sample, these values cancel, and the percentage of desired constituent becomes equal to one hundred times the gravimetric factor.   Other ratios may be inserted in the expression, and the calculation made in a similar way.

EXAMPLE. The gravimetric factor of a certain analysis is 0.3427. It is desired to regulate the weight of sample taken so that (a) each centigram of the precipitate obtained will represent 1 per cent of the desired constituent; (b) every 2 centigrams of precipitate will represent 1 per cent of the desired constituent; (c) the percentage will be twice the number of centigrams of precipitate; (d) three-fourths of the weight in grams of precipitate will be one-fiftieth of the percentage of desired constituent. What weight of sample should be taken in each case?

SOLUTION: (a) The relation between the weight of precipitate and the percentage of constituent is such that 0.01 gram ≈ 1 per cent. Hence,

$$\frac{0.01 \times 0.3427}{x} \times 100 = 1$$

$$x = 0.3427 \text{ gram.} \quad Ans.$$

(b)
$$\frac{0.02 \times 0.3427}{x} \times 100 = 1$$

$$x = 0.6854 \text{ gram.} \quad Ans.$$

(c)
$$\frac{0.01 \times 0.3427}{x} \times 100 = 2$$

$$x = 0.1714 \text{ gram.} \quad Ans.$$

(d)
$$\frac{\frac{4}{3} \times 0.3427}{x} \times 100 = 50$$

$$x = 0.9135 \text{ gram.} \quad Ans.$$

Problems

8.34. In the analysis of a sample of feldspar for silica, the sample is fused, dissolved in HCl, and the solution is evaporated to dryness, heated, and treated with acid. The residue is filtered off and weighed as SiO_2. What weight of sample should be taken for analysis so that (a) each centigram of residue will represent 1 per cent SiO_2, (b) the number of centigrams will represent directly the percengage SiO_2, (c) every 2 centigrams of residue will represent 1 per cent SiO_2, (d) twice the number of centigrams will equal the percentage of SiO_2?

Ans. (a) 1.000 gram, (b) 1.000 gram, (c) 2.000 grams, (d) 0.5000 gram.

8.35. What weight of cast iron should be taken for analysis so that the weight of ignited SiO_2 in centigrams will be equal to one-third of the percentage of Si in the cast iron?

Ans. 0.156 gram.

8.36. Calculate the weight of limestone to be taken so that the number of centigrams of CaO obtained and the percentage of Ca in the sample will be in the respective ratio of 7:5.

Ans. 1.001 grams.

8.37. What weight of impure ferrous sulfate should be taken for analysis so that each milligram of Fe_2O_3 obtained will correspond to 0.120 per cent FeO in the sample?

8.38. What weight of dolomite should be taken for analysis so that, in the determination of magnesium, the number of centigrams of $Mg_2P_2O_7$ obtained will be twice the percentage of Mg in the mineral?

8.39. In the analysis of potassium in a silicate, the mineral is decomposed and the potassium subsequently weighed as $KClO_4$. What weight of sample was taken if it was found that the percentage of K_2O in the mineral could be found by dividing the number of milligrams of $KClO_4$ obtained by 12?

8.40. What weight of magnetite (impure Fe_3O_4) should be taken for analysis so that after decomposition of the sample, precipitation of the iron as $Fe(OH)_3$, and ignition to Fe_2O_3 (*a*) the number of centigrams of Fe_2O_3 obtained will be equal to the percentage of Fe_3O_4 in the sample, (*b*) the number of milligrams of Fe_2O_3 obtained will be five times the percentage of Fe_3O_4, (*c*) the percentage of Fe in the sample and the number of centigrams of Fe_2O_3 obtained will be in the ratio of 3:2?

60. Calculation of the Volume of a Reagent Required for a Given Reaction.

The volume of a solution required to carry out a given reaction can be calculated if the concentration of the solution is known. If the concentration is expressed in terms of normality, the calculation is best made by the methods of volumetric analysis, *i.e.*, in terms of milliequivalents (see Sec. 28); if the concentration is expressed as grams of solute per unit volume of solution or in terms of specific gravity and percentage composition, the calculation is usually easiest made by the use of the gravimetric factor.

EXAMPLE I. How many milliliters of barium chloride solution containing 90.0 grams of $BaCl_2.2H_2O$ per liter are required to precipitate the sulfate as $BaSO_4$ from 10.0 grams of pure $Na_2SO_4.10H_2O$?

SOLUTION: The weight of $BaCl_2.2H_2O$ for the precipitation is found by means of the gravimetric factor, thus:

$$10.0 \times \frac{BaCl_2.2H_2O}{Na_2SO_4.10H_2O} = 10.0 \times \frac{244}{322} = 7.58 \text{ grams of } BaCl_2.2H_2O$$

Since each milliliter of reagent contains 0.0900 gram of $BaCl_2.2H_2O$, the volume of solution required is

$$\frac{7.58}{0.0900} = 84.2 \text{ ml.} \quad Ans.$$

. When the concentration of the required reagent is expressed in terms of the percentage by weight of the solute, the specific gravity of the solution must also be known in order to determine the volume required. As stated in Sec. 25, there is no exact mathematical relationship between these two factors, but tables are given in all standard chemical handbooks showing this relationship for solutions of common substances experimentally determined at many different concentrations. Consequently, when a problem includes only one of these factors, tables must be consulted in order to determine the other. In the Appendix, specific-gravity-percentage tables are given for a few common acids and bases. These tables apply to weighings in vacuo at definite temperatures, but since three-significant figure accuracy is all that is needed in most calculations involving specific gravity of solutions, it is usually not necessary to make corrections for temperature and buoyancy differences.

EXAMPLE II.   How many milliliters of ammonia water of specific gravity 0.950 (containing 12.72 per cent of NH_3 by weight) are required to precipitate the iron from 0.800 gram of pure ferrous ammonium sulfate, $FeSO_4.(NH_4)_2SO_4.6H_2O$, after oxidation of the iron to the ferric state?

SOLUTION: Since 3 molecules of ammonia are required to precipitate one atom of ferric iron

$$Fe^{+++} + 3NH_3 + 3H_2O \rightarrow \underline{Fe(OH)_3} + 3NH_4^+$$

it follows that the weight of NH_3 necessary to precipitate the iron from 0.800 gram of ferrous ammonium sulfate will be

$$0.800 \times \frac{3NH_3}{FeSO_4.(NH_4)_2SO_4.6H_2O} = 0.800 \times \frac{51.10}{392.1} = 0.1043 \text{ gram of } NH_3$$

Since the ammonia water has a specific gravity of 0.950 and contains 12.74 per cent of NH_3 by weight, one milliliter of the solution weighs 0.950 gram of which 12.74 per cent by weight is NH_3 and 87.26 per cent by weight is water.   The actual weight of NH_3 in one milliliter of solution is therefore $0.950 \times 0.1274 = 0.121$ gram.   Since 0.1043 gram of NH_3 is required to precipitate the iron and since each milliliter of the solution contains 0.121 gram of NH_3, it follows that the volume of solution required is

$$\frac{0.1043}{0.121} = 0.862 \text{ ml.} \quad Ans.$$

As explained in Sec. 55, in calculations of this type the computations should not be carried through unnecessary steps.   In the example above, it is not necessary to compute the weight of iron contained in the ferrous ammonium sulfate, the weight of ammonium hydroxide required to precipitate the iron, and the weight of anhydrous ammonia contained in the ammonium hydroxide.   On expressing the whole, the common factors cancel.

$$0.800 \times \frac{\cancel{(Fe)}}{FeSO_4.(NH_4)_2SO_4.6H_2O} \times \frac{\cancel{(3NH_4OH)}}{\cancel{(Fe)}} \times \frac{3NH_3}{\cancel{(3NH_4OH)}}$$
$$= 0.1043 \text{ gram of } NH_3$$

$$\frac{0.1043}{0.121} = 0.862 \text{ ml.}$$

In general, with problems of this type, time will be saved if the final multiplications and divisions are not made until all the factors are combined and expressed as a whole.   In the above example the only essential factors are

$$\frac{0.800 \times 51.10}{392.1 \times 0.950 \times 0.1274} = 0.862 \text{ ml.}   \textit{Ans.}$$

A very similar type of problem is one in which it is required to calculate the volume of a solution of given percentage composition required to react with a certain volume of another solution of given percentage composition.   By computing the weight of reacting component in the given volume of the latter solution, the problem becomes exactly like the one discussed above.

EXAMPLE III.   How many milliliters of sulfuric acid (sp. gr. 1.135, 18.96 per cent H_2SO_4 by weight) are required to neutralize 75.0 ml. of ammonium hydroxide (sp. gr. 0.960, containing 9.91 per cent NH_3 by weight)?

SOLUTION: In 75.0 ml. of the ammonia solution there are

$$75.0 \times 0.960 \times 0.0991 \text{ grams of } NH_3$$

The required weight of H_2SO_4 for this NH_3 is

$$75.0 \times 0.960 \times 0.0991 \times \frac{H_2SO_4}{2NH_3} =$$

$$75.0 \times 0.960 \times 0.0991 \times \frac{98.08}{34.06} \text{ grams}$$

Since each milliliter of the acid contains 1.135×0.1896 gram of H_2SO_4, the volume of acid required is

$$\frac{75.0 \times 0.960 \times 0.0991 \times 98.08}{1.135 \times 0.1896 \times 34.06} = 95.6 \text{ ml.}   \textit{Ans.}$$

61. Calculation of the Concentration of a Reagent Mixture.   This type of problem is frequently encountered by the chemical engineer and industrial chemist.   It involves fairly concentrated solutions, and as stated in the preceding section, since the percentage composition of such a solution does not bear a direct mathematical relationship to its specific gravity, appropriate tables (see Appendix) must be used in order to find one from the other.   For this reason, too, the required amounts of solutions should be calculated on the basis of weight rather than on the basis of volume.   Standard conditions of temperature are assumed in the following examples and problems.   A precision of three significant figures is adequate.

EXAMPLE I. What weight of water must be added to 100 ml. of sulfuric acid containing 26.0 per cent by weight of H_2SO_4 in order that the resulting solution shall contain 12.3 per cent by weight of H_2SO_4?

SOLUTION: The original solution is of specific gravity 1.19 (Table VI, Appendix) and therefore weighs 119 grams. It contains $119 \times 0.260 = 30.9$ grams of pure H_2SO_4. The desired solution contains 12.3 per cent H_2SO_4. Let x = number of grams of water added.

$$\frac{\text{Weight of } H_2SO_4}{\text{Weight of solution}} \times 100 = \text{per cent}$$

$$\frac{30.9}{119 + x} \times 100 = 12.3$$

$$x = 132 \text{ grams.} \quad Ans.$$

EXAMPLE II. What is the percentage-by-weight composition and the specific gravity of a reagent made by mixing equal volumes of water, HNO_3 (sp. gr. 1.40), and HNO_3 (49.1 per cent HNO_3 by weight)?

SOLUTION: Assume 1.00 ml. of each liquid to be used.

1.00 ml. H_2O = 1.00 gram.

1.00 ml. HNO_3 (sp. gr. 1.40) weighs 1.40 grams and contains $1.40 \times 0.653 = 0.914$ gram of HNO_3 (Table VI, Appendix).

1.00 ml. HNO_3 (49.1 per cent) weighs 1.31 grams (Table VI) and contains $1.31 \times 0.491 = 0.643$ gram of HNO_3.

The mixture therefore weighs $1.00 + 1.40 + 1.31 = 3.71$ grams and contains $0.914 + 0.643 = 1.56$ grams of HNO_3.

Percentage by weight of $HNO_3 = 1.56/3.71 = 42.0$ per cent. *Ans.*

Specific gravity (Table VI) = 1.26. *Ans.*

EXAMPLE III. Given two solutions of hydrochloric acid. Solution A is of specific gravity 1.160; solution B is of specific gravity 1.060. In what proportion by weight should these be mixed in order to obtain a solution containing 20.0 per cent HCl by weight?

SOLUTION:

Solution A contains 31.5 per cent by weight of HCl (Table VI, Appendix).

Solution B contains 12.2 per cent by weight of HCl.

Assume 100 grams of A to be used.

Let x = number of grams of B required.

$$\frac{\text{Weight of HCl}}{\text{Weight of solution}} \times 100 = \text{per cent HCl}$$

$$\frac{(100 \times 0.315) + (x \times 0.122)}{100 + x} \times 100 = 20.0$$

$$x = 147 \text{ grams}$$

$$\text{Ratio:} \frac{A}{B} = \frac{100}{147}. \quad Ans.$$

A somewhat more complicated problem arises when a chemical reaction takes place between components of the mixed solutions. A common example of this occurs in the preparation of oleum mixtures. Oleum (fuming sulfuric acid) consists of free SO_3 dissolved in 100 per cent H_2SO_4. If an oleum is mixed with ordinary concentrated sulfuric acid (*i.e.*, containing a little water), some of the free SO_3 of the oleum unites with the free H_2O in the sulfuric acid and forms $H_2SO_4(SO_3 + H_2O \rightarrow H_2SO_4)$.

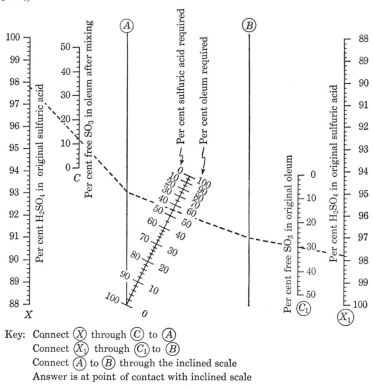

Key: Connect Ⓧ through Ⓒ to Ⓐ
     Connect Ⓧ₁ through Ⓒ₁ to Ⓑ
     Connect Ⓐ to Ⓑ through the inclined scale
     Answer is at point of contact with inclined scale

FIG. 2. Nomograph for calculating the relative amounts by weight of concentrated sulfuric acid and oleum required to prepare an oleum of desired composition. From an article by C. S. Davis in *Chemical and Metallurgical Engineering*, Vol. 43, No. 3, p. 150 (March, 1936) (*by permission*).

EXAMPLE IV. What relative weights of sulfuric acid (containing 97.8 per cent H_2SO_4 and 2.2 per cent H_2O) and oleum (containing 30.0 per cent SO_3 and 70.0 per cent H_2SO_4) must be mixed in order to prepare an oleum containing 12.0 per cent free SO_3?

SOLUTION: Assume 100 grams of the 97.8 per cent H_2SO_4 are taken. Let x = number of grams of 30.0 per cent oleum needed. One-hundred grams of the 97.8 per cent H_2SO_4 would unite with

$$2.2 \times \frac{SO_3}{H_2O} = 9.80 \text{ grams of } SO_3$$

Free SO_3 remaining $= 0.30x - 9.80$ grams

Weight of mixture $= 100 + x$

$$\text{Per cent free } SO_3 = \frac{0.30x - 9.80}{100 + x} = 0.12$$

$$x = 121 \text{ grams}$$

$$\text{Ratio} = 100\!/\!121$$

$$= \text{approx.} \begin{cases} 45 \text{ per cent sulfuric acid} \\ 55 \text{ per cent oleum} \end{cases} \quad Ans.$$

Figure 2 shows a nomograph which has been constructed for solving this last type of problem. It is typical of nomographs in general (see Sec. 12).

To solve the above problem by means of the nomograph, first locate on scale X the percentage of H_2SO_4 in the concentrated sulfuric acid ($= 97.8$). Then locate on scale C the percentage of SO_3 in the desired oleum ($= 12.0$). Connect these two points by means of a straight line and extend the line to the A axis. On scale X_1 again locate the percentage of H_2SO_4 in the concentrated sulfuric acid ($= 97.8$), and on scale C_1 locate the percentage of SO_3 in the original oleum ($= 30.0$). Connect these two points by means of a straight line and extend the line to the B axis. Now connect the points on the A and B axes by means of a straight line. The point where this line intersects the inclined scale shows the relative percentages by weight of the two original solutions required for mixing ($= 45$ per cent sulfuric acid, 55 per cent oleum).

Problems

8.41. What volume of ammonium oxalate solution [35.1 grams of $(NH_4)_2C_2O_4.H_2O$ per liter] will be required to precipitate the calcium as CaC_2O_4 from 0.124 gram of $3Ca_3(PO_4)_2.CaCl_2$? What volume of "magnesia mixture" containing 1 F.W. of $MgCl_2$ per liter will be necessary to precipitate the phosphate as $MgNH_4PO_4$ from the filtrate from the calcium determination?

Ans. 4.82 ml. 0.71 ml.

8.42. How many milliliters of silver nitrate solution containing 20.00 grams of $AgNO_3$ per 100 ml. are required to precipitate all the chloride as $AgCl$ from a solution containing 2.012 grams of dissolved $BaCl_2.2H_2O$? How many milliliters of H_2SO_4 (sp. gr. 1.105) are required to precipitate the barium as $BaSO_4$ from the same solution?

Ans. 14.00 ml. 4.86 ml.

8.43. In the precipitation of arsenic as $MgNH_4AsO_4$ from a solution of 0.4000 gram of pure As_2O_3 that has been oxidized to arsenic acid, it is desired to add sufficient magnesium chloride reagent (64.00 grams $MgCl_2$ per liter) to precipitate the arsenic and also have 200 mg. of Mg remaining in solution. What volume is required?

Ans. 18.26 ml.

8.44. Chloride samples are to be prepared for student analysis by using the chlorides of sodium, potassium, and ammonium, alone or mixed in various proportions. How many milliliters of 5.00 per cent silver nitrate of specific gravity 1.041 must be added to a 0.300-gram sample in order to ensure complete precipitation in every possible case?

Ans.   18.3 ml.

8.45. How many milliliters of aqueous ammonia (sp. gr. 0.900) are required to precipitate the iron as $Fe(OH)_3$ from a half-gram sample of pure $Fe_2(SO_4)_3.9H_2O$?

Ans.   0.36 ml.

8.46. Calculate the volume of hydrochloric acid (sp. gr. 1.050, containing 10.17 per cent HCl by weight) to neutralize (*a*) 48.6 ml. of a solution of KOH (sp. gr. 1.100, containing 12.0 per cent KOH by weight), (*b*) 152.1 ml. of a solution of NaOH (sp. gr. 1.327), (*c*) a solution containing 10.0 grams of pure KOH, (*d*) a solution containing 10.0 grams of impure KOH (96.6 per cent KOH, 2.2 per cent K_2CO_3, 1.2 per cent H_2O), (*e*) 25.3 ml. of ammonia water containing 15.04 per cent by weight of NH_3.

Ans.   (*a*) 39.0 ml., (*b*) 508 ml., (*c*) 60.9 ml., (*d*) 59.8 ml., (*e*) 72.0 ml.

8.47. The following are added to water: 1.60 grams of pure Na_2CO_3, 2.21 ml. of H_2SO_4 solution (sp. gr. 1.700), and 16.0 ml. of KOH solution (56.0 grams of solid per liter). This solution is to be brought to the exact neutral point. The solutions available for this purpose are hydrochloric acid (sp. gr. 1.141) and ammonia water (sp. gr. 0.930). Which should be used? What volume is required?

Ans.   1.26 ml. of ammonia water.

8.48. In the reaction $2NaCl + H_2SO_4 \rightarrow Na_2SO_4 + 2HCl$, it is desired to add sufficient sulfuric acid (sp. gr. 1.835) to liberate that amount of HCl which when absorbed in water will furnish 250 ml. of solution of specific gravity 1.040. Calculate the volume necessary.

Ans.   16.7 ml.

8.49. A solution of ferrous ammonium sulfate is prepared by dissolving 2.200 grams of pure $FeSO_4.(NH_4)_2SO_4.6H_2O$ in 500 ml. of water containing 15.0 ml. H_2SO_4 (sp. gr. 1.135, containing 18.96 per cent H_2SO_4 by weight). The iron is then oxidized by bromine water ($2Fe^{++} + Br_2 \rightarrow 2Fe^{+++} + 2Br^-$). What total volume of NH_4OH (sp. gr. 0.950, containing 12.74 per cent NH_3 by weight) is required to neutralize the acid and just precipitate all of the iron as $Fe(OH)_3$?

Ans.   11.6 ml.

8.50. What is the specific gravity of a solution made by mixing the following liquids in the respective volume ratio of $1:2:3$? (*a*) KOH solution (40.9 per cent KOH by weight), (*b*) KOH solution (sp. gr. 1.20), (*c*) H_2O.

Ans.   1.14.

8.51. What is the percentage-by-weight composition of a solution made by mixing sulfuric acid (sp. gr. 1.205) and water in the respective ratio by volume of $2:1$? What is the specific gravity of the mixture?

Ans.   19.8 per cent.   1.14.   •

8.52. Given two solutions of sulfuric acid. Solution *A* has a specific gravity of 1.140. Solution *B* contains 48.0 per cent of *combined* $SO_3(H_2SO_4 = SO_3 + H_2O)$.

In what proportion by weight should these two solutions be mixed in order to obtain a solution containing 34.0 per cent of H_2SO_4?

Ans. $\dfrac{A}{B} = \dfrac{1.00}{0.58}$.

8.53. How many grams of water should be added to 200 ml. of sodium hydroxide solution of specific gravity 1.32 in order that the specific gravity of the resulting solution shall be 1.16?

Ans. 273 grams.

8.54. Equal volumes of NH_4OH (sp. gr. 0.960) and NH_4OH (sp. gr. 0.900) are mixed. What is the percentage of NH_3 in the resulting solution? What would be the percentage of NH_3 in the resulting solution if equal weights of the initial solutions were mixed?

Ans. 18.8 per cent. 19.1 per cent.

8.55. An oleum weighing 10.0 grams and consisting of 36.0 per cent free SO_3 and 64.0 per cent H_2SO_4 is to be diluted by adding sulfuric acid containing 97.0 per cent H_2SO_4 and 3.0 per cent H_2O. It is desired to obtain an oleum containing 18.0 per cent SO_3 and 82.0 per cent H_2SO_4. Calculate the weight of the sulfuric acid required, and verify the answer by means of the nomograph given in the text.

Ans. 5.75 grams.

8.56. If 140 grams of oleum containing 40.0 per cent free SO_3 and 60.0 per cent H_2SO_4 are mixed with 60 grams of sulfuric acid containing 99.0 per cent H_2SO_4 and 1.0 per cent H_2O, what is the percentage of free SO_3 in the resulting mixture? Show how this result can be obtained from the nomograph given in the text.

Ans. 26.7 per cent.

8.57. How many milliliters of barium chloride solution containing 21.05 grams of $BaCl_2.2H_2O$ per liter are required to precipitate all the sulfate as $BaSO_4$ from a solution containing 1.500 grams of dissolved $Fe_2(SO_4)_3.9H_2O$? How many milliliters of $NaOH$ solution (sp. gr. 1.200) are required to precipitate all the iron as $Fe(OH)_3$ from the same solution?

8.58. A sample of $MgCO_3$ contaminated with SiO_2 weighs 0.5000 gram and loses 0.1002 gram on ignition to MgO. What volume of disodium phosphate solution (90.0 grams $Na_2HPO_4.12H_2O$ per liter) will be required to precipitate the magnesium as $MgNH_4PO_4$?

8.59. How many milliliters of a solution of potassium dichromate containing 26.30 grams of $K_2Cr_2O_7$ per liter must be taken in order to yield 0.6033 gram of Cr_2O_3 after reduction, precipitation, and ignition of the chromium?

8.60. The arsenic in a half-gram sample of As_2S_3 is oxidized to arsenic acid, and is precipitated with a solution of "magnesia mixture" ($MgCl_2 + NH_4Cl$). If exactly 12.6 ml. of the mixture are required, how many grams of $MgCl_2$ per liter does the solution contain? ($H_3AsO_4 + MgCl_2 + 3NH_4OH \rightarrow MgNH_4AsO_4 + 2NH_4Cl + 3H_2O$.)

8.61. How many grams of silver chloride will be formed by the addition of an excess of silver nitrate to 10.00 ml. of hydrochloric acid (sp. gr. 1.160, containing 31.52 per cent HCl by weight)?

8.62. Sulfuric acid of specific gravity 1.800 is to be used to precipitate the barium as barium sulfate from 1.242 grams of pure $BaCl_2.2H_2O$. Calculate the volume of acid necessary for precipitation.

8.63. How many milliliters of ammonia (sp. gr. 0.940) will neutralize 40.00 ml. of H_2SO_4 solution (sp. gr. 1.240)?

8.64. According to the following equation what volume of HNO_3 (sp. gr. 1.050) is required to oxidize the iron in 1.000 gram of $FeSO_4.7H_2O$ in the presence of sulfuric acid?   [$6FeSO_4 + 2HNO_3 + 3H_2SO_4 \rightarrow 3Fe_2(SO_4)_3 + 2NO + 4H_2O$.]

8.65. How many milliliters of ammonia (sp. gr. 0.960 containing 9.91 per cent of NH_3 by weight) will be required to precipitate the aluminum as $Al(OH)_3$ from a solution containing 50.0 grams of alum [$KAl(SO_4)_2.12H_2O$] and 100 ml. of HCl (sp. gr. 1.120, containing 23.82 per cent HCl by weight)?

8.66. Alum, $KAl(SO_4)_2.12H_2O$, weighing 0.6000 gram is dissolved in water and 10.0 ml. of hydrochloric acid (sp. gr. 1.120, containing 23.82 per cent HCl by weight) are added.   It takes 5.11 ml. of ammonia (containing 28.33 per cent NH_3 by weight) to neutralize the acid and precipitate the aluminum as $Al(OH)_3$.   Find the specific gravity of the ammonia, the normality of the acid, and the ratio of the base to the acid.

8.67. To a suspension of 0.310 gram of $Al(OH)_3$ in water are added 13.0 ml. of aqueous ammonia (sp. gr. 0.900).   How many milliliters of sulfuric acid (sp. gr. 1.18) must be added to the mixture in order theoretically to bring the aluminum into solution?

8.68. What must be the specific gravity of a solution of HNO_3 if when mixed with an equal weight of a solution of HNO_3 containing 47.5 per cent HNO_3 by weight the resulting solution has the same specific gravity as that of a solution of HCl containing 35.4 per cent HCl by weight?

8.69. In what proportion by weight should one mix an oleum containing 20.0 per cent free SO_3 and 80.0 per cent H_2SO_4 and a sulfuric acid solution containing 96.0 per cent H_2SO_4 and 4.0 per cent H_2O in order that the resulting liquid shall be 100.0 per cent hydrogen sulfate?   Solve the problem by numerical calculation and verify the result from the nomograph given in the text.

8.70. What is the percentage by weight of NH_3 in a solution made by mixing the following liquids in the respective volume ratio of 3:2:1?   (*a*) NH_4OH (sp. gr. 0.900), (*b*) NH_4OH (containing 11.6 per cent NH_3 by weight), (*c*) water.

8.71. In what ratio by volume must water and NH_4OH (sp. gr. 0.900) be mixed in order that the resulting solution shall contain 12.75 per cent NH_3?

62. Indirect Methods.

Problems relating to indirect methods of gravimetric analysis differ from those relating to direct methods in much the same way that algebraic equations involving two or more unknown quantities differ from those involving only one unknown quantity.

The simplest type of indirect analysis is that in which two pure chemical substances are isolated and weighed together.   Then either by further chemical action on the substance or by chemical analysis of a new sample of the material, additional data are derived by which one of the components is determined.   The other component is then found by difference.

In any case, results of analyses of this type are usually less precise than results of analyses in which a single component is determined by a direct method.   In solving simultaneous algebraic equations, for example, there is often a decrease in the number of significant figures that may properly be retained. For example, in solving the following simultaneous equations:

$$0.2395x + 0.2689y = 1.937$$
$$0.2067x + 0.2689y = 1.222$$
$$\overline{0.0328x \qquad\qquad = 0.715}$$
$$x = 2.18$$

there is a decrease from four-significant- to three-significant-figure precision.

EXAMPLE I. In the analysis of a two-gram sample of limestone, the weight of combined oxides of iron and aluminum ($Fe_2O_3 + Al_2O_3$) is found to be 0.0812 gram. By volumetric methods, the percentage of total iron calculated as FeO is found to be 1.50 per cent. What is the percentage of Al_2O_3 in the sample?

SOLUTION:

$$\text{Weight of FeO} = 2.00 \times \frac{1.50}{100} = 0.0300 \text{ gram}$$

$$\text{Weight of } Fe_2O_3 = 0.0300 \times \frac{Fe_2O_3}{2FeO} = 0.0333 \text{ gram}$$

$$\text{Weight of } Al_2O_3 = 0.0812 - 0.0333 = 0.0479 \text{ gram}$$

$$\text{Percentage of } Al_2O_3 = \frac{0.0479}{2.00} \times 100 = 2.40 \text{ per cent.} \quad Ans.$$

A second general type of indirect analysis is that in which two chemical substances are isolated and weighed together. Then another measure of the two substances is obtained either by converting them to two different compounds and again finding the combined weights or by determining the amount of reagent required to effect such conversion. In this way, by the use of algebraic symbols to represent the unknown quantities, two independent equations can be formulated, and from them the values of the unknowns can be determined. It is evident that this type of problem may be extended to any number of unknown quantities, provided sufficient data are given to allow the formulation of as many independent algebraic equations as there are unknowns.

EXAMPLE II. In the analysis of a 0.5000-gram sample of feldspar, a mixture of the chlorides of sodium and potassium is obtained which weighs 0.1180 gram. Subsequent treatment with silver nitrate furnishes 0.2451 gram of silver chloride. What is the percentage of Na_2O and K_2O in the sample?

SOLUTION:

$$\text{Let } x = \text{weight of KCl}$$
$$y = \text{weight of NaCl}$$
$$(1) \quad x + y = 0.1180$$

Number of grams of AgCl obtainable from x grams of KCl

$$= x \left(\frac{\text{AgCl}}{\text{KCl}} \right)$$
$$= 1.923x$$

Number of grams of AgCl obtainable from y grams of NaCl

$$= y \left(\frac{\text{AgCl}}{\text{NaCl}} \right)$$
$$= 2.452y$$

Therefore,

$$(2)\ \ 1.923x + 2.452y = 0.2451$$

Solving (1) and (2) simultaneously,

$$x = 0.0837 \text{ gram of KCl}$$
$$y = 0.0343 \text{ gram of NaCl}$$

$$\left. \begin{array}{l} \text{Percentage of } K_2O = \left(\dfrac{K_2O}{2KCl} \right) \dfrac{0.0837 \times 100}{0.500} = 10.6 \\[3mm] \text{Percentage of } Na_2O = \left(\dfrac{Na_2O}{2NaCl} \right) \dfrac{0.0343 \times 100}{0.500} = 3.64 \end{array} \right\} Ans.$$

The standard J. Lawrence Smith method for determining sodium and potassium in a silicate is an example of an indirect analysis of this type. By this method the sample is decomposed and the alkalies are isolated and weighed as combined chlorides. These are dissolved and the potassium alone is precipitated from water-alcohol solution as K_2PtCl_6 (or as $KClO_4$) and weighed as such. The K_2PtCl_6 can also be ignited and weighed as $2KCl + Pt$, or (after washing) as metallic platinum (see also Part V).

EXAMPLE III. In the analysis of a sample of feldspar weighing 0.4150 gram, a mixture of $KCl + NaCl$ is obtained weighing 0.0715 gram. From these chlorides 0.1548 gram of K_2PtCl_6 is obtained. Calculate the percentage of Na_2O in the feldspar.

SOLUTION:

Let x = weight of NaCl in combined chlorides

Then

$$0.0715 - x = \text{weight of KCl}$$
$$(0.0715 - x) \times \frac{K_2PtCl_6}{2KCl} = 0.1548$$

Solving,

$$x = 0.0415 \text{ gram}$$
$$\frac{0.0415 \times (Na_2O/2NaCl)}{0.4150} \times 100 = 5.30 \text{ per cent } Na_2O. \quad Ans.$$

Problems

8.72. A mixture of 0.2600 gram of ferric oxide and 0.4500 gram of aluminum oxide is ignited in hydrogen, the ferric oxide alone being reduced to metallic iron. What is the final weight?

Ans. 0.6318 gram.

8.73. A silicate weighing 0.6000 gram yields a mixture of pure NaCl and pure KCl weighing 0.1800 gram. In this residue the KCl is converted to K_2PtCl_6 weighing 0.2700 gram. Find the percentage of K_2O and the percentage of Na_2O in the silicate.

Ans. 8.72 per cent K_2O, 8.60 per cent Na_2O.

8.74. In the analysis of a sample of feldspar weighing 0.7500 gram there is obtained 0.2200 gram of NaCl + KCl. These chlorides are dissolved in water-alcohol mixture and treated with chloroplatinic acid. The precipitate of K_2PtCl_6 is filtered on a porous-base crucible, dried, and ignited in hydrogen. After washing with hot water, the residual platinum then weighs 0.0950 gram. Compute the percentages of Na_2O and K_2O in the feldspar. What weight of precipitate would have been obtained if perchloric acid had been used as the precipitating agent and the precipitate had been dried and weighed without ignition?

Ans. 10.42 per cent Na_2O, 6.11 per cent K_2O. 0.1349 gram.

8.75. A mixture of silver chloride and silver bromide is found to contain 66.35 per cent of silver. What is the percentage of bromine?

Ans. 21.3 per cent.

8.76. A sample of carbonate rock weighing 1.250 grams yields a precipitate of the hydrated oxides of iron and aluminum. These are filtered off and ignited. The combined oxides $Fe_2O_3 + Al_2O_3$ are found to weigh 0.1175 gram. Iron is determined by a volumetric method on a separate sample of the rock and the results show 3.22 per cent Fe. Calculate the percentage of Al in the rock.

Ans. 2.54 per cent.

8.77. An alloy weighing 0.2500 gram when treated with HNO_3 gives a residue of the hydrated oxides of tin and antimony. These on ignition yield 0.1260 gram of the combined oxides $SnO_2 + Sb_2O_4$. This residue is brought into solution and is found by a volumetric method to contain 32.56 per cent Sn. Calculate the percentage of antimony in the original alloy.

Ans. 23.4 per cent.

8.78. A mixture of silver chloride and silver bromide weighs 0.5267 gram. By treatment with chlorine, the silver bromide is converted into silver chloride, and the total weight of silver chloride becomes 0.4269 gram. What is the weight of bromine in the original mixture?

Ans. 0.179 gram.

8.79. A mixture of pure CaO and pure BaO weighing 0.6411 gram yields 1.1201 grams of pure mixed sulfates. Find the percentages of Ba and of Ca in the original mixture.

Ans. 17.6 per cent Ca, 67.4 per cent Ba.

8.80. A sample of silicate weighing 0.6000 gram yields 0.1803 gram of a mixture of pure NaCl and pure KCl. When these are dissolved and treated with $AgNO_3$, the resulting precipitate of AgCl is found to weigh 0.3904 gram. Calculate the percentages of Na_2O and K_2O.

Ans. 7.32 per cent Na_2O, 10.27 per cent K_2O.

8.81. From a sample of feldspar a mixture of KCl and NaCl is obtained that weighs 0.1506 gram and contains 55.00 per cent chlorine. What weight of K_2PtCl_6 could be obtained from the KCl?

Ans. 0.212 gram.

8.82. A mixture of $BaCl_2.2H_2O$ and LiCl weighs 0.6000 gram and with silver nitrate solution yields 1.440 grams AgCl. Calculate the percentage of Ba in the original mixture.

Ans. 25.0 per cent.

8.83. A mixture of pure NaCl and pure NaI weighs 0.4000 gram and yields with $AgNO_3$ a precipitate of AgCl and AgI that weighs 0.8981 gram. Find the percentage of iodine present in the original mixture.

Ans. 19.8 per cent.

8.84. What percentage of $MgCO_3$ is present with pure $BaCO_3$ so that the mixture contains the same CO_2 content as if it were pure $CaCO_3$?

Ans. 72.5 per cent.

8.85. A 1.0045-gram sample containing only $CaCO_3$ and $MgCO_3$ is strongly ignited. The weight of the ignited product (CaO and MgO) is 0.5184 gram. Calculate the percentages of Ca and of Mg in the original sample and in the ignited sample.

8.86. A mixture of BaO and CaO weighing 1.792 grams, when treated with sulfuric acid and transformed to mixed sulfates, weighs twice the original amount. What is the percentage of BaO in the mixture?

8.87. Iron and aluminum are precipitated from a sample of a mineral weighing 0.9505 gram and the combined oxides Al_2O_3 + Fe_2O_3 are found to weigh 0.1083 gram. By a volumetric method this oxide residue is found to contain 10.50 per cent Fe. What is the percentage of Al in the original mineral?

8.88. An alloy weighing 0.5180 gram yields a residue of the hydrated oxides of tin and antimony which on ignition produces 0.1661 gram of the combined oxides SnO_2 + Sb_2O_4. By a titration method a separate sample of the alloy shows the presence of 10.12 per cent Sb. Calculate the percentage of Sn in the alloy.

8.89. A silicate rock weighing 0.7410 gram is analyzed by the J. L. Smith method, and a mixture of the chlorides of sodium and potassium weighing 0.2172 gram is obtained. These chlorides are dissolved in a mixture of alcohol and water and treated with $HClO_4$. The dried precipitate of $KClO_4$ weighs 0.3330 gram. What is the percentage of Na_2O in the silicate? If the potassium had been precipitated as K_2PtCl_6 and the precipitate converted to metallic platinum, what weight of platinum would have been obtained?

8.90. How many grams of $BaCO_3$ must be added to 2.40 grams of $MgCO_3$ so that the mixture will contain the same percentage of CO_2 as $CaCO_3$ does?

8.91. A mixture of NaBr, NaI, and $NaNO_3$ weighs 0.6500 gram. With silver nitrate, a precipitate of the halides of silver is obtained and is found to weigh 0.9390 gram. When heated in a current of chlorine gas the precipitate is converted entirely into AgCl weighing 0.6566 gram. What is the percentage composition of the original sample?

8.92. A precipitate of AgCl + AgBr weighs 0.8132 gram.   On heating in a current of chlorine, the AgBr is converted into AgCl, the mixture losing 0.1450 gram in weight. What was the percentage of chlorine in the original precipitate?

8.93. A mixture of NH_4Cl and KCl weighs 0.5000 gram.   With chloroplatinic acid a precipitate is obtained that, when ignited, weighs 1.0400 grams.   What is the percentage of NH_3 in the mixture?   If the ignited precipitate were washed with water and reignited, what would be the weight obtained?

8.94. A mixture of AgCl and AgBr contains chlorine and bromine in the proportion by weight of Cl: Br = 1: 2.   What is the percentage of silver in the mixture?   If one gram of the sample were heated in a current of chlorine, thereby converting the AgBr into AgCl, what would be the weight of the resulting mixture?

8.95. A sample of an impure mixture of NaCl, NaBr, and NaI weighing 1.5000 grams is dissolved in water, and the solution is divided into two equal portions.   One portion gives a precipitate of PdI_2 weighing 0.1103 gram.   The other portion gives a precipitate of AgCl + AgBr + AgI weighing 1.2312 grams; and when these salts are heated in a current of chlorine they are all converted into AgCl weighing 1.0500 grams. What are the percentages of NaCl, NaBr, and NaI in the original sample?

8.96. A mixture of silver bromide and silver iodide weighs x grams.   After the mixture has been heated in a current of chlorine, the resulting silver chloride is found to weigh y grams.   Derive an expression for the percentages of bromine and of iodine in the original mixture.

8.97. A mixture of silver chloride and silver iodide on being heated in a current of chlorine is converted entirely into silver chloride and is found to have lost 6.00 per cent of its weight.   What is the percentage of chlorine in the original mixture?

CHAPTER 9

ELECTROLYTIC METHODS

63. Electrolysis. In analytical chemistry the term *electrolysis* is applied to a reaction in which a chemical change is caused to take place by the passage of a current through a solution of an electrolyte. Oxidation (loss of electrons) takes place at the anode; reduction (gain of electrons) takes place at the cathode. Typical electrolytic reactions in analytical chemistry are:

Cathode:

$$2H^+ + 2\epsilon \rightarrow H_2$$
$$Cu^{++} + 2\epsilon \rightarrow Cu$$

Anode:

$$2H_2O \rightarrow O_2 + 4H^+ + 4\epsilon$$
$$Pb^{++} + 2H_2O \rightarrow PbO_2 + 4H^+ + 2\epsilon$$

64. Ohm's Law. When a current is passed through a solution, its total energy is distributed among three factors: (1) its potential, E (measured in volts); (2) the current strength, I (measured in amperes); and (3) the resistance of the conducting medium, R (measured in ohms). The relationship existing among these factors is:

$$E = IR$$

65. Faraday's Laws. Quantitative analysis by means of electrochemical methods is usually restricted to the determination of metals. An electric current is passed, under suitable conditions, through a solution of the salt of a metal, and the metal itself is gradually deposited, usually in the elementary condition, upon one of the electrodes. The calculation of the amount of metal which will be deposited at the end of a given time is founded on Faraday's laws which may be stated as follows:

1. *The mass of any substance deposited at an electrode is proportional to the quantity of electricity which passes through the solution.*

2. *The amounts of different substances liberated at the electrodes by the passage of the same quantity of electricity are proportional to the equivalent weights of the substances.*

Current strength is expressed in terms of the *ampere*, which is defined as that strength of current which, when passed through a solution of silver nitrate under certain standard conditions, will deposit silver at the rate of 0.001118 gram per second.

Quantities of electricity are expressed in terms of the *coulomb*, which is defined as that quantity of electricity which passes through a conductor in 1 second when the current is 1 ampere. That is,

$$Q = It$$

where Q = quantity of electricity, coulombs

I = current strength, amperes

t = time, seconds

From Faraday's first law, it follows that the weight of a substance liberated from solution by electrolysis during a given time will be directly proportional to the current strength and under a given amperage will be directly proportional to the time.

Faraday's second law states that the weights of different substances liberated at the electrodes by a given quantity of electricity are proportional to the respective equivalent weights. The equivalent weight of a substance in this case is the atomic or molecular weight divided by the total *change* in oxidation number. It is found by experiment that 96,500 coulombs are required to liberate a gram-equivalent weight (equivalent weight in grams) of any substance. Thus, 96,500 coulombs of electricity are capable of depositing at the cathode:

$$\frac{Ag}{1} = 107.88 \text{ grams of silver from a solution of a silver salt}$$

$$\frac{Fe}{2} = 27.92 \text{ grams of iron from a solution of a ferrous salt}$$

$$\frac{Fe}{3} = 18.61 \text{ grams of iron from a solution of a ferric salt}$$

The value 96,500 coulombs is therefore a unit of quantity in electrochemical measurements, and in that capacity it is called a *faraday*. One faraday = 96,500 coulombs = 96,500 ampere-seconds = 26.81 ampere-hours.

The above reactions may be expressed by equations, as follows:

(a) $Ag^+ + \epsilon \rightarrow Ag$

(b) $Fe^{++} + 2\epsilon \rightarrow Fe$

(c) $Fe^{+++} + 3\epsilon \rightarrow Fe$

where the symbol ϵ represents the electron, or unit of negative electricity. If the equations are considered as representing gram-atomic or gram-molecular ratios, then the symbol represents the faraday. That is, 1, 2, and 3 faradays are required to deposit a gram-atomic weight of metal from a solution of silver salt, ferrous salt, and ferric salt, respectively.

EXAMPLE I.   How many grams of copper will be deposited in 3.00 hours by a current of 4.00 amperes, on the assumption that no other reactions take place at the cathode?

SOLUTION:

$$t = 3.00 \times 3,600 = 10,800 \text{ seconds}$$
$$\text{Number of coulombs} = It = 4.00 \times 10,800 = 43,200$$
$$1 \text{ faraday would deposit } \frac{Cu^{++}}{2} = 31.8 \text{ grams of copper}$$
$$43,200 \text{ coulombs would deposit } \frac{43,200}{96,500} \times 31.8 = 14.2 \text{ grams Cu.}\quad Ans.$$

Faraday's laws apply to each electrode.   A current of 1 ampere flowing for 96,500 seconds through a copper sulfate solution is not only capable of depositing $Cu/2 = 31.79$ grams of copper at the cathode, but at the same time will liberate $O/2 = 8.000$ grams of oxygen at the anode.

$$Cu^{++} + 2\epsilon \rightarrow Cu \qquad \text{(cathode)}$$
$$H_2O \rightarrow 2H^+ + \tfrac{1}{2}O_2 + 2\epsilon \text{ (anode)}$$

The passage of 2 faradays therefore deposits one gram-atomic weight of copper (63.57 grams) and liberates $\tfrac{1}{2}$ mole, or 16 grams, of oxygen gas, occupying 11.2 liters under standard conditions.   As seen from the equation, the acidity of the solution increases by one gram equivalent ($\backsimeq$ 1 mole $HNO_3 \backsimeq \tfrac{1}{2}$ mole H_2SO_4, etc.) per faraday passed.   This gain in acidity may be expressed in terms of acid normality (see Secs. 28 and 77).   It is possible to prepare a solution suitable as a standard in acidimetry by electrolyzing a neutral solution of copper sulfate and determining the acid concentration of the resulting solution from the weight of copper deposited.

The electrolysis of a dilute sulfuric acid solution causes the following reactions to take place:

$$2H^+ + 2\epsilon \rightarrow H_2 \qquad \text{(cathode)}$$
$$H_2O \rightarrow 2H^+ + \tfrac{1}{2}O_2 + 2\epsilon \text{ (anode)}$$

The passage of 1 faraday liberates $\tfrac{1}{2}$ mole of hydrogen (1.008 grams; 11.2 liters under standard conditions) and $\tfrac{1}{4}$ mole of oxygen (8.000 grams; 5.6 liters under standard conditions).   The total amount of gas evolved per faraday is therefore $\tfrac{3}{4}$ mole (16.8 liters).   In this electrolysis, there is no net change in acidity if the volume of the solution is kept constant, for the loss in acidity at the cathode is balanced by the gain in acidity at the anode.

The electrolysis of a dilute nitric acid solution of lead causes the deposition of lead dioxide on the anode:

$$Pb^{++} + 2H_2O \rightarrow PbO_2 + 4H^+ + 2\epsilon \text{ (anode)}$$
$$2H^+ + 2\epsilon \quad \rightarrow H_2 \qquad\qquad \text{(cathode)}$$

One faraday therefore deposits $PbO_2/2$ = 119.6 grams of PbO_2, liberates $\frac{1}{2}$ mole of hydrogen, and increases the acidity by 1 gram-equivalent weight (1.008 grams) of hydrogen ion.

EXAMPLE II. A neutral solution containing 0.4000 gram of copper is electrolyzed until all the copper is plated out, and the electrolysis is continued 7 minutes longer. The volume of the solution is kept at 100 ml. and the current strength is maintained at an average of 1.20 amperes. On the basis of 100 per cent current efficiency (*a*) how long did it take for the copper to deposit, (*b*) what total volume of gas was evolved during the entire electrolysis, (*c*) what was the acidity of the solution at the end of the electrolysis?

SOLUTION:

$$1 \text{ faraday deposits } \frac{Cu}{2} = 31.8 \text{ grams Cu}$$

$$\text{Number of faradays to deposit 0.4000 gram Cu} = \frac{0.4000}{31.8} = 0.0126$$

$$\text{Time required} = \frac{0.0126 \times 96,500}{1.20} = 1,012 \text{ seconds} = 16.9 \text{ minutes.} \quad Ans.$$

During deposition of Cu, each faraday (*i.e.*, each $\frac{1}{2}$ mole Cu) corresponds to $\frac{1}{4}$ mole O_2.

$$\text{Moles } O_2 \text{ evolved} = 0.0126 \times \frac{1}{4} = 0.00315$$

After Cu deposited, number faradays passed =

$$\frac{7 \times 60 \times 1.20}{96,500} = 0.00522$$

Each faraday evolves $\frac{1}{2}$ mole H_2 and $\frac{1}{4}$ mole O_2

$$\text{Moles } H_2 + O_2 \text{ evolved} = 0.00522 \times \frac{3}{4} = 0.00392$$
$$\text{Total gas evolved} = 0.00315 + 0.00392 = 0.00707 \text{ mole.} \quad Ans.$$

During Cu deposition each faraday corresponds to a gain of 1 gram atom of H^+.

After Cu deposition, acidity does not change
Gain in acidity = 0.0126 gram-equivalent of H^+. *Ans.*

(Resulting solution is $10 \times 0.01258 = 0.1258$ normal as an acid.)

In the above calculations involving Faraday's second law, it has been assumed that all the current serves for the decomposition of the substance in question; *i.e.*, 100 per cent current efficiency has been assumed.

In actual analyses, this is not usually the case. The electrolysis of an acid solution of a copper salt will not only cause the deposition of copper at the cathode, but small amounts of hydrogen will usually be given off at the same electrode before the copper has all plated out. In such cases, the *sum* of the weights of the products discharged at each electrode exactly corresponds to the law. That is, in the copper electrolysis, for each faraday of electricity passed, the number of gram-equivalent weights of copper deposited added to the number of gram-equivalent weights of hydrogen liberated will be unity. In problems of electroanalyses, unless otherwise specified, 100 per cent current efficiency may be assumed.

Other electrical units which are frequently used in electrochemical computations are as follows:

The *ohm*, R, is the unit of resistance. It is the resistance offered to a constant current of electricity at $0°C$. by a column of mercury 1 sq. mm. in cross section and 106.3 cm. long.

The *volt*, E, is the unit of electromotive force or electrical pressure. Its relation to the ampere and ohm is expressed by Ohm's law.

$$E = IR$$

The *joule*, J, is the unit of work. It is represented by the energy expended in 1 second by a current of 1 ampere against a resistance of 1 ohm.

$$J = EIt = EQ = 10^7 \text{ ergs}$$

The *watt*, W, is the unit of power. It is represented by the work done at the rate of 1 joule per second.

$$W = EI$$
$$J = Wt$$

66. Decomposition Potentials. The electrode potentials existing between metals and their ions and the effect of concentration on these potentials were considered in the discussions of Secs. 44, 47, and 48, and these sections should be reviewed at this point.

The *decomposition potential* of an electrolyte is the lowest e.m.f. that must be applied in order to bring about continuous decomposition of cation and anion at the electrodes.

If a nitric or sulfuric acid solution of copper is electrolyzed between platinum electrodes, the copper plates out on the cathode.

$$Cu^{++} + 2\epsilon \rightarrow Cu$$

Water is decomposed at the anode.

$$H_2O \rightarrow \tfrac{1}{2}O_2 + 2H^+ + 2\epsilon$$

As a result there is produced a voltaic cell of the type

$$Cu \mid Cu^{++} \parallel 2H^+, \tfrac{1}{2}O_2 \mid Pt$$

This cell exerts a "back e.m.f." which opposes the applied voltage and which can be calculated from the formula

$$E = E_1 - E_2 =$$
$$\left(E_{H_2O}{}^0 - \frac{0.0591}{2} \log [H^+]^2 [press.\ O_2]^{\frac{1}{2}} \right) - \left(E_{Cu}{}^0 - \frac{0.0591}{2} \log [Cu^{++}] \right)$$

In order to continue the electrolysis, a voltage at least equal to this must be applied. In addition, enough voltage to overcome the simple ohmic resistance of the solution is necessary, and in cases where polarization effects occur, the e.m.f. must be still further increased.

67. Polarization and Overvoltage. The term *polarization* is used to indicate a condition at an electrode which causes the potential of the corresponding half cell to differ from the normal value. It can be attributed to a counterelectromotive force brought about either by the accumulation at the electrode of products of the reaction or by the exhaustion at the electrode of substances necessary for the reaction. When such conditions exist, in order to cause electrodeposition to take place it is necessary to apply a voltage somewhat greater than that calculated from the back e.m.f. and the ohmic resistance of the solution. This excess potential is called *overvoltage*.

Decomposition potential = back e.m.f. + IR + overvoltage

The extent of overvoltage depends on several factors, such as current density (amperes per square centimeter of electrode surface), concentration, temperature, nature of the substances liberated, and character of the electrodes. Overvoltages are relatively low when metals are deposited; they are relatively high when gases are liberated, particularly when the gases are liberated at electrodes composed of such metals as copper, nickel, zinc, or mercury.

68. Electrolytic Separations. If the difference between the decomposition potentials of two metals in solution is sufficiently great, it is usually possible to effect a separation of those metals by electrolytic means. Thus, if a solution containing silver ions and cupric ions at moderate concentrations is electrolyzed under proper conditions, the silver plates out first, and the plating can be continued until the concentration of the remaining silver ions has been reduced to such a value that the decomposition potential is equal to that of the copper. Any attempt to plate out the copper would cause simultaneous deposition of the remaining silver, but that amount of silver is negligibly small.

EXAMPLE I.   A solution is 0.0010 molar in Cu^{++} and contains Ag^+ ions. Neglecting overvoltage, what approximate value would the concentration of Ag^+ have to be before silver would deposit simultaneously with the copper in the electrolysis of the solution?

SOLUTION:

$$\text{Standard potentials: Cu} - Cu^{++} \qquad -0.344 \text{ volt}$$
$$\text{Ag} - Ag^+ \qquad -0.800 \text{ volt}$$

$$-0.344 - \frac{0.0591}{2} \log 0.0010 = -0.800 - \frac{0.0591}{1} \log [Ag^+]$$

Solving,

$$\log [Ag^+] = -9.23$$
$$[Ag^+] = 6 \times 10^{-10}. \quad Ans.$$

Many other separations are possible.   The separation of metals below hydrogen in the potential series from those above hydrogen is especially easy.   In the electrolysis of brass (Cu + Zn), for example, essentially all the copper plates out at the cathode.   After that, hydrogen ions are reduced to hydrogen gas, and no zinc can be reduced so long as the solution remains acidic.

Under certain conditions however, zinc, and several other metals relatively high in the potential series, can be electrolyzed from solution.   It is necessary to use an alkaline solution since the decomposition potential of the hydrogen ion is thereby raised.   The high overvoltage of hydrogen on the zinc electrode (that results from the plating of the zinc on the original platinum electrode) is a help in this process in that it permits the electrolytic reduction of zinc ions in only moderately alkaline solutions.

EXAMPLE II.   What must be the pH value of a solution which is 2.0×10^{-4} molar in Zn^{++} to allow deposition of the zinc?   Assume the hydrogen overvoltage to be 0.30 volt.

SOLUTION:

$$\text{Standard potential} \quad \text{Zn} - Zn^{++} \qquad +0.762 \text{ volt}$$
$$\tfrac{1}{2}H_2 - H^+ \qquad 0.000 \text{ volt}$$

$$+0.762 - \frac{0.0591}{2} \log (2.0 \times 10^{-4}) = 0.00 - \frac{0.0591}{1} \log [H^+] + 0.30$$

Solving,

$$-\log [H^+] = \frac{+0.762 + 0.109 - 0.30}{0.0591} = 9.67$$
$$pH = -\log [H^+] = 9.67. \quad Ans.$$

Problems

9.1. A 100-watt 110-volt incandescent lamp is connected in series with an electrolytic cell.   What weight of cadmium could be deposited from solution by the current in 30 minutes?

Ans.   0.953 gram.

9.2. How many minutes will it take for a current of 0.500 ampere to cause the deposition of 500 mg. of silver from nitric acid solution on the basis of 80 per cent current efficiency?

Ans. 18.6 minutes.

9.3. How many coulombs of electricity are required to deposit 0.1000 gram of cobalt from a solution of cobaltous salt? How many amperes would be required to deposit that amount in 20 minutes 20 seconds? How many grams of nickel would be deposited under identical conditions?

Ans. 327.3 coulombs. 0.2682 ampere. 0.09951 gram.

9.4. With a current at 8.00 volts, how much electrical energy is theoretically required to deposit (a) 0.100 gram of gold, (b) 0.100 gram of mercury from solutions containing these metals in the higher state of oxidation?

Ans. (a) 1,180 joules, (b) 770 joules.

9.5. What weights of Cu, of Zn, and of PbO_2 will be deposited in separate electrolytic cells, on the assumption of 100 per cent current yield by a current of 0.0800 ampere flowing for 30 hours?

Ans. 2.85 grams Cu, 2.93 grams Zn, 10.7 grams PbO_2.

9.6. Using a rotating electrode, Sand obtained 0.240 gram of copper from a nitric acid solution of copper sulfate in 6 minutes. A current of 10.0 amperes under 2.80 volts was used. What electrical energy was expended and what was the current efficiency?

Ans. 10,080 joules, 20.2 per cent.

9.7. Using a rotating electrode, Langness found that with a current of 17.0 amperes and a potential of 10.0 volts, 0.200 gram of platinum could be deposited in 5 minutes from a solution of potassium chloroplatinate. How much electrical energy was expended per second? What quantity of electricity was used? What was the current efficiency?

Ans. 170 joules. 5,100 coulombs. 7.75 per cent.

9.8. What quantity of electricity is required for (a) the electrolytic deposition of 1.196 grams of PbO_2, (b) the liberation of 0.800 gram of oxygen gas, (c) the liberation of 30.0 ml. of chlorine when measured under standard conditions (one molecular weight in grams occupies 22.4 liters)?

Ans. (a) 965 coulombs, (b) 9.650 coulombs, (c) 259 coulombs.

9.9. For how long a time must a current of 1.00 ampere be passed through a dilute solution of sulfuric acid in order to liberate a total volume of 600 ml. of gas when measured dry and under standard conditions?

Ans. 57.4 minutes.

9.10. With a current of 1.00 ampere, what weight of silver would be deposited in 1 minute in a silver coulometer? What volume of gas (under standard conditions) would be evolved in 60 seconds in a water coulometer?

Ans. 0.06708 gram. 10.44 ml.

9.11. Pure crystals of copper sulfate are dissolved in water, and the solution is electrolyzed until the solution is colorless. The cathode gains 0.4280 gram. What is the acidity of the solution in terms of moles of H_2SO_4?

Ans. 0.006731 mole.

9.12. What would be the net gain or loss in gram-equivalents of H^+ per faraday in the electrolysis of a solution of HNO_3 in which 80 per cent of the current goes to the simple decomposition of water and 20 per cent goes to the reaction involving the reduction of nitrate to free nitrogen at the cathode and liberation of oxygen at the anode?

Ans.   0.040 gram-equivalent lost.

9.13. An alloy consists of 20.72 per cent lead and 79.30 per cent zinc. A 1-gram sample is dissolved in acid and the solution diluted to exactly one liter. A 100-ml. pipetful is titrated with 0.1000 N NaOH and requires 30.00 ml. to neutralize the acid present. The remaining 900 ml. are electrolyzed under 2.00 amperes for exactly 5 minutes (100 per cent current efficiency) with the deposition of the lead as PbO_2. (a) How many milliliters of gas (standard conditions) are evolved during this time? (b) If the volume of the solution after electrolysis is brought again to 900 ml., what would be the acid normality of the solution.

Ans.   (a) 94.4 ml.   (b) 0.034 N.

9.14. An average current of 0.5000 ampere is passed through a dilute acid solution of an alloy containing 0.5000 gram of copper, 0.2000 gram of zinc, and 0.1000 gram of lead. Assuming 100 per cent efficiency, compute the total gain in acidity in terms of moles of H_2SO_4 (a) at the end of the PbO_2 deposition at the anode, (b) at the end of the Cu deposition at the cathode, (c) after the current has been continued 5 minutes longer. What volume of gas (standard conditions) has been evolved during the entire process?

Ans.   (a) 0.0009652 mole, (b) 0.008347 mole, (c) 0.008347 mole.   108.8 ml.

9.15. A solution is 0.0010 molar in Ag^+ and contains auric ions (Au^{+++}). Neglecting overvoltage effects, at approximately how high a concentration of auric ions would the two metals deposit simultaneously on electrolysis? The standard potential of $Au - Au^{+++}$ is -1.42 volts; that of $Ag - Ag^+$ is -0.800 volt.

Ans. 2×10^{-41} molar.

9.16. What overvoltage of hydrogen would allow nickel to be electrolyzed out of a solution that is 0.010 molar in Ni^{++} and 0.10 molar in H^+?

Ans.   0.36 volt.

9.17. A solution is 0.10 molar in Cd^{++} and 0.10 molar in H^+. What is the difference between the potential of $Cd - Cd^{++}$ and that of $\frac{1}{2}H_2 - H^+$? To the solution is added a sufficient amount of NH_3 and of ammonium salt to convert nearly all of the Cd^{++} to $Cd(NH_3)_4^{++}$ and to make the solution 0.10 molar in free NH_3 and 0.60 molar in NH_4^+. Assuming the volume of the solution to be the same as before, what is the difference between the two potentials?

Ans.   0.372 volt.   Practically zero.

9.18. How many milligrams of silver can be deposited from solution in 23 minutes by a current of 0.700 ampere at 100 per cent efficiency? How long would it take the same current to deposit the same weight of nickel?

9.19. If a current of 0.250 ampere is passed through a copper sulfate solution and a 90 per cent current yield is obtained, compute (a) the weight of copper which can be deposited in one hour, (b) the gain in acidity in moles of sulfuric acid during that time.

9.20. If 6.30 amperes will deposit 0.532 gram of tin in 20 minutes from a solution of stannous salt, what is the current efficiency?

9.21. A pure alloy of copper and zinc is dissolved in acid and electrolyzed under 0.500 ampere (100 per cent efficiency). It is found that just 40 minutes are required to deposit all the copper. From the filtrate the zinc is precipitated and ignited to 0.245 gram of $Zn_2P_2O_7$. Calculate (a) grams of copper deposited, (b) percentage of copper in the alloy, (c) volume of gas liberated, (d) gain in acid normality of the solution assuming the volume at the end of the electrolysis to be 500 ml.

9.22. Assuming the volume of an electrolytic cell to be kept at 125 ml., find the normal acid concentration of a solution containing 0.42 gram of copper, 0.20 gram of lead, and 0.26 gram of zinc and 144 milliequivalents of acid at the start (a) after just enough current has been passed to deposit all the lead as PbO_2 and assuming no other reaction takes place at the anode during that time, (b) after all the copper has deposited, (c) when the current of 1.8 amperes has been continued 30 minutes longer. Compute the total volume of gas evolved during the entire electrolysis, measured under standard conditions.

9.23. On the basis of 30 per cent current yield, compute the cost of the power required to produce 1 pound of $NaMnO_4$ from a manganese anode and 0.3 N Na_2CO_3 solution. E.m.f. = 8 volts. Cost of current = 3 cents per kilowatt-hour.

9.24. The following represents the net reaction for the discharge of an ordinary lead storage battery: $Pb + PbO_2 + 2H^+ + 2HSO_4^- \rightarrow 2PbSO_4 + 2H_2O$. Write the two half-cell reactions involved. If the charged battery contains two liters of sulfuric acid of specific gravity 1.28 (36.9 per cent H_2SO_4 by weight) and in 1 hour the cell is discharged to the point where the specific gravity of the acid is 1.11 (15.7 per cent H_2SO_4 by weight), what is the average amperage produced? Assume no change in volume of the electrolyte.

9.25. A current of one ampere is passed for one hour through a saturated solution of sodium chloride connected in series with a copper coulometer consisting of copper electrodes dipping in a solution of cupric sulfate. Write equations for the anode and cathode reactions that take place in the NaCl cell and in the $CuSO_4$ cell. Assuming 100 per cent current efficiency, calculate (a) grams of copper deposited on the cathode of the coulometer, (b) number of liters of Cl_2 gas evolved (standard conditions), (c) number of milliliters of $N/10$ HCl required to titrate one-tenth of the cathode portion of the NaCl cell.

9.26. A copper coulometer, consisting of copper electrodes dipping in a solution of cupric sulfate, is connected in series with a cell containing a concentrated solution of sodium chloride. After a direct current is passed through both the cell and the coulometer for exactly 50 minutes, it is found that 0.636 gram of copper has been dissolved from the coulometer anode. (a) What is the average amperage used during the electrolysis? (b) Assuming 100 per cent efficiency, how many grams of $NaClO_3$ could be produced from the Cl_2 and NaOH formed during the electrolysis ($3Cl_2 + 6OH^- \rightarrow ClO_3^- + 5Cl^- + 3H_2O$)?

9.27. What weight of $CuSO_4.5H_2O$ must be dissolved in water so that after complete deposition of the copper by electrolysis, a solution will be obtained which is equivalent to 100 ml. of 0.100 N acid?

9.28. Pure crystals of $CuSO_4.5H_2O$ weighing 1.0000 gram are dissolved in water, and the solution is electrolyzed with an average current of 1.30 amperes for 20 minutes. What weight of copper has been deposited? What volume of gas measured dry and under standard conditions has been liberated? If the resulting solution is made up to 100 ml. with water, what is its normality as an acid?

9.29. Pure crystals of $CuSO_4.5H_2O$ are dissolved in water, and the solution is electrolyzed with an average current of 0.600 ampere. The electrolysis is continued for 5 minutes after all the copper has been deposited, and it is found that a total volume of 62.5 ml. of gas measured dry at 18°C. and 745 mm. pressure has been evolved.   What weight of crystals was taken for electrolysis?   (Assume all the copper is deposited before hydrogen is evolved.)   How many milliliters of 0.100 N NaOH will the resulting solution neutralize?

9.30. A solution of brass in nitric acid contains 1.10 grams of copper and 0.50 gram of zinc and is 2.00 N in acid.   It is electrolyzed at 1.50 amperes, and the volume is kept at 100 ml.   If all the current goes to the deposition of copper at the cathode, what is the acid normality of the solution when all the copper has just deposited? What is the acid normality of the solution if the current is continued 20 minutes longer and 40 per cent of it goes to the reduction of nitrate ions to ammonium ions: (cathode) $NO_3^- + 8\epsilon + 10H^+ = NH_4^+ + 3H_2O$; (anode) $4H_2O - 8\epsilon = 8H^+ + 2O_2$.   How long before the acid would be entirely destroyed?

9.31. Assuming 100 per cent current efficiency and assuming that the electrolysis is discontinued as soon as the copper is deposited, compute the time required, the volume of gas evolved, and the gain in acidity in terms of millimoles of hydrogen ions when 0.8000 gram of brass in dilute HNO_3 is electrolyzed.   Cathode gains 0.6365 gram; anode gains 0.0240 gram.   Current = 0.900 ampere.   Compute also the percentage composition of the brass.

9.32. Calculate the minimum concentration of Zn^{++} required for the deposition of zinc on a zinc electrode from a solution having a pH value of 7.5, assuming the overvoltage of hydrogen on zinc to be 0.50 volt.

CHAPTER 10

CALCULATIONS FROM REPORTED PERCENTAGES

69. Calculations Involving the Elimination or Introduction of a Constituent. It is occasionally necessary to eliminate from or introduce into a report of an analysis one or more constituents, and calculate the results to a new basis. Thus, a mineral may contain hygroscopic water which is not an integral part of the molecular structure. After complete analysis, it may be desirable to calculate the results to a dry basis as being more representative of the mineral under normal conditions. On the other hand, a material may contain a very large amount of water, and because of the difficulty of proper sampling, a small sample may be taken for the determination of the water while the bulk of the material is dried, sampled, and analyzed. It may then be desirable to convert the results thus obtained to the basis of the original wet sample. This applies equally well to constituents other than water, and, in any case, the method by which these calculations are made is based upon the fact that the constituents other than the ones eliminated or introduced are all changed in the same proportion, and the total percentage must remain the same.

EXAMPLE I. A sample of lime gave the following analysis:

$$
\begin{array}{lcr}
\text{CaO} & = & 90.15 \text{ per cent} \\
\text{MgO} & = & 6.14 \text{ per cent} \\
\text{Fe}_2\text{O}_3 + \text{Al}_2\text{O}_3 & = & 1.03 \text{ per cent} \\
\text{SiO}_2 & = & 0.55 \text{ per cent} \\
\text{H}_2\text{O} + \text{CO}_2 \text{ (by loss on ignition)} & = & \underline{2.16 \text{ per cent}} \\
& & 100.03 \text{ per cent}
\end{array}
$$

What is the percentage composition of the ignited sample on the assumption that the volatile constituents are completely expelled?

SOLUTION: In the sample as given, total percentage of all constituents is 100.03. The slight variation from the theoretical 100 per cent is due to experimental errors in the analysis. The total percentage of nonvolatile constituents is $100.03 - 2.16 = 97.87$ per cent. Ignition of the sample would therefore increase the percentage of each of the nonvolatile constituents in the ratio of 100.03:97.87, and the percentage composition of the ignited sample would be

$$
\begin{aligned}
\text{CaO} &= 90.15 \times \frac{100.03}{97.87} = 92.14 \text{ per cent} \\
\text{MgO} &= 6.14 \times \frac{100.03}{97.87} = 6.28 \text{ per cent} \\
\text{Fe}_2\text{O}_3 + \text{Al}_2\text{O}_3 &= 1.03 \times \frac{100.03}{97.87} = 1.05 \text{ per cent} \\
\text{SiO}_2 &= 0.55 \times \frac{100.03}{97.87} = 0.56 \text{ per cent} \\
&\hspace{3.2cm} \overline{100.03 \text{ per cent}}
\end{aligned}
\quad \Bigg\} \quad Ans.
$$

EXAMPLE II.   If the original sample of lime mentioned in the preceding problem were heated only sufficiently to reduce the percentage of volatile constituents from 2.16 to 0.50 per cent, what would be the percentage composition of the product?

SOLUTION: In the original sample, total percentage of nonvolatile constituents is $100.03 - 2.16 = 97.87$ per cent.   In the ignited sample, the total percentage of residual constituents would be $100.03 - 0.50 = 99.53$ per cent.   The loss of volatile matter would therefore have caused the percentage of the various constituents to increase in the ratio of 99.53 to 97.87.   Hence, the percentage composition would be

$$
\begin{aligned}
\text{CaO} &= 90.15 \times \frac{99.53}{97.87} = 91.68 \text{ per cent} \\
\text{MgO} &= 6.14 \times \frac{99.53}{97.87} = 6.24 \text{ per cent} \\
\text{Fe}_2\text{O}_3 + \text{Al}_2\text{O}_3 &= 1.03 \times \frac{99.53}{97.87} = 1.05 \text{ per cent} \\
\text{SiO}_2 &= 0.55 \times \frac{99.53}{97.87} = 0.56 \text{ per cent} \\
\text{Volatile matter} &= 0.50 \text{ per cent} \\
&\hspace{3.2cm} \overline{100.03 \text{ per cent}}
\end{aligned}
\quad \Bigg\} \quad Ans.
$$

70. Cases Where Simultaneous Volatilization and Oxidation or Reduction Occur.   Occasionally a material on ignition may not only lose volatile constituents but may also undergo changes due to oxidation or reduction effects.   In such cases the percentages of the constituents after ignition can best be calculated by assuming that oxidation or reduction occurs first, and loss of volatile material afterward.   In other words, it is easiest to solve the problem in two separate steps.

EXAMPLE. A mineral analyzes as follows:

$$CaO = 45.18 \text{ per cent}$$
$$MgO = 8.10 \text{ per cent}$$
$$FeO = 4.00 \text{ per cent}$$
$$SiO_2 = 6.02 \text{ per cent}$$
$$CO_2 = 34.67 \text{ per cent}$$
$$H_2O = \underline{2.03} \text{ per cent}$$
$$100.00 \text{ per cent}$$

After heating in oxygen the ignited material shows the presence of no water and 3.30 per cent CO_2. The iron is all oxidized to the ferric state. Calculate the percentage of CaO and of Fe_2O_3 in the ignited material.

SOLUTION: Assume first that 100 grams of the original mineral are taken and that the only change is that of oxidation of FeO to Fe_2O_3. Here 4.00 grams of FeO would form $4.00 \times Fe_2O_3/2FeO = 4.44$ grams of Fe_2O_3 and the resulting material would gain in weight by 0.44 gram due to this change alone. The material now weighs 100.44 grams and the percentages of the constituents (other than Fe_2O_3) are decreased in the ratio of 100/100.44. The percentages are now

$$CaO = 45.18 \times 100/100.44 = 44.98 \text{ per cent}$$
$$MgO = 8.10 \times 100/100.44 = 8.07 \text{ per cent}$$
$$Fe_2O_3 = 4.44 \times 100/100.44 = 4.42 \text{ per cent}$$
$$SiO_2 = 6.02 \times 100/100.44 = 5.99 \text{ per cent}$$
$$CO_2 = 34.67 \times 100/100.44 = 34.52 \text{ per cent}$$
$$H_2O = 2.03 \times 100/100.44 = \underline{2.02} \text{ per cent}$$
$$100.00 \text{ per cent}$$

Assume now that the second change takes place, namely, that all the water is lost and that the percentage of CO_2 in the ignited material is brought down to 3.30 per cent due to loss of most of the CO_2. The calculation then becomes similar to that of the preceding example:

$$\text{Percentage of CaO} = 44.98 \times \frac{100.00 - 3.30}{100.00 - (34.52 + 2.02)}$$
$$= 66.97 \text{ per cent. } Ans.$$
$$\text{Percentage of } Fe_2O_3 = 4.42 \times \frac{100.00 - 3.30}{100.00 - (34.52 + 2.02)}$$
$$= 6.61 \text{ per cent. } Ans.$$

Problems

10.1. The percentage of copper in a sample of copper ore with a moisture content of 8.27 per cent is found to be 36.47 per cent. Calculate the percentage on a dry sample.

Ans. 39.76 per cent.

10.2. A sample of coal as taken from the mine contains 8.32 per cent ash. An air-dried sample of the same coal contains 10.03 per cent ash and 0.53 per cent moisture. Calculate the percentage of moisture in the original sample.

Ans. 17.50 per cent.

10.3. A powder consisting of a mixture of pure $BaCl_2.2H_2O$ and silica contains 20.50 per cent Cl. What would be the percentage of Ba in the material after all the water of crystallization is expelled by ignition?

Ans. 44.34 per cent.

10.4. A sample of lime gives the following analysis:

$$
\begin{aligned}
CaO &= 75.12 \text{ per cent} \\
MgO &= 15.81 \text{ per cent} \\
SiO_2 &= 2.13 \text{ per cent} \\
Fe_2O_3 &= 1.60 \text{ per cent} \\
CO_2 &= 2.16 \text{ per cent} \\
H_2O &= \underline{3.14} \text{ per cent} \\
&99.96 \text{ per cent}
\end{aligned}
$$

What is the percentage of each constituent after superficial heating in which the CO_2 content has been reduced to 1.08 per cent and the water content to 1.00 per cent?

Ans. $CaO = 77.66$, $MgO = 16.35$, $SiO_2 = 2.21$, $Fe_2O_3 = 1.66$, $CO_2 = 1.08$, $H_2O = 1.00$.

10.5. Lime is to be manufactured by the ignition of a sample of dolomite. The only data as to the composition of the dolomite are as follows:

96.46 per cent $CaCO_3 + MgCO_3$
2.21 per cent SiO_2
10.23 per cent MgO
1.33 per cent H_2O

The analysis of the lime shows no water and 1.37 per cent carbon dioxide. Calculate the percentages of CaO, MgO, and SiO_2 in the lime.

Ans. $CaO = 76.14$, $MgO = 18.52$, $SiO_2 = 4.00$, $CO_2 = 1.37$.

10.6. The oil in a sample of paint is extracted, and the residual pigment is found to be 66.66 per cent of the original weight. An analysis of the pigment gives

$$
\begin{aligned}
\text{Zinc oxide} &= 24.9 \text{ per cent} \\
\text{Lithopone} &= 51.6 \text{ per cent} \\
\text{Barium chromate} &= \underline{23.5} \text{ per cent} \\
&100.0 \text{ per cent}
\end{aligned}
$$

Calculate the percentage composition of the original paint.

Ans. Zinc oxide = 16.6, lithopone = 34.4, barium chromate = 15.7, oil = 33.3.

10.7. The same sample of iron ore is analyzed by two chemists. Among other constituents, Chemist *A* reports: $H_2O = 1.62$ per cent, $Fe = 43.92$ per cent. Chemist *B* reports: $H_2O = 0.96$ per cent, $Fe = 44.36$ per cent. Calculate the percentage of iron in both cases on a dry sample. Analysis of a dry sample shows *A* to be correct. What are the error and percentage error in the constituent iron in *B*'s analysis as reported?

Ans. $A = 44.64$ per cent, $B = 44.79$ per cent. 0.15 per cent, 0.34 per cent.

10.8. A cargo of wet coal is properly sampled and the loss in weight at 105°C. is determined as 10.60 per cent. The dried sample is used for the analysis of other constituents, as follows:

$$\text{Volatile combustible matter} = 21.60 \text{ per cent}$$
$$\text{Coke} = 60.04 \text{ per cent}$$
$$\text{`Ash} = 18.36 \text{ per cent}$$

The air-dried coal (moisture content = 1.35 per cent) costs $8.80 a ton at the mine. What is its percentage of ash? Neglecting other factors except water content, calculate the value of the wet coal.

Ans. 18.11 per cent. $7.98 a ton.

10.9. The moisture content of a sample of $Al_2(SO_4)_3.18H_2O$ is reduced from the theoretical to 7.36 per cent. Calculate the analysis of the partly dried material reporting percentage of Al_2O_3, SO_3, and H_2O. The original salt costs $0.0262 per pound. Calculate the cost of the dried material, considering only the loss in water content.

Ans. $Al_2O_3 = 27.64$ per cent, $SO_3 = 64.98$ per cent, $H_2O = 7.36$ per cent. $0.0473.

10.10. In the paper industry "air-dry" paper pulp is considered as containing 10 per cent of water. A sample of wet pulp weighs 737.1 grams and when heated to "bone dryness" weighs 373.6 grams. What is the percentage of air-dry pulp in the original sample?

Ans. 56.30 per cent.

10.11. Ignition in air of MnO_2 converts it quantitatively into Mn_3O_4. A sample of pyrolusite is of the following composition: $MnO_2 = 80.0$ per cent; SiO_2 and other inert constituents = 15.0 per cent; $H_2O = 5.0$ per cent. The sample is ignited in air to constant weight. Calculate the percentage of Mn in the ignited sample.

Ans. 59.4 per cent.

10.12. A salt mixture is found to contain 60.10 per cent UO_3 (essentially in the form of ammonium diuranate). It is also found that 10.00 per cent of the mixture is combined and uncombined volatile matter (essentially NH_3 and H_2O) and 29.90 per cent is nonvolatile inert matter. What is the percentage of the element uranium in the material after ignition if the volatile matter is all lost and the uranium is converted to the oxide U_3O_8?

Ans. 56.27 per cent.

10.13. A sample of a mineral containing water as its only volatile constituent contains 26.40 per cent SiO_2 and 8.86 per cent water. What would be the percentage of SiO_2 in the material after heating sufficiently to drive off all the water, assuming that no chemical changes occur? What would be the percentage of SiO_2 if the ignited material still showed the presence of 1.10 per cent water?

10.14. A powder consisting of a mixture of pure $CuSO_4.5H_2O$ and silica contains 18.10 per cent Cu. What would be the percentage of combined sulfur in the material after the water of crystallization is all driven off by ignition?

10.15. One pound of an ore lost 0.500 ounce of water by drying at 110°C. to constant weight. The dried ore upon strong ignition with a flux lost 1.50 per cent of its weight as moisture and was also found to contain 20.10 per cent SiO_2. Find the percentage of water and of silica in the ore as received.

10.16. A sample of crude copperas ($FeSO_4.7H_2O$) representing a large shipment was purchased at 1.25 cents per pound. An analysis for iron content gave 20.21 per cent Fe. The shipment was stored for a considerable period during which time water of crystallization was lost. To fix the price at which the copperas was to be sold, it was found that an increase of 0.023 cent per pound would be necessary, due entirely to the change in the percentage of iron. Calculate the percentage of iron in the sample after storage. Assume the increase to be due wholly to loss of water.

10.17. A sample of dolomite analyzes as follows:

$$SiO_2 = 0.31 \text{ per cent}$$
$$Al_2O_3 = 0.07 \text{ per cent}$$
$$Fe_2O_3 = 0.09 \text{ per cent}$$
$$MgO = 21.54 \text{ per cent}$$
$$CaO = 30.52 \text{ per cent}$$
$$CO_2 = 47.55 \text{ per cent}$$

The dolomite is ignited, and a 5.00-gram sample of the ignited material shows the presence of 0.80 per cent CO_2. What weight of $Mg_2P_2O_7$ could be obtained from a 0.500-gram sample of the ignited material?

10.18. A shipment of meat scrap is sold with the specification that it contains a minimum of 55.00 per cent protein and a maximum of 10.00 per cent fat when calculated to a dry basis. The analyst for the sender reports 53.20 per cent protein, 9.59 per cent fat, and 3.60 per cent moisture. The material takes on moisture during shipment and the analyst for the receiver reports 50.91 per cent protein, 9.31 per cent fat, and 7.50 per cent moisture. Do either or both of the analyses show conformity of the material to specifications? On the dry basis, what is the percentage variation between the two protein values and between the two fat values as reported by the analysts?

10.19. A sample of limestone analyzes as follows:

$$CaCO_3 = 86.98 \text{ per cent}$$
$$MgCO_3 = 3.18 \text{ per cent}$$
$$Fe_2O_3 = 3.10 \text{ per cent}$$
$$Al_2O_3 = 0.87 \text{ per cent}$$
$$SiO_2 = 5.66 \text{ per cent}$$
$$H_2O = \underline{0.30} \text{ per cent}$$
$$100.09 \text{ per cent}$$

Analysis of the ignited material shows no moisture and only 1.30 per cent CO_2. What is the percentage of Fe in the ignited material?

10.20. A sample of pyrolusite analyzes as follows: MnO_2 = 69.80 per cent; SiO_2 and other inert constituents = 26.12 per cent; CO_2 = 1.96 per cent; H_2O = 2.15 per cent. On ignition in air all the H_2O and CO_2 are lost and the MnO_2 is converted to Mn_3O_4. Calculate the percentage of Mn_3O_4 in the ignited material.

10.21. A carbonate rock analyzes as follows: CaO = 43.18 per cent; MgO = 8.82 per cent; FeO = 3.10 per cent; Fe_2O_3 = 1.90 per cent; SiO_2 = 7.30 per cent; CO_2 = 33.69 per cent; H_2O = 2.00 per cent. A portion of this rock is ignited and a sample of the ignited material on analysis shows 2.00 per cent CO_2 and no water. It also shows that the ferrous iron has been completely oxidized. Calculate the percentage of total Fe_2O_3 and of CaO in the ignited material.

71. Calculation of Molecular Formulas from Chemical Analyses. Given a compound of unknown composition, a chemical analysis will determine the proportion in which the constituents of the compound exist. The results of such an analysis may then be used to calculate the empirical formula of the compound. Thus, the analysis of a certain salt gives the following results:

$$\begin{aligned}
\text{Zinc} &= 47.96 \text{ per cent} \\
\text{Chlorine} &= \underline{52.04} \text{ per cent} \\
&\ \ 100.00 \text{ per cent}
\end{aligned}$$

Dividing the percentage of each constituent by its atomic weight will give the number of gram-atoms of that constituent in 100 grams of the compound. In 100 grams of the above salt there are present $47.96/65.38 = 0.7335$ gram-atom of zinc and $52.04/35.46 = 1.4674$ gram-atoms of chlorine. These numbers are seen to be in the ratio of 1 to 2. The empirical formula of the salt is therefore $ZnCl_2$, although, as far as the above analysis is concerned, the actual formula might be Zn_2Cl_4, Zn_3Cl_6, or any other whole multiple of the empirical formula. In general, the determination of the molecular weight of a compound is necessary in order to determine which multiple of the empirical formula will give the actual formula. The usual methods of establishing molecular weights by means of vapor density, freezing-point lowering, boiling-point raising, and other physico-chemical phenomena should already be familiar to the student but the following will serve as a brief review.

Equal volumes of gases under identical conditions of temperature and pressure contain the same number of molecules (Avogadro). Therefore the molecular weights of gases are proportional to their densities. Since under standard conditions of temperature and pressure (0°C., 760 mm.) a gram-molecular weight of a gas (*e.g.*, 32 grams of O_2; 28.016 grams of N_2) occupies 22.4 liters, an experimental method of determining the molecular weight of a gas is to measure its density under known conditions of temperature and pressure and calculate the weight of 22.4 liters of it under standard conditions (see Sec. 125). The molecular weight of a solid or liquid can also be determined in this way if the substance can be converted to a gas without decomposition or change in degree of molecular association.

A soluble substance lowers the freezing point and raises the boiling point of a definite weight of a solvent in proportion to the number of molecules or ions of solute present. In the case of a nonpolar (un-ionized) solute dissolved in water, one gram-molecular weight of the solute dissolved in 1,000 grams of water raises the boiling point of the water by 0.52°C. (*i.e.*, to 100.52°C.) and lowers the freezing point of the water by 1.86° (*i.e.*, to -1.86°C.). In general, for aqueous solutions of nonpolar solutes,

$$\frac{\text{Grams of solute}}{\text{Mol. wt. of solute}} \times \frac{1,000}{\text{grams of water}} \begin{cases} \times 0.52 = \text{raising of boiling point} \\ \times 1.86 = \text{lowering of freezing point} \end{cases}$$

Ionized solutes change the boiling point or freezing point of a solvent to a greater degree owing to the greater number of particles present. Thus, NaCl at ordinary concentrations depresses the freezing point of water and raises the boiling point by about twice as much as calculated from the above formula, owing to ionization into Na^+ and Cl^- ions. Similarly, $CaCl_2$ and Na_2SO_4 give an effect about three times as great as that of a nonpolar solute.

Solutes dissolved in solvents other than water show analogous behavior in that the changes in freezing point and boiling point brought about by a mole of solute in 1,000 grams of solvent are fixed values (but of course different from those values given by water as the solvent).

The determination of the molecular weight of a soluble substance can therefore be made by preparing a solution of a known weight of it in a known weight of solvent (preferably water) and measuring the point at which the solution begins to freeze or boil.

EXAMPLE I.   A certain organic compound is found by analysis to contain 40.00 per cent carbon, 6.71 per cent hydrogen, and the rest oxygen. When converted to a gas it has a density 2.81 times that of oxygen at the same temperature and pressure.   What is the formula of the compound?

SOLUTION: In 100 grams of substance there are 40.00 grams of C, 6.71 grams of H, and 53.29 grams of O.   This corresponds to

$$\frac{40.00}{12.01} = 3.33 \text{ gram-atoms of C}$$

$$\frac{6.71}{1.008} = 6.66 \text{ gram-atoms of H}$$

$$\frac{53.29}{16.00} = 3.33 \text{ gram-atoms of O}$$

These are in the ratio of $1:2:1$

Empirical formula = CH_2O
Formula weight of CH_2O = 30 (approx.)
Molecular weight of compound = 2.81×32 = 90 (approx.)

Therefore,

Formula of compound = $C_3H_6O_3$.   *Ans.*

EXAMPLE II.   Butandione is a yellow liquid containing 55.8 per cent carbon, 7.00 per cent hydrogen, and 37.2 per cent oxygen.   It is soluble in water, and the solution does not conduct electricity.   A water solution containing 10.0 grams of the compound in 100 grams of water freezes at $-2.16°C$.   What is the formula of butandione?

SOLUTION:

$$\text{Gram-atoms per 100 grams} = \frac{55.8}{12.0} = 4.65 \text{ of C}$$

$$= \frac{7.00}{1.00} = 7.00 \text{ of H}$$

$$= \frac{37.2}{16.0} \doteq 2.32 \text{ of O}$$

These are in the approx. ratio of $2:3:1$

$$\text{Empirical formula} = C_2H_3O$$
$$\text{Formula weight of } C_2H_3O = 43$$
$$\frac{10.0}{\text{Mol. wt.}} \times \frac{1,000}{100} \times 1.86 = 2.16$$

Solving,

$$\text{Mol. wt.} = 86$$

Therefore,

$$\text{Actual formula} = C_4H_6O_2. \quad Ans.$$

72. Calculation of Empirical Formula of a Mineral. The calculation of molecular formulas plays an important part in the analysis of natural minerals. A careful analysis furnishes a means of establishing the empirical formula of a mineral of high degree of purity, although its actual formula is usually impossible to determine by ordinary physicochemical methods since minerals cannot be vaporized or dissolved unchanged. The method of calculation is similar to that of the preceding examples, except that the basic constituents of a mineral are usually expressed in terms of their oxides. If the percentage of each constituent is divided by its molecular weight, the number of moles (gram-molecular weights) of that constituent in 100 grams of the mineral is obtained. From the ratios of the number of moles of the various constituents thus obtained, the formula of the mineral may be determined. It should be remembered, however, that analytical methods are subject to errors. It can hardly be expected, therefore, that the number of moles of the various constituents as determined analytically will be *exactly* in the ratio of small whole numbers, although in the actual molecule (except in cases involving isomorphism, discussed below) the molar ratios are small whole numbers. In a few cases, some judgment must be exercised in order to determine from the analysis the true molar ratios of the constituents in the molecule. A slide rule will be found to be almost indispensable for this purpose, since, with two settings of the rule, all possible ratios are visible.

EXAMPLE. The analysis of a certain mineral gives the following results:

$$Al_2O_3 = 38.07 \text{ per cent}$$
$$K_2O\ \ = 17.70 \text{ per cent}$$
$$CaO\ \ = 10.46 \text{ per cent}$$
$$SiO_2\ \ = \underline{33.70} \text{ per cent}$$
$$99.93 \text{ per cent}$$

What is the empirical formula of the mineral?

SOLUTION: In 100 grams of the mineral there are present

$$\frac{38.07}{Al_2O_3} = \frac{38.07}{102.0} = 0.3733 \text{ mole of } Al_2O_3$$

$$\frac{17.70}{K_2O} = \frac{17.70}{94.20} = 0.1879 \text{ mole of } K_2O$$

$$\frac{10.46}{CaO} = \frac{10.46}{56.07} = 0.1865 \text{ mole of } CaO$$

$$\frac{33.70}{SiO_2} = \frac{33.70}{60.3} = 0.559 \text{ mole of } SiO_2$$

It is seen that the moles of these constituents are near enough in the ratio of $2:1:1:3$ to be within the limits of experimental error. The molecule is therefore made up of $2Al_2O_3.K_2O.CaO.3SiO_2$ and may be written $K_2CaAl_4Si_3O_{14}$.

73. Calculation of Formulas of Minerals Exhibiting Isomorphic Replacement.   Complications arise in the calculation of formulas in the cases of minerals exhibiting isomorphic replacement, *i.e.*, the partial replacement of one constituent by one or more other constituents having the same general properties.   It therefore happens that, owing to different degrees of replacement, samples of the same kind of mineral obtained from different localities often give on analysis numerical results which apparently bear little resemblance to one another.

As a general rule, a constituent may be replaced only by another of the same type and valence.   Thus, Fe_2O_3 is often partially or wholly replaced by Al_2O_3, and vice versa.   CaO may be replaced by MgO, MnO, FeO, etc.   Exceptions are sometimes met with, but, for purposes of calculation, this assumption may be safely made.   Since the isomorphic replacement occurs in no definite proportion, it follows that the molar amounts of the constituents in such minerals do not necessarily bear any simple relation to one another.   On the other hand, if constituent B partially replaces constituent A, since the valences are the same, the *sum* of the molar amounts of A and B would be the same as the molar amount of A if it had not been replaced.   Consequently, when the molar quantities of the constituents of a mineral in themselves bear no simple ratio to one another, the quantities of constituents of the same type should be combined in an effort to obtain *sums* that do exist in ratios of simple whole numbers.

EXAMPLE. A certain mineral gives the following analysis:

$$Al_2O_3 = 20.65 \text{ per cent}$$
$$Fe_2O_3 = 7.03 \text{ per cent}$$
$$CaO = 27.65 \text{ per cent}$$
$$SiO_2 = \underline{44.55} \text{ per cent}$$
$$99.88 \text{ per cent}$$

What is the empirical formula?

SOLUTION: The number of moles of each constituent in 100 grams of the mineral is found to be

$$\frac{20.65}{Al_2O_3} = 0.2025 \text{ mole of } Al_2O_3$$
$$\frac{7.03}{Fe_2O_3} = 0.0440 \text{ mole of } Fe_2O_3$$
$$\left.\begin{array}{l}\end{array}\right\} = 0.2465 \text{ mole}$$

$$\frac{27.65}{CaO} = 0.4932 \text{ mole of } CaO$$

$$\frac{44.55}{SiO_2} = 0.7389 \text{ mole of } SiO_2$$

Only when the molar quantities of the first two constituents are combined are all the above numerical results found to be in simple ratio to one another, these being approximately as $1:2:3$. This shows isomorphic replacement between Fe_2O_3 and Al_2O_3, and the formula of the mineral may therefore be written

$$(Al,Fe)_2O_3.2CaO.3SiO_2$$

or

$$Ca_2(Al,Fe)_2Si_3O_{11}. \quad Ans.$$

Problems

10.22. From the following percentage composition of ethylamine, calculate its empirical formula: C = 53.27 per cent, H = 15.65 per cent, N = 31.08 per cent.

Ans. C_2H_7N.

10.23. Calculate the empirical formula of the compound having the following composition: Ca = 23.53 per cent, H = 2.37 per cent, P = 36.49 per cent, O = 37.61 per cent.

Ans. $Ca(H_2PO_2)_2$.

10.24. Calculate the empirical formula of an organic compound having the following composition: C = 68.83 per cent, H = 4.96 per cent, O = 26.21 per cent.

Ans. $C_7H_6O_2$.

10.25. Show that the following analysis of diethylhydrazine agrees with the formula $(C_2H_5)_2:N.NH_2$:

$$\text{Carbon} = 54.55 \text{ per cent}$$
$$\text{Hydrogen} = 13.74 \text{ per cent}$$
$$\text{Nitrogen} = \underline{31.80} \text{ per cent}$$
$$100.09 \text{ per cent}$$

10.26. Calculate the molecular formula of a compound that has a molecular weight of approximately 90 and has the following composition: C = 26.67 per cent, H = 2.24 per cent, O = 71.09 per cent.

Ans. $H_2C_2O_4$.

10.27. A certain compound of carbon and oxygen has an approximate molecular weight of 290 and by analysis is found to contain 50 per cent by weight of each constituent. What is the molecular formula of the compound?

Ans. $C_{12}O_9$.

10.28. What is the molecular weight of a substance, 0.0850 gram of which dissolved in 10.0 grams of water gives a solution freezing at −0.465°C. and not conducting electricity? What is the molecular formula of the substance if it contains 5.94 per cent hydrogen and 94.06 per cent oxygen?

Ans. 34.0. H_2O_2.

10.29. A certain organic compound contains 48.64 per cent carbon, 43.19 per cent oxygen, and the rest hydrogen. A solution of 7.408 grams of the solid in 100 grams of water boils at 100.52°C. and does not conduct electricity. What is the molecular formula of the compound?

Ans. $C_3H_6O_2$.

10.30. A certain gaseous compound is found by analysis to consist of 87.44 per cent nitrogen and 12.56 per cent hydrogen. If 500 ml. of the compound has almost exactly the same weight as that of 500 ml. of oxygen at the same temperature and pressure, what is the molecular formula of the compound?

Ans. N_2H_4.

10.31. A certain organic compound contains almost exactly 60 per cent carbon, 5 per cent hydrogen, and 35 per cent nitrogen. A solution of 20.0 grams of the compound in 300 grams of water does not conduct electricity and freezes at −1.55°C. What is the molecular formula of the compound?

Ans. $C_4H_4N_2$.

10.32. A certain sugar in a compound of carbon, hydrogen, and oxygen. Combustion in oxygen of a sample weighing 1.200 grams yields 1.759 grams of CO_2 and 0.720 gram of H_2O. A solution of 8.10 grams of the substance in 150 grams of water boils at 100.156°C. What is the molecular formula of the sugar? At what temperature will the above solution freeze?

Ans. $C_6H_{12}O_6$.   −0.558°C.

10.33. At a certain temperature and pressure 250 ml. of a certain gas consisting of 90.28 per cent silicon and 9.72 per cent hydrogen has a weight equal to that of 555 ml. of nitrogen at the same temperature and pressure. What is the molecular formula of the gas?

Ans. Si_2H_6.

10.34. When 0.500 gram of a certain hydrocarbon is completely burned in oxygen, 0.281 gram of H_2O and 1.717 grams of CO_2 are formed. When a certain weight of this compound is vaporized, it is found to have a volume almost exactly one-quarter that of the same weight of oxygen under the same conditions of temperature and pressure. Calculate the molecular formula of the compound.

Ans. $C_{10}H_8$.

10.35. An analysis of a mineral gave the following results: H_2O = 4.35 per cent, CaO = 27.15 per cent, Al_2O_3 = 24.85 per cent, SiO_2 = 43.74 per cent. Calculate the empirical formula of the mineral.

Ans. $H_2Ca_2Al_2Si_3O_{12}$.

10.36. Dana gives the composition of vivianite as follows: P_2O_5 = 28.3 per cent, FeO = 43.0 per cent, H_2O = 28.7 per cent. Show that this conforms to the formula $Fe_3P_2O_8.8H_2O$.

10.37. The percentage composition of a certain silicate is as follows: K_2O = 21.53 per cent, Al_2O_3 = 23.35 per cent, SiO_2 = 55.12 per cent. Calculate the empirical formula of the silicate.

Ans. $KAlSi_2O_6$.

10.38. A certain compound contains only the following constituents: CaO, Na_2O, SO_3. The percentages of these constituents are in the respective approximate ratios of 9:10:26. What is the empirical formula of the compound?

Ans. $Na_2CaS_2O_8$.

10.39. What is the empirical formula of a simple basic cupric carbonate which, according to Rogers, contains 57.4 per cent Cu and 8.1 per cent H_2O?

Ans. $Cu_2(OH)_2CO_3$.

10.40. The composition of bismutite is given by Ramm as follows: CO_2 = 6.38 per cent, Bi_2O_3 = 89.75 per cent, H_2O = 3.87 per cent. Calculate the empirical formula.

Ans. $2Bi_8C_3O_{18}.9H_2O$.

10.41. What is the empirical formula of a silicate which gives the following analysis:

$$
\begin{aligned}
\text{CaO} &= 24.72 \text{ per cent}\\
\text{MgO} &= 11.93 \text{ per cent}\\
\text{FeO} &= 10.39 \text{ per cent}\\
\text{SiO}_2 &= \underline{53.09 \text{ per cent}}\\
&100.13 \text{ per cent}
\end{aligned}
$$

Ans. $Ca(Mg,Fe)(SiO_3)_2$.

10.42. A silicate gives the following analysis. If two-thirds of the water exists as water of crystallization, what is the empirical formula?

$$
\begin{aligned}
\text{H}_2\text{O} &= 17.22 \text{ per cent}\\
\text{CaO} &= 8.22 \text{ per cent}\\
\text{Na}_2\text{O} &= 0.76 \text{ per cent}\\
\text{Al}_2\text{O}_3 &= 16.25 \text{ per cent}\\
\text{SiO}_2 &= \underline{57.48 \text{ per cent}}\\
&99.93 \text{ per cent}
\end{aligned}
$$

Ans. $H_4(Ca,Na_2)Al_2(SiO_3)_6.4H_2O$.

10.43. Calculate the empirical formula of a mineral that analyzes as follows:

$$
\begin{aligned}
\text{MnO} &= 46.36 \text{ per cent}\\
\text{CaO} &= 6.91 \text{ per cent}\\
\text{SiO}_2 &= \underline{46.78 \text{ per cent}}\\
&100.05 \text{ per cent}
\end{aligned}
$$

Ans. $(Mn,Ca)SiO_3$.

10.44. The analysis of samples of microcline and of albite are given below. Show that these minerals are of the same type. Give the general empirical formula. Assume the percentages of silica and alumina to be the most reliable.

MICROCLINE	ALBITE
Na_2O = 1.61 per cent	Na_2O = 11.11 per cent
K_2O = 13.56 per cent	K_2O = 0.51 per cent
Al_2O_3 = 19.60 per cent	CaO = 0.38 per cent
SiO_2 = 64.79 per cent	Al_2O_3 = 19.29 per cent
99.56 per cent	SiO_2 = 68.81 per cent
	100.10 per cent

Ans. $(K,Na)AlSi_3O_8$.

10.45. Calculate the empirical formula of axinite from the following analysis:

$$H_2O = \quad 1.58 \text{ per cent}$$
$$CaO = 19.63 \text{ per cent}$$
$$FeO = \quad 9.54 \text{ per cent}$$
$$MnO = \quad 3.01 \text{ per cent}$$
$$Al_2O_3 = 17.92 \text{ per cent}$$
$$B_2O_3 = \quad 6.12 \text{ per cent}$$
$$SiO_2 = 42.23 \text{ per cent}$$
$$\overline{100.03 \text{ per cent}}$$

Ans. $HCa_2(Fe,Mn)Al_2B(SiO_4)_4$.

10.46. A sample of the mineral biotite gave the following analysis:

$$H_2O = \quad 1.10 \text{ per cent}$$
$$FeO = \quad 9.60 \text{ per cent}$$
$$Al_2O_3 = 22.35 \text{ per cent}$$
$$K_2O = 14.84 \text{ per cent}$$
$$MgO = 12.42 \text{ per cent}$$
$$SiO_2 = 39.66 \text{ per cent}$$
$$\overline{99.97 \text{ per cent}}$$

What is the empirical formula of the mineral?

Ans. $(H,K)_2(Mg,Fe)_2Al_2Si_3O_{12}$.

10.47. What is the empirical formula of a compound of the following composition: K = 38.68 per cent, H = 0.50 per cent, As = 37.08 per cent, O = 23.74 per cent?

10.48. Analysis of an organic compound gave the following results: C = 60.86 per cent, H = 4.38 per cent, O = 34.76 per cent. Calculate the empirical formula of the compound.

10.49. An organic acid is found to have a molecular weight of approximately 160 and to give the following analysis: carbon = 57.82 per cent, hydrogen = 3.64 per cent, oxygen (by difference) = 38.54 per cent. Calculate the molecular formula of the acid.

10.50. Calculate the empirical formula of the compound of the following composition: Sb = 49.55 per cent, O = 6.60 per cent, Cl = 43.85 per cent.

10.51. Metaformaldehyde contains 40.00 per cent carbon, 6.67 per cent hydrogen, and 53.33 per cent oxygen. A solution of 10.01 grams of the compound in 250 grams of water freezes at $-0.827°C.$ and does not conduct electricity. What is the molecular formula of metaformaldehyde?

10.52. A certain derivative of benzene contains only carbon, hydrogen, and nitrogen, and is not ionized in aqueous solution. Analysis of the compound shows 58.51 per cent carbon and 7.37 per cent hydrogen. A solution of 30.0 grams of the compound in 150 grams of water freezes at $-3.02°C$. What is the molecular formula of the compound?

10.53. What is the molecular weight of a substance 4.50 grams of which, when dissolved in 50.0 grams of water, gives a solution freezing at $-0.93°C$. but not conducting electricity? What is its molecular formula if it contains 40.00 per cent carbon, 6.67 per cent hydrogen, and 53.33 per cent oxygen? At what temperature would the solution boil?

10.54. A certain hydrocarbon contains 79.89 per cent carbon and has a density 1.07 times that of N_2 at the same temperature and pressure. What is the molecular formula of the hydrocarbon?

10.55. A sample of a certain compound of carbon, hydrogen, and oxygen weighing 2.000 grams yields on combustion in oxygen 2.837 grams of CO_2 and 1.742 grams of H_2O. A solution of 2.150 grams of the compound in 50.0 grams of water is nonconducting and freezes at $-1.288°C$. What is the molecular formula of the compound?

10.56. Under standard conditions a liter of a certain gaseous compound of boron and hydrogen weighs 2.38 grams. When 1.00 gram of this compound is heated, it is completely decomposed into boron and hydrogen, and the latter has a volume of 2.10 liters under standard conditions. Calculate the molecular formula of the boron hydride.

10.57. A certain gas is composed of 46.16 per cent carbon and the remainder nitrogen. Its density is 1.80 times that of air at the same temperature and pressure. What is the molecular formula of the gas? (Calculate the apparent molecular weight of air by considering it four-fifths nitrogen and one-fifth oxygen.)

10.58. Calculate the formula of a compound of carbon, hydrogen, nitrogen, and oxygen from the following data. Approximate mol. wt. 140. Decomposition of a 0.2-gram sample gives 32.45 ml. of nitrogen when measured dry under standard conditions. The same weight of sample on combustion in oxygen yields 0.3824 gram of CO_2 and 0.0783 gram of H_2O.

10.59. What is the empirical formula of a mineral containing 3.37 per cent water, 19.10 per cent aluminum oxide, 21.00 per cent calcium oxide, and 56.53 per cent silica?

10.60. Zircon is a pure silicate of zirconium containing 33.0 per cent of silica. What is its empirical formula?

10.61. A tungstate has the following composition: WO_3 = 76.5 per cent, FeO = 9.5 per cent, MnO = 14.0 per cent. Calculate the empirical formula.

10.62. Calamine is a basic zinc silicate of the following composition: ZnO = 67.5 per cent, H_2O = 7.5 per cent, SiO_2 = 25.0 per cent. Calculate its empirical formula.

10.63. A silicate of the composition given below is found to have 85 per cent of its water in the form of water of crystallization. What is the empirical formula?

$$H_2O = \quad 7.7 \text{ per cent}$$
$$K_2O = \quad 28.1 \text{ per cent}$$
$$CaO = \quad 20.4 \text{ per cent}$$
$$SiO_2 = \quad 43.8 \text{ per cent}$$
$$\overline{100.0 \text{ per cent}}$$

10.64. A sample of a certain hydrogen-potassium-magnesium-aluminum silicate weighing 1.2000 grams yields the following products: 0.0516 gram of water, 0.4000 gram of $KClO_4$, 0.9550 gram of $Mg_2P_2O_7$, and 0.1461 gram of alumina. What is the empirical formula of the mineral?

10.65. From the following data obtained from the analysis of a feldspar, calculate the percentage composition of the sample and determine the empirical formula of the mineral, omitting the calcium from the formula and assuming the percentages of silica and alumina to be the most reliable.

Sample taken	= 1.2000 grams
Silica obtained	= 0.7751 gram
Alumina obtained	= 0.2255 gram
Calcium oxide obtained	= 0.0060 gram
KCl + NaCl obtained	= 0.3193 gram
K_2PtCl_6 obtained	= 0.7240 gram

Part III

VOLUMETRIC ANALYSIS

CHAPTER 11

CALIBRATION OF MEASURING INSTRUMENTS

74. Measuring Instruments in Volumetric Analysis. The principle of volumetric analysis differs from that of gravimetric analysis in that, instead of isolating and weighing a product of a reaction directly or indirectly involving the desired substance, the volume of a reagent required to bring about a direct or indirect reaction with that substance is measured. From the volume of the reagent and its concentration, the weight of the substance is calculated.

Since volumetric analysis makes use of exact volume relationships, it is essential first to adopt a definite standard for a unit volume and then to calibrate all measuring instruments to conform to this standard. The measuring instruments most often used are burets, pipets, and measuring flasks, and the experimental methods of calibrating them may be found in any standard reference book on quantitative analysis.

75. Calculation of True Volume. A *liter* is the volume occupied by 1 kilogram of water at the temperature of its maximum density (approximately 4°C.). A *milliliter* (*ml.*) is 1/1,000 liter. A *cubic centimeter* (*cc.*) is the volume occupied by a cube 1 cm. on a side. One liter contains 1000.027 · · · cc. In calibrating a vessel, since the cubical content of the vessel holding the water to be weighed varies with the temperature, it is evident that the temperature of the container must be included in the specifications. Instead of taking the corresponding temperature of 4°C., the temperature of 20°C. has been accepted as the *normal temperature* by the Bureau of Standards at Washington.

To contain a *true liter* then, a flask must be so marked that at 20°C. its capacity will be equal to the volume of water which at 4°C. weighs 1 kilogram in vacuo. From the density of water at different temperatures (Table IV, Appendix), the coefficient of cubical expansion of glass (0.000026), and the relationship existing between the weight of a substance in air and the weight in vacuo (Sec. 53), it is possible to calculate the amount of water to be weighed into a container in order that it shall occupy a true liter at any given temperature.

141

EXAMPLE.   How much water at 25°C. should be weighed in air with brass weights so that when placed in a flask at the same temperature and under normal barometric pressure it will occupy 1 true liter at 20°C.?

SOLUTION: Density of water at 25°C. = 0.99707 (Table IV).

At 4°C. and in vacuo, 1,000 grams of water will occupy 1 true liter.

At 25°C. and in vacuo, 1,000 × 0.99707 grams of water will occupy 1 true liter.

At 25°C. and in air, the weight of water is found by substituting in the formula

$$W^0 = W + \left(\frac{W}{d} - \frac{W}{d'}\right) a$$

and solving for W (see Sec. 53).

Thus,

$$997.07 = W + \left(\frac{W}{0.99707} - \frac{W}{8.0}\right) 0.0012$$

Since the term to the right of the plus sign is required to only two significant figures, it is sufficiently accurate to write

$$997.07 = W + \left(\frac{1,000}{1.0} - \frac{1,000}{8.0}\right) 0.0012$$

whence

$$W = 996.02 \text{ grams}$$

Theoretically, to contain a true liter, the flask must be at 20°C. and yet contain this weight of water at 25°C.   Actually, the temperature of the flask is also 25°C.   It has therefore expanded, the cubical content is greater, and the true-liter volume is also greater.   The coefficient of cubical expansion of glass is 0.000026, and the increase in volume from 20 to 25°C. is 1,000 × 0.000026(25 − 20) = 0.13 ml.   This volume is represented by 0.13 × 0.99707 = 0.13 gram of water.   The required weight of water is therefore

$$996.02 + 0.13 = 996.15 \text{ grams.}   \textit{Ans.}$$

A general formula may now be written for calculating the weight of water required for a true liter.

$$W = \frac{1,000 \times d}{1 + \dfrac{a}{d} - \dfrac{a}{d'}} + [1,000 \times d \times c(t - 20)]$$

where W = grams of water required for 1 true liter
t = temperature of water and flask
d = density of water at $t°$
a = weight of 1 ml. of air under given conditions
d' = density of balance weights
c = coefficient of cubical expansion of the container

(The values of these last three terms are usually 0.0012, 8.0, and 0.000026, respectively.)

The correction for the expansion or contraction of the container is in each case small compared with the quantity to which it is added. Consequently, only an approximate value containing two or three significant figures need be used. Indeed, in the case of instruments of 50-ml. content or less and for small differences in temperature, this correction may ordinarily be neglected.

By using the third column of Table IV, calculations like the above can be simplified. This column gives the weight of 1 ml. of water at a given temperature when the weighing is made in air against brass weights and the water is in a glass container. In other words, corrections for expansion of glass and for conversion to vacuo are incorporated in the values given. It is seen, for example, that the answer to the above problem is found directly by multiplying by 1,000 the weight of 1 ml. of water at 25°C. under the conditions specified.

$$0.99615 \times 1,000 = 996.15 \text{ grams.} \quad Ans.$$

Problems

11.1. Calculate accurately the amount of water which should be weighed into a tared flask at 18°C. and 770 mm. pressure against brass weights in order that the flask may be marked to contain exactly 250 true milliliters.

Ans. 249.37 grams.

11.2. A flask which has been marked to contain 1 true liter is filled with water at 15°C. to the mark, and the temperature of the water is allowed to rise to 25°C. How many milliliters above the mark does the water now stand (inner diameter of the neck of the flask = 15.0 mm.)?

Ans. 10.2 mm.

11.3. In calibrating a flask to contain $\frac{1}{2}$ true liter, if the water is weighed at 26°C. against brass weights, what percentage error would be introduced in the weight of water necessary if the expansion of glass were neglected? What weight of water should be taken?

Ans. 0.016 per cent. 498.07 grams.

11.4. What is the true volume of a flask that contains 746.24 grams of water at 30°C. when weighed in air against brass weights?

Ans. 750.06 ml.

11.5. A flask is accurately marked to contain a true liter, and the inner diameter of the neck of the flask is 16.0 mm. If 996.00 grams of water are weighed out in air against brass weights at 20°C. and placed in the flask at this temperature, how far above or below the true-liter mark does the meniscus of the water lie?

Ans. 5.9 mm. below.

11.6. To calibrate a flask to contain a true liter at 20°C., how much water at 31°C. and 760 mm. pressure must be weighed into the flask in air against brass weights?

11.7. In calibrating a flask to contain $\frac{1}{2}$ true liter using water at 30°C., what percentage error would be introduced by neglecting the expansion of glass in the calculation of the weight of water required?

11.8. What is the true volume of a flask that contains 398.70 grams of water at 26°C. when weighed in air against brass weights?

11.9. A pipet is marked to contain 100 ml. according to the true-liter standard. It is filled with water at 12°C. How much would the water weigh in air under normal barometric pressure against gold weights?

11.10. The inner diameter of the neck of a flask is 14 mm., and the flask contains 498.00 grams of water at 28°C. weighed in air against brass weights. How far above or below the meniscus of the water should a mark be placed in order to represent a volume of 500 ml. according to the true-liter standard?

11.11. A 50-ml. buret is calibrated by weighing in air (against brass weights) the water delivered between 10-ml. intervals in the graduations. Calculate from the following data the true volume of solution that the buret will deliver between each 10-ml. interval, calculate the true total volume delivered between the 0- and the 50-ml. mark, and make a graph showing the correction that must be applied to the buret reading to obtain the true volume in any titration where the buret is initially filled to the zero mark (temperature of the water = 25°C.).

GRADUATION INTERVALS, ML.	WEIGHT OF WATER OBTAINED, GRAMS
0.03–10.07	10.04
10.07–19.93	9.84
19.93–29.97	10.07
29.97–40.03	10.13
40.03–49.96	10.05

If this buret is used in a titration and the initial and final readings are 0.11 and 46.38, respectively, what volume of solution has actually been delivered?

CHAPTER 12

NEUTRALIZATION METHODS
(ACIDIMETRY AND ALKALIMETRY)

76. Divisions of Volumetric Analysis. It is customary to divide the reactions of volumetric analysis into four groups, *viz.*,
1. Acidimetry and alkalimetry
2. Oxidation and reduction ("redox") methods
3. Precipitation methods
4. Complex formation methods

In Secs. 28 and 29 the principles underlying the use of equivalents, milliequivalents, and normal solutions were taken up in a general way. In this and succeeding chapters these principles are reviewed, developed, and applied to the above four types of volumetric analysis.

77. Equivalent Weights Applied to Neutralization Methods. The fundamental reaction of acidimetry and alkalimetry is as follows:

$$H^+ + OH^- \to H_2O$$

i.e., the neutralization of an acid by a base, or the neutralization of a base by an acid.

The gram-equivalent weight of a substance acting as an acid is that weight of it which is equivalent in total neutralizing power to one gram-atom (1.008 grams) of hydrogen as hydrogen ions. The gram-equivalent weight of a substance acting as a base is that weight of it which will neutralize one gram-atom of hydrogen ions (or is equivalent in total neutralizing power to 17.008 grams of hydroxyl ions).

A normal solution of an acid or base contains one gram-equivalent weight of the acid or base in one liter of solution, or one gram-milliequivalent weight in one milliliter of solution (see also Sec. 28).

When hydrochloric acid reacts as an acid, the gram-molecular weight (36.47 grams) of hydrogen chloride furnishes for the neutralization of any base one gram-atom (1.008 grams) of reacting hydrogen. According to the definition, the value 36.47 grams constitutes the gram-equivalent weight of hydrogen chloride, and a liter of solution containing this amount is a normal solution of the acid. In this case, the normal solution and the molar solution are identical. On the other hand, the amount of hydrogen sulfate required to furnish in reaction one gram-atomic weight of hydrogen is only one-half the gram-molecular weight, or

$H_2SO_4/2 = 49.04$ grams, and a normal solution of sulfuric acid would contain 49.04 grams of hydrogen sulfate per liter of solution. A molar solution of sulfuric acid is therefore 2 normal and contains 2 gram-equivalent weights per liter, or 2 gram-milliequivalent weights per milliliter.

Acetic acid, $HC_2H_3O_2$, contains 4 hydrogen atoms in its molecule; but, when the compound acts as an acid, only one of these hydrogens is involved in active reaction, thus:

$$HC_2H_3O_2 + OH^- \rightarrow C_2H_3O_2^- + H_2O$$

Consequently, $HC_2H_3O_2/1 = 60.05$ grams of acetic acid constitute the gram-equivalent weight, and the normal solution contains this weight of acid in a liter, or 0.06005 gram of acetic acid per milliliter.

Sodium hydroxide is neutralized as follows:

$$(Na^+)OH^- + H^+ \rightarrow H_2O\ (+Na^+)$$

$NaOH/1$, or 40.00 grams, of sodium hydroxide constitutes one gram-equivalent weight of the alkali, because that amount will furnish 17.008 grams of hydrogen ions in a neutralization process and will therefore just react with one gram-atom (1.008 grams) of hydrogen ions. Therefore, a weight of 40.00 grams of sodium hydroxide in a liter of solution represents the normal solution. When calcium oxide is used as a base, each gram-molecule reacts with two gram-atoms of hydrogen, thus:

$$CaO + 2H^+ \rightarrow Ca^{++} + H_2O$$

or $CaO/2 = 28.04$ grams of calcium oxide are needed to involve in reaction one gram-atom of hydrogen. Therefore, 28.04 grams of calcium oxide constitute the gram-equivalent weight in this case.

Total neutralizing power should not be confused with degree of ionization. Equal volumes of normal solutions of hydrochloric acid and acetic acid have the same total neutralizing power, but the acids have very different degrees of ionization. In other words, equivalent weight is based on neutralizing power and not on relative "strength" or degree of ionization.

Problems

12.1. What is the equivalent weight of zinc oxide as a base? Of $KHSO_4$ as an acid?

Ans.   40.69.   136.2

12.2. What is the milliequivalent weight in grams of each of the following acids or bases, assuming complete neutralization unless otherwise specified: (a) Na_2CO_3, (b) K_2O, (c) NH_4OH, (d) B_2O_3 (assume neutralization by the NaOH only to the point of forming NaH_2BO_3), (e) P_2O_5 (assume neutralization only to the point of forming $H_2PO_4^-$ ions).

Ans.   (a) 0.05300 gram, (b) 0.04710 gram, (c) 0.03505 gram, (d) 0.03482 gram, (e) 0.07098 gram.

12.3. What is the equivalent weight of the following acids or bases, assuming complete neutralization in each case: (a) N_2O_5, (b) Ag_2O, (c) $Ba(OH)_2$, (d) NH_3, (e) SO_2?

Ans. (a) 54.01, (b) 115.9, (c) 85.69, (d) 17.03, (e) 32.03.

12.4. What is the gram-milliequivalent weight of K_2CO_3 in the reaction $K_2CO_3 + HCl \rightarrow KHCO_3 + KCl$? What is the gram-equivalent weight of H_3PO_4 in the reaction $H_3PO_4 + 2NaOH \rightarrow Na_2HPO_4 + 2H_2O$?

Ans. 0.1382 gram. 49.00 grams.

12.5. How many grams of oxalic acid, $H_2C_2O_4.2H_2O$, are required to make (a) a liter of molar solution, (b) a liter of normal solution, (c) 400 ml. of half-normal solution?

Ans. (a) 126.1 grams, (b) 63.03 grams, (c) 12.61 grams.

12.6. Formic acid ($HCHO_2$) is a monobasic acid that is 3.2 per cent ionized in 0.20-normal solution. What weight of the pure acid should be dissolved in 250.0 ml. in order to prepare a 0.2000-normal solution?

Ans. 2.301 grams.

12.7. What weight of CaO is necessary to prepare the following: (a) 500 ml. of a one-hundredth molar solution of $Ca(OH)_2$, (b) 30.63 ml. of $N/100$ $Ca(OH)_2$?

Ans. (a) 0.2804 gram, (b) 0.008589 gram.

12.8. What is the normality of a sulfurous acid solution containing 6.32 grams of SO_2 per liter? Of an ammonium hydroxide solution containing 17.5 grams of NH_3 in 480 ml. of solution?

Ans. 0.197 N. 2.14 N.

12.9. A solution of hydrochloric acid has a specific gravity of 1.200 and contains 39.11 per cent HCl by weight. Calculate (a) the molar concentration of the solution, (b) the normality of the solution, (c) the number of gram-equivalent weights of HCl in every 750 ml. of solution.

Ans. (a) 12.87 molar, (b) 12.87 N, (c) 9.65.

12.10. A solution of sulfuric acid has a specific gravity of 1.100 and contains 15.71 per cent H_2SO_4 by weight. What is the normality of the solution?

Ans. 3.524 N.

12.11. Assuming complete neutralization in each case, what are the equivalent weights of the following substances when acting as acids and bases? (a) LiOH, (b) N_2O_3, (c) Fe_2O_3, (d) $HC_2H_3O_2$, (e) cream of tartar ($KHC_4H_4O_6$).

12.12. What is the gram-milliequivalent weight of P_2O_5 in a neutralization process in which the final products are HPO_4^- ions?

12.13. How many grams of H_2SO_4 does a liter of 0.1000 N sulfuric acid solution contain?

12.14. How many grams of hydrated oxalic acid ($H_2C_2O_4.2H_2O$) must be dissolved and diluted to exactly one liter to make a 0.1230 N solution for use as an acid?

12.15. Chloracetic acid, $CH_2Cl.COOH$ (mol. wt. = 94.50), is a monobasic acid with an ionization constant of 1.6×10^{-3}. How many grams of the acid should be dissolved in 300.0 ml. of solution in order to prepare a half-normal solution?

12.16. How many grams of pure potassium tetroxalate ($KHC_2O_4.H_2C_2O_4.2H_2O$) must be dissolved in water and diluted to 780 ml. to make a 0.05100 N solution for use as an acid?

12.17. How many milliliters of sulfuric acid (sp. gr. 1.200, containing 27.32 per cent H_2SO_4 by weight) are required to make one liter of 0.4980 N solution by dilution with water?

12.18. What is the normality of a sulfuric acid solution that has a specific gravity of 1.839 and contains 95.0 per cent H_2SO_4 by weight?

12.19. If 75.0 milliliters of hydrochloric acid (sp. gr. 1.100, containing 20.01 per cent hydrochloric acid by weight) have been diluted to 900 ml., what is the normality of the acid?

12.20. A 0.2000 N solution of barium hydroxide is to be prepared from pure Ba-$(OH)_2.8H_2O$ crystals that have lost part of their water of crystallization. How may the solution be made if no standardized reagents are available? State specifically the treatment given and the weight and volume used.

78. Normality of a Solution Made by Mixing Similar Components.

When several similar components are mixed and dissolved in water, the normality of the resulting solution is determined by calculating the total number of equivalent weights present in a liter of solution.

EXAMPLE. If 3.00 grams of solid KOH and 5.00 grams of solid NaOH are mixed, dissolved in water, and the solution made up to 1,500 ml., what is the normality of the solution as a base?

SOLUTION: The number of equivalent weights (see footnote, Sec. 28) of KOH in 1,500 ml. is $\dfrac{3.00}{KOH} = \dfrac{3.00}{56.10}$. In 1 liter there is $\dfrac{3.00}{56.10} \times \dfrac{1,000}{1,500} =$ 0.0356 equivalent weight of KOH. In a liter of the solution there is also $\dfrac{5.00}{40.00} \times \dfrac{1,000}{1,500} = 0.0833$ equivalent weight of NaOH. A total of 0.0356 + 0.0833 = 0.1189 equivalent weight of base in a liter makes the normality of the solution as a base 0.1189 N. *Ans.*

Problems

12.21. What is the normality of an alkali solution made by dissolving 6.73 grams of NaOH (99.5 per cent NaOH, 0.5 per cent H_2O) and 9.42 grams of pure $Ba(OH)_2.8H_2O$ in water and diluting to 850 ml.?

Ans. 0.267 N.

12.22. If 50.00 ml. of sulfuric acid (sp. gr. 1.420, containing 52.15 per cent of H_2SO_4 by weight) and 50.00 ml. of sulfuric acid (sp. gr. 1.840, containing 95.60 per cent H_2SO_4 by weight) are mixed and diluted to 1,500 ml., what is the normality of the solution as an acid?

Ans. 1.699 N.

12.23. If a sample of NaOH contains 2.00 per cent by weight of Na_2CO_3 and 6.00 per cent by weight of H_2O and if 40.0 grams are dissolved in water and diluted to a liter, what is the normality of the resulting solution as a base? Assume complete neutralization.

Ans. 0.935 N.

12.24. If 50.00 grams of a solid dibasic acid (mol. wt. 126.0) are mixed with 25.00

grams of a solid monobasic acid (mol. wt. 122.0) and the mixture is dissolved and diluted to 2,500 ml., what is the normality of the solution as an acid?

Ans. 0.3995 N.

12.25. What is the normality as an acid of a solution made by mixing the following components? Assume no change in volume due to chemical effects. (*a*) 160 ml. of 0.3050 N HCl, (*b*) 300 ml. of half-molar H_2SO_4, (*c*) 140 ml. containing 1.621 grams of HCl, (*d*) 200 ml. containing 1.010 grams of H_2SO_4.

Ans. 0.517 N.

12.26. In preparing an alkaline solution for use in volumetric work, a student mixed exactly 46.32 grams of pure KOH and 4.63 grams of pure $Na_2CO_3.10H_2O$ and, after dissolving in water, diluted the solution to exactly one liter. How many gram-milliequivalents of total alkali are present in each milliliter? Assume complete neutralization.

12.27. What would be the approximate normality of an acid solution made by mixing the following amounts of H_2SO_4 solutions? (*a*) 160 ml. of 0.3050 N solution, (*b*) 300 ml. of 0.4163 molar solution, (*c*) 175 ml. of solution containing 22.10 grams H_2SO_4, (*d*) 250 ml. of solution (sp. gr. 1.120, containing 17.01 per cent H_2SO_4 by weight).

12.28. What is the normality of an alkali solution made by mixing 50.0 ml. of a solution containing 5.00 grams of NaOH with 100 ml. of a solution containing 2.90 grams of $Ba(OH)_2.8H_2O$ and diluting with water to 250 ml.?

79. Volume-normality-milliequivalent Relationship. A normal solution contains one gram-equivalent of solute per liter of solution, or one gram-milliequivalent weight per milliliter of solution. It follows that the product of the number of milliliters of a given solution and the normality of the solution must give the number of gram-milliequivalents of solute present, or

$$ml. \times N = number\ of\ gram\text{-}milliequivalents$$

where *ml.* = volume, milliliters
N = normality
This simple relationship is the basis of most calculations involving simple volume relationships between solutions and is illustrated in the following sections.

80. Adjusting Solution to a Desired Normality. A solution with a given normality is often found to be too concentrated or too dilute for the purpose for which it is to be used. In order to decrease its concentration, water is usually added; and in order to increase its concentration, a solution is added which contains the solute in greater concentration than the one given. The amounts required in each case may be determined by simple calculation.

EXAMPLE I. To what volume must 750.0 ml. of a 2.400 normal solution be diluted in order to make it 1.760 normal?

SOLUTION:

Before diluting, number of gram-milliequivalents
$$= 750.0 \times 2.400 = 1{,}800$$

After diluting to x ml., these would be
$$1{,}800 \text{ gm.-milliequivalents in } x \text{ ml.}$$

$$\frac{1{,}800}{x} = \text{normality} = 1.760$$

Solving,
$$x = 1{,}023 \text{ ml.} \quad Ans.$$

EXAMPLE II.   How much 0.600 normal base must be added to 750 ml. of a 0.200 normal base in order that the resulting solution shall be 0.300 normal?

SOLUTION:

Let x = milliliters of $0.600\ N$ base added
Total volume after dilution $= 750 + x$
Total number of gram-milliequivalents present
$$= (750 \times 0.200) + (0.600x)$$
Resulting normality (number of gram-milliequivalents per milliliter)
$$= 0.300$$

$$\frac{(750 \times 0.200) + 0.600x}{750 + x} = 0.300$$

$$x = 250 \text{ ml.} \quad Ans.$$

Problems

12.29. Each milliliter of a solution of sodium carbonate contains 0.0109 gram of pure Na_2CO_3.   To what volume must 100 ml. of the solution be diluted to make it $0.0100\ N$?

Ans.   2,056 ml.

12.30. What volumes of $3.00\ N$ and $6.00\ N$ hydrochloric acid must be mixed to make a liter of $5.00\ N$ acid?

Ans.   667 ml. 6 N, 333 ml. 3 N.

12.31. A solution of sulfuric acid is standardized gravimetrically, and it is found that 25.00 ml. will precipitate 0.3059 gram of $BaSO_4$.   To what volume must a liter of the acid be diluted in order to be $0.1000\ N$?

Ans.   1,047 ml.

12.32. A solution of sodium hydroxide is found on analysis to be 0.537 normal, and a liter of it is available.   How many milliliters of $1.00\ N$ NaOH solution must be added in order to make the resulting solution 0.600 normal?

Ans.   158 ml.

12.33. How much water must be added to 760 ml. of $0.2500\ M$ barium hydroxide solution in order to prepare a tenth-normal solution?   How many grams of $Ba(OH)_2.\text{-}8H_2O$ must be dissolved and diluted to 400 ml. to prepare a twelfth-normal solution?

How many moles per liter, and how many gram-equivalent weights per liter does this last solution contain?

Ans. 3,040 ml. 5.26 grams. 0.04167 mole, 0.08333 gram-equivalent weight.

12.34. A 10-ml. pipetful of H_2SO_4 (sp. gr. 1.80, containing the equivalent of 80.0 per cent SO_3 by weight) is diluted to 500 ml. What is the normality of the solution as an acid? How many milliliters of 4.00 *molar* H_3PO_4 should be added to this solution so that the resulting mixture will be 1.00 *normal* as an acid in reactions where neutralization to Na_2SO_4 and Na_2HPO_4 takes place?

Ans. 0.719 N. 20.1 ml.

12.35. What volume of 0.206 N KOH must be added to 150 ml. of 0.132 N KOH in order that the resulting solution shall have the same basic strength as a solution which contains 15.5 grams of $Ba(OH)_2$ per liter?

Ans. 289 ml.

12.36. What volumes of 0.500 N and 0.100 N HCl must be mixed to give 2.00 liters of 0.200 N acid?

12.37. How many milliliters of water must be added to a liter of 0.167 N sulfuric acid to make it 0.100 N?

12.38. If 10.0 ml. of H_2SO_4 (sp. gr. 1.50 containing the equivalent of 48.7 per cent of combined SO_3 by weight) are diluted to 400 ml., what is the normality of the solution as an acid? What volume of 6.00 molar H_2SO_4 should be added to this in order to make the resulting mixture 1.00 normal as an acid?

12.39. If 10.0 ml of Na_2CO_3 solution (sp. gr. 1.080, containing 8.00 per cent Na_2CO_3 by weight) are diluted to 50.0 ml., what is the normality of the resulting solution as a base? What volume of 4.00 molar K_2CO_3 solution should be added to this solution so that the resulting mixture will be 1.00 normal?

12.40. A 500-ml. graduated flask contains 150 ml. of 0.200 N sulfuric acid. By addition of more concentrated sulfuric acid, the solution is brought up to the mark and after mixing is found to be exactly 0.300 N. What was the normality of the acid added?

12.41. A chemist desires to prepare approximately 14.00 liters of 0.5000 N NaOH. How many grams of the solid should be weighed out? After preparing 14.00 liters of the solution, the analyst standardizes it and finds it to be actually 0.4895 N. What volume of 6.00 N NaOH should be added to bring the solution up to half normal? After adding approximately this amount, the analyst standardizes the solution and finds it to be 0.5010 N. How much water should now be added?

81. Volume and Normality Relationships between Reacting Solutions.
Since a gram-milliequivalent weight of an acid will just neutralize a gram-milliequivalent weight of a base and since the number of milliequivalents in each case is found by multiplying the number of milliliters of solution by its normality, we have the following simple relationship between two reacting solutions:

$$ml._A \times N_A = ml._B \times N_B$$

A solution can therefore be standardized by determining what volume of it will exactly react with a definite volume of another solution the normality of which is already known. The normalities of the two solutions will then be in inverse ratio to the respective volumes used. Thus 50 ml. of any half-normal acid will neutralize 50 ml. of any half-normal base, or 100 ml. of quarter-normal base, since the solutions contain the same number of equivalent weights of reacting substance (*i.e.*, 25 gram-milliequivalents). To neutralize 60 ml. of 0.5 N alkali solution (30 milliequivalents), 15 ml. of 2 N acid (30 milliequivalents) will be required regardless of the chemical composition of the acid or alkali used. The chemical compositions of the reacting substances are taken into account in preparing their standard solutions.

EXAMPLE. What is the normality of a solution of H_2SO_4 if 27.80 ml. are required to neutralize a 25-ml. pipetful of 0.4820 N alkali?

SOLUTION:

$$27.80 \times x = 25.00 \times 0.4820$$
$$x = 0.4334 \ N. \quad Ans.$$

Problems

12.42. A solution of HCl contains 0.1243 gram-equivalent of HCl per liter. How many milliliters of half-normal KOH solution are necessary to neutralize 10.00 ml. of the acid?

Ans. 2.486 ml.

12.43. A solution of H_2SO_4 is 0.1372 normal. How many milliliters of 0.1421 normal KOH solution are required to neutralize 13.72 ml. of the acid?

Ans. 13.24 ml.

12.44. Convert 42.95 ml. of 0.1372 normal hydrochloric acid to the equivalent volume of normal solution.

Ans. 5.892 ml.

12.45. Subtract 34.37 ml. of 0.1972 N HCl from 42.00 ml. of 0.2000 N HCl by converting both values to the equivalent volumes of normal acid. Express the answer in terms of (*a*) milliliters of 1.000 N HCl, (*b*) number of milliequivalents of HCl, (*c*) number of milliliters of 0.5000 N NaOH.

Ans. (*a*) 1.622 ml., (*b*) 1.622, (*c*) 3.244 ml.

12.46. To neutralize 10.00 ml. of dilute acetic acid, 13.12 ml. of 0.1078 N KOH were required. What was the normality of the acid?

Ans. 0.1415 N.

12.47. A solution containing 31.21 ml. of 0.1000 N HCl is added to a solution containing 98.53 ml. of 0.5000 N H_2SO_4, and 50.00 ml. of 1.002 N KOH are added. Is the resulting solution acid or alkaline? How many milliliters of 0.3333 N acid or alkali will make it exactly neutral?

Ans. Acid. 6.85 ml. of alkali.

12.48. If 50.00 ml. of 1.087 normal HCl are added to 28.00 ml. of a solution of a solid substance having an alkaline reaction, the alkali is more than neutralized. It then requires 10.00 ml. of 0.1021 N alkali to make the solution exactly neutral. How many milliequivalents of base per milliliter did the original solution of solid substance contain, and what was its normality as an alkali?

Ans. 1.904, 1.904 *N*.

12.49. Given: Standard sulfuric acid = $0.1072 \, N$
Standard sodium hydroxide = $0.1096 \, N$

How many milliliters of the sodium hydroxide solution are equivalent to 26.42 ml. of the sulfuric acid solution?

12.50. If 50.0 ml. of 6.00 *N* ammonium hydroxide and 50.0 ml. of 6.00 *N* hydrochloric acid are mixed, what is the approximate normality of the resulting ammonium chloride solution?

12.51. How many milliliters of 0.300 *N* H_2SO_4 will be required to (*a*) neutralize 30.0 ml. of 0.500 *N* KOH, (*b*) neutralize 30.0 ml. of 0.500 *N* $Ba(OH)_2$, (*c*) neutralize 20.0 ml. of a solution containing 10.02 grams of $KHCO_3$ per 100 ml., (*d*) give a precipitate of $BaSO_4$ weighing 0.4320 gram?

12.52. 1.000 ml. NaOH $\approx$ 1.012 ml. HCl
HCl = 0.4767 *N*

If 100.0 ml. of the alkali have been diluted to 500.0 ml. with the idea of preparing a tenth-normal solution, how much too large is the volume?

82. Determination of the Normality of a Solution.

A solution may be standardized (*i.e.*, its normality may be determined) in a variety of ways. In a few specific cases, it is possible to prepare a standard solution by accurately weighing out the solute, dissolving, and diluting to a definite volume. This method is applicable only to solutions of such substances as can be weighed out accurately and the composition and purity of which are definitely known.

In some cases, it is possible to determine the normality of a given solution by gravimetric methods, *i.e.*, by taking a definite volume of solution and precipitating the principal constituent in the form of a weighable compound of known composition. From the weight of this compound the weight of the solute in the volume of solution taken is calculated. This gives a direct measure of the normality. For example, if a certain volume of hydrochloric acid is treated with an excess of silver nitrate, the weight of the precipitated silver chloride is a measure of the weight of hydrogen chloride in a liter of the acid. Since a liter of normal hydrochloric acid contains 36.47 grams of HCl, the normality of the solution is found by direct proportion.

A solution is most often standardized, however, by determining the exact volume of it required to react with a known weight of substance of known purity (usually, but not necessarily, 100 per cent pure). One liter of a normal solution of an acid, for example, contains one gram-equivalent weight of that acid and therefore must just neutralize one gram-equivalent weight of any base, or one milliliter (a more convenient unit for ordinary experimental work) of the acid will neutralize one gram-milliequivalent weight of any base. One milliliter of normal acid will just neutralize one milliequivalent weight in grams of any base. For example, it will neutralize $Na_2CO_3/2,000 = 0.05300$ gram of pure sodium carbonate, $K_2CO_3/2,000 = 0.06910$ gram of pure potassium carbonate, or $NaOH/1,000 = 0.04000$ gram of pure sodium hydroxide. If 1.000 ml. of an acid solution were found to neutralize 0.1060 gram (*i.e.*, two gram-milliequivalents) of pure sodium carbonate, the acid would be 2.000 N. If 1.000 ml. of an acid solution were found to neutralize 0.02000 gram (½ gram-milliequivalent) of pure sodium hydroxide, the acid would be 0.5000 N. The same reasoning holds true for the standardization of alkali solutions against acids and, as will be seen later, for the standardization of solutions of oxidizing, reducing, and precipitating agents. In calculating the normality of a solution standardized in this way, the number of grams of pure standardizing agent divided by its milliequivalent weight gives the number of gram-milliequivalents present. This must be the same as the number of gram-milliequivalents of substance in the solution used. Since this equals the number of milliliters times the normality,

$$ml._s \times N_s = \frac{grams_x}{mew_x}$$

or

$$N_s = \frac{grams_x}{ml._s \times mew_x}$$

where mew_x is the milliequivalent weight (in grams) of pure substance x which is titrated with solution s.

EXAMPLE.   A sample of pure oxalic acid ($H_2C_2O_4.2H_2O$) weighs 0.2000 gram and requires exactly 30.12 ml. of potassium hydroxide solution for complete neutralization.   What is the normality of the KOH solution?

SOLUTION: The milliequivalent weight of oxalic acid is

$$\frac{H_2C_2O_4.2H_2O}{2,000} = 0.06303$$

The number of milliequivalents of oxalic acid present is 0.2000/0.06303. The number of milliequivalents of KOH required is 30.23 × N.

$$30.12 \times N = \frac{0.2000}{0.06303}$$
$$N = 0.1053. \quad Ans.$$

83. Conversion of Data to Milliequivalents.   In general, the student will usually find that the most satisfactory initial step in solving problems in analytical chemistry is to convert amounts of reacting substances to the corresponding number of gram-milliequivalents of these substances. Since the number of milliequivalents of reacting substances are the same, such problems resolve themselves into the simplest types of algebraic equations. The following three formulas are of general applicability.

1. Solution s of given normality:

$$ml._s \times N_s = no.\ of\ me.\text{-}wts.\ of\ solute$$

2. Solution s of given specific gravity and percentage composition:

$$\frac{ml._s \times sp.\ gr._s \times \dfrac{percentage\ x\ in\ solution}{100}}{mew_x} = no.\ of\ me.\text{-}wts.\ of\ solute$$

3. Solid x:

$$\frac{grams_x}{mew_x} = no.\ of\ me.\text{-}wts.\ of\ solid$$

where mew_x = gram-milliequivalent weight of solid or solute

Even in gravimetric analysis, the gravimetric factor (Sec. 56) expresses nothing more than a ratio between two equivalent or milliequivalent weights. For example, the gravimetric factor $2Fe/Fe_2O_3$ represents the weight of iron *equivalent* to a unit weight of ferric oxide. It is identical to the fraction $\dfrac{Fe/1,000}{Fe_2O_3/2,000}$, which is the ratio of the milliequivalent weights of the two substances.

Problems

12.53. A hydrochloric acid solution is of such strength that 45.62 ml. are equivalent to 1.600 grams of pure Na_2CO_3. Calculate: (*a*) the number of gram-equivalents of Na_2CO_3 neutralized by 1.00 liter of the acid, (*b*) the number of gram-milliequivalents of Na_2CO_3 neutralized by 1.000 ml. of the acid, (*c*) the normality of the acid.

Ans. (*a*) 0.6616, (*b*) 0.6616, (*c*) 0.6616 N.

12.54. What is the normality of a solution of HCl if 20.00 ml. are required to neutralize the NH_3 that can be liberated from 4 millimoles of $(NH_4)_2SO_4$?

Ans. 0.4000 N.

12.55. How many milliliters of 3.100 N NaOH will be neutralized by (*a*) 105.0 ml. of H_2SO_4 (sp. gr. 1.050), (*b*) 10.50 grams of SO_3?

Ans. 53.44 ml., 84.61 ml.

12.56. Three millimoles of pure thiourea, $CS(NH_2)_2$, are digested with concentrated H_2SO_4 and the nitrogen thereby converted to ammonium bisulfate. Excess NaOH is added and the liberated NH_3 is caught in 25.0 ml. of H_2SO_4 (1.00 ml. $\backsimeq$ 2.00 ml. NaOH $\backsimeq$ 0.0315 gram $H_2C_2O_4.2H_2O$). The excess acid then requires 20.0 ml. of KOH. How many millimoles of P_2O_5 would each milliliter of the KOH be equivalent to in the neutralization of H_3PO_4 to the point of forming K_2HPO_4?

Ans. 0.0813 millimoles.

12.57. A 10-ml. pipetful of dilute sulfuric acid was standardized gravimetrically by adding an excess of $BaCl_2$, filtering, igniting, and weighing the resulting precipitate. The weight was found to be 0.2762 gram. Calculate the normality of the acid.

Ans. 0.2366 N.

12.58. The normality of a sulfuric acid solution is 0.5278.   If 38.61 ml. of the acid are equivalent to 31.27 ml. of a solution of NaOH, calculate the normality of the NaOH.   If 38.61 ml. of the acid are equivalent to 62.54 ml. of a solution of $Ba(OH)_2$, what is the normality of the $Ba(OH)_2$?

Ans.   0.6516 N.   0.3258 N.

12.59. Calculate the normality of a solution of hydrochloric acid and of sodium hydroxide from the following data:

$$1.000 \text{ ml. of HCl} \backsimeq 0.9492 \text{ ml. of NaOH}$$
$$39.81 \text{ ml. of HCl} \backsimeq 0.6293 \text{ gram of AgCl}$$

Ans.   HCl = 0.1105 N, NaOH = 0.1162 N.

12.60. A sample of pure $CaCO_3$ weighs 1.0000 gram and requires 40.10 ml. of a solution of HCl for neutralization.   What is the normality of the acid?   What volume of sulfuric acid of the same normality would be required for the same weight of $CaCO_3$?   What volume of KOH solution of which 20.00 ml. will neutralize 1.420 grams of $KHC_2O_4.H_2O$ would be neutralized by 50.32 ml. of the acid?

Ans.   0.4985 N.   40.10 ml.   51.59 ml.

12.61. To a sample of sodium carbonate (99.20 per cent pure Na_2CO_3) weighing 1.0500 grams are added 48.24 ml. of a solution of acid.   This is in excess of the amount required for complete neutralization.   The resulting solution is brought back to the neutral point with exactly 1.31 ml. of sodium hydroxide solution of which 1.000 ml. is equivalent to 1.010 ml. of the acid.   Calculate the normality of the acid.

Ans.   0.4189 N.

12.62. In standardizing an alkali against 0.1200 gram of sulfamic acid (NH_2SO_3H), 38.92 ml. of the alkali are added before it is realized that the end point has been overstepped.   By introducing 0.0050 gram of pure $H_2C_2O_4.2H_2O$ into the solution, it is found that 0.58 ml. of the alkali is required to make the solution neutral.   What is the normality of the alkali?

Ans.   0.03330 N.

12.63. A solution of sulfuric acid was standardized against calcium carbonate containing 91.90 per cent $CaCO_3$ and no other basic material.   The sample weighing 0.7242 gram was titrated by adding an excess of acid (29.97 ml.), and the excess was titrated with 10.27 ml. of NaOH solution (1.000 ml. of the acid $\backsimeq$ 1.024 ml. of the NaOH).   Calculate the normality of each solution.

Ans. H_2SO_4 = 0.6664 N.   NaOH = 0.6507 N.

12.64. A sample of pure potassium acid phthalate (a monobasic acid, $KHC_8H_4O_4$) weighing 4.070 grams is titrated with NaOH solution and back-titrated with HCl. NaOH required = 46.40 ml.; HCl required = 5.35 ml.   One milliliter HCl $\backsimeq$ 0.01600 gram Na_2O.   How much water or how much 6.00 N NaOH must be added to 500 ml. of the NaOH to bring it to 0.5000 N?

Ans.   0.96 ml. of 6 N NaOH.

12.65.   10.0 ml. NaOH $\backsimeq$ 0.0930 $H_2C_2O_4.2H_2O$
       1.00 ml. NaOH $\backsimeq$ 0.850 ml. HCl.
       What is the normality of the HCl solution?

12.66. What would be the normality of a solution of (*a*) HCl and (*b*) H_2SO_4, if

40.0 ml. of the acid are required to neutralize 0.500 gram of pearl ash containing 95.0 per cent total alkali calculated as K_2CO_3?

12.67. Three millimoles of pure urea, $CO(NH_2)_2$, are digested with concentrated H_2SO_4 and the nitrogen is thereby converted to ammonium bisulfate. Excess NaOH is added and the liberated NH_3 is caught in a 25-ml. pipetful of $0.5200\ N\ H_2SO_4$. How many milliliters of NaOH (each milliliter will neutralize 0.01640 gram $H_2C_2O_4.$-$2H_2O$) will be required to neutralize the excess acid? How many millimoles of hydrated Al_2O_3 will each milliliter of the above H_2SO_4 be capable of reacting with to form $Al_2(SO_4)_3$?

12.68. An acid solution is prepared by dissolving 19.264 grams of pure $KHC_2O_4.$-$H_2C_2O_4.2H_2O$ in water and diluting to exactly 900 ml. Fifty milliliters of this solution are neutralized by 35.00 ml. of KOH solution. What is the normality of each solution? How many grams of sulfamic acid (NH_2SO_3H, monobasic) will each milliliter of the KOH neutralize?

12.69. 1.000 ml. NaOH $\approx$ 0.0302 gram $H_2C_2O_4.2H_2O$
      1.000 ml. HCl $\approx$ 0.1123 gram $BaCO_3$
What is the ratio by volume of HCl to NaOH? How much solid NaOH must be added to 800 ml. of the alkali solution so that when the resulting solution is diluted to 1,000 ml. it will be $0.5000\ N$? How much water must be added to 1,000 ml. of the HCl to make it $0.5000\ N$? What is the value of 1.000 ml. of the original NaOH in terms of grams of benzoic acid (C_6H_5COOH)?

12.70. What is the normality of a solution of KOH if 20.60 ml. are required to neutralize (*a*) 32.35 ml. of H_2SO_4 (sp. gr. 1.160), (*b*) 1.000 gram of P_2O_5 (forming K_2HPO_4)?

12.71. How many milliliters of H_2SO_4 (sp. gr. 1.105) will be neutralized by (*a*) 20.00 ml. of $2.680\ N$ NaOH, (*b*) 5.100 grams of Fe_2O_3?

12.72. 1.000 ml. NaOH $\approx$ 1.342 ml. HCl
      1.000 ml. HCl $\approx$ 0.0225 gram $CaCO_3$
How much water must be added to 1,000 ml. of the sodium hydroxide solution to make it half normal? How much hydrochloric acid (sp. gr. 1.190, containing 37.23 per cent HCl by weight) must be added to 1,000 ml. of the acid solution to make it half normal?

12.73. Pure dry sodium carbonate weighing 0.1042 gram is dissolved in 50.00 ml. of $0.1024\ N$ sulfuric acid and the solution heated to boiling to expel the carbon dioxide liberated by the reaction. The solution is then titrated with $0.1120\ N$ sodium hydroxide. What volume of the base is necessary to neutralize the solution?

12.74. Calculate the normality of a solution of NaOH from the following data:

> Weight of potassium acid phthalate ($KHC_8H_4O_4$) = 4.119 grams.
> NaOH used = 42.18 ml.
> HCl used = 3.10 ml.
> 1.000 ml. HCl $\approx$ 0.02577 gram K_2O

What volume of $2.000\ N$ NaOH or of water should be added to 750 ml. of the NaOH in order to bring it to $0.5000\ N$?

84. Calculation of Percentage Purity from Titration Values.

Just as the normality of a solution can be found from the volume required to react with a definite weight of substance of known purity, the percentage purity of a substance can be determined from the volume of a solution of known normality required to react with a definite weight of the substance. For example, one milliliter of normal alkali solution will neutralize one milliequivalent weight in grams of any acid. If an acid is titrated with normal alkali and exactly *two* milliliters of the latter are required, it follows that *two* gram-milliequivalent weights of the acid must be present. If *two* milliliters of *two* normal alkali are required, then *four* gram-milliequivalent weights of the acid must be present. In other words, the number of milliliters multiplied by the normal value of the solution will give the number of milliequivalents (in grams) of substance reacted upon. The number of gram-milliequivalents thus found multiplied by the milliequivalent weight of the substance reacted upon will give the number of grams of that substance. If the percentage is desired, all that is necessary is to divide this weight by the weight of sample taken and multiply by 100.

In general, therefore, if a substance x requires a certain number of milliliters of a solution s of normality N and if mew_x is the milliequivalent weight of the substance,

$$ml._s \times N_s \times mew_x = grams_x$$

and

$$\frac{ml._s \times N_s \times mew_x}{Weight\ of\ sample} \times 100 = per\ cent_x$$

EXAMPLE I. A sample of soda ash (impure Na_2CO_3) is titrated with half-normal sulfuric acid. If the sample weighs 1.100 grams and requires 35.00 ml. of the acid for complete neutralization, what is the percentage of Na_2CO_3 in the ash, assuming no other active component to be present?

SOLUTION: One milliliter of normal acid will neutralize one gram-milliequivalent weight of any base. Thirty-five milliliters of 0.5000 N acid will neutralize $35.00 \times 0.5000 = 17.50$ gram-milliequivalent weights of any base. Since the milliequivalent weight of Na_2CO_3 is $Na_2CO_3/2,000 = 0.05300$, 35.00 ml. of the 0.5000 N sulfuric acid will react with

$$35.00 \times 0.5000 \times 0.05300 = 0.9275 \text{ gram of } Na_2CO_3$$

As this weight is contained in a sample weighing 1.100 grams, the percentage of Na_2CO_3 in the sample is

$$\frac{0.9275}{1.100} \times 100 = 84.32 \text{ per cent.} \quad Ans.$$

It is important to remember that the normality of a solution merely expresses the ratio of its concentration to that of a solution containing one gram-equivalent weight of solute per liter (*i.e.*, a normal solution). Consequently, if the normality of a solution is known, the value of a definite volume of it in terms of other elements, compounds, or radicals can be found directly, even though the solution may not be capable of reacting directly with these elements, compounds, or radicals. Thus, the weight of hydrogen chloride in 10.00 ml. of 0.1000 N hydrochloric acid is

$$10.00 \times 0.1000 \times \frac{HCl}{1,000} = 0.03647 \text{ gram}$$

The weight of silver chloride precipitated by adding an excess of silver nitrate to 10.00 ml. of 0.1000 N hydrochloric acid is

$$10.00 \times 0.1000 \times \frac{AgCl}{1,000} = 0.1433 \text{ gram}$$

The weight of silver sulfate equivalent to the silver in the silver chloride precipitated by adding an excess of silver nitrate to 10.00 ml. of 0.1000 N hydrochloric acid is

$$10.00 \times 0.1000 \times \frac{Ag_2SO_4}{2,000} = 0.1559 \text{ gram}$$

The weight of barium in the barium sulfate obtained by adding an excess of barium chloride to the silver sulfate above is

$$10.00 \times 0.1000 \times \frac{Ba}{2,000} = 0.06868 \text{ gram}$$

In other words, as in the case of gravimetric computations, it is not necessary to calculate the weights of the intermediate products of a reaction. From the milliequivalent weight of the substance required, the weight of that substance can be determined directly.

EXAMPLE II. Given the same conditions as in Example I, what would be the percentage of CO_2 in the soda ash?

SOLUTION:

$$35.00 \times 0.5000 = 17.50 \text{ gram-milliequivalents of } CO_2$$

$$17.50 \times \frac{CO_2}{2,000} = 0.3850 \text{ gram of } CO_2$$

$$\frac{0.3850}{1.100} \times 100 = 35.00 \text{ per cent } CO_2. \quad Ans.$$

EXAMPLE III. A 0.3000-gram sample of impure magnesium oxide is titrated with hydrochloric acid solution of which 3.000 ml. $\approx$ 0.04503 gram $CaCO_3$. The end point is overstepped on the addition of 48.00 ml. of the acid, and the solution becomes neutral on the further addition of 2.40 ml. of 0.4000 N sodium hydroxide. What is the percentage of MgO in the sample?

SOLUTION:

$$1 \text{ ml. HCl} \backsimeq \frac{0.04503}{3.000} \backsimeq 0.01501 \text{ gram of } CaCO_3$$

$$\text{Normality of HCl} = \frac{0.01501}{CaCO_3/2,000} = 0.3000$$

$$48.00 \times 0.3000 = 14.40 \quad \text{milliequivalents of HCl}$$
$$2.40 \times 0.4000 = 0.96 \quad \text{milliequivalents of NaOH}$$
$$14.40 - 0.96 = 13.44 = \text{net milliequivalents}$$

$$\frac{13.44 \times MgO/2,000}{0.3000} \times 100 = 90.33 \text{ per cent } MgO. \quad Ans.$$

85. Volumetric Indirect Methods. Instead of titrating a substance directly with a standard solution, it is frequently more feasible to allow the substance to react with a measured amount of a given reagent and then to titrate that part of the reagent left over from the reaction. This is an indirect method and is characterized by the fact that, other factors being fixed, a greater degree of purity of the sample corresponds to a smaller buret reading.

In acidimetry and alkalimetry an outstanding example of an indirect method is the *Kjeldahl method* for determining nitrogen in organic material. The sample is digested with concentrated H_2SO_4 in the presence of a catalyst and the nitrogen in the material thus converted to ammonium bisulfate. The resulting solution is made alkaline with NaOH and the liberated ammonia gas distilled (through a condenser) into a measured volume of standard acid ($NH_3 + H^+ \rightarrow NH_4^+$). The acid remaining in the receiving flask, after all the NH_3 has been liberated, is then titrated with standard NaOH solution.

Calculation of a volumetric indirect method is usually best made by determining the total number of milliequivalents of reagent added, and subtracting the number of milliequivalents used in the titration. This difference is the number of milliequivalents of desired substance.

EXAMPLE. A sample of meat scrap weighing 2.000 grams is digested with concentrated sulfuric acid and a catalyst. The resulting solution is made alkaline with NaOH and the liberated ammonia distilled into 50.00 ml. of 0.6700 N H_2SO_4. The excess acid then requires 30.10 ml. of 0.6520 N NaOH for neutralization. What is the percentage of nitrogen in the meat?

SOLUTION:

$$\text{Milliequivalents of } H_2SO_4 = 50.00 \times 0.6700 = 33.50$$
$$\text{Milliequivalents of NaOH} = 30.10 \times 0.6520 = 19.62$$
$$\text{Net milliequivalents} = 33.50 - 19.62 = 13.88$$

Since, in the above process, $NH_3 + H^+ \rightarrow NH_4^+$, the milliequivalent weight of NH_3 is $NH_3/1,000$ and that of nitrogen is $N/1,000$.

$$\frac{13.88 \times N/1,000}{2.000} \times 100 = 9.72 \text{ per cent.} \quad Ans.$$

Problems

12.75. Calculate the percentage of carbon dioxide in a sample of calcium carbonate from the following data:

Total volume of 0.5000 N HCl = 35.00 ml.
Total volume of 0.1000 N NaOH = 17.50 ml.
Weight of sample = 1.000 gram

Ans. 34.65 per cent.

12.76. Given the following data, calculate the percentage purity of a sample of cream of tartar ($KHC_4H_4O_6$):

Weight of sample = 2.527 grams
NaOH solution used = 25.87 ml.
H_2SO_4 solution used = 1.27 ml.
1.000 ml. of H_2SO_4 ≈ 1.120 ml. of NaOH
1.000 ml. of H_2SO_4 ≈ 0.02940 gram $CaCO_3$

Ans. 95.50 per cent.

12.77. A sample of pearl ash (technical grade of K_2CO_3) weighing 2.000 grams is titrated with HCl, requiring 25.00 ml. What is the alkaline strength of the ash in terms of per cent of K_2O if 20.00 ml. of the HCl will just neutralize the NH_3 that can be liberated from four millimoles of $(NH_4)_2HPO_4$?

Ans. 23.55 per cent.

12.78. Calculate the percentage of K_2CO_3 in a sample of pearl ash from the following data:

Weight of sample = 2.020 grams
HCl used = 49.27 ml.
NaOH used = 2.17 ml.
1.000 ml. HCl ≈ 0.02926 gram $CaCO_3$
NaOH = 0.3172 N

Ans. 96.25 per cent.

12.79. Given four 10.00-ml. portions of 0.1000 normal hydrochloric acid solution. (*a*) How many grams of pure sodium carbonate will be neutralized by one portion? (*b*) How many grams of K_2O are contained in that weight of potassium hydroxide neutralized by another portion of the acid? (*c*) A sample of calcium carbonate is decomposed by a portion of the acid. Calculate the weight of $CaCO_3$ decomposed, the weight of CO_2 liberated, and the weight of $CaCl_2$ formed. (*d*) Calculate the weight of $KHC_2O_4.H_2C_2O_4.2H_2O$ equivalent in acid strength to a portion of the HCl.

Ans. (*a*) 0.05300 gram. (*b*) 0.04710 gram. (*c*) 0.05004 gram, 0.02200 gram, 0.05550 gram. (*d*) 0.08473 gram.

12.80. Strong KOH will liberate NH_3 from ammonium salts. The liberated ammonia can be distilled and determined by absorbing it in standard acid and titrating the excess acid with standard alkali. From the following data, calculate the percentage of NH_3 in a sample of impure ammonium salt:

Sample = 1.009 grams
Standard acid used = 50.00 ml. of 0.5127 N
Standard alkali required = 1.37 ml. of 0.5272 N

Ans. 42.06 per cent.

12.81. Rochelle salt is $KNaC_4H_4O_6.4H_2O$ and on ignition is converted to $KNaCO_3$. The original sample of 0.9546 gram is ignited and the product titrated with sulfuric acid.   From the data given, calculate the purity of the sample:

$$H_2SO_4 \text{ used} = 41.72 \text{ ml.}$$
$$10.27 \text{ ml. } H_2SO_4 \backsimeq 10.35 \text{ ml. NaOH}$$
$$NaOH = 0.1297 \text{ } N$$
$$NaOH \text{ used in titrating excess acid} = 1.91 \text{ ml.}$$

Ans.   **76.95** per cent.

12.82. A sample of zinc oxide is digested with 50.00 ml. of normal sulfuric acid. The excess acid is titrated with 2.96 ml. of 0.1372 normal alkali.   The weight of sample is 2.020 grams.   Calculate the percentage of purity of the sample.

Ans.   **99.89** per cent.

12.83. If all of the nitrogen in 10.00 millimoles of urea, $CO(NH_2)_2$, is converted by concentrated H_2SO_4 into ammonium bisulfate and if, with excess NaOH, the NH_3 is liberated and caught in 50.00 ml. of HCl (1.000 ml. $\backsimeq$ 0.03000 gram $CaCO_3$), how much NaOH solution (1.000 ml. $\backsimeq$ 0.03465 gram $H_2C_2O_4.2H_2O$) would be required to complete the titration?

Ans.   **18.18** ml.

12.84. The percentage of protein in meat products is determined by multiplying the percentage of nitrogen as determined by the Kjeldahl method by the arbitrary factor 6.25.   A sample of dried meat scrap weighing 2.000 grams is digested with concentrated H_2SO_4 and mercury (catalyst) until the nitrogen present has been converted to ammonium bisulfate.   This is treated with excess NaOH and the liberated NH_3 caught in a 50-ml. pipetful of H_2SO_4 (1.000 ml. $\backsimeq$ 0.01860 gram NaO_2).   The excess acid requires 28.80 ml. of NaOH (1.000 ml. $\backsimeq$ 0.1266 gram potassium acid phthalate, $KHC_8H_4O_4$).   Calculate the percentage of protein in the meat scrap.

Ans.   **53.11** per cent.

12.85. A sample of milk weighing 5.00 grams is digested with concentrated H_2SO_4 (plus a catalyst) which converts the protein nitrogen in the milk to ammonium bisulfate.   Excess NaOH is added and the liberated NH_3 is evolved and caught in 25.0 ml. of dilute H_2SO_4.   The excess acid then requires 28.2 ml. of NaOH of which 31.0 ml. are equivalent to 25.8 ml. of the dilute H_2SO_4.

The acid and base are standardized by evolving the NH_3 from 1.00 gram of pure NH_4Cl, passing it into 25.0 ml. of the above dilute H_2SO_4 and titrating the excess acid with the above NaOH.   A volume of 11.3 ml. of the NaOH is required.

The arbitrary factor for converting nitrogen in milk and milk products to protein is 6.38.   Calculate the percentage of protein in the above sample of milk.

Ans.   **3.30** per cent.

12.86. From the following data, calculate the percentage purity of a sample of $KHSO_4$:

$$1.000 \text{ ml. HCl} \backsimeq 1.206 \text{ ml. NaOH}$$
$$1.000 \text{ ml. HCl} \backsimeq 0.02198 \text{ gram } Na_2CO_3$$
$$\text{Sample} = 1.2118 \text{ grams}$$
$$\text{HCl used} = 1.53 \text{ ml.}$$
$$\text{NaOH used} = 26.28 \text{ ml.}$$

12.87. A sample of Rochelle salt ($KNaC_4H_4O_6.4H_2O$), after ignition in platinum to convert it to the double carbonate, is titrated with sulfuric acid, methyl orange being employed as an indicator. From the following data, calculate the percentage purity of the sample:

$$\text{Weight of sample} = 0.9500 \text{ gram}$$
$$H_2SO_4 \text{ used} = 43.65 \text{ ml.}$$
$$NaOH \text{ used} = 1.72 \text{ ml.}$$
$$1.000 \text{ ml. } H_2SO_4 \backsim 1.064 \text{ ml. } NaOH$$
$$NaOH = 0.1321 \, N$$

12.88. A sample of milk of magnesia [suspension of $Mg(OH)_2$] weighing 5.000 grams is titrated with standard HNO_3, requiring 40.10 ml. What is the percentage of MgO in the sample if 20.11 ml. of the HNO_3 will just neutralize the NH_3 that can be liberated from five millimoles of $(NH_4)_3AsO_4.5H_2O$?

12.89. The *saponification number* of a fat or oil is defined as the number of milligrams of potassium hydroxide required to saponify one gram of the fat or oil. To a sample of butter weighing 2.010 grams are added 25.00 ml. of 0.4900 N KOH solution. After saponification is complete, 8.13 ml. of 0.5000 N HCl solution are found to be required to neutralize the excess alkali. What is the saponification number of the butter?

12.90. Samples of oxalic acid mixed with inert matter are given out for student analysis to determine by acidimetric titration the acid strength in terms of percentage of $H_2C_2O_4.2H_2O$. However, a sample of pure potassium acid tartrate $KHC_4H_4O_6$, is included among the samples. What percentage of $H_2C_2O_4.2H_2O$ would the student report in this case?

12.91. A sample of vinegar weighing 10.52 grams is titrated with standard NaOH. The end point is overstepped, and the solution is titrated back with standard HCl. From the following data, calculate the acidity of the vinegar in terms of percentage of acetic acid $(HC_2H_3O_2)$:

$$NaOH \text{ used} = 19.03 \text{ ml.}$$
$$HCl \text{ used} = 1.50 \text{ ml.}$$
$$1.000 \text{ ml. HCl} \backsim 0.02500 \text{ gram } Na_2CO_3$$
$$1.000 \text{ ml. NaOH} \backsim 0.06050 \text{ gram benzoic acid } (C_6H_5COOH)$$

12.92. The arbitrary factor 6.25 is used by agricultural chemists to convert percentages of nitrogen in meat products to percentages of protein. A sample of dried pork scrap is sold under a guarantee of a minimum of 70.00 per cent protein. A one-gram sample is digested with sulfuric acid and a catalyst, which converts all the nitrogen to ammonium bisulfate. Treated with excess NaOH, the ammonia is liberated and caught in a 25-ml. pipetful of H_2SO_4 (1.000 ml. $\backsim$ 0.02650 gram Na_2CO_3). What is the maximum volume of 0.5110 N NaOH required to titrate the excess acid if the sample conforms to the guarantee?

86. Problems in Which the Volume of Titrating Solution Bears a Given Relation to the Percentage.

In commercial laboratories where many similar titrations are made each day, it is often convenient to simplify computation by taking each time for analysis a weight of sample such that the volume of standard solution used will bear some simple relation to the percentage of desired constituent. The advantages derived from such a procedure are the same as those discussed in Sec. 59, and the computations involved are similar in principle. In the volumetric problem, it is also possible to fix the weight of sample and determine the normality of the titrating solution which must be used to fulfill a similar condition, although this type of problem is less often met with in practice. It is easier in practical work to vary a sample weight than it is to vary a solution concentration. In either case, however, the required weight of sample or normality of solution is best found by directly applying the formula previously derived, *viz.*,

$$\frac{ml._s \times N_s \times mew_x}{Weight\ of\ sample} \times 100 = per\ cent_x$$

In this type of problem, it will always be found that, of the five factors involved, two will be known and a ratio will be given between two others, thus making possible the determination of the fifth factor.

EXAMPLE.   What weight of soda ash should be taken for analysis such that the percentage of Na_2O present may be found by multiplying by 2 the number of milliliters of 0.2000 *N* acid solution used in the titration?

SOLUTION:

$$\frac{ml._s \times N_s \times mew_x}{Weight\ of\ sample} \times 100 = per\ cent_x$$

In the problem given, N_s and mew_x are known.   A relation also exists between the *ml.* and the *per cent* whereby

$$ml. \times 2 = per\ cent$$

Upon substitution,

$$\frac{ml._s \times 0.2000 \times Na_2O/2,000}{Weight\ of\ sample} \times 100 = ml._s \times 2$$

$$\frac{0.2000 \times 62.00/2,000}{Weight\ of\ sample} \times 100 = 2$$

$$Weight\ of\ sample = 0.3100\ gram. \quad Ans.$$

The same precautions should be taken in solving this type of problem as were emphasized in the examples in Sec. 59, namely, that a numerical difference exists between a statement such as "the number of milliliters is three times the per cent," and the statement "the per cent is found by multiplying the number of milliliters by 3."   Thus, in the above example, the weight of soda ash to be taken so that *each milliliter of* 0.2000 *N acid shall equal* ½ *of* 1 *per cent* of Na_2O is found as follows:

$$\frac{1 \times 0.2000 \times 0.03100}{Weight\ of\ sample} \times 100 = \frac{1}{2}$$

$$Weight\ of\ sample = 1.240\ grams. \quad Ans.$$

Problems

12.93. A sample of oxalic acid is to be analyzed by titrating with a solution of NaOH that is 0.1000 N. What weight of sample should be taken so that each milliliter of NaOH will represent $\frac{1}{2}$ of 1 per cent of $H_2C_2O_4.2H_2O$?

Ans. 1.261 grams.

12.94. In the analysis of oxalic acid using a one-gram sample, what must be the normality of the alkali used for titration so that the buret reading will equal one-half the percentage of $H_2C_2O_4.2H_2O$?

Ans. 0.3173 N.

12.95. In the analysis of a sample of soda ash, what weight of sample should be taken so that the volume in milliliters of 0.4205 normal acid required for complete neutralization and the percentage of Na_2CO_3 in the sample will be in the respective ratio of 8:17?

Ans. 1.049 grams.

12.96. A sample of a certain acid weighed 0.8250 gram and was titrated with 0.2000 N alkali. After the purity of the sample was calculated in terms of the percentage of constituent A, it was found that the percentage obtained was just equal to the equivalent weight of A as an acid. What volume of titrating solution was used?

Ans. 41.25 ml.

12.97. A sample of limestone is titrated for its value as a neutralizing agent. A one-gram sample is always taken. What must be the normality of the titrating acid so that every 10 ml. will represent $4\frac{1}{2}$ per cent of the neutralizing value expressed in terms of percentage CaO?

Ans. 0.1605 N.

12.98. Samples of pickling solution are to be analyzed volumetrically for acidity, and results are to be expressed in terms of milliliters H_2SO_4 (sp. gr. 1.84, containing 95.60 per cent H_2SO_4 by weight). The specific gravity of the pickling solution is 1.270, and a 25-ml. pipetful is taken for analysis. (*a*) What must be the normality of the standard alkali so that each milliliter used will represent 0.100 ml. of the H_2SO_4? (*b*) So that every 10.0 ml. will represent 1.00 per cent of pure H_2SO_4?

Ans. (*a*) 3.59 N. (*b*) 0.647 N.

12.99. What weight of soda ash must be taken for analysis so that by using 0.5000 N HCl for titrating (*a*) the buret reading will equal the percentage of Na_2O, (*b*) three times the buret reading will equal the percentage of Na_2O, (*c*) every 3 ml. will represent 1 per cent Na_2O, (*d*) each milliliter will represent 3 per cent Na_2O, (*e*) the buret reading and the percentage of Na_2O will be in the respective ratio of 2:3?

Ans. (*a*) 1.550 grams, (*b*) 0.5167 gram, (*c*) 4.650 grams, (*d*) 0.5167 gram, (*e*) 1.033 grams.

12.100. What weight of calcite (impure $CaCO_3$) should be taken for analysis so that the buret reading will be $2\frac{1}{2}$ times the percentage of Ca in the sample? The solution used for the titration is HNO_3 of which 2.00 ml. $\approx$ 1.00 ml. $Ba(OH)_2$ solution $\approx$ 0.0400 gram potassium acid phthalate ($KHC_8H_4O_4$).

12.101. What weight of soda ash (technical Na_2CO_3) should be taken for analysis so that when titrated with HCl [1.00 ml. $\approx$ 2.00 ml. $Ba(OH)_2$ solution $\approx$ 0.0254 gram

$KHC_2O_4.H_2C_2O_4.2H_2O$] the buret reading will be three-quarters of the percentage of Na_2O in the ash?

12.102. In the standardization of an acid, it was titrated against 1.000 gram of calcium carbonate (98.56 per cent pure). If 46.86 ml. of HCl were added, the $CaCO_3$ dissolved, and the excess acid titrated with 5.21 ml. of NaOH solution of which 1.000 ml. $\backsim$ 0.7896 ml. HCl, calculate the weight of crude pearl ash to be taken for analysis so that each milliliter of this HCl will represent 2.00 per cent K_2O.

12.103. If 1.500 grams of crude K_2CO_3 are taken for analysis, what must be the strength of the HCl used in order that the buret reading will indicate twice the percentage of K_2O in the sample?

12.104. A 2.000-gram sample of nitrogenous organic matter is digested with concentrated H_2SO_4 and a catalyst until the nitrogen in the sample has been converted to NH_4HSO_4. By adding excess NaOH, NH_3 is liberated and is completely caught in a cold 5 per cent solution of boric acid. It is then titrated directly with standard HCl. What must be the value of each milliliter of the acid in terms of pure Na_2CO_3 if the buret reading is $2\frac{1}{2}$ times the percentage of nitrogen in the material?

12.105. A sample of quicklime is to be analyzed for CaO and $CaCO_3$ by titrating with 0.3572 N HCl. It is desired to start with a 10.0-gram sample, mix with water, dilute, and take aliquot portions of such size (*a*) that when titrated with HCl [phenolphthalein being used as an indicator, in which case only the $Ca(OH)_2$ is neutralized] the number of milliliters will represent directly the percentage of CaO and (*b*) that, when titrated by adding an excess of HCl, heating, and titrating back with NaOH of the same normality as the HCl, the net number of milliliters of HCl used will represent directly the percentage of total calcium in terms of CaO. What portions should be taken?

87. Determination of the Proportion in Which Components Are Present in a Pure Mixture.
Problems involving the determination from titration values of the proportion in which components are present in a pure mixture are identical in principle with the so-called double chloride problems of gravimetric analysis (see Sec. 62, Example II), and the same algebraic method of solution may conveniently be used. The same type of analysis may be applied equally well to methods of oxidation and reduction.

As shown in Sec. 62, the precision of the result of an analysis of this type is usually less than that of the data given, and there is often a decrease in the number of significant figures that may properly be retained in the numerical answer.

• EXAMPLE. If 0.5000 gram of a mixture of calcium carbonate and barium carbonate requires 30.00 ml. of 0.2500 N hydrochloric acid solution for neutralization, what is the percentage of each component?

SOLUTION:

$$\text{Let } x = \text{ number of grams of } CaCO_3$$
$$y = \text{ number of grams of } BaCO_3$$

Then

$$(1)\ x + y = 0.5000$$

Number of gram-milliequivalents of $CaCO_3$ present

$$= \frac{x}{CaCO_3/2,000} = \frac{x}{0.05004}$$

Number of gram-milliequivalents of $BaCO_3$ present

$$= \frac{y}{BaCO_3/2,000} = \frac{y}{0.09869}$$

Number of gram-milliequivalents of HCl used $= 30.00 \times 0.2500$
Therefore

$$(2) \quad \frac{x}{0.05004} + \frac{y}{0.09869} = 30.00 \times 0.2500$$

Solving equations (1) and (2) simultaneously,

$$x = 0.247$$
$$y = 0.253$$

$$\text{Percentage of } CaCO_3 = \frac{0.247}{0.5000} \times 100 = 49.4 \text{ per cent}$$
$$\text{Percentage of } BaCO_3 = \frac{0.253}{0.5000} \times 100 = 50.6 \text{ per cent}$$

Ans.

88. Analysis of Fuming Sulfuric Acid. *Case A.* An important titration is that involved in the analysis of fuming sulfuric acid (oleum). This substance may be considered to be a solution of sulfur trioxide, SO_3, in hydrogen sulfate, H_2SO_4, and when no other component is present, the analysis is made by dissolving a weighed sample in water and titrating with standard alkali.

EXAMPLE I. A sample of fuming sulfuric acid weighing 1.000 gram when dissolved in water requires 21.41 ml. of 1.000 *N* NaOH solution for neutralization. What is the percentage of each component?

SOLUTION:

Method I. Since fuming sulfuric acid is a mixture of two pure components, the problem can be solved by the method of the preceding section.

$$\text{Let } x = \text{weight of free } SO_3$$
$$y = \text{weight of } H_2SO_4$$
$$x + y = 1.000$$

$$\frac{x}{SO_3/2,000} + \frac{y}{H_2SO_4/2,000} = 21.41 \times 1.000$$

When the simultaneous equations are solved,

$$x = 0.222 \text{ gram } SO_3 \quad = 22.2 \text{ per cent}$$
$$y = 0.778 \text{ gram } H_2SO_4 = 77.8 \text{ per cent}$$

Ans.

Method II. In dissolving the oleum, the SO_3 unites with part of the water to form H_2SO_4. If the total percentage of acid is computed in terms of H_2SO_4, the following result is obtained:

$$\frac{21.41 \times 1.000 \times H_2SO_4/2,000}{1.000} \times 100 = 105.0 \text{ per cent}$$

Since, in the original mixture, $SO_3 + H_2SO_4 = 100.00$ per cent, the difference of 5.0 per cent is caused by the water which has combined with the SO_3. The SO_3 and H_2O combine mole for mole.

$$5.0 \times \frac{SO_3}{H_2O} = \text{percentage of } SO_3$$

$$\left. \begin{array}{l} = 22.2 \text{ per cent } SO_3 \\ 100.0 - 22.2 = 77.8 \text{ per cent } H_2SO_4 \end{array} \right\} \ Ans.$$

Case B. Fuming sulfuric acid often contains small amounts of SO_2 which with water forms H_2SO_3 and is included in the alkali titration:

$$H_2SO_3 + 2OH^- \rightarrow SO_3^{=} + 2H_2O$$

This is when phenolphthalein is used as the indicator. With methyl orange, the color change takes place at the bisulfite stage:

$$H_2SO_3 + OH^- \rightarrow HSO_3^- + H_2O$$

In case SO_2 is present, its amount is usually determined in a separate sample by titration with a standard oxidizing agent, and the other components are then computed from the alkali titration values in the usual way, with a correction for the volume of alkali used by the SO_2.

EXAMPLE II. A sample of fuming sulfuric acid containing H_2SO_4, SO_3, and SO_2 weighs 1.000 gram and is found to require 23.47 ml. of 1.000 N alkali for neutralization (phenolphthalein as indicator). A separate sample shows the presence of 1.50 per cent SO_2. Find the percentages of SO_3 and H_2SO_4.

SOLUTION:

$$\text{Volume of alkali used by } SO_2 = \frac{0.0150}{1.000 \times SO_2/2,000} = 0.47 \text{ ml.}$$

Volume of alkali used for $H_2SO_4 + SO_3 = 23.47 - 0.47 = 23.00$ ml.
Percentage of $H_2SO_4 + SO_3 = 100.00 - 1.50 = 98.50$ per cent

$$\text{Let } x = \text{weight of } SO_3$$
$$y = \text{weight of } H_2SO_4$$
$$x + y = 0.9850$$

$$\frac{x}{SO_3/2,000} + \frac{y}{H_2SO_4/2,000} = 23.00 \times 1,000$$

Solving,

$$x = 0.635 \text{ gram } SO_3 \quad = 63.5 \text{ per cent}$$
$$y = 0.350 \text{ gram } H_2SO_4 = 35.0 \text{ per cent}$$

$Ans.$

Problems

12.106. A mixture consisting entirely of lithium carbonate and barium carbonate weighs 1.000 gram and requires 15.00 ml. of 1.000 N HCl for neutralization. Calculate the percentage of $BaCO_3$ in the sample.

Ans. 7.12 per cent.

12.107. A mixture of pure lithium carbonate and pure strontium carbonate weighs 0.5280 gram and requires 19.82 ml. of 0.5060 N acid for neutralization. What is the composition of the sample expressed in terms of the percentages of Li_2O and SrO?

Ans. $Li_2O = 16.3$ per cent, SrO $= 41.8$ per cent.

12.108. What weight of barium carbonate must be added to 1.000 gram of lithium carbonate so that the mixture will require the same volume of standard acid for neutralization as would the same weight of pure calcium carbonate?

Ans. 0.716 gram.

12.109. A half-gram sample of a mixture of pure $CaCO_3$ and pure $SrCO_3$ requires 30.00 ml. of 0.2726 N sulfuric acid for neutralization. (*a*) What would be the loss in weight of the original sample on strong ignition? (*b*) Calculate the combined weight of $CaSO_4$ and $SrSO_4$ obtained above. (*c*) What is the weight of $CaCO_3$ in the original sample?

Ans. (*a*) 0.180 gram. (*b*) 0.647 gram. (*c*) 0.218 gram.

12.110. The combined weight of LiOH, KOH, and $Ba(OH)_2$ in a mixture is 0.5000 gram, and 25.44 ml. of 0.5000 N acid are required for neutralization. The same amount of material with CO_2 gives a precipitate of $BaCO_3$ that when filtered is found to require 5.27 ml. of the above acid for neutralization. Calculate the weights of LiOH, KOH, and $Ba(OH)_2$ in the original sample.

Ans. LiOH $= 0.217$ gram, KOH $= 0.0567$ gram, $Ba(OH)_2 = 0.226$ gram.

12.111. A sample of fuming sulfuric acid, containing no SO_2 or other impurity, on titration is found to contain 108.5 per cent acid expressed in terms of H_2SO_4. Calculate the percentage of free SO_3 in the sample.

Ans. 37.8 per cent.

12.112. A sample of fuming sulfuric acid containing only SO_3 and H_2SO_4 is titrated, and the percentage of total SO_3 (free and combined) is found to be 84.00 per cent. What is the percentage of H_2SO_4 in the original sample?

Ans. 87.1 per cent.

12.113. A sample of fuming sulfuric acid containing only SO_3 and H_2SO_4 weighs 1.4000 grams and requires 36.10 ml. of 0.8050 N NaOH for neutralization. What is the percentage of each component in the sample?

Ans. 91.98 per cent H_2SO_4, 8.02 per cent SO_3.

12.114. A solution of SO_3 in H_2SO_4 requires 65.10 ml. of 0.9000 N alkali for the titration of a sample weighing 2.604 grams. What is the proportion by weight of free SO_3 to H_2SO_4 in the sample?

Ans. 0.850.

12.115. A sample of fuming sulfuric acid consisting of a solution of SO_3 and SO_2 in H_2SO_4 is found to contain 2.06 per cent SO_2. A sample weighing 1.500 grams requires 21.64 ml. of 1.500 N KOH when phenolphthalein is used as the indicator. What are the percentages of free SO_3 and H_2SO_4 in the sample?

Ans.   22.4 per cent free SO_3, 75.6 per cent H_2SO_4.

12.116. A mixture of pure sodium carbonate and pure barium carbonate weighing 0.2000 gram requires 30.00 ml. of 0.1000 N acid for complete neutralization. What is the percentage of each component in the mixture?

12.117. A sample supposed to be pure calcium carbonate is used to standardize a solution of HCl. The substance really was a mixture of $MgCO_3$ and $BaCO_3$, but the standardization was correct in spite of the erroneous assumption. Find the percentage of MgO in the original powder.

12.118. A mixture of $BaCO_3$ and $CaCO_3$ weighs 0.5000 gram. The mixture is titrated with HCl, requiring 12.90 ml. From the following data, calculate the percentage of barium in the mixture:

$$30.40 \text{ ml. HCl} \approx 45.60 \text{ ml. NaOH}$$
$$2.000 \text{ ml. of NaOH will neutralize } 0.07460 \text{ gram of NaHC}_2O_4$$

12.119. Glacial acetic acid often consists of a mixture of two acids, namely, pure acetic acid, $HC_2H_3O_2$ or CH_3COOH, and a small amount of acetic anhydride, $(CH_3CO)_2O$. When dissolved in water, the anhydride forms acetic acid: $(CH_3CO)_2O + H_2O \rightarrow 2CH_3COOH$. A sample of the original substance weighing A grams is dissolved in water and requires B ml. of C normal NaOH for neutralization. Set up an expression showing how the percentage of acetic anhydride in the sample can be determined from this single titration. Express clearly the correct milliequivalents involved.

12.120. A sample of P_2O_5 is known to contain H_3PO_4 as its only impurity. A sample is weighed in a closed container, the container is opened under water ($P_2O_5 + 3H_2O \rightarrow 2H_3PO_4$) and the solution is titrated with standard NaOH to form Na_2HPO_4 at the end point. If A ml. of B normal NaOH were used, set up an expression to show how the number of grams of P_2O_5 in the original mixture could be determined. Express all milliequivalent weights.

12.121. The titration of a sample of fuming sulfuric acid containing no SO_2 shows the presence of an equivalent of 109.22 per cent H_2SO_4. Calculate the percentage composition of the sample and the percentage of combined SO_3.

12.122. A sample of oleum weighing 1.762 grams requires 42.80 ml. of 0.8905 N NaOH for neutralization. Calculate the proportion by weight of free SO_3 to combined SO_3 in the sample.

12.123. A mixture of SO_3 and H_2SO_4 contains 91.18 per cent of total SO_3. Calculate the volume of half-normal alkali required to titrate a solution of 1.030 grams of the mixture. What is the percentage of free SO_3 in the mixture? What is the equivalent of the mixture in terms of aqueous sulfuric acid containing 93.19 per cent H_2SO_4?

12.124. A mixture of pure acetic acid and acetic anhydride is dissolved in water and titrated with NaOH. The acidity of the sample expressed in terms of $HC_2H_3O_2$ is found to be 114.0 per cent. What is the composition of the original mixture? Acetic anhydride reacts with water to form acetic acid: $(CH_3CO)_2O + H_2O \rightarrow 2HC_2H_3O_2$.

89. Indicators. An indicator is used in volumetric analysis for the purpose of detecting the point at which a reaction is just completed.

The indicators used in acidimetry and alkalimetry are usually organic dyestuffs which are of one color in acid solution and of a distinctly different color in alkaline solution. They are usually in themselves either weak acids (*e.g.*, phenolphthalein) or weak bases (*e.g.*, methyl orange), and the change in color that they undergo can be attributed to the fact that the arrangement of the atoms in their molecules is somewhat different from the arrangement of the atoms in the molecules of their corresponding salts.

Consider a weak organic acid indicator of the general formula HX. This acid ionizes as follows: $HX \rightleftarrows H^+ + X^-$. The undissociated molecule HX is, for example, colorless; the ion X^- is colored, usually because of a rearrangement of atoms to form a quinoid structure. In water solution the ionization of the acid is so slight that the color of the ion is too faint to be seen. The addition of an alkaline substance to the solution, however, by reacting with the hydrogen ion, displaces the above equilibrium to the right and increases the concentration of the X^- ion to the point where its color becomes visible. The ionization constant of the above indicator is as follows: $\dfrac{[H^+][X^-]}{[HX]} = K$, and is called an *indicator constant*. If it is assumed that with this type of indicator a titration is stopped when one half of the un-ionized molecules have been converted by a base to the colored ionic form, then $[HX] = [X^-]$ and the indicator constant is equal to the hydrogen-ion concentration of the solution at the end point.

Similarly, a weak basic indicator of the general formula XOH ionizes as follows: $XOH \rightleftarrows X^+ + OH^-$, and the ionization constant (= indicator constant) is $\dfrac{[X^+][OH^-]}{[XOH]} = K$. In water solution the color of the XOH molecule predominates, but the addition of acid increases the concentration of the X^+ form and the color changes. If it is assumed that the color change is seen when three-fourths of XOH has been converted to X^+, then the hydroxyl-ion concentration at the end point is equal to $\frac{1}{3}K$.

With a given concentration of indicator, the color change takes place at a point where the hydrogen-ion or the hydroxyl-ion concentration in the solution has attained a definite value that is characteristic of the indicator in question. Thus, a solution containing about 0.001 per cent of phenolphthalein turns from colorless to pink when the hydroxyl-ion concentration has attained the value of about 1×10^{-5} mole per liter, and the corresponding hydrogen-ion concentration has therefore been reduced to about 1×10^{-9} mole per liter (pH = 9). Figure 3 shows the approximate hydrogen-ion and hydroxyl-ion concentrations at which dilute solutions of the common indicators change color. It will be noted that on this chart each color change is spread over a certain range of pH values. Each indicator may be said to have a *pH differential* over which the

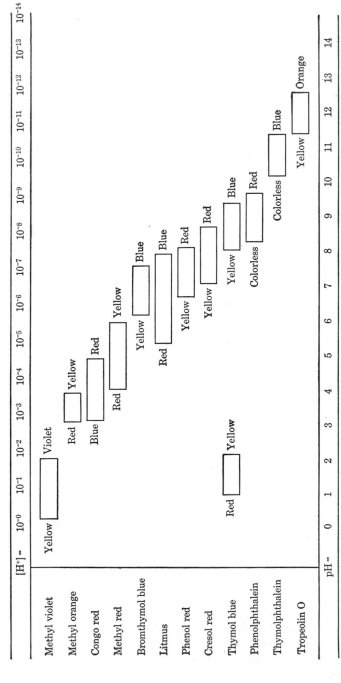

FIG. 3. Hydrogen-ion concentrations and pH values required to produce the indicated change of color in dilute solutions (0.001 per cent) of some of the more common indicators.

transition in shade of color is gradual; the average analyst might stop a titration anywhere within the range in question.

90. Equivalence Point. The *equivalence point* in any titration is the point where the amount of titrating solution added is chemically equivalent to the amount of substance being titrated; the analyst attempts to make the *end point* (*i.e.*, the point where the indicator changes color) coincide with this. In an acidimetric or alkalimetric titration the equivalence point is not necessarily the same as the *neutral point* (pH = 7). For example, in the titration of acetic acid with sodium hydroxide, when the latter has been added in an amount equivalent to the former, the acidity of the solution is the same as that resulting from dissolving the corresponding amount of sodium acetate in water. Such a solution is basic owing to hydrolysis of the salt. Similarly, in the titration of a weak base with a strong acid, the equivalence point is at a point where the solution is slightly acidic (pH < 7).

Other conditions being equal, the correct indicator for a given titration is one of which the color change takes place when the solution has that pH value which exists in a solution obtained by dissolving in the same volume of water the salt formed by the neutralization. In other words, an indicator should be chosen that will change color at a pH value approximately equal to the pH value at the equivalence point. Just how that pH value can be determined is shown in the following section.

91. Change in Hydrogen-ion Concentration during Titrations. During an acidimetric or alkalimetric titration the pH value of the solution changes progressively, and when pH values are plotted (usually as ordinates) against corresponding buret readings (usually as abscissas) a *titration curve* is obtained which is a very valuable aid in determining the proper indicator to use, in establishing the equivalence point in a potentiometric titration (see Chap. 16), and in obtaining information as to the precision of the titration.

Four general types of acidimetric titrations are considered below, and the method of establishing the titration curve in each case is illustrated by calculating the pH values at different points in the titration. The following symbols will be used:

$$pH = \log \frac{1}{[H^+]} = -\log [H^+]$$

$$pOH = \log \frac{1}{[OH^-]} = -\log [OH^-]$$

Kw = ion-product constant of water = $[H^+][OH^-] = 1.0 \times 10^{-14}$ (at 25°C.)

$$pW = \log \frac{1}{Kw} = -\log Kw = 14.0 \text{ (at 25°C.)}$$

Ka = ionization constant of the weak acid being titrated = $[H^+][X^-]/[HX]$

$$pA = \log \frac{1}{Ka} = -\log Ka$$

Kb = ionization constant of the weak base being titrated = $[X^+][OH^-]/[XOH]$

$$pB = \log \frac{1}{Kb} = -\log Kb$$

C = molar concentration at the equivalence point, of the salt formed by the neutralization process

Case A.   Strong Acid Titrated with Strong Base
Strong Base Titrated with Strong Acid

EXAMPLE I.   Twenty milliliters of 0.50 N HCl are diluted with water to 100 ml., and the resulting solution is titrated with 0.50 N NaOH. Calculate the pH value (a) at the start; (b) when 8.0 ml. of the NaOH have been added; (c) at the equivalence point (*i.e.*, when 20 ml. of the NaOH have been added); (d) when 30 ml. of the NaOH have been added. Show the general form of the titration curve and show the form of the curve in the reverse titration of 20 ml. of 0.50 N NaOH with 0.50 N HCl.

SOLUTION: (a) At the beginning of the titration $[H^+] = 20 \times 0.50 = 10$ milliequivalents per 100 ml. = 0.10 normal = 0.10 molar.   Therefore pH = 1.0.

(b) When 8.0 ml. of 0.50 N NaOH have been added, the unneutralized HCl is at a concentration of $12 \times 0.50 = 6.0$ milliequivalents per 108 ml. $[H^+]$ is therefore $6/108 = 5.56 \times 10^{-2}$ N, and pH = $-\log (5.56 \times 10^{-2})$ = 1.26.

(c) At the equivalence point (20 ml. NaOH added), the solution contains only sodium chloride dissolved in water, and since there is no appreciable hydrolysis, pH = 7.0.

(d) When 30 ml. of 0.50 N NaOH have been added, the volume of the solution is 130 ml. and $10 \times 0.50 = 5.0$ milliequivalents of NaOH are in excess.   The $[OH^-]$ concentration is therefore $5/130 = 3.84 \times 10^{-2}$ normal, pOH = 1.42, and pH = 12.58.

The graph for this titration in which the above buret readings (and others similarly obtained) are plotted against corresponding pH values is shown in Fig. 4, curve (A)(A).   The curve, as it crosses the 20-ml. line, is nearly but not quite vertical and crosses the 20-ml. line at pH 7.   At the right of the figure are shown the approximate pH values at which four of the common indicators (phenolphthalein, bromthymol blue, methyl red, and methyl orange) change color.   The figure shows that in titrations of this type, not only is the equivalence point at pH = 7.0, but near the equivalence point the change in pH is so rapid that any indicator changing color between about pH = 3 and pH = 11 should be suitable. In other words, in titrations of strong acids with strong bases, although an indicator changing at pH = 7 is indicated (*e.g.*, bromthymol blue), yet the error involved in the use of such indicators as phenolphthalein or methyl orange is negligible, being usually within the error of reading a buret.

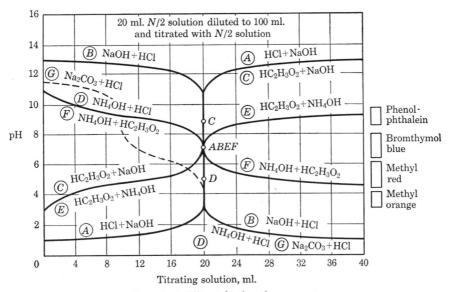

Fig. 4. Acidimetric titration curves.

The curve for the titration of 20 ml. of 0.50 N NaOH (diluted to 100 ml.) with 0.50 N HCl is shown in curve (*B*)(*B*) of Fig. 4. Here each pH value is 14 minus the corresponding value in the titration of the HCl. There is a very slight left-to-right slope in the curve as it crosses the 20-ml. line, but the proper indicator is established as in the preceding case.

Case B. Weak Acid Titrated with Strong Base

EXAMPLE II. Twenty milliliters of 0.50 N HC₂H₃O₂ are diluted with water to 100 ml., and the resulting solution is titrated with 0.50 N NaOH. Calculate the pH value (*a*) at the start; (*b*) when 8.0 ml. of the NaOH have been added; (*c*) at the equivalence point (when 20 ml. of NaOH have been added); (*d*) when 30 ml. of the NaOH have been added. Show the general form of the titration curve.

(*a*) At the beginning of the titration the pH value can be calculated from the ionization constant of acetic acid, $K_a = 1.86 \times 10^{-5}$, thus:

$$HC_2H_3O_2 \rightleftarrows H^+ + C_2H_3O_2^-$$

$$\frac{[H^+][C_2H_3O_2^-]}{[HC_2H_3O_2]} = Ka = 1.86 \times 10^{-5}$$

$$\frac{x \times x}{(0.10 - x)} = 1.86 \times 10^{-5}$$

$$x = 1.36 \times 10^{-3} = [H^+]$$

$$pH = \log \frac{1}{1.36 \times 10^{-3}} = 2.87$$

(b) When 8.0 ml. of 0.50 N NaOH have been added, an excess of 12.0 ml. of 0.50 N (= 6.0 milliequivalents) of acetic acid are still present, but the acid is considerably buffered by the sodium acetate formed during the titration. The acetate-ion concentration (mostly from the salt formed) at this point is 8.0 $\times$ 0.50 = 4.0 milliequivalents. The total volume is 108 ml.

Since

$$\frac{[H^+][C_2H_3O_2^-]}{[HC_2H_3O_2]} = Ka = 1.86 \times 10^{-5}$$

$$[H^+] = Ka \frac{[HC_2H_3O_2]}{[C_2H_3O_2^-]} = 1.86 \times 10^{-5} \times \frac{6.0/108}{4.0/108}$$

$$= 2.79 \times 10^{-5}$$

$$pH = -\log [H^+] = 4.55$$

(c) At the equivalence point (20 ml. NaOH added), the pH value of the solution can be calculated from either of the following formulas (which are general for titrations of this type):

$$\textbf{pH} = -\tfrac{1}{2} \log \textbf{Kw} - \tfrac{1}{2} \log \textbf{Ka} + \tfrac{1}{2} \log \textbf{C}$$

or

$$\textbf{pH} = \tfrac{1}{2} \, \textbf{pW} + \tfrac{1}{2}\textbf{pA} + \tfrac{1}{2} \log \textbf{C}$$

This may be derived by considering the numerical equilibrium relationships at the equivalence point in the titration just cited. The salt, sodium acetate, formed at the equivalence point at concentration C, hydrolyzes as follows:

$$NaC_2H_3O_2 + H_2O \rightleftarrows HC_2H_3O_2 + NaOH$$

or

$$C_2H_3O_2^- + H_2O \rightleftarrows HC_2H_3O_2 + OH^-$$

The mass-action expression for this hydrolysis is

$$(1) \quad \frac{[HC_2H_3O_2][OH^-]}{[C_2H_3O_2^-]} = K$$

but

$$(2) \quad [H^+][OH^-] = Kw$$

and

$$(3) \quad \frac{[H^+][C_2H_3O_2^-]}{[HC_2H_3O_2]} = Ka$$

Dividing (2) by (3) gives (1). Hence,

$$\frac{[HC_2H_3O_2][OH^-]}{[C_2H_3O_2^-]} = \frac{Kw}{Ka}$$

but, as seen from the above hydrolysis equilibrium,

$$[HC_2H_3O_2] = [OH^-]$$

and, if the extent of hydrolysis is not too great,

$$[C_2H_3O_2^-] = C \text{ (approx.)}$$

Therefore,

$$[OH^-]^2 = C \frac{Kw}{Ka}$$

$$[OH^-] = \sqrt{C \frac{Kw}{Ka}}$$

$$[H^+] = \frac{Kw}{[OH^-]}$$

$$= \frac{Kw}{\sqrt{C \frac{Kw}{Ka}}}$$

$$pH = -[\log Kw - (\tfrac{1}{2} \log C + \tfrac{1}{2} \log Kw - \tfrac{1}{2} \log Ka)]$$
$$= -\tfrac{1}{2} \log Kw - \tfrac{1}{2} \log Ka + \tfrac{1}{2} \log C$$
$$= \tfrac{1}{2} pW + \tfrac{1}{2} pA + \tfrac{1}{2} \log C$$

In the case at hand, we have $Kw = 1.0 \times 10^{-14}$, $Ka = 1.86 \times 10^{-5}$, and

$$C = \frac{0.010 \text{ mole } NaC_2H_3O_2}{120 \text{ ml. solution}} = 0.0833 \text{ molar}$$

$$pH = \frac{14.0}{2} + \frac{4.73}{2} + \frac{(-1.08)}{2} = 8.83$$

(*d*) Beyond the equivalence point excess NaOH is present and the pH values are the same as in the preceding titration of HCl with NaOH. The right-hand arms of the curves therefore coincide.

The titration curve in this case is represented by curve (*C*)(*C*) in Fig. 4. Point *C* shows the pH value (8.83) at the equivalence point. The common indicator that changes color at this point is phenolphthalein and is the indicator suitable for the titration. As can be seen from the titration graph, the use of an indicator like methyl orange would give erroneous results.

If half-normal bases are used, the titration of acids with ionization constants less than about 10^{-7} is not feasible; if tenth-normal bases are used, the titration of acids with ionization constants less than about 10^{-6} is not feasible.   In either case, the inflection at the equivalence point is not sharp and the change of color of even the most nearly appropriate indicator is gradual and extends over a considerable volume of titrating solution.

The titration of a weak polybasic acid (H_3PO_4) is illustrated in Prob. 12.154.

Case C.   Weak Base Titrated with Strong Acid

EXAMPLE III.   Twenty milliliters of 0.50 N NH_4OH are diluted to 100 ml. with water and titrated with 0.50 N HCl.   Calculate the pH value (a) at the start; (b) at the equivalence point.   Show the general form of the titration curve.

(a) The calculation of the hydroxyl-ion concentration at the start is exactly similar to the calculation of the hydrogen-ion concentration in the acetic acid solution of Case B [see Example II(a) above], except that the ionization constant of NH_4OH ($Kb = 1.75 \times 10^{-5}$) is used.   The corresponding pH value is 11.1.

(b) At the equivalence point, the pH value can be calculated from either of the following formulas (which are general for titrations of this type):

$$pH = -\tfrac{1}{2} \log Kw + \tfrac{1}{2} \log Kb - \tfrac{1}{2} \log C$$

or

$$pH = \tfrac{1}{2}pW - \tfrac{1}{2}pB - \tfrac{1}{2} \log C$$

These equations are derived from the hydrolysis constant of ammonium chloride by a method analogous to that in Case B.

In the case at hand, we have $Kw = 1.0 \times 10^{-14}$, $Kb = 1.75 \times 10^{-5}$, and $C = 0.0833$.

$$pH = \frac{14.0}{2} - \frac{4.76}{2} - \frac{(-1.08)}{2}$$
$$= 5.16$$

This is point D on the titration curve (D) (D).

The common indicator that changes color at approximately this point is methyl red.   As seen from the chart an indicator like phenolphthalein would give erroneous results.   The change of color would be gradual, and the end point would occur considerably before the true equivalence point.

Case D.   Weak Acid Titrated with Weak Base
Weak Base Titrated with Weak Acid

The titration curves for the neutralization of a weak acid like acetic acid with a weak base like ammonium hydroxide and for the reverse titration are represented by curves (E) (E) and (F) (F) in Fig. 4. The pH value at the equivalence point can be found from either of the following formulas (which are general for titrations of this type):

$$\textbf{pH} = -\tfrac{1}{2} \textbf{ log Kw} - \tfrac{1}{2} \textbf{ log Ka} + \tfrac{1}{2} \textbf{ log Kb}$$

or

$$\textbf{pH} = \tfrac{1}{2}\textbf{pW} + \tfrac{1}{2}\textbf{pA} - \tfrac{1}{2}\textbf{pB}$$

Such titrations are of no value in general analytical work, for as seen from the figure, there is no sudden inflection of the curve at the equivalence point, and no indicator has a sharp enough change in color to indicate the equivalence point with satisfactory precision.

92. Calculation of the Degree of Hydrolysis of a Salt. Not only are the above formulas useful for calculating the pH value at the equivalence point in a given titration, but they can be used to calculate the approximate extent of hydrolysis of a salt of a weak acid or of a weak base. For example, in the hydrolysis of sodium acetate $(C_2H_3O_2^- + H_2O \rightarrow HC_2H_3O_2 + OH^-)$, the value of the concentration of OH^- can be found from the pH value calculated from the appropriate formula above; the value of the concentration of acetate is that of the concentration of the salt (C) in the formula. The ratio of $[OH^-]$ to $[C_2H_3O_2^-]$ indicates the degree of hydrolysis of the salt.

EXAMPLE. What is the percentage hydrolysis of a 0.0010-molar solution of NH_4Cl $(NH_4^+ + H_2O \rightarrow NH_4OH + H^+)$?

SOLUTION:

$$pH = \tfrac{1}{2} pW - \tfrac{1}{2} pB - \tfrac{1}{2} \log C$$

where pW $= 14$

$pB = -\log K_{NH_4OH} = -\log 1.75 \times 10^{-5}$

$C = 0.0010$

Solving,

$$pH = 6.12$$

$$[H^+] = \log \frac{1}{6.12} = 7.6 \times 10^{-7}$$

$$[NH_4^+] = 0.0010$$

$$\text{Percentage hydrolysis} = \frac{[H^+]}{[NH_4^+]} \times 100 = 0.076 \text{ per cent.} \quad Ans.$$

Problems

12.125. What is the pH value of a solution that at 25°C. has a hydroxyl-ion concentration of 4.2×10^{-8}? What color would be given to the solution by a drop of methyl orange? Of thymol blue?

Ans. 6.62. Yellow. Yellow.

12.126. What is the hydrogen-ion concentration of a solution that at 25°C. has a pOH value of 8.85?   What common indicator would change color at approximately this concentration?

Ans. 7.08×10^{-6}.   Methyl red.

12.127. A certain weak monobasic acid is colorless in acid solution and blue in alkaline solution.   Assuming that the blue is seen when two-fifths of the indicator has been converted to ions and that at this point the pOH value of the solution is 3.6, what is the indicator constant of the indicator?

Ans. 2.7×10^{-11}.

12.128. A certain weak monobasic acid has an ionization constant of 2.0×10^{-4}. If 1/100 mole is dissolved in water and the solution diluted to 200 ml. and titrated with 0.250 *N* NaOH, calculate the pH value of the solution at the following points: (*a*) the original solution, (*b*) one-fifth of the way to the equivalence point, (*c*) at the equivalence point.

Ans.   (*a*) 2.50, (*b*) 3.10, (*c*) 8.16.

12.129. What is the pH value of a 0.0100-molar solution of KCN?   Of NH_4Cl? What common indicator is therefore suitable for the titration with HCl of a solution approximately *N*/100 in NH_4OH?

Ans.   10.57.   5.62.   Methyl red.

12.130. What is the percentage hydrolysis at 25°C. in a 0.0050-molar solution of potassium acetate?

Ans.   0.032 per cent.

12.131. What are the pH value and the percentage hydrolysis at 25°C. in a 0.010-molar solution of sodium formate ($K_{HCHO_2} = 2.1 \times 10^{-4}$)?

Ans.   7.84, 0.0069 per cent.

12.132. What is the percentage hydrolysis at 25°C. in a 0.10-molar solution of $Na_2CO_3(CO_3^- + H_2O \rightleftarrows HCO_3^- + OH^-)$?

Ans.   4.5 per cent.

12.133. What are the pH value, the hydroxyl-ion concentration, and the percentage hydrolysis at 25°C. in a 0.10-molar solution of NaCN?

Ans.   11.07, 1.1×10^{-3}, 1.1 per cent.

12.134. How many moles per liter of KClO are required to give a solution with a hydroxyl-ion concentration of 2.0×10^{-6} at 25°C.?

Ans. 1.6×10^{-5}.

12.135. A sample of vinegar weighing 6.00 grams is dissolved in water, diluted to 50.0 ml., and titrated with 0.505 *N* NaOH, phenolphthalein being used.   After 12.40 ml. of the base have been added, it is found necessary to back-titrate with 2.00 ml. of 0.606 *N* HCl.   What is the acidity of the vinegar in terms of percentage of acetic acid, $HC_2H_3O_2$?   Assuming that this is the only acid present in appreciable amounts in the vinegar, calculate the pH value of the solution at the equivalence point at the end of the above titration.   Is phenolphthalein shown to be suitable for this titration?

Ans.   5.05 per cent.   8.82.   Yes.

12.136. When a solution of a certain weak organic base of the formula type ROH is titrated with HCl, the pH value at the point two-thirds of the way to the equivalence point is 8.90.   What is the ionization constant of the base?

Ans. 8.0×10^{-6}.

12.137. If 400 ml. of a solution containing NH_4OH are titrated with 0.250 N HCl, 40.0 ml. of the acid are required to reach the equivalence point. What is the pH value of the solution at the start of the titration, halfway to the equivalence point, and at the equivalence point? What indicator is thus shown to be suitable?

Ans. 10.82, 9.24, 5.44. Methyl red.

12.138. Formic acid (HCOOH) is a monobasic acid that is 4.6 per cent ionized in tenth-molar aqueous solution at 25°C. Calculate the ionization constant of formic acid. If 50.0 ml. of 0.100 N HCOOH are diluted to 250 ml. and titrated with 0.200 N NaOH, what would be the pH value at the equivalence point? What indicator is suitable for the titration?

Ans. 2.13 × 10^{-4}. 7.97. Cresol red.

12.139. What is the pOH value of a solution the hydrogen-ion concentration of which at 25°C. is 9.0 × 10^{-10}? What common indicator would change color at approximately this concentration?

12.140. What is the hydroxyl-ion concentration of a solution that at 25°C. has a pH value of 6.30? What color would be given to the solution by a drop of congo red? Of cresol red?

12.141. Derive the formula pH = ½pW − ½pB − ½ log C, which represents the pH value at the equivalence point in the titration of a weak base with a strong acid.

12.142. A certain weak monoacidic organic base serves as an indicator. Assuming that the color change is seen when one-third of the indicator has been converted to ions and that at that point the pH value of the solution is 4.8, what is the indicator constant of the indicator?

12.143. In the titration of a solution of a certain monoacidic base with HCl, with methyl red as the indicator, the appearance of a shade of pink in the solution is taken as the end point. On the assumption that the concentration of the resulting salt is 0.100 N and that the indicator used is best suited for this titration, what is the approximate ionization constant of the base?

12.144. Benzoic acid (C_6H_5COOH) is a monobasic acid with an ionization constant of 6.6 × 10^{-5}. A sample of the pure acid weighing 0.610 gram is dissolved in 500 ml. of water and titrated with 0.500 N NaOH. Calculate the pH value of the solution at the start of the titration, halfway to the equivalence point and at the equivalence point. What indicator is shown to be suitable for this titration? Sketch the titration curve.

12.145. What is the percentage hydrolysis in a solution of 0.050 molar $NaNO_2$?

12.146. By how many times is the percentage hydrolysis of NH_4NO_3 increased when its 0.10-molar solution is diluted tenfold?

12.147. What are the pH value and the percentage hydrolysis in a solution 0.10 molar in $KHCO_3$ at 25°C.? ($HCO_3^- + H_2O \rightleftarrows H_2CO_3 + OH^-$).

12.148. How many grams of each of the following substances must be dissolved in 100 ml. in order that the resulting solution shall have a pH value of 9.0: (a) NH_3, (b) NaOH, (c) KNO_2, (d) $NaHCO_3$?

12.149. What is the percentage hydrolysis in 0.10 M solution at 25°C. of (a) Na_3PO_4- ($PO_4^{\equiv} + H_2O \rightleftarrows HPO_4^= + OH^-$), (b) $Na_2HPO_4(HPO_4^= + H_2O \rightleftarrows H_2PO_4^- + OH^-$)?

12.150. A certain organic amine is a monoacidic base like NH_4OH and is soluble in water. Calculate its ionization constant from the fact that a tenth-molar solution of the base is 6.6 per cent ionized. What is the hydroxyl-ion concentration at the equivalence point in the titration of 200 ml. of a 0.20-molar solution of the base with 0.500 N HCl? What indicator is suitable?

12.151. A certain organic amine is a weak monoacidic base like NH_4OH. Its ionization constant is 1.0×10^{-4}. If 100 ml. of a 0.020-molar solution is titrated with 0.020 N HCl, what is the hydroxyl-ion concentration at the equivalence point? Which of the following four indicators would be best suited for the titration: methyl orange, phenolphthalein, methyl red, bromthymol blue? Carefully sketch the titration curve (pH against ml.) and show from it why the other three indicators would not be as satisfactory. Show clearly the positions of pH 4, 7, and 10 on the graph.

12.152. Propionic acid is a monobasic acid with an ionization constant of 1.6×10^{-5}. If 0.100 mole of the pure acid is dissolved in 100 ml. and titrated with 4.00 N NaOH, calculate the pH value (*a*) of the original solution, (*b*) of the solution when the acid is two-thirds neutralized, (*c*) at the equivalence point.

12.153. When a solution of a certain weak organic monobasic acid is titrated with NaOH, the equivalence point is found to be the point where 40.0 ml. of NaOH have been added.   If at the point where 16.0 ml. of NaOH have been added the pH value of the solution is 6.20, what is the ionization constant of the organic acid?

12.154. In the titration of a certain solution of H_3PO_4 with 0.300 N NaOH, the pH values corresponding to the added volumes of NaOH were found experimentally to be the following: 0.01 ml. = 1.71; 4.0 ml. = 1.81; 8.0 ml. = 1.99; 10.0 ml. = 2.13; 11.0 ml. = 2.30; 11.5 ml. = 2.51; 12.0 ml. = 3.50; 12.5 ml. = 4.59; 13.0 ml. = 4.81; 14.0 ml. = 5.01; 16.0 ml. = 5.22; 18.0 ml. = 5.53; 20.0 ml. = 6.04; 22.0 ml. = 6.80; 23.0 ml. = 7.35; 24.0 ml. = 8.55; 25.0 ml. = 9.76; 26.0 ml. = 10.15; 28.0 ml. = 10.46; 32.0 ml. = 10.75; 36.0 ml. = 10.85; 40.0 ml. = 10.95; 44.0 ml. = 11.04.

Sketch the titration curve from the above data and calculate from the first inflection the number of grams of H_3PO_4 present in the original solution.   From the curve determine the *difference* between the pH values (*a*) at 1.0 ml. before the first equivalence point and 1.0 ml. beyond the first equivalence point; (*b*) at 1.0 ml. before the second equivalence point and 1.0 ml. beyond the second equivalence point; (*c*) at 1.0 ml. before the theoretical third equivalence point and 1.0 ml. beyond the theoretical third equivalence point. Explain why these three values are different. From Fig. 3 determine what indicator would be suitable for the first inflection point and the second inflection point, and explain why no indicator is suitable for the theoretical third step in the titration.

93. Titration of Sodium Carbonate.

In Fig. 4 (Sec. 91) curve (*G*) (*G*) represents the titration of a solution of sodium carbonate with a half-normal solution of hydrochloric acid. It will be noted that there are two points of inflection. The first is at about pH $= 9$ and corresponds to the completion of the reaction

$$CO_3^= + H^+ \rightarrow HCO_3^-$$

The second is at about pH $= 4$ and corresponds to the completion of the reaction

$$HCO_3^- + H^+ \rightarrow CO_2 + H_2O$$

Phenolphthalein should therefore indicate the conversion of sodium carbonate to bicarbonate, and methyl orange should change color only when complete neutralization has taken place.   Use is made of this principle in titrations of certain mixtures of substances as illustrated in the following section.

94. Analyses Involving the Use of Two Indicators. The fact that certain indicators change color at different stages of a neutralization is sometimes made use of in volumetric work to determine the proportions of the components of certain mixtures by the employment of two end points in a single titration. This may be brought about by means of two indicators, and the volumes of titrating solution required for the respective end points give a direct measure of the amounts of substances present. Only the two common indicators, methyl orange and phenolphthalein, will be considered.

Assume a solution to contain only sodium hydroxide and inert impurities. The weight of NaOH present may be found by direct titration with a standard solution of any strong acid and with either methyl orange or phenolphthalein as the indicator. In either case, the color change will take place only when the alkali is completely neutralized, and the volume of standard acid used in the titration is a direct measure of the weight of NaOH present.

If a solution contains only sodium carbonate and inert impurities and is titrated with standard acid, with methyl orange as the indicator, the color change takes place only when the Na_2CO_3 has been completely neutralized.

$$CO_3^= + H^+ \rightarrow HCO_3^-$$
$$HCO_3^- + H^+ \rightarrow H_2O + CO_2$$

The volume of acid required is a measure of the total alkaline strength of the sample and of the actual weight of Na_2CO_3 present. In calculating, the equivalent weight of the Na_2CO_3 would be taken as one-half of the molecular weight. On the other hand, if phenolphthalein were used as the indicator and the titration were carried out in the cold, the color change from pink to colorless would occur when the carbonate had been changed to bicarbonate.

$$CO_3^= + H^+ \rightarrow HCO_3^-$$

The volume of standard acid required to titrate sodium carbonate to an end point with methyl orange as the indicator is twice that required if phenolphthalein is used as the indicator, since twice the number of hydrogen-ion equivalents is involved. The equivalent weight of sodium carbonate is $Na_2CO_3/1$, and the calculated weight of Na_2CO_3 present is the same in the two cases. It is important to note that if, with phenolphthalein as the indicator, an excess of standard acid is added to the carbonate solution and *the carbon dioxide is expelled by boiling*, the sodium carbonate will be completely neutralized. Neutralization of the excess acid with standard alkali will give a *net* volume of acid which will be the same as that used with methyl orange as the indicator.

If a solution contains sodium bicarbonate and inactive impurities, the $NaHCO_3$ may be titrated with standard acid, with methyl orange as the indicator, or in *boiling solution* with phenolphthalein, in the latter case by adding excess acid and titrating back with alkali.

$$HCO_3^- + H^+ \rightarrow H_2O + CO_2$$

The equivalent weight of $NaHCO_3$ in either case is identical to the molecular weight. As stated above, a *cold* solution of pure sodium bicarbonate gives no color with phenolphthalein and therefore cannot be titrated with phenolphthalein as the indicator.

There now remains the question of possible mixtures of the three alkalies just discussed. Altogether, there are the following theoretical possibilities:

(a) $NaOH$
(b) Na_2CO_3
(c) $NaHCO_3$
(d) $NaOH + Na_2CO_3$
(e) $Na_2CO_3 + NaHCO_3$
(f) $NaOH + NaHCO_3$
(g) $NaOH + Na_2CO_3 + NaHCO_3$

Inert impurities may be present in each case. The last two mixtures, however, cannot exist in solution, for sodium hydroxide and sodium bicarbonate interact mole for mole to form the normal carbonate

$$OH^- + HCO_3^- \rightarrow CO_3^= + H_2O$$

Strictly speaking, these last two mixtures can exist when in the *perfectly dry* form, although this condition would be difficult to realize in practice. When they are treated with water the reaction takes place, forming the carbonate and leaving a possible excess of hydroxide or bicarbonate as the case may be.

The mixtures ordinarily encountered in practice are those of (d) and (e), *viz.*, sodium hydroxide with sodium carbonate and sodium carbonate with sodium bicarbonate. Two end points being used, it is possible to determine the proportions of the components of either of these mixtures even when inactive impurities are present.

EXAMPLE I. MIXTURE OF HYDROXIDE AND CARBONATE. A 1.200-gram sample of a mixture of sodium hydroxide and sodium carbonate containing inert impurities is dissolved and titrated cold with half-normal hydrochloric acid solution. With phenolphthalein as an indicator, the solution turns colorless after the addition of 30.00 ml. of the acid. Methyl orange is then added, and 5.00 ml. more of the acid are required before this indicator changes color. What is the percentage of NaOH and of Na_2CO_3 in the sample?

SOLUTION: If the acid is added slowly, the stronger base (NaOH) is neutralized first, as follows:

$$OH^- + H^+ \rightarrow H_2O$$

After this reaction is complete, the carbonate is converted to bicarbonate.

$$CO_3^= + H^+ \rightarrow HCO_3^-$$

At this point, the phenolphthalein changes from pink to colorless and a total of 30.00 ml. of acid has been added. Then the bicarbonate formed is neutralized by 5.00 ml. more of acid.

$$HCO_3^- + H^+ \rightarrow H_2O + CO_2$$

Since each mole of Na_2CO_3 reacts with 1 mole of HCl to give 1 mole of $NaHCO_3$ and this, in turn, is neutralized by 1 mole of HCl, it follows that the volume of acid required to convert the Na_2CO_3 into $NaHCO_3$ is the same as the volume required to neutralize the $NaHCO_3$, *viz.*, 5.00 ml.

Therefore, the volume of acid necessary to neutralize completely the Na_2CO_3 is 10.00 ml. Since the total volume added was 35.00 ml., it is evident that $35.00 - 10.00 = 25.00$ ml. were necessary to neutralize the NaOH. Hence,

Percentage of NaOH

$$= \frac{25.00 \times 0.5000 \times \dfrac{NaOH}{1,000}}{1.200} \times 100 = 41.68 \text{ per cent}$$

Percentage of Na_2CO_3

$$= \frac{10.00 \times 0.5000 \times \dfrac{Na_2CO_3}{2,000}}{1.200} \times 100 = 22.08 \text{ per cent}$$

$\left. \right\} Ans.$

These volume relationships are shown diagrammatically in Fig. 5.

EXAMPLE II. MIXTURE OF CARBONATE AND BICARBONATE. A 1.200-gram sample of an impure mixture of sodium carbonate and sodium bicarbonate containing only inert impurities is dissolved and titrated cold with half-normal hydrochloric acid solution. With phenolphthalein as an indicator, the solution turns colorless after the addition of 15.00 ml. of the acid. Methyl orange is then added, and 22.00 ml. more of the acid are required to change the color of this indicator. What is the percentage of Na_2CO_3 and of $NaHCO_3$ in the sample?

SOLUTION: When the acid is added slowly, the Na_2CO_3 is converted into $NaHCO_3$. At this point, the phenolphthalein changes color, and

15.00 ml. of HCl have been added.   As in Example I, the same volume of HCl as was used for the conversion of the Na_2CO_3 into $NaHCO_3$ would be required to convert this $NaHCO_3$ formed from the Na_2CO_3 into NaCl, H_2O, and CO_2.   It follows that 15.00 + 15.00 = 30.00 ml. of acid were required to neutralize completely the Na_2CO_3 present in the sample.

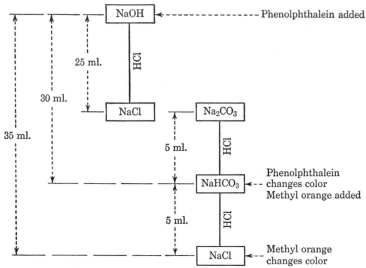

Fig. 5. Titration of NaOH + Na_2CO_3 mixture.

The total volume being 15.00 + 22.00 = 37.00 ml., it is evident that 37.00 − 30.00 = 7.00 ml. of HCl were required to neutralize the $NaHCO_3$ present in the original sample.   Hence,

Percentage of Na_2CO_3

$$= \frac{30.00 \times 0.5000 \times \dfrac{Na_2CO_3}{2,000}}{1.200} \times 100 = 66.25 \text{ per cent}$$

Percentage of $NaHCO_3$

$$= \frac{7.00 \times 0.5000 \times \dfrac{NaHCO_3}{1,000}}{1.200} \times 100 = 24.50 \text{ per cent}$$

$\left. \begin{array}{c} \\ \\ \\ \\ \\ \\ \\ \\ \end{array} \right\} Ans.$

These volume relationships are shown diagrammatically in Fig. 6.

95. Relation of Titration Volumes to Composition of Sample.   In an analysis of the type discussed in this section, it is not always true that the analyst is previously aware of the exact composition of the sample. He may not know whether the sample contains hydroxide, carbonate, bicarbonate, or possible combinations of these components, and a qualitative test is not always conclusive.   By means of a simple titration, however, and the use of a double indicator or double end point, the composition of the alkali can be determined so far as these negative radicals are concerned.

In this connection, let A represent the volume of standard acid required to titrate the cold solution to a change of color of phenolphthalein, and

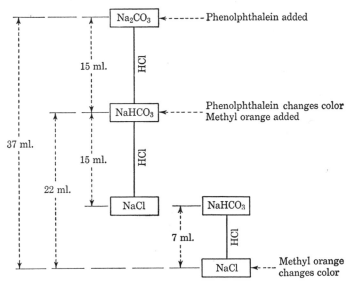

Fig. 6. Titration of $Na_2CO_3 + NaHCO_3$ mixture.

let B represent the *additional* volume of the acid to continue the titration to a change of color of methyl orange. The following relationships exist:

Active ions present	Volume for first end point	Additional volume for second end point
OH^-	A	0
HCO_3^-	0	B
CO_3^-	A	$B = A$
$CO_3^- + OH^-$	A	$B < A$
$CO_3^- + HCO_3^-$	A	$B > A$

Problems

12.155. A sample of sodium carbonate containing sodium hydroxide and only inert impurities weighs 1.197 grams. It is dissolved and titrated in the cold with phenolphthalein as the indicator. The solution turns colorless when 48.16 ml. of 0.2976 N HCl have been added. Methyl orange is added, and 24.08 ml. more of the acid are required for complete neutralization. Calculate the percentages of NaOH and Na_2CO_2 in the sample. Show the general appearance of the titration curve.

Ans. NaOH = 23.95 per cent, Na_2CO_3 = 63.46 per cent.

12.156. From the following data, calculate the percentages of Na_2CO_3 and $NaHCO_3$ in a mixture in which they are the only alkaline components. Sample = 1.272 grams.

Volume of $0.2400 \, N$ HCl required for phenolphthalein end point $= 26.92$ ml.   After addition of an excess of the standard acid and the boiling out of the CO_2, net additional volume of the acid required for the phenolphthalein end point $= 50.21$ ml. Show the general appearance of the titration curve.

Ans. $Na_2CO_3 = 53.84$ per cent, $NaHCO_3 = 36.93$ per cent.

12.157. A sample of material contains for its active components NaOH, Na_2CO_3, $NaHCO_3$, or possible mixtures of these.   Two samples, each weighing 1.000 gram, are dissolved in water.   To one sample phenolphthalein is added and the solution is titrated cold with $1.038 \, N$ acid, of which 17.96 ml. are required.   The other sample is titrated cold with methyl orange as an indicator, and 21.17 ml. of the same acid are required.   What alkalies are present?   Calculate the percentage of each.

Ans.   NaOH $= 61.28$ per cent, $Na_2CO_3 = 35.31$ per cent.

12.158. A chemist received different mixtures for analysis with the statement that they contained either NaOH, $NaHCO_3$, Na_2CO_3, or possible mixtures of these substances with inert material.   From the data given, identify the respective materials and calculate the percentage of each component.   One-gram samples and 0.2500 normal HCl were used in all cases.

Sample I.   With phenolphthalein as an indicator, 24.32 ml. were used.   A duplicate sample required 48.64 ml. with methyl orange as an indicator.

Sample II.   The addition of phenolphthalein caused no color change.   With methyl orange, 38.47 ml. of the acid were required.

Sample III.   To cause a color change in the cold with phenolphthalein 15.29 ml. of the acid were necessary, and an additional 33.19 ml. were required for complete neutralization.

Sample IV.   The sample was titrated with acid until the pink of phenolphthalein disappeared; this process required 39.96 ml.   On adding an excess of the acid, boiling, and titrating back with alkali, it was found that the alkali was exactly equivalent to the excess acid added.

Ans.   I. 64.45 per cent Na_2CO_3.   II. 80.79 per cent $NaHCO_3$.   III. 40.52 per cent Na_2CO_3, 37.60 per cent $NaHCO_3$.   IV. 39.97 per cent NaOH.

12.159. A sample is known to contain either NaOH or $NaHCO_3$ or Na_2CO_3 or possible mixtures of these, together with inert matter.   A 1.200-gram sample requires 42.20 ml. of $N/2$ HCl, with methyl orange as indicator.   The same weight of sample requires 36.30 ml. of the acid with phenolphthalein indicator.   Calculate the percentage of inert matter in the sample.

Ans.   23.27 per cent.

12.160. Pure dry NaOH and pure dry $NaHCO_3$ are mixed in the respective proportion by weight of 2:1, and the mixture is dissolved in water.   Calculate to three significant figures the ratio of the volume of standard acid required with phenolphthalein as an indicator to the additional volume required with methyl orange.

Ans.   4.20.

12.161. A mixture that contains KOH and K_2CO_3 weighs a grams and, in the cold solution with phenolphthalein, requires b ml. of c normal acid.   After methyl orange is added, d ml. of the acid are required.   Calculate the percentage of KOH and of K_2CO_3.   Reduce to simplest terms.

Ans.   Per cent KOH $= \dfrac{5.611(b - d)c}{a}$.

Per cent $K_2CO_3 = \dfrac{13.82cd}{a}$.

12.162. Solve the preceding problem with respect to a mixture of Na_2CO_3 and $NaHCO_3$. Reduce to simplest terms.

Ans. Per cent $Na_2CO_3 = \dfrac{10.60bc}{a}$.

Per cent $NaHCO_3 = \dfrac{8.401(d - b)c}{a}$.

12.163. A liter of an alkali solution is prepared from 38.00 grams of pure NaOH and 2.00 grams of pure Na_2CO_3. What is the true normality of the solution if completely neutralized? If this solution were used in a titration in the cold with phenolphthalein as an indicator, what normality should be taken for the alkali?

Ans. $0.9874 \ N$. $0.9687 \ N$.

12.164. Calculate the grams of NaOH and the grams of Na_2CO_3 present in a mixture that on analysis gives the following data: Sample = 10.00 grams. The sample is dissolved in water, the solution is diluted to 250.0 ml., and 25.00 ml. are taken for analysis. An end point with phenolphthalein in cold solution is obtained with 44.52 ml. of $0.5000 \ N$ HCl. A new portion of the same volume requires 46.53 ml. of $0.5000 \ N$ HCl for an end point with methyl orange.

12.165. A mixture of soda ash and caustic soda weighs 0.7500 gram. It is dissolved in water, phenolphthalein is added, and the mixture is titrated cold with $0.5000 \ N$ HCl; the color disappears when 21.00 ml. have been added. Methyl orange is then added, and the titration continued until the pink color appears. This requires 5.00 ml. of acid in addition. Calculate the percentage of NaOH and of Na_2CO_3 in the sample. Show the general appearance of the titration curve.

12.166. A sample is known to contain NaOH or $NaHCO_3$ or Na_2CO_3 or possible mixtures of these, together with inert matter. With methyl orange, a 1.100-gram sample requires 31.40 ml. of HCl (1.00 ml. $\approx$ 0.01400 gram CaO). With phenolphthalein, the same weight of sample requires 13.30 ml. of the acid. Calculate the percentage of inert matters in the sample. Show the general appearance of the titration curve.

12.167. The qualitative analysis of a powder shows the presence of sodium, a carbonate, and a little chloride. Titrated with methyl orange as an indicator, 0.8000 gram of the powder reacts with 25.10 ml. of half-normal HCl, and the same weight reacts with 18.45 ml. of the acid with phenolphthalein in the cold solution. Compute the percentage composition of the original powder.

12.168. A substance reacts alkaline in aqueous solution, and the alkalinity is due either to K_2CO_3 and KOH or to K_2CO_3 and $KHCO_3$. Compute the percentage of each alkaline constituent from the following data:

When phenolphthalein is the indicator (in a cold solution), 1.500 grams of powder react with 26.27 ml. of $0.3333 \ N$ HCl, and with 59.17 ml. when methyl orange is the indicator. Sample = 1.5000 grams.

12.169. A solution of alkali is prepared from NaOH contaminated with Na_2CO_3. With phenolphthalein in the cold, 36.42 ml. of the alkali are required to neutralize 50.00 ml. of $0.5280 \ N$ H_2SO_4. With methyl orange as the indicator, 35.60 ml. of the alkali are required for the same amount of acid. How many grams of NaOH and of Na_2CO_3 are contained in each milliliter of the alkali solution?

96. Analysis of Phosphate Mixtures.
Phosphoric acid ionizes in three steps. The ionization constant for the first hydrogen is 1.1×10^{-2}; for the second, 2.0×10^{-7}; and for the third, 3.6×10^{-13}. In the titration of phosphoric acid with an alkali like NaOH, the replacement of the

first hydrogen results in the formation of NaH_2PO_4 ($H_3PO_4 + OH^- \rightarrow$ $H_2PO_4^- + H_2O$). At approximately this point, methyl orange changes color. The replacement of the second hydrogen results in the formation of Na_2HPO_4 ($H_2PO_4^- + OH^- \rightarrow HPO_4^= + H_2O$). At approximately this point, phenolphthalein changes color. The reverse titration of Na_3PO_4 with a strong acid like HCl results first in the formation of $HPO_4^=$, at which point phenolphthalein changes color, and then in the formation of $H_2PO_4^-$, at which point methyl orange changes color. A titration of this sort is shown in Fig. 7.

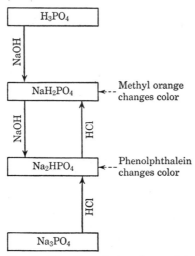

FIG. 7. Titration of phosphate mixture.

Only adjacent substances shown on the diagram can exist together in solution. Other combinations interact. As in the case of the carbonate titrations of the preceding section, it is possible to analyze certain mixtures of phosphates by means of titrations involving the use of two indicators. Actually, the titrations should be carried out on fairly concentrated solutions and at a temperature of about 55°C.

EXAMPLE. A sample, which is known to contain either Na_3PO_4, NaH_2PO_4, Na_2HPO_4, or possible mixtures of these, together with inert impurity, weighs 2.00 grams. When this sample is titrated with 0.500 *N* HCl, using methyl orange, 32.0 ml. of the acid are required. The same weight of sample when titrated with 0.500 *N* HCl, using phenolphthalein, requires 21.0 ml. of the acid. What is the percentage composition of the sample?

SOLUTION: From simple inspection of the diagram and consideration of the two volumes involved, it is evident that both Na_3PO_4 and Na_2HPO_4 are present. A volume of 12.0 ml. must have been required to convert the Na_3PO_4 to Na_2HPO_4; and, since 12.0 ml. more would be required to convert the Na_2HPO_4 *formed* to NaH_2PO_4, a volume of $32.0 - (2 \times 12.0)$ = 8.0 ml. is required to convert the *original* Na_2HPO_4 to NaH_2PO_4.

$$\frac{12.0 \times 0.500 \times \dfrac{Na_3PO_4}{1,000}}{2.00} \times 100 = 49.2 \text{ per cent } Na_3PO_4$$

$$\frac{8.0 \times 0.500 \times \dfrac{Na_2HPO_4}{1,000}}{2.00} \times 100 = 28.4 \text{ per cent } Na_2HPO_4$$

Ans.

Problems

12.170. A sample that contains $Na_3PO_4.12H_2O$, or $Na_2HPO_4.12H_2O$, or $NaH_2PO_4.-$ H_2O, or possible mixtures of these weighs 3.00 grams. When it is titrated with 0.500 N HCl, methyl orange being used, 14.0 ml. of the acid are required. A similar sample requires 5.00 ml. of 0.600 N NaOH, with phenolphthalein. What is the percentage composition of the sample?

Ans. 13.8 per cent $NaH_2PO_4.H_2O$, 83.6 per cent $Na_2HPO_4.12H_2O$.

12.171. A certain solution is known to contain any possible combinations of the following substances: HCl, Na_2HPO_4, NaH_2PO_4, H_3PO_4, NaOH. Titration of a sample with 0.500 N NaOH, phenolphthalein being used, requires 27.0 ml. of the base. With the same weight of sample and methyl orange indicator, 17.2 ml. of the 0.500 N NaOH are required to obtain a color change. What components are present, and how many grams of each are present in the sample taken?

Ans. 0.135 gram HCl, 0.481 gram H_3PO_4.

12.172. A certain solution is known to contain either HCl + H_3PO_4, or H_3PO_4 + NaH_2PO_4, or the three compounds existing alone. A sample is titrated with NaOH, requiring A ml. with methyl orange indicator; but the same weight of sample requires B ml. of the NaOH with phenolphthalein indicator. What relationship would exist between A and B to indicate the first combination, and what relationship would indicate the second combination? What relationship would indicate the presence of H_3PO_4 alone?

Ans. $B > A$, but $B < 2A$; $B > 2A$. $B = 2A$.

12.173. A solution known to contain H_3PO_4, Na_2HPO_4, or NaH_2PO_4, or possible mixtures of these, weighs 1.10 grams. When it is titrated with 0.520 N NaOH, 27.0 ml. are required to change the color of phenolphthalein, but only 10.0 ml. to change the color of methyl orange. What is the percentage composition of the solution?

12.174. A certain solution is known to contain any possible combinations of the following substances: HCl, Na_2HPO_4, NaH_2PO_4, H_3PO_4, NaOH, Na_3PO_4. Titration of a sample with 0.510 N HCl, methyl orange being used, requires 28.1 ml. of the acid. With the same weight of sample and phenolphthalein indicator, 17.1 ml. of the HCl are required. What components are present, and how many grams of each are in the sample taken?

12.175. A series of solutions are known to contain H_3PO_4, NaH_2PO_4, Na_2HPO_4, alone or mixed in varying proportions. In each case, the titration is made with 1.000 N NaOH to a pink color with phenolphthalein and the solution is then back-titrated with 1.000 N HCl to a pink color with methyl orange. In each of the following four cases, determine which components are present and the number of millimoles of each:

a. Initial titration 48.36 ml.; back-titration 33.72 ml.
b. Initial titration 37.33 ml.; back-titration 39.42 ml.
c. Initial titration 24.36 ml.; back-titration 24.36 ml.
d. Initial titration 36.24 ml.; back-titration 18.12 ml.

CHAPTER 13

OXIDATION AND REDUCTION (REDOX) METHODS
(OXIDIMETRY AND REDUCTIMETRY)

97. Fundamental Principles. This phase of volumetric analysis has to do with the titration of an oxidizing agent with a standard solution of a reducing agent or the titration of a reducing agent with a standard solution of an oxidizing agent. This type of determination embraces the greater part of volumetric analysis, for the number of substances capable of oxidation or reduction is comparatively large.

Oxidation is the increase in the positive direction of the electrical valence or oxidation number of an element or radical; reduction is the decrease in electrical valence or oxidation number of an element or radical. Oxidation and reduction must evidently take place simultaneously, for in any reaction of this type the oxidizing agent is always reduced and the reducing agent is always oxidized, and to the same degree. The methods of expressing concentration and the definitions given in Chap. 4 hold true for solutions of oxidizing and reducing agents. Therefore, the relationships existing between these agents are the same as those existing between acids and bases. However, it is necessary in the case of concentrations of solutions expressed in terms of normality to consider the hydrogen equivalent from a slightly different point of view.

98. Equivalent Weights of Oxidizing and Reducing Agents. As in acidimetry and alkalimetry, the concentration of a solution of an oxidizing or reducing agent is best expressed in terms of its relation to the normal solution, and the gram-atom of hydrogen is taken as the ultimate unit. We must, however, consider the unit from the point of view of oxidation and reduction, thus:

$$H^0 \rightleftarrows H^+ + \epsilon$$

Hydrogen ion is an oxidizing agent and is capable of being reduced to hydrogen gas (*e.g.*, $Zn + 2H^+ \rightarrow Zn^{++} + H_2$). Free hydrogen is a reducing agent and is capable of being oxidized to hydrogen ion (*e.g.*, $2Fe^{+++} + H_2 \rightarrow 2Fe^{++} + 2H^+$).

The conversion of one atom of hydrogen to the ion, or vice versa, involves a change of 1 in oxidation number and a transfer of one electron. To find the equivalent weight of an oxidizing or reducing agent we must, therefore, take that fraction of its formula weight so that in the oxidation or reduction process there will be involved the equivalent of a transfer of one electron. This will be accomplished (1) by dividing the formula weight of the substance by the total change in oxidation number involved in the oxidation-reduction process, or (2) by dividing the formula weight of the substance by the number of electrons transferred per formula weight of substance. The gram-equivalent weight of an oxidizing agent is the equivalent weight in grams and is equivalent in oxidizing power to 1.008 grams of hydrogen as hydrogen ion. It is likewise equivalent in oxidizing power to 8.000 grams of oxygen. The gram-equivalent weight of a reducing agent is equivalent in reducing power to 1.008 grams of elementary hydrogen gas. As will be seen later, a substance may have two different equivalent weights depending on whether it is used as an acid or as an oxidizing or reducing agent. As in acidimetry, a normal solution of an oxidizing or reducing agent contains one gram-equivalent weight of substance per liter of solution, or one gram-milliequivalent per milliliter. Hence, as in acidimetry,

$$ml. \times N = number\ of\ gram\text{-}milliequivalents$$

and

$$ml._s \times N_s \times mew_x = grams_x$$

EXAMPLE I. How many grams of the following reducing substances constitute the gram-equivalent weight in each case: (a) $FeSO_4.7H_2O$, (b) $SnCl_2$, (c) $H_2C_2O_4.2H_2O$ (oxalic acid), (d) $KHC_2O_4.H_2O$ (potassium binoxalate), (e) $KHC_2O_4.H_2C_2O_4.2H_2O$ (potassium tetroxalate), (f) H_2S (oxidized to S), (g) H_2S (oxidized to H_2SO_4), (h) $Na_2S_2O_3.5H_2O$ (oxidized to $Na_2S_4O_6$), (i) H_2O_2?

SOLUTION: (a) $FeSO_4.7H_2O$. In solution, this gives ferrous ions which can be oxidized to ferric ions.

$$Fe^{++} \rightarrow Fe^{+++} + \epsilon$$

e.g.,

$$2Fe^{++} + Br_2 \rightarrow 2Fe^{+++} + 2Br^-$$

Each ferrous ion changes in oxidation number by one unit and hence is equivalent in reducing power to the hydrogen unit. The molecular weight of $FeSO_4.7H_2O$ is therefore the equivalent weight as a reducing agent, and, expressed in grams, is equivalent in reducing power to 1.008 grams of hydrogen.

$$\frac{FeSO_4.7H_2O}{1} = 278.0\ grams.\quad Ans.$$

(b) $SnCl_2$. In solution, this gives stannous ions which can be oxidized to stannic ions: $Sn^{++} \rightarrow Sn^{++++} + 2\epsilon$. The change in oxidation number is 2. The gram-molecular weight of $SnCl_2$ is, therefore, equivalent in reducing power to 2 gram atoms of hydrogen, or one-half the molecular weight represents the equivalent weight.

$$\frac{SnCl_2}{2} = 77.08 \text{ grams.} \quad Ans.$$

(*c*) $H_2C_2O_4.2H_2O$. In solution, this gives oxalate ions, $C_2O_4^{=}$, which can be oxidized to CO_2 gas.

$$C_2O_4^{=} \rightarrow 2CO_2 + 2\epsilon$$

e.g.,

$$5C_2O_4^{=} + 2MnO_4^{-} + 16H^{+} \rightarrow 10CO_2 + 2Mn^{++} + 8H_2O$$

The *average* oxidation number of carbon in the oxalate radical is +3 (actually one is +2, the other is +4). The oxidation number of carbon in CO_2 is +4. Each carbon, on an average, changes by one unit in oxidation number; but, since there are 2 carbon atoms in the oxalate radical, the average change for the oxalate radical is 2. The radical is, therefore, equivalent in reducing power to 2 hydrogen atoms.

$$\frac{H_2C_2O_4.2H_2O}{2} = 63.03 \text{ grams.} \quad Ans.$$

(*d*) $KHC_2O_4.H_2O$. Here again, each molecule of the dissolved salt gives an oxalate ion which is oxidized to CO_2 as in the preceding case.

$$\frac{KHC_2O_4.H_2O}{2} = 73.07 \text{ grams.} \quad Ans.$$

It should be noted that the equivalent weight of this salt *as an acid* is the molecular weight, or 146.14. Hence, a solution of potassium binoxalate which is 0.1 *N* as an acid is 0.2 *N* as a reducing agent.

(*e*) $KHC_2O_4.H_2C_2O_4.2H_2O$. Since each molecule of this salt in solution gives 2 oxalate ions which are oxidized as above to CO_2, the equivalent weight of potassium tetroxalate as a reducing agent is

$$\frac{KHC_2O_4.H_2C_2O_4.2H_2O}{4} = 63.55 \text{ grams.} \quad Ans.$$

When this salt is reacting as an acid, its equivalent weight is one-third of the molecular weight, or 84.73. A given solution of potassium tetroxalate has four-thirds the normality as a reducing agent that it has as an acid.

(*f*) H_2S. When this substance is oxidized to free sulfur, the change in oxidation number of sulfur is 2.

$$\frac{H_2S}{2} = 17.04 \text{ grams.} \quad Ans.$$

(*g*) H_2S. When this substance is oxidized to sulfate, the change in oxidation number of sulfur is from -2 to $+6$.

$$\frac{H_2S}{8} = 4.260 \text{ grams.} \quad Ans.$$

(*h*) $Na_2S_2O_3.5H_2O$. In aqueous solution, this salt gives thiosulfate ions which can be oxidized to tetrathionate ions.

$$2S_2O_3^{=} \rightarrow S_4O_6^{=} + 2\epsilon$$

e.g.,

$$2S_2O_3^{=} + I_2 \rightarrow S_4O_6^{=} + 2I^-$$

In the thiosulfate radical, the *average* oxidation number of sulfur is $+2$; in tetrathionate, the *average* oxidation number of sulfur is $+2\frac{1}{2}$. The average change for each sulfur is $\frac{1}{2}$; but, since in thiosulfate there are two sulfurs, the total change in oxidation number is 1.

$$\frac{Na_2S_2O_3.5H_2O}{1} = 248.2 \text{ grams.} \quad Ans.$$

(*i*) H_2O_2. When hydrogen peroxide acts as a reducing agent, it is oxidized to free oxygen; *e.g.,*

$$5H_2O_2 + 2MnO_4^- + 6H^+ \rightarrow 5O_2 + 2Mn^{++} + 8H_2O$$

Average change in oxidation number of each oxygen atom in the hydrogen peroxide molecule is from -1 to 0. Total change for the molecule is 2.

$$\frac{H_2O_2}{2} = 17.01 \text{ grams.} \quad Ans.$$

EXAMPLE II. How many grams of the following oxidizing substances constitute the gram-milliequivalent weight in each case: (*a*) $K_3Fe(CN)_6$, (*b*) $KMnO_4$, (*c*) $K_2Cr_2O_7$, (*d*) I_2, (*e*) $KBrO_3$ (reduced to bromide), (*f*) H_2O_2?

SOLUTION: (*a*) $K_3Fe(CN)_6$. In solution, this salt gives ferricyanide ions which are capable of being reduced to ferrocyanide ions.

$$Fe(CN)_6^{\equiv} + \epsilon \rightarrow Fe(CN)_6^{\equiv}$$

The change in oxidation number of the iron is from $+3$ to $+2$.

$$\frac{K_3Fe(CN)_6}{1,000} = 0.3293 \text{ gram.} \quad Ans.$$

(*b*) $KMnO_4$. When reduced *in the presence of acid*, permanganate ions form manganous ions.

$$MnO_4^- + 8H^+ + 5\epsilon \rightarrow Mn^{++} + 4H_2O$$

e.g.,

$$MnO_4^- + 5Fe^{++} + 8H^+ \rightarrow Mn^{++} + 5Fe^{+++} + 4H_2O$$

Change in oxidation number of manganese is from $+7$ to $+2$.

$$\frac{KMnO_4}{5,000} = 0.03161 \text{ gram.} \quad Ans.$$

In alkaline solution, permanganate is reduced to MnO_2 with a change in oxidation number of 3 (from $+7$ to $+4$).

$$MnO_4^- + 2H_2O + 3\epsilon \rightarrow MnO_2 + 4OH^-$$

Here the equivalent weight is *one-third* of the molecular weight.

(c) $K_2Cr_2O_7$.   Dichromate ions are ordinarily reduced to chromic ions.

$$Cr_2O_7^= + 14H^+ + 6\epsilon \rightarrow 2Cr^{+++} + 7H_2O$$

e.g.,

$$Cr_2O_7^= + 6Fe^{++} + 14H^+ \rightarrow 2Cr^{+++} + 6Fe^{+++} + 7H_2O$$

The change in oxidation number of each chromium atom is from $+6$ to $+3$, or the change of the dichromate ion (since it contains 2 chromium ions) is 6.

$$\frac{K_2Cr_2O_7}{6,000} = 0.04903 \text{ gram.} \quad Ans.$$

(d) I_2.   Iodine is reduced to iodide.

$$I_2 + 2\epsilon \rightarrow 2I^-$$

There is one unit change in oxidation number for each iodine atom, or two unit changes for the molecule.

$$\frac{I_2}{2,000} = 0.1269 \text{ gram.} \quad Ans.$$

(e) $KBrO_3$.   Bromate reduced to bromide involves a change in oxidation number of the bromine from $+5$ to -1, or a change of 6 units.

$$BrO_3^- + 6H^+ + 6\epsilon \rightarrow Br^- + 3H_2O$$
$$\frac{KBrO_3}{6,000} = 0.02784 \text{ gram.} \quad Ans.$$

(f) H_2O_2.   As an oxidizing agent, hydrogen peroxide is reduced to water.

$$H_2O_2 + 2H^+ + 2\epsilon \rightarrow 2H_2O$$

Average change of each oxygen is from -1 to -2.   Total change for the molecule is 2.

$$\frac{H_2O_2}{2,000} = 0.01701 \text{ gram.} \quad Ans.$$

99. Calculations of Oxidation and Reduction Processes. Since the concentration of solutions in oxidation and reduction titrations, like those in acidimetry and alkalimetry, is based on the hydrogen equivalent, the methods of calculation are identical. Thus, 1 liter of a normal solution of an oxidizing agent will exactly oxidize 1 liter of a normal solution of a reducing agent, or 2 liters of a half-normal solution.

In titrating a reducing agent with a solution of oxidizing agent or an oxidizing agent with a solution of reducing agent, reasoning similar to that described in Secs. 82, 83, and 84 will evolve the same general formulas as were there derived: *viz.*,

$$ml._s \times N_s \times mew_x = grams_x$$

and

$$\frac{ml._s \times N_s \times mew_x}{Weight\ of\ sample} \times 100 = per\ cent_x$$

The methods of solving the various types of problems described under Secs. 85, 86, and 87 likewise apply to oxidation and reduction titrations.

Problems

13.1. Thirty milliliters of ferrous ammonium sulfate solution contain 1.176 grams of pure $FeSO_4.(NH_4)_2SO_4.6H_2O$. Twenty milliliters of potassium dichromate solution contain 0.2940 gram of $K_2Cr_2O_7$. Calculate (*a*) normality of the ferrous ammonium sulfate, (*b*) normality of the dichromate, (*c*) value of 1.000 ml. of ferrous solution in terms of the dichromate solution.

Ans. (*a*) 0.1000 *N*, (*b*) 0.2998 *N*, (*c*) 0.3335 ml.

13.2. A solution of nitric acid is 3.00 *N* as an acid. How many milliliters of water must be added to 50 ml. of the acid to make it 3.00 *N* as an oxidizing agent? Assume reduction of HNO_3 to NO.

Ans. 100 ml.

13.3. If 10.00 grams of $K_4Fe(CN)_6.3H_2O$ are dissolved in water and the volume made up to 500 ml., what is the normality of the solution as a reducing agent?

Ans. 0.04736 *N*.

13.4. From the following data, calculate the ratio of the nitric acid as an oxidizing agent to the tetroxalate solution as a reducing agent (assume reduction of NO_3^- to NO).

$$1.000\ ml.\ HNO_3 \backsimeq 1.246\ ml.\ NaOH$$
$$1.000\ ml.\ KHC_2O_4.H_2C_2O_4.2H_2O \backsimeq 1.743\ ml.\ NaOH$$
$$Normality\ NaOH = 0.1200$$

Ans. 1.608

13.5. To oxidize the iron in 1.00 gram of $FeSO_4.(NH_4)_2SO_4.6H_2O$ requires 5.00 ml. of HNO_3 ($3Fe^{++} + NO_3^- + 4H^+ \rightarrow 3Fe^{+++} + NO + H_2O$). How much water must be added to 500 ml. of this acid to make the concentration as an acid one-tenth normal?

Ans. 350 ml.

13.6. A certain volume of a solution of $KHC_2O_4.H_2O$ would be oxidized in the presence of acid by an equal volume of 0.01000 molar $KMnO_4$. How many milliliters of 0.01000 molar $Ba(OH)_2$ solution would be neutralized by 20.00 ml. of the binoxalate?

Ans. 25.00 ml.

13.7. A method of standardizing $KMnO_4$ solution against a standard solution of NaOH has been suggested. This consists in dissolving a small (unweighed) amount of oxalic acid (or acid oxalate) in water and titrating with the standard alkali, using phenolphthalein indicator. The resulting solution is acidified with H_2SO_4 and titrated with the $KMnO_4$. If $KHC_2O_4.H_2O$ were used as the intermediate compound and the titrations required 10.58 ml. of 0.2280 N NaOH and 38.10 ml. of $KMnO_4$, calculate the normality of the $KMnO_4$ as an oxidizing agent.

Ans. 0.1266 N.

13.8. $KHC_2O_4.H_2C_2O_4.2H_2O$ and $Na_2C_2O_4$ are to be mixed in the proper proportion so that the normality of a solution of the mixture as a reducing agent will be 2.15 times the normality as an acid. Calculate the proportion.

Ans. $1:0.644$.

13.9. Calculate the normality as an acid and as a reducing agent of a solution made by dissolving a mixture of 20.00 grams of $H_2C_2O_4.2H_2O$, 10.00 grams of KHC_2O_4, and 15.00 grams of $KHC_2O_4.H_2C_2O_4.2H_2O$ in water and diluting to $1,000$ ml.

Ans. 0.5728 N, 0.7096 N.

13.10. In the analysis of chrome iron ore, chromium is oxidized by fusion to chromate and determined by titration with ferrous ammonium sulfate. What is the equivalent weight in terms of (*a*) Cr_2O_3 and (*b*) Cr?

13.11. What volume of HCl solution is theoretically required to dissolve 1.000 gram of pure iron out of contact with the air, if 3.00 ml. of the acid will neutralize that volume of KOH solution which will react with 6.00 ml. of a potassium acid oxalate solution that is 2.00 N as a reducing agent?

13.12. When 25.00 ml. of HCl are treated with $AgNO_3$, a precipitate of AgCl weighing 0.5465 gram is obtained; 24.36 ml. of the HCl react with 27.22 ml. of NaOH solution; 26.24 ml. of the NaOH react with 30.17 ml. of $KHC_2O_4.H_2C_2O_4.2H_4O$ solution. How much water must be added to a liter of the oxalate solution to make it 0.02500 N as a reducing agent?

13.13. The hydrogen peroxide sold for medicinal purposes is often labeled "10 volume" which means that on ordinary decomposition it yields ten times its volume of oxygen. What would be the normality of such a solution as an oxidizing agent? As a reducing agent?

13.14. A certain volume of $KHC_2O_4.H_2C_2O_4.2H_2O$ solution would be neutralized by an equal volume of 0.01000 molar Na_2CO_3 solution. How many milliliters of 0.02000 molar $K_2Cr_2O_7$ would be required to oxidize 25.00 ml. of the tetroxalate solution?

100. Permanganate Process. Potassium permanganate is extensively used as an oxidimetric standard. It serves as its own indicator. A normal solution contains one-fifth the gram-molecular weight per liter (see Sec. 98, Example II*b*) if used in the presence of acid. A standard solution of potassium permanganate is used in three ways:

1. It is used in the presence of acid in the direct titration of a large number of oxidizable cation and anions. Among them are the following:

SUBSTANCE	OXIDIZED TO
Fe^{++}	Fe^{+++}
Sn^{++}	Sn^{++++}
VO^{++}	VO_3^-
$C_2O_4^-$	CO_2
NO_2^-	NO_3^-
SO_3^-	SO_4^-
H_2O_2	O_2
Mo^{+++}	MoO_4^-
Ti^{+++}	TiO^{++}
U^{++++}	UO_2^{++}

2. It is used in the presence of acid in the indirect titration of a large number of reducible substances. In each case a measured amount of a reducing agent (*e.g.*, a ferrous salt or an oxalate) is added, and, after reduction is complete, the excess reducing agent is titrated with standard permanganate (see Sec. 85). Among the many substances that can be determined in this way are the following:

SUBSTANCE	REDUCED TO
MnO_4^-	Mn^{++}
$Cr_2O_7^-$	Cr^{+++}
MnO_2, Mn_3O_4	Mn^{++}
PbO_2, Pb_2O_3, Pb_3O_4	Pb^{++}

3. It is used in neutral or alkaline solution in the titration of a few substances. In these cases the permanganate is reduced to MnO_2, which precipitates. The permanganate, therefore, has an oxidizing power only three-fifths of what it has when used in the presence of acid (see Sec. 98). This fact must be made use of in the calculations of such analyses (see Example VI below).

SUBSTANCE	OXIDIZED TO
Mn^{++}	MnO_2
HCOOH (formic acid)	CO_2

EXAMPLE I. What is the normality of a solution of potassium permanganate if 40.00 ml. will oxidize that weight of potassium tetroxalate, $KHC_2O_4.H_2C_2O_4.2H_2O$, which requires 30.00 ml. of 0.5000 N sodium hydroxide solution for its neutralization?

SOLUTION: The amount of tetroxalate that requires 30.00 ml. of 0.5000 N NaOH for neutralization is

$$30.00 \times 0.5000 \times \frac{KHC_2O_4.H_2C_2O_4.2H_2O}{3,000} = 1.271 \text{ grams}$$

The normality of the permanganate is therefore

$$\frac{1.271}{40.00 \times \dfrac{KHC_2O_4.H_2C_2O_4.2H_2O}{4,000}} = 0.5000 \; N. \quad Ans.$$

The same result is more simply obtained by setting up the entire equation before performing any of the operations, when it will be found that the molecular weights of the potassium tetroxalate cancel and need not be calculated. Thus, the weight of potassium tetroxalate neutralized by 30.00 ml. of 0.5000 N NaOH is

$$30.00 \times 0.5000 \times \frac{KHC_2O_4.H_2C_2O_4.2H_2O}{3,000}$$

and the weight of potassium tetroxalate oxidized by 40.00 ml. of x normal $KMnO_4$ is

$$40.00 \times x \times \frac{KHC_2O_4.H_2C_2O_4.2H_2O}{4,000}$$

Since these two expressions are equal to each other, the equality may be expressed by an equation in which the molecular weights of the potassium tetroxalate cancel and x gives the value 0.5000 for the normality of the permanganate.

EXAMPLE II. What is the percentage of iron in a sample of iron ore weighing 0.7100 gram if, after solution and reduction of the iron with amalgamated zinc, 48.06 ml. of $KMnO_4$ (1.000 ml. $\approx$ 0.006700 gram $Na_2C_2O_4$) are required to oxidize the iron? How many grams of $KMnO_4$ are contained in each milliliter of the solution?

SOLUTION:

$$\text{Normality of the } KMnO_4 = \frac{0.006700}{\dfrac{Na_2C_2O_4}{2,000}} = 0.1000 \; N$$

$$\frac{48.06 \times 0.1000 \times \dfrac{Fe}{1,000}}{0.7100} \times 100 = 37.79 \text{ per cent Fe.} \quad Ans.$$

Each milliliter of normal $KMnO_4$ contains $KMnO_4/5,000 = 0.03161$ gram.

Each milliliter of this $KMnO_4$ contains $0.03161 \times 0.1000 = 0.003161$ gram. $Ans.$

EXAMPLE III. How many grams of H_2O_2 are contained in a solution that requires for titration 14.05 ml. of $KMnO_4$ of which 1.000 ml. $\approx$ 0.008378 gram Fe ($i.e.$, will oxidize that amount of iron from the divalent to the trivalent state)? How many grams and how many milliliters of oxygen measured dry and under standard conditions are evolved during the titration?

SOLUTION:

$$\text{Normality KMnO}_4 = \frac{0.008378}{\text{Fe}/1,000} = 0.1500 \, N$$

$$\text{Grams H}_2\text{O}_2 = 14.05 \times 0.1500 \times \frac{\text{H}_2\text{O}_2}{2,000} = 0.03584 \text{ gram.} \quad Ans.$$

Each mole of H_2O_2 corresponds to a mole of O_2 evolved [see Sec. 98, Example I(i)]. Therefore,

$$\text{Grams O}_2 \text{ evolved} = 14.05 \times 0.1500 \times \frac{\text{O}_2}{2,000} = 0.03372 \text{ gram.} \quad Ans.$$

Each mole of O_2 occupies 22,400 ml.
Therefore,

$$\text{Milliliters O}_2 \text{ evolved} = 14.05 \times 0.1500 \times \frac{22,400}{2,000} = 23.60 \text{ ml.} \quad Ans.$$

EXAMPLE IV. What is the percentage of MnO_2 in impure pyrolusite if a sample weighing 0.4000 gram is treated with 0.6000 gram of pure $H_2C_2O_4.2H_2O$ and dilute H_2SO_4 and after reduction has taken place $(MnO_2 + H_2C_2O_4 + 2H^+ \rightarrow Mn^{++} + 2CO_2 + 2H_2O)$ the excess oxalic acid requires 26.26 ml. of 0.1000 N $KMnO_4$ for titration?

SOLUTION:

$$\text{Milliequivalents of H}_2\text{C}_2\text{O}_4.2\text{H}_2\text{O used} = \frac{0.6000}{\text{H}_2\text{C}_2\text{O}_4.2\text{H}_2\text{O}/2,000} = 9.526$$

$$\text{Milliequivalents of KMnO}_4 \text{ used} = 26.26 \times 0.1000 = 2.626$$

$$\text{Net milliequivalents} = 9.526 - 2.626 = 6.900$$

$$\frac{6.900 \times \text{MnO}_2/2,000}{0.4000} \times 100 = 74.97 \text{ per cent MnO}_2. \quad Ans.$$

EXAMPLE V.   What would be the milliequivalent weight of Pb_3O_4 and of Pb in the calculation of the analysis of red lead (impure Pb_3O_4) by a method similar to that of the preceding example $(Pb_3O_4 + H_2C_2O_4 + 3SO_4^= + 6H^+ \rightarrow 3PbSO_4 + 2CO_2 + 4H_2O)$?

SOLUTION: The oxidation number of lead changes from an average of $2\frac{2}{3}$ (in Pb_3O_4) to 2 (in $PbSO_4$). Each lead therefore changes by an average of $\frac{2}{3}$ unit; 3 leads change by 2 units.   Hence,

$$\text{Me. wt. Pb}_3\text{O}_4 = \frac{\text{Pb}_3\text{O}_4}{2,000} = 0.3428. \quad Ans.$$

$$\text{Me. wt. Pb} = \frac{3\text{Pb}}{2,000} = 0.3108. \quad Ans.$$

EXAMPLE VI.   A steel containing 0.90 per cent Mn is analyzed by the three standard methods below, in each case with a 2.50-gram sample, 0.0833 N KMnO$_4$ and 0.100 N FeSO$_4$ solutions.   Calculate in each case the volume of KMnO$_4$ required.

SOLUTION: *Bismuthate Method.*   The Mn is oxidized to KMnO$_4$ and after reduction with 25.0 ml. of the standard FeSO$_4$ (MnO$_4^-$ + 5Fe^{++} + 8H$^+$ → Mn^{++} + 5Fe^{+++} + 4H$_2$O) the excess ferrous iron is titrated with the standard KMnO$_4$.

Let x = milliliters of KMnO$_4$ used in the titration.

$$\text{Milliequivalents of FeSO}_4 \text{ used} = 25.0 \times 0.100 = 2.50$$
$$\text{Milliequivalents of KMnO}_4 \text{ used} = x \times 0.0833$$
$$\text{Net milliequivalents} = 2.50 - 0.0833x$$
$$\frac{(2.50 - 0.0833x) \times \text{Mn}/5{,}000}{2.50} \times 100 = 0.90$$
$$x = 5.42 \text{ ml.}   Ans.$$

Chlorate (Williams) Method.   The Mn is oxidized with KClO$_3$ to MnO$_2$ which is filtered and dissolved in 25.0 ml. of the standard FeSO$_4$ (MnO$_2$ + 2Fe^{++} + 4H$^+$ → Mn^{++} + 2Fe^{+++} + 2H$_2$O).   The excess FeSO$_4$ is titrated with the standard KMnO$_4$.

Let x = milliliters of KMnO$_4$ used in the titration.
$$\text{Milliequivalents of FeSO}_4 \text{ used} = 25.0 \times 0.100 = 2.50$$
$$\text{Milliequivalents of KMnO}_4 \text{ used} = x \times 0.0833$$
$$\text{Net milliequivalents} = 2.50 - 0.0833x$$
$$\frac{(2.50 - 0.0833x) \times \text{Mn}/2{,}000}{2.50} \times 100 = 0.90$$
$$x = 20.2 \text{ ml.}   Ans.$$

Volhard Method.   The Mn is titrated directly with KMnO$_4$ in a solution kept neutral with ZnO (3Mn^{++} + 2MnO$_4^-$ + 2ZnO → 5MnO$_2$ + 2Zn^{++}).
Let x = milliliters of KMnO$_4$ used in the titration.
In this case the normality of the KMnO$_4$ cannot be taken as 0.0833 because it is used in neutral solution where the change in oxidation number of its manganese is 3 instead of 5.   In other words, the oxidizing power of KMnO$_4$ in neutral solution is only three-fifths as great as it is in acid solution.   In this particular case the normality is 0.0833 × ⅗. The change in oxidation number of the titrated Mn is 2.

$$\frac{x(0.0833 \times ⅗)\text{Mn}/2{,}000}{2.50} \times 100 = 0.90$$
$$x = 16.4 \text{ ml.}   Ans.$$

EXAMPLE VII.   A 1.00-gram sample of steel containing 0.90 per cent Mn is analyzed by the persulfate method whereby the manganese is oxidized to permanganate by ammonium persulfate and the resulting permanganate is titrated with a standard solution of sodium arsenite. If 7.68 ml. of arsenite solution (0.0400 molar in Na_3AsO_3) are required and the arsenite is oxidized to arsenate in the titration, to what average oxidation number was the manganese reduced in the titration?

SOLUTION:

$$0.0400 \text{ molar } Na_3AsO_3 = 0.0800 \text{ normal}$$

Let x = change in oxidation number of Mn during titration

$$7.68 \times 0.0800 \times \frac{Mn}{x \times 1,000} = 0.0090$$

Solving,

$$x = 3.75$$

Oxidation number of Mn in reduced form = $7 - 3.75 = 3.25$. *Ans.*

EXAMPLE VIII. If 1.000 ml. of a solution of $KMnO_4$ is equivalent to 0.1000 millimole of $NaCHO_2$ (sodium formate) in the following titration: $3CHO_2^- + 2MnO_4^- + H_2O \rightarrow 3CO_2 + 2MnO_2 + 5OH^-$, what is the value of the $KMnO_4$ in terms of grams of CaO in the volumetric method for calcium in which that element is precipitated as $CaC_2O_4.H_2O$ and the precipitate is filtered, dissolved in dilute H_2SO_4, and the oxalate titrated with permanganate?

SOLUTION:

$$0.1000 \text{ millimole } NaCHO_2 = 0.2000 \text{ milliequivalent}$$

(since in the titration the oxidation number of C changes from $+2$ to $+4$)

$$\text{Normality } KMnO_4 = 0.2000 \ N$$

This normality applies only to the above type of titration in which the oxidation number of Mn in $KMnO_4$ changes by 3 units. Therefore,

$$\text{Normality } KMnO_4 \text{ (presence of acid)} = 0.2000 \times \tfrac{5}{3} = 0.3333 \ N$$

Each atom of Ca is combined with and equivalent to 1 mole of oxalate. Since the milliequivalent weight of the oxalate radical is its molecular weight over 2,000, the milliequivalent weight of CaO must be its molecular weight over 2,000.

$$1.000 \times 0.3333 \times \frac{CaO}{2,000} = 0.009347 \text{ gram } CaO. \quad Ans.$$

101. Dichromate Process. Potassium dichromate is occasionally used as an oxidimetric standard. With chemical indicators (*e.g.*, potassium ferricyanide as an external indicator, or diphenylamine sulfate as an internal indicator), the use of dichromate in direct titrations is restricted to the titration of ferrous iron.   Oxidizing substances can be determined by the dichromate process, as in the permanganate process, by the addition of a measured excess of a ferrous salt and the titration of the excess with the standard solution. Potassium dichromate titrations have greater applicability in potentiometric titrations where chemical indicators are not necessary.

The normal solution of potassium dichromate contains one-sixth of the gram-molecular weight of $K_2Cr_2O_7$ per liter (see Sec. 98).

EXAMPLE I.   What is the percentage of Fe_2O_3 in a sample of limonite ore (impure Fe_2O_3) if the iron from a 0.5000-gram sample is reduced and titrated with 35.15 ml. of a potassium dichromate solution of which 15.00 ml. are equivalent in oxidizing power to 25.00 ml. of a potassium permanganate solution which has an "iron value" of 0.004750 gram?   (This last expression is a conventional means of signifying that 1.000 ml. of the solution will oxidize 0.004750 gram of iron *from the divalent to the trivalent state.*)

SOLUTION:

$$\text{Normality of } KMnO_4 = \frac{0.004750}{1.000 \times Fe/1,000} = 0.08506$$

$$\text{Normality of } K_2Cr_2O_7 = 0.08506 \times 25.00/15.00 = 0.1418$$

$$\frac{35.15 \times 0.1418 \times \dfrac{Fe_2O_3}{2,000}}{0.5000} \times 100 = 79.60 \text{ per cent } Fe_2O_3. \quad \textit{Ans.}$$

EXAMPLE II.   Fusion with Na_2O_2 oxidizes the chromium in a 0.2000-gram sample of chromite ore to chromate.   The addition of a 50-ml. pipetful of ferrous sulfate solution reduces this in acid solution to chromic ions $(Cr_2O_7^= + 6Fe^{++} + 14H^+ \rightarrow 2Cr^{+++} + 6Fe^{+++} + 7H_2O)$, and the excess ferrous ions are titrated with 7.59 ml. of $0.1000\ N\ K_2Cr_2O_7$.   Each pipetful of ferrous solution is equivalent to 47.09 ml. of the standard $K_2Cr_2O_7$ solution.   What is the percentage of Cr in the sample?   What weight of sample of the chromite ore should be taken so that the milliliters of standard $0.1000\ N\ K_2Cr_2O_7$ that are equivalent to the ferrous solution added, minus the milliliters of K_2CrO_7 used in the titration, will equal the percentage of Cr_2O_3 in the sample?

SOLUTION: Net $K_2Cr_2O_7$ solution (equivalent to the Cr in the ore) = 47.09 − 7.59 = 39.50 ml.

$$\frac{39.50 \times 0.1000 \times \dfrac{Cr}{3,000}}{0.2000} \times 100 = 34.23 \text{ per cent Cr.} \quad \textit{Ans.}$$

The second part of this problem merely states that the net volume of

$0.1000\ N\ K_2Cr_2O_7$ (*i.e.*, the milliliters equivalent to the Cr in the sample) is equal in value to the percentage of Cr_2O_3.

$$\frac{a \times 0.1000 \times Cr_2O_3/6,000}{x} \times 100 = a$$

$$x = 0.2533 \text{ gram.} \quad Ans.$$

102. Ceric Sulfate or Cerate Process. Cerium in the valence of 4 is a very powerful oxidizing agent, the yellow 4-valent ceric or complex cerate ions being reduced to colorless 3-valent cerous ions.

$$Ce^{++++} + \epsilon \rightarrow Ce^{+++}$$

A solution of ceric sulfate is satisfactory for oxidimetry titrations and has certain advantages over potassium permanganate, particularly with respect to its greater stability and its lesser tendency to oxidize chloride ions. In the titration of reducing substances that in solution are colorless, the yellow color of the excess ceric ions serves as a fairly satisfactory indicator. Titration of ferrous ions can be accomplished with orthophenanthroline ("ferroin") as an internal indicator. The potential of the indicator in its two states of oxidation lies between those of ferrous-ferric iron and cerous-ceric cerium.

$$Fe^{++} = Fe^{+++} + \epsilon$$
$$Ferroin' \text{ (red)} = ferroin'' \text{ (blue)} + \epsilon$$
$$Ce^{+++} = Ce^{++++} + \epsilon$$

Ceric sulfate is particularly satisfactory in potentiometric titrations.

EXAMPLE. What weight of limonite should be taken so that after solution in HCl and reduction of the iron, the volume of a standard ceric solution required for titration will be one-half the percentage of Fe_2O_3 in the sample (6.00 ml. of the ceric solution $\approx$ 2.00 ml. KHC_2O_4 solution $\approx$ 3.00 ml. of $0.0800\ N$ NaOH)?

SOLUTION:

$$KHC_2O_4 \text{ soln.} = 0.0800 \times 3.00/2.00$$
$$= 0.120\ N \text{ as an acid}$$
$$= 0.240\ N \text{ as a reducing agent}$$
$$\text{Ceric soln.} = 0.240 \times 2.00/6.00 = 0.0800\ N$$
$$\frac{1 \times 0.0800 \times Fe_2O_3/2,000}{x} \times 100 = 2$$
$$x = 0.320 \text{ gram.} \quad Ans.$$

Problems

13.15. A solution of permanganate contains 2.608 grams of $KMnO_4$ per 750 ml. What is the normality of the solution and what is the value of 1.000 ml. in terms of (*a*) Fe_2O_3, (*b*) As_2O_3, (*c*) KHC_2O_4, (*d*) H_2O_2, (*e*) $U(SO_4)_2$ (oxidized to UO_2^{++})?

Ans. 0.1100 N. (*a*) 0.005440 gram, (*b*) 0.006144 gram, (*c*) 0.007046 gram, (*d*) 0.001871 gram, (*e*) 0.02367 gram.

13.16. Given a solution of $KMnO_4$ of which 1.000 ml. $\approx$ 1.000 ml. KHC_2O_4 solution $\approx$ 1.000 ml. $NaOH$ $\approx$ 0.1000 millimole of $KHC_8H_4O_4$ (potassium acid phthalate). What is the value of 1 ml. of it in terms of grams of Fe_2O_3? How many millimoles of Mn are present in each milliliter?

Ans. 0.01597 gram. 0.04000 millimoles.

13.17. How many grams of $KMnO_4$ are contained in a liter of potassium permanganate if a certain volume of it will oxidize a weight of potassium tetroxalate requiring one-half that volume of 0.2000 N potassium hydroxide solution for neutralization?

Ans. 4.214 grams.

13.18. What is the normality of a solution of potassium permanganate if 50.13 ml. will oxidize that weight of KHC_2O_4 which requires 43.42 ml. of 0.3010 N sodium hydroxide for neutralization?

Ans. 0.5214 N.

13.19. 1.000 ml. $KHC_2O_4.H_2C_2O_4.2H_2O$ $\approx$ 0.2000 ml. $KMnO_4$
          1.000 ml. $KMnO_4$ $\approx$ 0.1117 gram Fe

What is the normality of the tetroxalate solution when used as an acid?

Ans. 0.3000 N.

13.20. Given two permanganate solutions. Solution A contains 0.01507 gram of $KMnO_4$ per milliliter. Solution B is of such strength that 20.00 ml. $\approx$ 0.1200 gram Fe. In what proportion must the two solutions be mixed in order that the resulting solution shall have the same oxidizing power in the presence of acid as 0.3333 N $K_2Cr_2O_7$ has?

Ans. $\dfrac{\text{Vol. } A}{\text{Vol. } B} = 1.576$.

13.21. How many milliliters of $K_2Cr_2O_7$ solution containing 25.00 grams of anhydrous salt per liter would react with 3.402 grams of $FeSO_4.7H_2O$ in dilute acid solution?

Ans. 24.00 ml.

13.22. If 25.0 ml. of ferrous sulfate solution in sulfuric acid require 31.25 ml. of 0.100 N $K_2Cr_2O_7$ solution for oxidation, how much water must be added to 200 ml. of the reducing solution to make it one-twentieth normal?

Ans. 300 ml.

13.23. How many grams of pure $K_2Cr_2O_7$ must be weighed out, dissolved, and diluted to exactly 700 ml. to make a solution which, when used in the titration of iron in a sample of ore, shall be of such a strength that four times the number of milliliters used with a half-gram sample will represent one-half the percentage of FeO in the sample?

Ans. 19.12 grams.

13.24. How many grams of pure Pb_3O_4 (= $PbO_2.2PbO$) must be dissolved in a mixture of 30 ml. of 6 N H_2SO_4 and 2.000 millimoles of $KHC_2O_4.H_2C_2O_4.2H_2O$ so that 30.00 ml. of 0.1000 N $KMnO_4$ will be required for the excess oxalate?

Ans. 1.714 grams.

13.25. What weight of spathic iron ore (impure $FeCO_3$) should be taken for analysis so that the number of milliliters of $KMnO_4$ (1.000 ml. $\approx$ 0.3000 ml. of potassium tetroxalate solution which is one-fourth normal as an acid) used in titration will be twice the percentage of FeO in the ore?

Ans. 1.438 grams.

13.26. If 0.9000 gram of oxalic acid ($H_2C_2O_4.2H_2O$) is allowed to react with 0.5000 gram of pyrolusite and the excess oxalic acid is titrated with permanganate, what must be the normality of the permanganate in order that one-half the percentage of MnO_2 may be obtained by subtracting the buret reading from the volume A of the permanganate equivalent to the 0.9000 gram of oxalic acid used? What is the value of A?

Ans. 0.2300 N. 62.09 ml.

13.27. A sample of steel weighing 2.20 grams and containing 0.620 per cent of Mn is dissolved, and the manganese is eventually titrated in neutral solution with standard $KMnO_4$. ($3Mn^{++} + 2MnO_4^- + 2H_2O \rightarrow 5MnO_2 + 4H^+$.) If 6.88 ml. are required, what is the value of each milliliter of the $KMnO_4$ in terms of (a) $H_2C_2O_4.2H_2O$, (b) As_2O_3?

Ans. (a) 0.00756 gram, (b) 0.00593 gram.

13.28. Balance the following equation:

$$K_2Na[Co(NO_2)_6] + MnO_4^- + H^+ \rightarrow K^+ + Na^+ + Co^{++} + NO_3^- + Mn^{++} + H_2O$$

This represents a volumetric method for determining potassium. Calculate from the molar relationships the value of 1.00 ml. of $KMnO_4$ (of which 1.00 ml. $\backsimeq$ 0.0080 gram Fe_2O_3) in terms of grams of K.

Ans. 0.00071 gram.

13.29. Sodium formate, $NaCHO_2$, can be titrated in neutral solution according to the equation: $3CHO_2^- + 2MnO_4^- + H_2O \rightarrow 2MnO_2 + 3CO_2 + 5OH^-$. If 10.00 ml. of the $KMnO_4$ are equivalent to 0.08161 gram of sodium formate by this method, (a) what is the "iron value" of each milliliter of the $KMnO_4$, (b) what is the value of each milliliter in terms of millimoles of H_2O_2, (c) what is the value of each milliliter in terms of grams of CaO, and (d) what is the value of each milliliter in terms of grams of Mn by the Volhard method?

Ans. (a) 0.02234 gram, (b) 0.2000 millimole, (c) 0.01122 gram, (d) 0.006598 gram.

13.30. Calcium can be precipitated as $CaC_2O_4.H_2O$, and the precipitate filtered, washed, and dissolved in dilute H_2SO_4. The oxalic acid formed can then be titrated with potassium permanganate. If a 0.1000 N solution of $KMnO_4$ is used, calculate the value of 1.000 ml. in terms of (a) Ca, (b) CaO, (c) $CaCO_3$.

Ans. (a) 0.002004 gram, (b) 0.002804 gram, (c) 0.005004 gram.

13.31. If the iron in a 0.1500-gram sample of iron ore is reduced and subsequently requires 15.03 ml. of permanganate for oxidation, what is the purity of the ore expressed as percentage of (a) Fe, (b) FeO, (c) Fe_2O_3? (4.000 ml. $KMnO_4$ $\backsimeq$ 3.000 ml. $KHC_2O_4.$ $H_2C_2O_4$ solution $\backsimeq$ 3.000 ml. 0.1000 N NaOH.)

Ans. (a) 55.95 per cent, (b) 71.96 per cent, (c) 80.00 per cent.

13.32. What is the percentage purity of a sample of impure $H_2C_2O_4.2H_2O$ if a sample weighing 0.2003 gram requires 29.30 ml. of permanganate solution, of which 1.000 ml. $\backsimeq$ 0.006023 gram Fe?

Ans. 99.53 per cent.

13.33. To a half-gram sample of pyrolusite is added a certain weight of oxalic acid ($H_2C_2O_4.2H_2O$). After reaction in acid solution is complete, the excess oxalic acid requires 30.00 ml. of 0.1000 N KMnO$_4$ for oxidation. If the pyrolusite is calculated to contain 86.93 per cent MnO$_2$, what is the weight of oxalic acid added? (MnO$_2$ + H$_2$C$_2$O$_4$ + 2H$^+$ → Mn^{++} + 2CO$_2$ + 2H$_2$O.)

Ans. 0.8194 gram.

13.34. One hundred milliliters of K$_2$Cr$_2$O$_7$ solution (10.0 grams per liter), 5.00 ml. of 6 N H$_2$SO$_4$, and 75.0 ml. of FeSO$_4$ solution (80.0 grams FeSO$_4$.7H$_2$O per liter) are mixed and the resulting solution is titrated with 0.2121 N KMnO$_4$. Calculate the volume required.

Ans. 5.63 ml.

13.35. In analyzing a one-gram sample of hydrogen peroxide with permanganate, what must be the normality of the KMnO$_4$ in order that the buret reading shall represent directly the percentage of H$_2$O$_2$?

Ans. 0.5880 N.

13.36. A sample of magnetite (impure Fe$_3$O$_4$) is fused with Na$_2$O$_2$ and all the iron thus oxidized to the ferric state. After leaching with water and acidifying, the total iron is determined by reduction in a Jones reductor and titration with standard KMnO$_4$. Volume of KMnO$_4$ required = 30.10 ml. It is of such concentration that 2.000 ml. ≎ 3.000 ml. KHC$_2$O$_4$ solution ≎ 2.000 ml. NaOH ≎ 1.000 ml. H$_2$SO$_4$ ≎ 0.008138 gram ZnO. What is the normality of the KMnO$_4$ and how many grams of Fe$_3$O$_4$ are present in the sample of magnetite?

Ans. 0.2000 N, 0.4646 gram.

13.37. Six millimoles of MnO are ignited in air (6MnO + O$_2$ → 2Mn$_3$O$_4$) and the resulting Mn$_3$O$_4$ = (MnO$_2$.2MnO) is dissolved in a solution containing 25 ml. of 6 N H$_2$SO$_4$ and A grams of FeSO$_4$.(NH$_4$)$_2$SO$_4$.6H$_2$O. The manganese is reduced by the ferrous ions completely to the divalent form. If the excess ferrous ions require 12.00 ml. of KMnO$_4$ (containing 0.05000 millimole of KMnO$_4$ per ml.) calculate the value of A.

Ans. 2.745 grams.

13.38. A sample of steel weighs 2.00 grams and contains 0.55 per cent Mn. After dissolving in HNO$_3$ the manganese is oxidized to permanganate with solid BiO$_2$ and the excess BiO$_2$ is filtered off. Excess FeSO$_4$.7H$_2$O (dissolved in water) is now added and the excess ferrous ions require 20.0 ml. of 0.200 N KMnO$_4$. How many grams of FeSO$_4$.7H$_2$O were used? If the reduction had been made with Na$_2$C$_2$O$_4$ instead of with FeSO$_4$.7H$_2$O, how many millimoles of Na$_2$C$_2$O$_4$ should have been added in order for 20.0 ml. of the KMnO$_4$ to be required for the excess oxalate?

Ans. 1.39 grams. 2.50 millimoles.

13.39. A sample of chromite contains 30.08 per cent Cr$_2$O$_3$. After fusion of a 0.2000-gram sample with Na$_2$O$_2$ and dissolving in acid, how many grams of FeSO$_4$.-(NH$_4$)$_2$SO$_4$.6H$_2$O should be added so that the excess ferrous ions will require 15.00 ml. of 0.6011 N K$_2$Cr$_2$O$_7$? How many milligram-atoms of Cr does each milliliter of the dichromate contain? If 3.000 ml. of this dichromate ≎ 2.000 ml. of KHC$_2$O$_4$.-H$_2$C$_2$O$_4$.2H$_2$O solution ≎ 1.000 ml. KOH ≎ 3.000 ml. H$_2$SO$_4$, how many moles of Fe$_2$O$_3$.xH$_2$O is each milliliter of the H$_2$SO$_4$ capable of dissolving, and how many milli-equivalents as an oxidizing agent would this amount of Fe$_2$O$_3$.xH$_2$O represent?

Ans. 4.467 grams. 0.2006 mg.-atoms. 0.00007514 moles, 0.1503 me.

13.40. A sample of steel weighing 2.00 grams is analyzed for manganese by the bismuthate method. If a 25-ml. pipetful of 0.120 N FeSO$_4$ were used for the reduction of the oxidized manganese and 22.9 ml. of 0.0833 N $KMnO_4$ were used in the titration of the excess ferrous ions, what volume of the $KMnO_4$ would have been used if the same weight of sample had been analyzed (*a*) by the chlorate method (using the same 25-ml. pipetful of the above $FeSO_4$); (*b*) by the Volhard method on a ½ aliquot portion of the prepared solution? What is the percentage of Mn in the steel?

Ans. (*a*) 30.8 ml., (*b*) 4.37 ml. 0.600 per cent.

13.41. A sample of chrome iron ore weighing 0.3010 gram is fused with Na_2O_2, leached with water, and acidified with H_2SO_4. The resulting solution of dichromate is treated with a solution containing dissolved crystals of $FeSO_4.(NH_4)_2SO_4.6H_2O$, and the excess ferrous ions titrated with standard dichromate (containing 5.070 grams $K_2Cr_2O_7$ per liter). A maximum of 45.00 per cent Cr_2O_3 in the ore being allowed for, what minimum weight of $FeSO_4.(NH_4)_2SO_4.6H_2O$ should be used so that not more than a 50-ml. buretful of the standard dichromate would be required?

Ans. 4.124 grams.

13.42. A sample of pure sodium oxalate, $Na_2C_2O_4$, weighing 0.2500 gram, when dissolved in dilute H_2SO_4 requires 40.15 ml. of ceric sulfate solution to give a permanent yellow color to the solution. What is the normality of the ceric sulfate solution? How many grams of pure $Ce(SO_4)_2.2(NH_4)_2SO_4.2H_2O$ should be dissolved in 500 ml. of solution in order to prepare a solution of this normality? If a sample of limonite weighing 0.3000 gram is dissolved in HCl, the iron reduced by metallic silver and then requires 25.03 ml. of the above ceric sulfate solution, orthophenanthroline being used as indicator, what percentage of Fe_2O_3 is shown to be present in the limonite?

Ans. 0.09294 *N*. 29.40 grams. 62.03 per cent.

13.43. What is the normality of a solution of $KMnO_4$ and what is the value of each milliliter in terms of grams of Fe if when titrating a 0.1000-gram sample of impure KNO_2 (which is oxidized to nitrate) the buret reading is one-half the percentage of N_2O_3 in the sample? How many gram-atoms of Mn does each liter of the $KMnO_4$ contain?

13.44. What must be the value of 1.000 ml. of ceric sulfate in terms of grams of Fe_2O_3 so that in the titration of a half-gram sample of impute sodium arsenite (arsenite oxidized to arsenate), the percentage of As_2O_3 in the sample will be twice the buret reading? What is the molarity of the ceric solution?

13.45. A stock solution of $KMnO_4$ is made up and standardized. It is found that each milliliter is equivalent to 0.01597 gram of Fe_2O_3. A 10-ml. pipetful of the permanganate is reduced with H_2O_2 in the presence of acid and the excess H_2O_2 is destroyed by boiling. The resulting solution is then made neutral and the manganous ions in the solution are titrated with more of the original stock $KMnO_4$, the solution being kept neutral with ZnO (Volhard method). How many milliliters of $KMnO_4$ would be required in the titration?

13.46. A student standardized a solution of KOH and one of $KMnO_4$ against the same salt ($KHC_2O_4.H_2C_2O_4.2H_2O$). The normality of the former was found to be 0.09963 as a base and of the latter to be 0.1328 as an oxidizing agent. By coincidence, exactly 50.00 ml. of solution were used in each standardization. Calculate the ratio of the weight of tetroxalate used in the first case to that used in the second case.

13.47. A powder is composed of oxalic acid ($H_2C_2O_4.2H_2O$), potassium binoxalate ($KHC_2O_4.H_2O$), and an inert impurity. Find the percentage of each constituent from the following. A sample of the powder weighing 1.200 grams reacts with 37.80

ml. of 0.2500 N NaOH solution; 0.4000 gram of powder reacts with 43.10 ml. of 0.1250 N permanganate solution.

13.48. It requires 15.27 ml. of $SnCl_2$ solution to reduce an amount of iron that can be oxidized by 16.27 ml. of permanganate solution. This volume of the permanganate will also oxidize that amount of $KHC_2O_4.H_2C_2O_4.2H_2O$ solution which reacts with 16.24 ml. of 0.1072 N NaOH. Calculate the normality of the $SnCl_2$ solution.

13.49. Given the following data, calculate the percentage of MnO_2 in a sample of pyrolusite:

Sample = 0.5217 gram
$KHC_2O_4.H_2C_2O_4.2H_2O$ added to react with MnO_2 = 0.7242 gram
$KMnO_4$ used in titrating excess = 22.42 ml.
1.000 ml. $KMnO_4 \backsimeq 0.007620$ gram As_2O_3.

13.50. A 50.00-ml. pipetful of 0.2016 N oxalic acid is added to a sample of pure MnO_2 to reduce it. The excess of oxalic acid requires 10.15 ml. of 0.2008 N $KMnO_4$ for its oxidation. What weight of MnO_2 is present?

13.51. How many grams of Cr_2O_3 are present in a sample of chromite ore if when decomposed by fusion with Na_2O_2, acidified with H_2SO_4, and treated with 3.000 millimoles of $KHC_2O_4.H_2C_2O_4.2H_2O(Cr_2O_7^= + 3C_2O_4^= + 14H^+ \rightarrow 2Cr^{+++} + 6CO_2 + 7H_2O)$, the excess oxalate requires 20.00 ml. of 0.1000 N $KMnO_4$?

13.52. A sample of spathic iron ore is analyzed for calcium by the permanganate method, following the precipitation of the calcium as oxalate. What weight of sample must be taken so that one-half the number of milliliters of 0.1000 N $KMnO_4$ will represent the percentage of CaO in the sample?

13.53. What weight of iron ore should be taken for analysis so that the milliliters of 0.0833 N permanganate multiplied by 2 will give the percentage of Fe_2O_3 in the sample?

13.54. The qualitative analysis of a certain silicate shows the presence of a large quantity of calcium and only traces of other positive elements. In the quantitative analysis, the silica is removed and the calcium is precipitated from the filtrate as calcium oxalate. It is found that the milliliters of 0.1660 N $KMnO_4$ required to oxidize the oxalate in a half-gram sample is almost exactly equal to the percentage of silica in the sample. What is the empirical formula of the pure mineral?

13.55. Heulandite is hydrous acid calcium metasilicate and yields on analysis 14.8 per cent water and 16.7 per cent alumina. If the calcium were precipitated as calcium oxalate from a 1.00-gram sample, 32.8 ml. of 0.100 N $KMnO_4$ would be required for oxidation. Three-fifths of the water exists as water of crystallization. What is the empirical formula of heulandite?

13.56. A sample of alloy containing manganese and weighing 4.35 grams is dissolved and the manganese eventually titrated in *neutral* solution with a standard permanganate having an "iron value" of 0.00640 gram (*i.e.*, 1.000 ml. will oxidize that amount of ferrous iron in acid solution). A volume of 13.05 ml. is required. Calculate the percentage of Mn in the alloy.

13.57. A sample of magnetite (impure Fe_3O_4) is fused with Na_2O_2 and all the iron thus oxidized to the ferric state. After leaching with water, the iron in the solution is determine by reducing with $SnCl_2$, destroying the excess stannous ions, and titrating with 0.3000 N $K_2Cr_2O_7$. If 30.00 ml. are required, calculate the number of grams of Fe_3O_4 in the sample. How many grams of Cr are present in each milliliter of the $K_2Cr_2O_7$? How many milligrams of CeO_2 is each milliliter of the dichromate equivalent to as an oxidizing agent?

13.58. From the following data, compute the weight of iron ore to be taken for analysis such that the percentage of Fe_2O_3 present is numerically equal to twice the number of milliliters of $K_2Cr_2O_7$ used in the titration:

40.00 ml. HCl solution $\backsim$ 2.880 grams of AgCl.

35.00 ml. HCl solution $\backsim$ 40.00 ml. of $KHC_2O_4.H_2C_2O_4$ solution.

35.00 ml. of tetroxalate solution $\backsim$ 40.00 ml. of $K_2Cr_2O_7$ solution.

13.59. A solution of dichromate is prepared by dissolving 4.883 grams of pure $K_2Cr_2O_7$ and diluting to exactly one liter; a solution of ferrous salt is prepared by dissolving 39.46 grams of $FeSO_4.(NH_4)_2SO_4.6H_2O$ and diluting to one liter. What volume of the dichromate solution must be transferred to the ferrous solution and thoroughly mixed so that the normality of one solution as a reducing agent will be the same as the normality of the other solution as an oxidizing agent?

13.60. An oxide of iron weighing 0.1000 gram is fused with $KHSO_4$, and the fused material is dissolved in acid. The iron is reduced with stannous chloride, mercuric chloride is added to oxidize the excess stannous ions, and the iron is titrated with 0.1000 N dichromate solution. If 12.94 ml. were used, what is the formula of the oxide—FeO, Fe_2O_3, or Fe_3O_4?

13.61. Two millimoles of pure Pb_3O_4 ($= PbO_2.2PbO$) are dissolved in a solution containing a mixture of 25 ml. of 6 N H_2SO_4 and A grams of $FeSO_4.(NH_4)_2SO_4.6H_2O$, the 4-valent lead being reduced to Pb^{++}. The excess of ferrous ions requires 12.00 ml. of 0.2500 N $KMnO_4$ for oxidation (a) What is the value of A? (b) How many milligram-atoms of Mn are present in each milliliter of the $KMnO_4$? (c) If potassium tetroxalate, $KHC_2O_4.H_2C_2O_4.2H_2O$, had been substituted for the ferrous ammonium sulfate above, how many milliequivalents, how many millimoles, and how many grams of the oxalate would have been used for the reduction so that the excess oxalate would have required 12.00 ml. of 0.2500 N $KMnO_4$? (d) If lead sesquioxide, Pb_2O_3, were analyzed by a similar method, what would be the milliequivalent weight of Pb_2O_3?

13.62. From the following data, calculate the percentage of iron in a sample of limonite:

$$1.000 \text{ ml. } K_2Cr_2O_7 \backsim 0.006299 \text{ gram Fe}$$
$$\text{Dichromate solution used} = 47.56 \text{ ml.}$$
$$\text{Ferrous solution used} = 2.85 \text{ ml.}$$
$$\text{Sample taken for analysis} = 0.6170 \text{ gram}$$
$$1.000 \text{ ml. ferrous solution} \backsim 1.021 \text{ ml. } K_2Cr_2O_7$$

13.63. A certain chrome iron ore is known to contain 24.80 per cent Cr. A sample weighing 0.2580 gram is fused with Na_2O_2, leached with water, and acidified with H_2SO_4. The resulting solution of dichromate is treated with a weight of $FeSO_4.7H_2O$ crystals which happens to be just 50 per cent more than the amount necessary to reduce the dichromate. The excess of ferrous ions is titrated with standard dichromate (containing 0.02000 millimole $K_2Cr_2O_7$ per milliliter). What volume is required? (*Hint:* It is not necessary to calculate the amount of ferrous salt required.)

13.64. A solution of ceric sulfate is of such normality that 26.73 ml. are required to titrate the ferrous iron obtainable from 1.052 grams of $FeSO_4.(NH_4)_2SO_4.6H_2O$. How many grams of $Ce(SO_4)_2.2(NH_4)_2SO_4.2H_2O$ should be dissolved in 750 ml. of water and the resulting solution diluted to one liter in order to prepare a solution of such normality that each milliliter is equivalent to 0.006500 gram $KHC_2O_4.H_2C_2O_4.2H_2O$? What is the ratio of the normalities of the two solutions?

13.65. (a) What is the normality of a solution of $KMnO_4$ if each milliliter will oxidize 0.008377 gram of iron from the ferrous to the ferric state? (b) How many grams of Mn do 10.00 ml. of such a solution contain? (c) How many grams of Mn would 10.00 ml. of this $KMnO_4$ oxidize to MnO_2 by the Volhard method ($3Mn^{++} + 2MnO_4^- + 2ZnO \rightarrow 5MnO_2 + 2Zn^{++}$)? (d) How many milliliters of this $KMnO_4$ would be required to titrate 0.1200 millimole of sodium formate ($NaCHO_2$) according to the reaction: $3CHO_2^- + 2MnO_4^- + H_2O \rightarrow 2MnO_2 + 3CO_2 + 5OH^-$? (e) How many grams of CaO would each milliliter of the $KMnO_4$ be equivalent to in the volumetric method for calcium? (f) How many grams of As_2O_3 would each milliliter of the $KMnO_4$ be equivalent to in the titration of arsenite to arsenate?

13.66. Find the percentage of Pb_3O_4 in a sample of red lead that has been adulterated with PbO. 2.500 grams of the pigment are treated with 50.00 ml. of potassium tetroxalate solution which is 0.1500 N as an acid, and the excess of the latter requires 30.00 ml. of permanganate of which each milliliter is equivalent to 0.005584 gram of iron.

13.67. A sample of steel weighing 2.50 grams is analyzed for manganese by the chlorate method (see above). If a 25-ml. pipetful of 0.110 N $FeSO_4$ were used to dissolve the precipitated MnO_2 and 18.4 ml. of 0.125 N $KMnO_4$ were used to titrate the excess ferrous ions, what volume of the permanganate would have been used if the same weight of sample had been analyzed (a) by the bismuthate method (using the same 25-ml. pipetful of the above $FeSO_4$); (b) by the Volhard method on a $\frac{1}{2}$ aliquot portion of the prepared solution? What is the percentage of Mn in the steel?

103. Iodimetric Process.

The fundamental reaction in this process is that between iodine and sodium thiosulfate, with starch (or sometimes chloroform) as the indicator.

$$I_2 + 2S_2O_3^= \rightarrow 2I^- + S_4O_6^=$$

Titrations by this process may be divided into two groups, those involving direct titrations with standard iodine and those involving titrations with standard sodium thiosulfate.

Iodine solutions are prepared by dissolving iodine crystals, together with potassium iodide, in water. A normal solution contains $I_2/2 = 126.9$ grams of iodine per liter. Standard solutions are used to titrate directly certain reducing agents of which the following are typical:

SUBSTANCE	OXIDIZED TO
H_2S	S
SO_3^-	SO_4^-
$S_2O_3^-$	$S_4O_6^-$
$AsO_3^=$	$AsO_4^=$
$SbO_3^=$	$SbO_4^=$

Sodium thiosulfate solutions are prepared by dissolving crystals of the salt in water. A normal solution contains $Na_2S_2O_3.5H_2O/1 = 248.2$ grams of the hydrated salt per liter (see Sec. 98). Standard solutions of thiosulfate can be used to titrate almost any oxidizing substance. The titration is made, however, by adding to the solution of oxidizing substance a large excess (roughly measured) of potassium iodide. The oxidizing substance is reduced, liberating *an equivalent amount* of iodine, and the liberated iodine is titrated with thiosulfate. Typical oxidizing agents determined in this way are as follows:

SUBSTANCE	EQUATION
$Cr_2O_7^-$	$Cr_2O_7^- + 6I^- + 14H^+ \rightarrow 2Cr^{+++} + 3I_2 + 7H_2O$
MnO_4^-	$2MnO_4^- + 10I^- + 16H^+ \rightarrow 2Mn^{++} + 5I_2 + 8H_2O$
BrO_3^-	$BrO_3^- + 6I^- + 6H^+ \rightarrow Br^- + 3I_2 + 3H_2O$
IO_3^-	$IO_3^- + 6I^- + 6H^+ \rightarrow I^- + 3I_2 + 3H_2O$
Cu^{++}	$2Cu^{++} + 4I^- \rightarrow 2CuI + I_2$
Cl_2	$Cl_2 + 2I^- \rightarrow 2Cl^- + I_2$
H_2O_2	$H_2O_2 + 2I^- + 2H^+ \rightarrow I_2 + 2H_2O$

Since an oxidizing agent liberates its own equivalent of iodine, the volume of thiosulfate required for the liberated iodine in any given case is the same as would be required if the thiosulfate were used directly and reduced the substance to the form indicated. In calculations, therefore, the equivalent weight of the substance titrated is found in the usual way by dividing the formula weight of the substance by the total change in oxidation number.

In titrations in acid solution, a standard solution of potassium iodate containing an excess of potassium iodide is a convenient substitute for standard iodine. It is a colorless, stable solution, but when it comes in contact with acid the two ingredients immediately interact and liberate free iodine ($IO_3^- + 6I^- + 6H^+ \rightarrow I^- + 3I_2 + 3H_2O$). In the titration of a substance in acid solution, this standard solution, therefore, behaves as if it were a standard solution of iodine. It is used, for example, in the determination of sulfur in steel. Since the iodate molecule has the oxidizing equivalent of 6 iodine atoms, a tenth-normal solution contains $KIO_3/60 = 3.567$ grams of KIO_3 per liter and can be prepared by dissolving this amount of the pure crystals, together with an excess of potassium iodide, in water and diluting to exactly one liter.

EXAMPLE I. An excess of potassium iodide is added to a solution of potassium dichromate, and the liberated iodine is titrated with 48.80 ml. of 0.1000 N sodium thiosulfate solution. How many grams of $K_2Cr_2O_7$ did the dichromate solution contain?

SOLUTION: Potassium dichromate liberates an equivalent amount of iodine from an iodide (*i.e.*, 6 gram-atoms = 6 gram-equivalents of iodine per mole of dichromate):

$$Cr_2O_7^- + 6I^- + 14H^+ \rightarrow 2Cr^{+++} + 3I_2 + 7H_2O$$

and the liberated iodine is titrated with thiosulfate

$$2S_2O_3^- + I_2 \rightarrow S_4O_6^- + 2I^-$$

The volume of titrating solution is the same as it would have been if the original solution had been titrated directly to the indicated products.

$$\text{Grams of } K_2Cr_2O_7 = 48.80 \times 0.1000 \times \frac{K_2Cr_2O_7}{6,000} = 0.2393. \quad Ans.$$

EXAMPLE II.   The sulfur from 4.00 grams of steel is evolved as H_2S and titrated with 1.60 ml. of 0.05000 N iodine solution.   What is the percentage of S in the steel?   What is the value of 1.000 ml. of the iodine in terms of As_2O_3?   How many milliliters of the iodine will be reduced by 40.00 ml. of $Na_2S_2O_3$ solution of which 1.000 ml. $\approx$ 0.006357 gram Cu. What volume of iodate-iodide solution containing 10.0 millimoles of KIO_3 and 50.0 grams of KI per liter would be required to titrate the H_2S from 5.00 grams of the above steel?   The equations involved are as follows:

$$H_2S + I_2 \rightarrow \underline{S} + 2I^- + 2H^+$$
$$AsO_3^{\equiv} + 2HCO_3^- + I_2 \rightarrow AsO_4^{\equiv} + 2I^- + 2CO_2 + H_2O$$
$$2Cu^{++} + 4I^- \rightarrow 2\underline{CuI} + I_2$$
$$IO_3^- + 6I^- + 6H^+ \rightarrow 3\underline{I_2} + I^- + 3H_2O$$

SOLUTION:

$$\frac{1.60 \times 0.05000 \times \dfrac{S}{2,000}}{4.00} \times 100 = 0.0320 \text{ per cent S.} \quad Ans.$$

$$1.000 \times 0.05000 \times \frac{As_2O_3}{4,000} = 0.002473 \text{ gram } As_2O_3. \quad Ans.$$

The addition of KI to a copper solution will cause reduction of the Cu and the liberation of an amount of iodine equivalent to the copper present. This iodine may be titrated with thiosulfate and the normality of the latter found from the amount of Cu present.   In the above case,

$$\text{Normality of } Na_2S_2O_3 \text{ solution} = \frac{0.006357}{1.000 \times Cu/1,000} = 0.1000 \ N$$

$$\text{Volume of } 0.0500 \ N \ I_2 \text{ solution} = 40.00 \times \frac{0.1000}{0.05000} = 80.00 \text{ ml.} \quad Ans.$$

$$\text{10.0 millimoles } KIO_3 = 60.0 \text{ milliequivalents}$$
$$\text{Normality of } KIO_3 = 0.0600 \ N$$

$$\frac{x \times 0.0600 \times S/2,000}{5.00} \times 100 = 0.0320$$

$$x = 1.67 \text{ ml.} \quad Ans.$$

The reaction $AsO_3^{\equiv} + I_2 + H_2O \rightleftarrows AsO_4^{\equiv} + 2I^- + 2H^+$ is reversible, for 3-valent arsenic is oxidized by iodine in neutral solution, whereas 5-valent arsenic is reduced by iodide in the presence of acid with the liberation of free iodine.   These reactions can be made use of in the determination of the two forms of arsenic when present in the same solution.

EXAMPLE III.   A powder consists of $Na_2HAsO_3 + As_2O_5 + $ inert material.   A sample weighing 0.2500 gram is dissolved and titrated with standard iodine in a solution kept neutral by excess dissolved $NaHCO_3$ $(AsO_3^{\equiv} + I_2 + 2HCO_3^{-} \rightarrow AsO_4^{\equiv} + 2I^{-} + 2CO_2 + H_2O)$.   The titration requires 15.80 ml. of 0.1030 N I_2.   Hydrochloric acid and an excess of KI are added $(AsO_4^{\equiv} + 2I^{-} + 8H^{+} \rightarrow As^{+++} + I_2 + 4H_2O)$ and the liberated iodine requires 20.70 ml. of 0.1300 N $Na_2S_2O_3$.   Calculate the percentages of Na_2HAsO_3 and As_2O_5 in the sample.

SOLUTION:

$$15.80 \times 0.1030 = 1.628 \text{ milliequivalents 3-valent As}$$
$$20.70 \times 0.1300 = 2.691 \text{ milliequivalents total As}$$
$$2.691 - 1.628 \;\; = 1.063 \text{ milliequivalents 5-valent As}$$

$$\left.\begin{array}{l} \dfrac{1.628 \times \dfrac{Na_2HAsO_3}{2,000}}{0.2500} \times 100 = 55.33 \text{ per cent } Na_2HAsO_3 \\[4ex] \dfrac{1.063 \times \dfrac{As_2O_5}{4,000}}{0.2500} \times 100 = 24.42 \text{ per cent } As_2O_5 \end{array}\right\} \quad Ans.$$

Problems

13.68. A solution of iodine contains 15.76 grams of I_2 per liter.   What is the value of each milliliter as an oxidizing agent in terms of (a) SO_2, (b) H_2SO_3, (c) $Na_2S_2O_3$, (d) As?

Ans.   (a) 0.003978 gram, (b) 0.005097 gram, (c) 0.01963 gram, (d) 0.004655 gram.

13.69. What is the value of 1.000 ml. of 0.04000 N sodium thiosulfate solution in terms of Cu?   What is the normality of a thiosulfate solution if 25.00 ml. are required to titrate the iodine liberated by 0.01563 gram of copper?

Ans.   0.002543 gram.   0.009833 N.

13.70. What is the value of 1.000 ml. of an iodine solution (1.000 ml. $\backsim$ 0.03000 gram $Na_2S_2O_3$) in terms of As_2O_3?

Ans.   0.009386 gram.

13.71. From the following data calculate the normality and molarity of the $Na_2S_2O_3$ solution and the value of 1.000 ml. in terms of grams of potassium bi-iodate $[KH(IO_3)_2]$.
1.000 ml. $K_2Cr_2O_7$ $\backsim$ 0.005585 gram of Fe.
20.00 ml. $K_2Cr_2O_7$ liberates sufficient iodine from potassium iodide to require 32.46 ml. $Na_2S_2O_3$ solution for reduction.

Ans.   0.06162 N, 0.06162 M, 0.002003 gram.

13.72. Forty milliliters of $KMnO_4$ solution (1.000 ml. $\backsim$ 0.005000 gram Fe) are added to KI and the liberated iodine is titrated with sodium thiosulfate solution requiring 35.90 ml.   What is the value of 1.000 ml. of the thiosulfate solution in terms of copper?

Ans.   0.006345 gram.

13.73. A solution of sodium thiosulfate is freshly prepared, and 48.00 ml. are required to titrate the iodine liberated from an excess of KI solution by 0.3000 gram of pure KIO_3. What are the normality of the thiosulfate and its value in terms of iodine?

Ans. 0.1752 N, 0.02224 gram.

13.74. The thiosulfate solution of the preceding problem is allowed to stand, and 1.00 per cent of the $Na_2S_2O_3$ is decomposed by a trace of acid present in the solution $(S_2O_3^- + 2H^+ \rightarrow H_2SO_3 + S)$. What is the new normality of the solution as a reducing agent, assuming oxidation of sulfite to sulfate?

Ans. 0.1768 N.

13.75. A steel weighing 5.00 grams is treated with HCl and the H_2S is evolved and eventually titrated with a solution containing 0.0100 mole of KIO_3 and 60 grams of KI per liter. If 3.00 ml. are required, what is the percentage of sulfur in the steel?

Ans. 0.0576 per cent.

13.76. If 20.00 ml. of thiosulfate (1.000 ml. $\approx$ 0.03750 gram $CuSO_4.5H_2O$) are required for a certain weight of pyrolusite by the Bunsen iodimetric method, what weight of $H_2C_2O_4.2H_2O$ should be added to a similar sample to require 20.00 ml. of 0.1000 N $KMnO_4$ by the commonly used indirect method? In the Bunsen method MnO_2 is reduced by HCl, the Cl_2 liberated from the latter is passed into KI solution, and the liberated iodine is titrated with thiosulfate.

Ans. 0.3154 gram.

13.77. Titrating with 0.05000 N iodine, what weight of stibnite ore should be taken so that the percentage of Sb_2S_3 in the sample will be $1\frac{1}{2}$ times the buret reading? $(SbO_3^= + I_2 + 2HCO_3^- \rightarrow SbO_4^= + 2I^- + 2CO_2 + H_2O)$. How many millimoles of $Na_2S_2O_3.5H_2O$ is each liter of the above iodine equivalent to?

Ans. 0.2831 gram.   50.00 millimoles.

13.78. A sample of sodium sulfite weighing 1.468 grams was added to 100 ml. of 0.1000 N iodine. The excess iodine was titrated with 42.40 ml. of $Na_2S_2O_3.5H_2O$ solution of which 1.000 ml. was equivalent to the iodine liberated from 0.01574 gram of KI. Calculate the percentage of Na_2SO_3 in the sample.

Ans. 25.67 per cent.

13.79. A sample of stibnite containing 70.00 per cent Sb is given to a student for analysis. He titrates with a solution of iodine of which he had found 1.000 ml. to be equivalent to 0.004948 gram of As_2O_3. The normality of the solution, however, had changed, owing to volatilization of iodine, and the student reports 70.25 per cent Sb. What are the percentage error and the present normality of the iodine solution, and how much 0.2000 N iodine solution must be added to one liter of the solution to bring it back to its original strength? $(SbO_3^= + I_2 + 2HCO_3^- \rightarrow SbO_4^= + 2I^- + 2CO_2 + H_2O.)$

Ans. 0.36 per cent, 0.09965 N.   3.5 ml.

13.80. A solution contains dissolved Na_3AsO_3 and Na_3AsO_4. If 0.100 millimole of $KBrO_3$ is required to oxidize the As(III) and bleach methyl orange indicator, and if the total arsenate in the resulting solution gives with uranyl ions a precipitate of $UO_2NH_4AsO_4.xH_2O$ which ignites to 0.400 millimole of U_3O_8, how many grams of Na_3AsO_4 are shown to be originally present?

Ans. 0.250 gram.

13.81. A sample of impure potassium iodide weighing 0.3100 gram is treated with 0.1942 gram (= 1 millimole) of K_2CrO_4 and 20 ml. of 6 N H_2SO_4 and the solution is boiled to expel all the free iodine formed by the reaction. The solution containing the excess chromate is cooled, treated with excess KI, and the liberated I_2 titrated with 0.1000 N $Na_2S_2O_3$, requiring 12.00 ml. Calculate the percentage purity of the original potassium iodide.

Ans. 96.38 per cent.

13.82. A standard stock solution is made by dissolving 50.0 millimoles of KIO_3 and 100 grams of KI in water and diluting to 10.00 liters. A sample of Bureau of Standards steel weighing 5.00 grams and certified to contain 0.0530 per cent sulfur is treated with HCl. The sulfur is liberated as H_2S, caught in ammoniacal zinc sulfate solution, and eventually titrated in the presence of acid with the above-mentioned stock solution. What volume is required? What is the oxidizing normality of the iodate solution? How many grams of KI in excess of the theoretical amount were used in preparing the stock solution?

Ans. 5.52 ml. 0.0300 N. 58.5 grams.

13.83. The copper in a 0.2500-gram sample of copper ore is treated in solution with excess KI and the liberated iodine titrated with 16.50 ml. of $Na_2S_2O_3$ (1.000 ml. $\eqsim$ 0.003619 gram $KBrO_3$). What is the purity of the ore expressed in terms of percentage of Cu_2S?

Ans. 68.28 per cent.

13.84. If the arsenic trichloride from 50 grams of impure copper is distilled off, absorbed in dilute alkali, and finally oxidized by 20 ml. of 0.0200 N iodine solution, find the percentage of arsenic in the sample.

Ans. 0.030 per cent.

13.85. A mixture of As_2O_3 and As_2O_5 and inert matter is dissolved and titrated in neutral solution with 0.05000 N I_2, requiring 20.10 ml. The resulting solution is acidified and excess KI is added. The liberated I_2 requires 29.92 ml. of 0.1500 N $Na_2S_2O_3$. Calculate the number of grams of combined $As_2O_3 + As_2O_5$ in the sample.

Ans. 0.2498 gram.

13.86. A mixture of pure potassium permanganate and pure potassium chromate weighing 0.2400 gram, when treated with KI in acid solution, liberates sufficient iodine to react with 60.00 ml. of 0.1000 N sodium thiosulfate solution. Find the percentages of Cr and Mn in the mixture.

Ans. Cr = 11.0 per cent, Mn = 20.5 per cent.

13.87. A sample of pyrolusite is treated with HCl, the liberated chlorine is passed into potassium iodide, and the liberated iodine is titrated with $Na_2S_2O_3$ solution (49.64 grams of $Na_2S_2O_3.5H_2O$ per liter). If 38.70 ml. are required, what volume of 0.2500 N $KMnO_4$ would be required in an indirect determination in which a similar sample is reduced with 0.9000 gram of $H_2C_2O_4.2H_2O$ and the excess oxalic acid is titrated with the $KMnO_4$?

Ans. 26.16 ml.

13.88. One milliliter of a thiosulfate solution is equivalent to 0.005642 gram of copper and is also equivalent to 1.50 ml. of a certain iodine solution. Calculate the value of one milliliter of the iodine solution in terms of grams of (*a*) Sb, (*b*) As, (*c*) As_2S_3, (*d*) Sb_2O_3.

13.89. Calculate the percentage of iron in a sample of crude ferric chloride weighing 1.000 gram if the iodine liberated by its action on an excess of potassium iodide is reduced by the addition of 50.00 ml. of $Na_2S_2O_3$ solution and the excess thiosulfate is titrated with standard iodine, of which 7.85 ml. are required.

$$45.00 \text{ ml. iodine} \approx 45.95 \text{ ml. thiosulfate}$$
$$45.00 \text{ ml. arsenite solution} \approx 45.20 \text{ ml. iodine}$$
$$1.000 \text{ ml. arsenite solution} \approx 0.00516 \text{ gram } As_2O_3.$$

13.90. What weight of copper ore should be taken for analysis so that when the copper is determined by the regular iodimetric method using 0.05000 N sodium thiosulfate, the buret reading will be two-thirds the per cent CuS in the ore? What is the molarity of the thiosulfate solution? What volume of $KMnO_4$ (1.000 ml. $\approx$ 0.0005493 gram of Mn by the Volhard method: $3Mn^{++} + 2MnO_4^- + 2ZnO \rightarrow 5MnO_2 + 2Zn^{++} + 2H_2O$) will react with an excess of soluble iodide in the presence of acid to require 20.00 ml. of the above thiosulfate for reduction?

13.91. If 50.00 ml. of an iodine solution are exactly equivalent in oxidizing power to 49.47 ml. of a $K_2Cr_2O_7$ solution of which 1.000 ml. will liberate 0.004263 gram of iodine from KI, calculate the normality of each solution.

13.92. Pure $K_2Cr_2O_7$, weighing 0.3321 gram, was boiled with an excess of strong HCl. The evolved chlorine was passed into a solution of KI, and the I_2 liberated was titrated with 68.21 ml. of $Na_2S_2O_3$ solution. Calculate the normality of the $Na_2S_2O_3$ solution.

13.93. What must be the normality of a standard iodine solution so that, if a 0.5000-gram sample of stibnite (impute Sb_2S_3) is taken for analysis, the number of milliliters of iodine required to oxidize Sb(III) to Sb(V) will represent directly the percentage of antimony?

13.94. A powder consists of a mixture of $Na_3AsO_4.12H_2O$, Na_2HAsO_3, and inert matter. It is dissolved and titrated in neutral solution with 0.08100 N I_2, requiring 15.60 ml. The resulting solution is acidified and excess KI is added. The liberated iodine requires 18.58 ml. of 0.1200 molar $Na_2S_2O_3$ solution. Calculate the amount of 5-valent and of 3-valent arsenic in terms of grams of $Na_3AsO_4.12H_2O$ and grams of combined As_2O_3, respectively.

13.95. If the amount of copper in a carbonate ore, expressed in terms of percentage $Cu_2(OH)_2CO_3$ is 53.05 and if 25.72 ml. of $Na_2S_2O_3$ are eventually required to titrate the iodine liberated from excess KI by the copper from a half-gram sample, what is the value of 1.000 ml. of the thiosulfate in terms of grams of (*a*) $KBrO_3$, (*b*) $KH(IO_3)_2$?

13.96. The sulfur from a 5.00-gram sample of steel is evolved as H_2S and eventually titrated in the presence of acid with standard iodine solution (1.00 ml. $\approx$ 0.004945 gram As_2O_3), of which 1.90 ml. are required. What is the percentage of sulfur in the steel? If a standard potassium iodate-iodide solution had been substituted for the standard iodine and a volume identical with the above had been required, how many grams of KIO_3 would have been present in each milliliter of the solution? Could the iodate solution have been standardized against pure As_2O_3, as the iodine solution was? Explain your answer.

104. Potassium Iodate Process. Potassium iodate in the presence of dilute acid is a fairly strong oxidizing agent. Its behavior is indicated by the half-cell reaction:

$$IO_3^- + 6H^+ + 5\epsilon = \tfrac{1}{2}I_2 + 3H_2O \quad E^0 = -1.20 \text{ volts}$$

If the titration of an oxidizable substance is carried out with potassium iodate in a solution greater than 4 normal in hydrochloric acid, a secondary reaction takes place in which the liberated iodine is subsequently acted on by the iodate to form iodine chloride:

$$2I_2 + IO_3^- + 6H^+ + 5Cl^- \rightarrow 5ICl + 3H_2O$$

Chloroform (or carbon tetrachloride) serves as the indicator. Free iodine dissolves in chloroform to give a purple color, and iodine chloride dissolves to give a yellow color. The solution being titrated is vigorously agitated with chloroform. The violet color that forms subsequently fades to yellow, and the latter change is taken as the end point.

The following reducing agents can be satisfactorily determined by the iodate process, and the net reaction in each case is indicated by the accompanying equation:

Iodide: $2I^- + IO_3^- + 6H^+ + 3Cl^- \rightarrow 3ICl + 3H_2O$
Iodine: $2I_2 + IO_3^- + 6H^+ + 5Cl^- \rightarrow 5ICl + 3H_2O$
Arsenic: $2As^{+++} + IO_3^- + 5H_2O + Cl^- \rightarrow ICl + 2H_3AsO_4 + 4H^+$
Antimony: $2Sb^{+++} + IO_3^- + 5H_2O + Cl^- \rightarrow ICl + 2H_3SbO_4 + 4H^+$
Copper: $2Cu^{++} + H_2SO_3 + 2CNS^- + H_2O$
$$\rightarrow Cu_2(CNS)_2 + SO_4^= + 4H^+$$
$$\underline{2Cu_2(CNS)_2 + 7IO_3^- + 14H^+ + 7Cl^-}$$
$$\rightarrow 4Cu^{++} + 7ICl + 4HCN + 4SO_4^= + 5H_2O$$
Mercury: $Hg_2^{++} + 2Cl^- \rightarrow Hg_2Cl_2$
$$\underline{2Hg_2Cl_2 + IO_3^- + 6H^+ + 5Cl^- \rightarrow 4HgCl_2 + ICl + 3H_2O}$$
Tin: $2Sn^{++} + IO_3^- + 6H^+ + 13Cl^- \rightarrow 2SnCl_6^= + ICl + 3H_2O$

EXAMPLE. A solution of KIO_3 is 0.100 N as used in ordinary iodimetric processes (see Sec. 103). How many grams of $CuSO_4.5H_2O$ must be present in a solution in order to require 10.0 ml. of this KIO_3 in a direct titration to the disappearance of a violet color in $CHCl_3$?

SOLUTION: In iodimetric processes $KIO_3 \backsimeq 3I_2 \backsimeq 6$ hydrogen equivalents. Since $4Cu \backsimeq 7KIO_3$, $4Cu \backsimeq 42$ hydrogen equivalents.

$$10.0 \times 0.100 \times \frac{4CuSO_4.5H_2O}{42,000} = 0.0238 \text{ gram}. \quad Ans.$$

105. Potassium Bromate Process. Potassium bromate, like potassium iodate, is a strong oxidizing agent in the presence of acid. In a titration of a reducing agent with potassium bromate, the bromate is reduced to bromide, and the next drop of bromate results in the formation of free bromine:

$$5Br^- + BrO_3^- + 6H^+ \rightarrow 3Br_2 + 3H_2O$$

Any one of a number of organic dyes (*e.g.*, methyl red) serves as an indicator, for the liberated bromine oxidizes the dye to a colorless product. The oxidizable substance is therefore titrated with a standard solution of potassium bromate to the disappearance of the color of the indicator dye.

Arsenic and antimony are among the constituents that can be satisfactorily determined by the bromate process, and the net reaction in each case is as follows:

$$3As^{+++} + BrO_3^- + 9H_2O \rightarrow 3H_3AsO_4 + Br^- + 9H^+$$
$$3Sb^{+++} + BrO_3^- + 9H_2O \rightarrow 3H_3SbO_4 + Br^- + 9H^+$$

In addition, several metal ions can be precipitated by 8-hydroxyquinoline (oxine), which has one replaceable hydrogen. The precipitate can be dissolved in hydrochloric acid and the liberated oxine (C_9H_6NOH) titrated with potassium bromate in the presence of potassium bromide. As in the above cases, methyl red or some other similar oxidizable dye is used as the indicator. The net equation for the titration is as follows:

$$3C_9H_6NOH + 2BrO_3^- + 4Br^- + 6H^+ \rightarrow 3C_9H_4NBr_2OH + 6H_2O$$

Ions commonly determined in this way include Al^{+++}, Mg^{++}, Cd^{++}, Co^{++}, Ni^{++}, TiO^{++}, and Zn^{++}. In the case of aluminum, for example, the formula of the precipitate is $Al(C_9H_6NO)_3$, and therefore each atom of aluminum is equivalent to 2 molecules of potassium bromate or to 12 hydrogen equivalents.

EXAMPLE. What is the value of 1.00 ml. of 0.0100 molar $KBrO_3$ in terms of grams of Ti in the method whereby the titanium is precipitated as titanyl oxinate, $TiO(C_9H_6NO)_2$, and the oxine in the precipitate titrated with the bromate in the regular way?

SOLUTION: The 0.0100 molar $KBrO_3$ is 0.0600 normal (see Sec. 103). Each Ti is equivalent to 2 oxines, which in the bromate titration are equivalent to $\frac{4}{3}KBrO_3$ or to $\frac{4}{3} \times 6 = 8$ hydrogen equivalents.

$$1.00 \times 0.0600 \times \frac{Ti}{8,000} = 0.000359 \text{ gram.} \quad Ans.$$

Problems

13.97. A solution contains KI and free iodine. A 10.0-ml. portion requires 0.83 ml. of 0.120 N $Na_2S_2O_3$ to titrate to an end point with starch. Another 10.0-ml. portion, after acidification with concentrated HCl, requires 10.50 ml. of 0.0100 molar KIO_3 to titrate to an end point with chloroform indicator. Calculate the number of grams of I_2 and of KI in the 10.0-ml. portion.

Ans. 0.0127 gram I_2, 0.0265 gram KI.

13.98. A 25.0-ml. pipetful of H_2O_2 solution is diluted to 250 ml., and 25.0 ml. of the resulting solution are treated with NaOH and with 50.0 ml. of Na_3AsO_3 which is 0.100 N as a reducing agent ($H_2O_2 + AsO_3^\equiv \rightarrow AsO_4^\equiv + H_2O$). The unoxidized arsenite is determined by acidifying the solution with concentrated HCl and titrating with 20.0 ml. of 0.0250 molar KIO_3 to an end point with chloroform indicator. Calculate the number of grams of pure H_2O_2 contained in the original solution.

Ans. 0.51 gram.

13.99. What is the milliequivalent weight of magnesium in the determination of that element by precipitation with 8-hydroxyquinoline and titrating with standard $KBrO_3 + KBr$ the oxine liberated from the precipitate by HCl.

Ans. 0.003040 gram.

13.100. Addition of potassium periodate to a solution of a mercuric salt precipitates mercuric periodate, $Hg_5(IO_6)_2$. This precipitate can be dissolved in a mixture of potassium iodide and hydrochloric acid. Iodine is liberated and can be titrated with sodium thiosulfate. Balance the following equation which represents the reaction, and from it calculate the value of each milliliter of $Na_2S_2O_3$ solution (of which 1.00 ml. $\approx$ 0.0500 gram $CuSO_4.5H_2O$) in terms of grams of Hg.

$$Hg_5(IO_6)_2 + I^- + H^+ \rightarrow HgI_4^- + I_2 + H_2O$$

Ans. 0.00125 gram.

13.101. Write an equation to show the initial step in the titration of $Cu_2(CNS)_2$ with KIO_3 in which free iodine is liberated. How many milliliters of KIO_3 (0.0100 N as ordinarily used in iodimetric processes) are required to give the *maximum* intensity of violet color with $CHCl_3$ indicator?

13.102. Vanadium can be determined by adding a measured excess of KI to an HCl solution of vanadate (H_3VO_4) and titrating the liberated I_2 (VO^{++} is formed) plus the excess iodide with standard KIO_3 ($CHCl_3$ indicator). Write all equations and calculate the number of grams of elementary vanadium equivalent to each mililliter of 0.100 molar KIO_3.

CHAPTER 14

PRECIPITATION METHODS
(PRECIPITIMETRY)

106. Equivalent Weights in Precipitation Methods. In precipitation (or "saturation") methods a substance is titrated with a standard solution of a precipitating agent. At the completion of the precipitation the precipitating agent reacts with an indicator and a color change takes place. For example, in the *Volhard method* for silver, silver ions are titrated with a standard solution of potassium thiocyanate ($Ag^+ + CNS^- \rightarrow AgCNS$) and the end point is determined by the red color formed when an additional drop of the thiocyanate reacts with ferric alum indicator ($Fe^{+++} + 4CNS^- \rightarrow Fe(CNS)_4^-$).

Similarly silver ions and halide ions can be titrated in neutral solution with standard NaCl or standard $AgNO_3$ using certain so-called *adsorption indicators* (*e.g.*, dichlorofluorescein), which form colored compounds on the surface of the particles of precipitate and give a change of color at the equivalence point.

In determining the equivalent weight of a constituent being precipitated, 1.008 grams of hydrogen ion is again taken as the standard of reference. The equivalent weight is that weight which *in precipitation* reacts with the equivalent of that amount of hydrogen ion. Here the point of view is that of general metathesis rather than that of neutralization (as in acidimetry) or of oxidizing power (as in oxidimetry). Knowledge of valence and a simple inspection of the equation usually suffice to determine the correct equivalent weight. In a great majority of cases the gram-equivalent weight is found by dividing the formula weight by the net number of charges on the constituent actually taking part in the reaction.

In the reaction between silver nitrate and sodium chloride ($Ag^+ + Cl^- \rightarrow AgCl$) the equivalent weights of the reacting substances are $AgNO_3/1$ and $NaCl/1$, respectively. In the reaction between barium chloride and sodium sulfate ($Ba^{++} + SO_4^= \rightarrow BaSO_4$) the equivalent weight in each case is one-half of the molecular weight. The equivalent weight of anhydrous disodium phosphate as a sodium salt is $Na_2HPO_4/2 = 71.03$; and as a phosphate, $Na_2HPO_4/3 = 47.35$.

Reactions in this class may be direct or indirect. That is, the titrating solution may be added in amounts just sufficient to precipitate all of the substance to be determined; or in certain cases an excess of the precipitating agent may be added and the excess titrated by means of a precipitating agent. Because of the difficulty of finding suitable indicators to show the completion of the reactions, a great many precipitating reactions cannot be used satisfactorily for quantitative titrations.

The Volhard method for silver is a direct method and is illustrated in Example I below. The Volhard method can also be applied as an indirect process to the determination of chloride, bromide, iodide, cyanide, and thiocyanate. This is illustrated in Example II below.

EXAMPLE I. What is the percentage of silver in a coin, if a 0.2000-gram sample requires 39.60 ml. of potassium thiocyanate solution (0.4103 gram of KCNS per 100 ml.) for the precipitation of the silver?

$$Ag^+ + CNS^- \rightarrow \underline{AgCNS}$$

SOLUTION: A liter of the KCNS solution contains 4.103 grams of the salt. Its normality is

$$\frac{4.103}{KCNS/1} = \frac{4.103}{97.17} = 0.04223$$

$$\frac{39.60 \times 0.04223 \times \dfrac{Ag}{1,000}}{0.2000} \times 100 = 90.20 \text{ per cent Ag.} \quad Ans.$$

EXAMPLE II. A sample of impure strontium chloride weighs 0.5000 gram. After the addition of 50.00 ml. of 0.2100 N AgNO$_3$ and filtering out of the precipitated silver chloride, the filtrate requires 25.50 ml. of 0.2800 N KCNS to titrate the silver. What is the percentage of SrCl$_2$ in the sample?

SOLUTION:

Milliequivalents of AgNO$_3$ added   = 50.00 × 0.2100 = 10.50
Milliequivalents of KCNS required   = 25.50 × 0.2800 = 7.14
Net milliequivalents = 10.50 − 7.14 = 3.36

$$\text{Per cent SrCl}_2 = \frac{3.36 \times \dfrac{SrCl_2}{2,000}}{0.5000} \times 100 = 53.3 \text{ per cent.} \quad Ans.$$

EXAMPLE III. A sample of feldspar weighing 1.500 grams is decomposed, and eventually there is obtained a pure mixture of KCl and NaCl weighing 0.1801 gram. These chlorides are dissolved in water, a 50-ml. pipetful of 0.08333 N AgNO$_3$ is added, and the precipitate filtered off. The filtrate requires 16.47 ml. of 0.1000 N KCNS, with ferric alum as indicator. Calculate the percentage of K$_2$O in the silicate.

Let x = grams of KCl obtained

Then

$$0.1801 - x = \text{grams of NaCl}$$

$$\text{Total milliequivalents of mixed halides} = \frac{x}{\text{KCl}/1,000} + \frac{0.1801 - x}{\text{NaCl}/1,000}$$

$$\frac{x}{\text{KCl}/1,000} + \frac{0.1801 - x}{\text{NaCl}/1,000} = (50 \times 0.08333) - (16.47 \times 0.1000)$$

$$x = 0.1517 \text{ gram HCl}$$

$$\frac{0.1517 \times \text{K}_2\text{O}/2\text{KCl}}{1.500} \times 100 = 6.40 \text{ per cent.} \quad Ans.$$

Problems

14.1. What volume of 0.1233 N silver nitrate solution is required to precipitate the chlorine from a sample of rock salt weighing 0.2280 gram and containing 99.21 per cent NaCl and no other halide?

Ans. 31.37 ml.

14.2. What volume of 0.08333 N $BaCl_2$ solution is required to precipitate the sulfur from a solution containing 0.2358 gram of $FeSO_4.7H_2O$?

Ans. 20.36 ml.

14.3. A solution of a soluble phosphate that is 0.2000 N as a precipitating agent is used to precipitate the magnesium as $MgNH_4PO_4$ from a 1.000-gram sample of dolomite containing 14.01 per cent $MgCO_3$. What volume is required?

Ans. 16.62 ml.

14.4. A solution of $K_2Cr_2O_7$ which is 0.1121 normal as an oxidizing agent is used to precipitate $BaCrO_4$ from 0.5060 gram of $BaCl_2.2H_2O$. What is the normality of the solution of $K_2Cr_2O_7$ as a precipitating agent, and what volume is required?

Ans. 0.07473 N, 55.42 ml.

14.5. What volume of oxalic acid solution which is 0.2000 N as an acid is required to precipitate the calcium as $CaC_2O_4.H_2O$ from 0.4080 gram of cement containing 60.32 per cent CaO? What is the normality of the oxalic acid as a precipitating agent?

Ans. 43.88 ml. 0.2000 N.

14.6. In the volumetric analysis of a silver coin containing 90.00 per cent Ag, a 0.5000-gram sample being used, what is the least normality that a potassium thiocyanate solution may have and not require more than 50.00 ml. of solution in the analysis?

Ans. 0.08339 N.

14.7. Pure elementary arsenic weighing 0.1500 gram is dissolved in HNO_3 (forming H_3AsO_4). The resulting solution is made neutral and then treated with 150 ml. of 0.06667 M $AgNO_3$ which precipitates all the arsenic as Ag_3AsO_4. The precipitate is washed, dissolved in acid, and the silver in the resulting *solution of the precipitate* is titrated with 0.1000 M KCNS using ferric ions as indicator. How many milliliters are required?

Ans. 60.06 ml.

14.8. What is the percentage of bromine in a sample of bromide if to 1.600 grams of the sample are added 52.00 ml. of 0.2000 N $AgNO_3$ solution and the excess silver requires 4.00 ml. of 0.1000 N KCNS solution for the precipitation of AgCNS?

Ans. 49.95 per cent.

14.9. The purity of soluble iodides is determined by precipitating the iodine with an excess of standard silver nitrate and titrating the excess $AgNO_3$ with thiocyanate solution. The silver nitrate is made by dissolving 2.122 grams of metallic silver in nitric acid, evaporating just to dryness, dissolving the residue in water, and diluting to exactly 1,000 ml. From a buret 60.00 ml. of this solution are added to 100.0 ml. of a solution of an iodide and the excess is titrated with 1.03 ml. of thiocyanate solution of which 1.000 ml. will precipitate 0.001247 gram of silver as AgCNS. Calculate the grams of iodine present as iodide in the 100-ml. portion of the solution.

Ans. 0.1482 gram.

14.10. A mixture of pure LiCl and BaI_2 weighing 0.6000 gram is treated with 45.15 ml. of 0.2000 normal $AgNO_3$ solution, and the excess silver is then titrated with 25.00 ml. of 0.1000 N KCNS solution with ferric alum as an indicator. Find the percentage of iodine present in the mixture.

Ans. 44.61 per cent.

14.11. A sample of feldspar contains 7.58 per cent Na_2O and 9.93 per cent K_2O. What must be the normality of a silver nitrate solution if it takes 22.71 ml. of it to precipitate the chloride ions from the combined alkali chlorides from a 0.1500-gram sample?

Ans. 0.03005 N.

14.12. A sample of greensand weighing 2.000 grams yields a mixture of NaCl and KCl weighing exactly 0.2558 gram. After the chlorides have been dissolved, 35.00 ml. of 0.1000 N $AgNO_3$ are added to precipitate the chlorine and the excess is titrated with 0.92 ml. of 0.02000 N thiocyanate solution. Calculate the percentage of potassium in the sample.

Ans. 6.36 per cent.

14.13. How many milliliters of 0.2500 N $AgNO_3$ solution are required to precipitate all the chlorine from a solution containing 0.5680 gram of $BaCl_2.2H_2O$?

14.14. How many milliliters of a solution of $Na_2HPO_4.12H_2O$ which is tenth normal as a sodium salt are required to precipitate the calcium as $Ca_3(PO_4)_2$ from a solution containing 0.5000 gram of $Ca(NO_3)_2$?

14.15. How many milliliters of $K_2Cr_2O_7$ (1.000 ml. $\backsim$ 0.01597 gram Fe_2O_3) will precipitate all the lead as $PbCrO_4$ from a solution containing 0.2510 gram of $Pb(NO_3)_2$?

14.16. To precipitate the sulfur from a certain weight of ferrous ammonium sulfate contaminated with silica and water requires a number of milliliters of 0.2000 N barium chloride solution exactly equal to the percentage of iron in the sample. What is the weight of sample?

14.17. In the analysis of a sample of silicate weighing 0.8000 gram, a mixture of NaCl and KCl weighing 0.2400 gram was obtained. The chlorides were dissolved in water, 50.00 ml. of 0.1000 N $AgNO_3$ added, and the excess of silver titrated with KCNS solution, ferric alum being used as an indicator. In the last titration, 14.46 ml. were used, and the reagent was exactly 0.30 per cent stronger in normality than the $AgNO_3$ solution. Find the percentage of K_2O and of Na_2O in the silicate.

14.18. A sample of feldspar contains 7.73 per cent Na_2O and 9.17 per cent K_2O. What must be the normality of a silver nitrate solution if 25.18 ml. precipitates the chloride ions from the combined chlorides in a sample weighing 0.1500 gram?

14.19. A mixture of LiCl and $BaBr_2$ weighing 0.5000 gram is treated with 37.60 ml. of 0.2000 N silver nitrate and the excess of the latter titrated with 18.50 ml. of 0.1111 N thiocyanate solution. Find the percentage of Ba in the mixture.

14.20. Express the calculation of the per cent Na_2O in a silicate containing sodium and potassium from the following data: Weight of sample = A grams. Weight of NaCl + KCl obtained = B grams. Weight of $AgNO_3$ crystals added to precipitate the chlorine from these chlorides and give an excess = C grams. Volume of D normal KCNS required to titrate the excess silver ions = E ml.

CHAPTER 15

COMPLEX-ION FORMATION METHODS (COMPLEXIMETRY)

107. Equivalent Weights in Complex-ion Methods. Reactions in which complex ions are formed are common in chemistry, particularly in qualitative analysis, and many of them should already be familiar to the student. Typical cases where complex ions are formed are the following:

$$Ag^+ + 2NH_4OH \rightarrow Ag(NH_3)_2{}^+ + 2H_2O$$
$$Cd^{++} + 4CN^- \rightarrow Cd(CN)_4{}^=$$
$$Sn^{++++} + 6Cl^- \rightarrow SnCl_6{}^=$$
$$Hg^{++} + 4I^- \rightarrow HgI_4{}^=$$

Unfortunately, because of lack of suitable indicators, few of the many reactions of this class can be used as a basis for a volumetric analysis. Most of those that are in common use are covered by the examples and problems below.

The gram-equivalent weight of a substance involved in a complex-ion forming reaction is based as usual on 1.008 grams of H^+ as the standard of reference. As in all previous cases, if one formula weight of a substance reacts with A hydrogen equivalents, its equivalent weight is its formula weight divided by A. The milliequivalent weights of the metal ions in the above four equations are Ag/2,000, Cd/4,000, Sn/6,000, and Hg/4,000, respectively. Conversely, the equivalent weight of CN^- in the second reaction is $4CN/2,000 = CN/500$, each atom of Cd being considered as equivalent to 2 atoms of H^+.

EXAMPLE I. LIEBIG METHOD. How many grams of NaCN are present in a solution that is titrated just to a permanent turbidity with 26.05 ml. of $AgNO_3$ solution containing 8.125 grams of $AgNO_3$ per liter?

SOLUTION:

$$2CN^- + Ag^+ \rightarrow Ag(CN)_2{}^-$$

The next drop of $AgNO_3$ gives a permanent precipitate of $Ag[Ag(CN)_2]$, which serves as the indicator for the above reaction.

$$Ag(CN)_2{}^- + Ag^+ \rightarrow Ag[Ag(CN)_2] \text{ (indicator)}$$

$$\text{Normality of } AgNO_3 = \frac{8.125}{169.9} = 0.04782 \ N$$

The milliequivalent weight of NaCN in this case is not NaCN/1,000 since *two* cyanide ions react with *one* silver ion in the titration. The milliequivalent weight of NaCN may be considered here to be 2NaCN/1,000. Then,

$$\text{Grams NaCN} = 26.05 \times 0.04782 \times \frac{2\text{NaCN}}{1,000} = 0.1221 \text{ gram.} \quad Ans.$$

Or, from another point of view, if 26.05 ml. are necessary to form the complex ion as shown above, then *twice* that amount is necessary to *precipitate* the cyanide completely.

$$2CN^- + 2Ag^+ \rightarrow \underline{Ag[Ag(CN)_2]}$$

Therefore,

$$\text{Grams NaCN} = 2 \times 26.05 \times 0.04782 \times \frac{\text{NaCN}}{1,000} = 0.1221 \text{ gram.} \quad Ans.$$

EXAMPLE II.   A solution contains KCN and KCl.   It is titrated with 0.1000 N AgNO$_3$ to a faint turbidity, requiring 15.00 ml.   Then 32.10 ml. more of the AgNO$_3$ are added and the precipitates of Ag[Ag(CN)$_2$] and AgCl are filtered off.   The filtrate requires 7.20 ml. of 0.08333 N KCNS to give a red color with ferric indicator.   How many grams of KCN and of KCl are present in the original solution?

SOLUTION:

$$15.00 \times 0.1000 \times \frac{\text{KCN}}{500} = 0.1953 \text{ gram KCN.} \quad Ans.$$

Total volume AgNO$_3$ added = 15.00 + 32.10 = 47.10 ml.
AgNO$_3$ required to precipitate KCN completely as
$$\text{Ag[Ag(CN)}_2] = 2 \times 15.00 = 30.00 \text{ ml.}$$
47.10 − 30.00 = 17.10 ml. AgNO$_3$ (reacting with KCl and giving excess)
$$[(17.10 \times 0.1000) - (7.20 \times 0.08333)] \times \frac{\text{KCl}}{1,000}$$
$$= 0.08276 \text{ gram KCl.} \quad Ans.$$

EXAMPLE III.   VOLUMETRIC NICKEL.   How many grams of Ni are contained in an ammoniacal solution that is treated with 49.80 ml. of KCN solution (0.007810 gram per milliliter) and the excess KCN titrated with 5.91 ml. of 0.1000 N AgNO$_3$, KI being used as an indicator?

SOLUTION: The essential reactions are

$$Ni(NH_3)_6^{++} + 4CN^- + 6H_2O \rightarrow Ni(CN)_4^= + 6NH_4OH$$
$$2CN^- + Ag^+ \rightarrow Ag(CN)_2^-$$

Unlike the Liebig method above, the formation of Ag[Ag(CN)$_2$] cannot be used as an indicator since this salt is soluble in NH$_4$OH.   Instead, excess Ag^+ is indicated by the formation of AgI which is insoluble in NH_4OH.

$$\text{Normality KCN solution} = \frac{0.007810}{\text{KCN}/1,000} = 0.1200 \; N$$

$$5.91 \text{ ml. AgNO}_3 \eqsim 5.91 \times \frac{0.1000}{0.1200} \times 2 = 9.85 \text{ ml. KCN solution}$$

(see Example I)

Net milliliters of KCN $= 49.80 - 9.85 = 39.95$ ml.

$$39.95 \times 0.1200 \times \frac{\text{Ni}}{4,000} = 0.07032 \text{ gram Ni.} \quad Ans.$$

EXAMPLE IV. A volumetric method for zinc consists in titrating it in acid solution with a standard solution of $K_4Fe(CN)_6$. The reaction takes place in two steps, the net reaction being

$$3Zn^{++} + 2Fe(CN)_6^{=} + 2K^+ \rightarrow K_2Zn_3[Fe(CN)_6]_2$$

Ferric ions or uranyl ions are used to indicate the completion of the reaction (by forming a highly colored insoluble ferrocyanide). If 15.5 ml. of a solution of $K_4Fe(CN)_6$ which is tenth-normal as a potassium salt is used in a given titration, what weight of zinc is shown to be present?

SOLUTION:

$$1 \text{ F.W. } K_4Fe(CN)_6 \text{ as a salt} = 4 \text{ gm.-atoms } H^+$$

Therefore each gm.-atom $Zn^{++} \eqsim \frac{8}{3}$ gm.-atoms H^+

$$15.5 \times 0.100 \times \frac{3Zn}{8,000} = \text{grams Zn}$$

$$= 0.380 \text{ gram.} \quad Ans.$$

Problems

15.1. How many milliliters of $0.1000 \; N$ $AgNO_3$ are required to titrate to a faint permanent turbidity a solution containing 10.00 millimoles of KCN?

Ans. 50.00 ml.

15.2. A solution containing KCN and KCl requires 20.0 ml. of $0.100 \; N$ $AgNO_3$ solution to titrate the KCN to a faint turbidity by the Liebig method. After addition of 50.0 ml. more of the silver solution and filtering, the filtrate requires 16.0 ml. of $0.125 \; N$ KCNS, ferric alum being used as an indicator. Calculate the number of millimoles of KCN and of KCl in the original solution.

Ans. 4 millimoles KCN, 1 millimole KCl.

15.3. A sample consists of 80.00 per cent KCN, 15.00 per cent KCl, and 5.00 per cent K_2SO_4. A half-gram sample would require how many milliliters of 0.1000 molar $AgNO_3$ for titration to a faint permanent turbidity? If 80.00 ml. more of the $AgNO_3$ were added, how many milliliters of 0.2000 molar KCNS would be required to complete the titration?

Ans. 30.17 ml. 19.62 ml.

15.4. A powder containing KCN, KCNS, and inert material weighs 1.200 grams, and the solution of it requires 23.81 ml. of 0.08333 N $AgNO_3$ to titrate the KCN by the Liebig method.   A 50-ml. pipetful of the silver solution is then added, and the precipitated AgCN and AgCNS are filtered.   The filtrate requires 10.12 ml. of 0.09090 N KCNS for the excess silver, ferric ions being used as the indicator.   Calculate the percentage of KCN and of KCNS in the powder.

Ans.   21.53 per cent KCN, 10.21 per cent KCNS.

15.5. Zinc can be determined by direct titration with standard $K_4Fe(CN)_6$ and the net reaction is as follows: $3ZnCl_2 + 2K_4Fe(CN)_6 \rightarrow K_2Zn_3[Fe(CN)_6]_2 + 6KCl$. If the $K_4Fe(CN)_6$ is 0.1000 N as a potassium salt, what is the value of each milliliter of it in terms of grams of Zn?   If the $K_4Fe(CN)_6$ were 0.1000 N as a reducing agent (in reactions where it is oxidized to ferricyanide), what would be the value of 1 ml. of it in terms of zinc?

Ans.   0.002452 gram.   0.009807 gram.

15.6. Find the weights of dissolved KCl, KCN, and KCNS in 500 ml. of a solution that analyzed as follows: 30.0 ml. of the solution titrated for KCN by the Liebig method reacted with 9.57 ml. of $AgNO_3$ solution (15.0 grams per liter).   Then 75.0 ml. more of the silver solution were added, and the solution was filtered.   The filtrate contained enough silver to react with 9.50 ml. of 0.100 N KCNS.   The precipitate was heated with HNO_3 to decompose the AgCN and AgCNS, the H_2SO_4 formed was precipitated with barium nitrate, and the solution then reacted with 58.4 ml. of 0.100 N KCNS.

Ans.   KCl = 0.85 grams, KCN = 1.83 grams, KCNS = 6.73 grams.

15.7. A solution containing $\frac{1}{2}$ millimole of KCl, $\frac{1}{3}$ millimole of KCN, and $\frac{1}{4}$ millimole of KCNS is titrated with 0.0667 M $AgNO_3$ to a faint turbidity, requiring A ml. Then enough more of the $AgNO_3$ is added to make a total of 30.00 ml. of the $AgNO_3$. The precipitate is filtered off and the filtrate requires B ml. of 0.100 M KCNS to give a red color with ferric alum indicator.   The precipitate is decomposed with concentrated HNO_3 and the solution is diluted which leaves only AgCl as a residue.   The nitric acid solution containing the silver from the $Ag_2(CN)_2$ and the AgCNS is titrated with 0.100 M KCNS, requiring C ml.   What are the values of A, B, and C?

Ans. $A = 2.50$, $B = 9.17$, $C = 5.83$.

15.8. A nickel ore contains 10.11 per cent Ni.   A half-gram sample is decomposed and the ammoniacal solution treated with 60.00 ml. of a 0.08333 M solution of KCN. A little KI is added as an indicator and the solution is titrated with 0.06667 M $AgNO_3$ to a faint permanent turbidity.   What volume of the $AgNO_3$ is required?

Ans.   11.65 ml.

15.9. Find the percentage of nickel in an ore if the sample weighs 0.3000 gram and the ammoniacal solution is treated with 20.00 ml. of KCN (31.2 grams per liter) and then requires 14.00 ml. of $AgNO_3$ (25.5 grams per liter), KI being used as an indicator.

Ans.   26.4 per cent.

15.10. What weight of KCN is equivalent to 30.00 ml. of $AgNO_3$ solution containing 15.00 grams per liter (*a*) by the Volhard method for cyanide and (*b*) by the Liebig method?

15.11. A sample of impure KCN weighs 0.950 gram and requires 22.0 ml. of 0.0909 N $AgNO_3$ to obtain a turbidity in the Liebig titration.   What is the percentage of

KCN? If the sample contained also 0.102 gram of NaCl, what additional volume of $AgNO_3$ would be required for complete precipitation?

15.12. A sample containing KCN weighs 1.000 gram and requires 24.00 ml. of 0.08333 N $AgNO_3$ solution to obtain a faint permanent turbidity. What is the percentage of KCN? If the sample also contained 10.00 per cent KCl, what volume of the $AgNO_3$ solution would be required to precipitate the KCN and KCl completely?

15.13. A solution is known to contain dissolved KCl, KCNS, and KCN. The solution is titrated to a faint turbidity by the Liebig method for cyanide with 25.00 ml. of 0.0880 N $AgNO_3$ solution. A 100-ml. pipetful of the $AgNO_3$ is then added and the solution is filtered; the excess silver in the filtrate requires 50.4 ml. of 0.0833 N KCNS solution. The precipitate of the three silver salts is boiled with HNO_3, which decomposes the AgCN and AgCNS and leaves the AgCl, which is filtered off. The filtrate requires 65.0 ml. of the above-mentioned KCNS solution of the silver. Calculate the number of milligrams of KCN, KCl, and KCNS in the original solution.

15.14. A mixture of KCNS, KCN, KCl weighing 0.687 gram reacts with 30.0 ml. of 0.0500 N $AgNO_3$ in the Liebig titration and with 150 ml. more in the Volhard titration. Find the percentage composition of the original powder.

15.15. What is the percentage of nickel in an ore if the ammoniacal solution of a 1.000-gram sample is treated with 3.255 grams (= 50 millimoles) of KCN and the excess KCN requires 50.00 ml. of 0.1000 molar $AgNO_3$ to obtain a turbidity with KI indicator?

15.16. The Ni in a 0.9000-gram sample of millerite is converted to the ammonia complex, and to the solution are added 0.25 ml. of $AgNO_3$ solution, containing 20.00 grams $AgNO_3$ per liter, and 5.00 ml. of a KI solution that serves as the indicator. By addition of two 10-ml. pipetfuls of KCN solution (13.00 grams KCN per liter) the turbidity due to the AgI is found to have disappeared, but it just reappears on addition of 1.50 ml. more of the $AgNO_3$. Calculate the percentage of Ni in the millerite.

15.17. How many grams of copper are represented by each milliliter of KCN in the cyanide method for determining copper (see Part V, under Copper), if each milliliter of the KCN is equivalent to 0.01000 gram of silver by the Liebig method?

Part IV

SPECIAL METHODS

CHAPTER 16

POTENTIOMETRIC TITRATIONS

108. Potentiometric Acidimetric Titrations. In a potentiometric titration the principles discussed in Chap. 6 are applied in a practical way. Suppose a solution of hydrochloric acid is to be titrated potentiometrically with a standard solution of sodium hydroxide. One method is to use a hydrogen electrode (consisting of a platinum electrode coated with platinum black and over which pure hydrogen gas is allowed to bubble) immersed in the solution. This is one half cell. The other half cell is a calomel cell. This consists of a tube containing metallic mercury in contact with a solution saturated with mercurous chloride and usually either one molar with respect to chloride or saturated with potassium chloride. The two half cells are connected by means of a capillary tube filled with potassium chloride solution. The whole cell (assuming one-molar chloride to be used) is expressed as follows:

$$\text{Pt} \mid \tfrac{1}{2}\text{H}_2(1 \text{ atm.}), \text{ H}^+ \parallel \tfrac{1}{2}\text{Hg}_2\text{Cl}_2, \text{ Cl}^-(1 \text{ molar}) \mid \text{Hg}$$

At 25°C. the electrode potential of this so-called normal calomel cell (or calomel "electrode") is -0.285 volt (see Table XI, Appendix). When saturated KCl is used, the potential is -0.246 volt.

(1) $\tfrac{1}{2}\text{H}_2$ (1 atm.) $= \text{H}^+ + \epsilon$

$$E_1 = E_1{}^0 - \frac{0.0591}{1} \log \frac{[\text{H}^+]}{(\text{press. H}_2)^{\frac{1}{2}}}$$

$$= 0 - 0.0591 \log [\text{H}^+]$$

(2) $\text{Hg} + \text{Cl}^-$ (1 molar) $= \tfrac{1}{2}\text{Hg}_2\text{Cl}_2 + \epsilon$

$$E_2 = -0.285$$

$$E = E_1 - E_2 = -0.0591 \log [\text{H}^+] - (-0.285)$$

$$-\log [\text{H}^+] = \text{pH} = \frac{E - 0.285}{0.0591}$$

By measurement of the e.m.f. of the cell, the pH value of the solution can be determined from this formula. Furthermore, the pH values of

233

the solution can be determined in the same way at successive points in the titration and those pH values plotted against corresponding buret readings.   There is obtained a curve similar to curve (A) (A) in Fig. 4, Sec. 91.   The point of maximum slope of the curve is found (by bisecting the nearly vertical line of inflection), and this is the equivalence point in the titration.   Since the titration is independent of color indicators, the titration can be as successfully carried out in a dark-colored or turbid solution as in a colorless one.   Plotting the results of potentiometric titrations of weak acids like acetic acid and weak bases like ammonia gives curves like (C) (C) and (D) (D) in Fig. 4, and the pH value at the equivalence point or at any other stage of the titration can be readily found in each case.

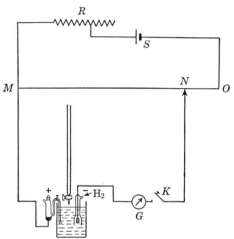

FIG. 8. Potentiometric titration hookup.

EXAMPLE.   If, at the equivalence point in the titration of a certain solution of acetic acid, pH = 9.10, what e.m.f. should be given by the cell made up of this solution in contact with a hydrogen electrode and a normal calomel half cell?

SOLUTION:

$$\text{pH} = \frac{E - 0.285}{0.0591}$$
$$9.10 \times 0.0591 = E - 0.285$$
$$E = 0.823 \text{ volt.} \textit{Ans.}$$

109. Simple Potentiometric Titration Apparatus.   The essential parts of a potentiometric titration apparatus of the type discussed above are shown in diagrammatic form in Fig. 8.   An outer circuit consists of a storage battery S, a rheostat R, and a slide wire MO, of uniform diameter. The inner circuit consists of a sensitive galvanometer G, a key K for closing the circuit, and the cell to be measured. The direction of the current in the inner circuit opposes that in the outer circuit so that, when the position of N on the slide wire is adjusted so that the two voltages are equal, no current will flow through the galvanometer. In determining the voltage of the cell to be measured, the position of N on the slide wire is adjusted until the galvanometer needle no longer deflects when the key is momentarily closed. The distance MN along the slide wire is then a measure of the desired voltage. If a standard Weston cell of known voltage is previously inserted in place of the cell to be measured, the resistance at R can be so adjusted that the scale divisions beside the wire will register millivolts directly.

110. Quinhydrone Electrode. Several substitutes for the cumbersome hydrogen electrode are available. Among these substitutes is the quinhydrone electrode. This consists of a few crystals of quinhydrone added directly to the solution to be titrated. A plain platinum wire serves as the metallic contact, and a calomel cell is used as the other half cell.

When quinhydrone is added to water, a very small amount dissolves and dissociates into an equimolecular mixture of quinone ($C_6H_4O_2$) and hydroquinone ($C_6H_4O_2H_2$). These two substances are in equilibrium with each other, as shown by the equation

$$C_6H_4O_2H_2 = C_6H_4O_2 + 2H^+ + 2\epsilon$$

The potential of this electrode is a function of the hydrogen-ion concentration.

$$E = E^0 - \frac{0.0591}{2} \log \frac{[C_6H_4O_2][H^+]^2}{[C_6H_4O_2H_2]}$$

$$= E^0 - \frac{0.0591}{2} \log [H^+]^2$$

$$= -0.700 - 0.0591 \log [H^+] \text{ at } 25°C.$$

Using a calomel cell as the other half cell and making it the negative electrode in the outer circuit (positive to quinhydrone in the inner circuit) we have

$$E_1 = -0.285$$
$$E_2 = -0.700 - 0.0591 \log [H^+]$$
$$E = E_1 - E_2 = -0.415 - 0.0591 \log [H^+]$$

or

$$pH = - \log [H^+] = \frac{0.415 - E}{0.0591}$$

In a titration in which the quinhydrone electrode is used, the value of E becomes zero at about pH = 7; and on the alkaline side of this point the calomel cell is used as the positive electrode, and the values of E are given a negative sign.   Correct values are not obtained in solutions where pH > 9.

111. Antimony Electrode.   Another substitute for the hydrogen gas electrode is the antimony electrode.   This consists of metallic antimony coated with a special crystalline form of antimonous oxide.   Although several equilibria are involved, the principal equilibrium can be considered to be the following:

$$Sb + \tfrac{3}{2}H_2O = \tfrac{1}{2}Sb_2O_3 + 3H^+ + 3\epsilon$$

The electrode potential is therefore a function of the hydrogen-ion concentration and has been found to be

$$-0.145 - 0.0591 \log [H^+]$$

The antimony-antimony oxide electrode is not satisfactory in the presence of any substance that will either oxidize Sb_2O_3 or form complexes with it.

112. Glass Electrode.   A glass electrode consists of a thin-walled bulb of special glass containing an electrode and standard reference solution. The exact mechanism of this electrode is not entirely understood, but hydrogen ions can apparently move in and out of the surface of the glass, and the glass bulb thus seems to act like a semipermeable membrane between the reference solution and the solution being tested.   Because of the high resistance of the glass bulb, electronic amplification of the current is necessary.

Because of variations in composition of the glass used in the glass electrode and the slight changes that occur over long periods of time, a general formula for calculating pH values cannot be given for this type of electrode.   It has to be established for each electrode.

Most modern portable pH meters use glass electrodes and calomel cells in compact form and are of such construction that pH values can be read directly from the instrument.   By means of such a meter a pH measurement can be made very quickly, and the manipulative technique involved is hardly more than that of turning a knob and pressing a button.

113. Potentiometric Redox Titrations.   The hookup for the potentiometric titration of a reducing or oxidizing agent is similar to that of an acidimetric titration except that a plain platinum wire serves as the electrode.   A calomel cell is used as the secondary half cell.

Suppose a solution of ferrous sulfate is titrated with a standard solution of ceric sulfate ($Fe^{++} + Ce^{++++} \rightarrow Fe^{+++} + Ce^{+++}$).[1]   At all times during the titration there is an equilibrium between ferrous and ferric ions ($Fe^{++} = Fe^{+++} + \epsilon$) and between cerous and ceric ions ($Ce^{+++} = Ce^{++++} + \epsilon$).   Before the equivalence point is reached, the most easily

---

[1] The possibility of the formation of complex ions is not considered in this discussion.

calculated ratios are those existing between ferrous and ferric ions, and during this part of the titration, the cell can be represented by

$$Hg \left| \frac{1}{2}Hg_2Cl_2, Cl^- (1 \text{ molar}) \left\| \begin{array}{c} Fe^{++} \\ Fe^{+++} \end{array} \right| Pt \right.$$

$$E = E_1 - E_2$$

$$= (-0.285) - \left(-0.771 - \frac{0.0591}{1} \log \frac{[Fe^{+++}]}{[Fe^{++}]} \right)$$

$$= 0.486 + 0.0591 \log \frac{[Fe^{+++}]}{[Fe^{++}]}$$

Beyond the equivalence point the most easily calculated ratios are those existing between cerous and ceric ions, and during this part of the titration the cell can be represented by

$$Hg \left| \frac{1}{2}Hg_2Cl_2, Cl^- (1 \text{ molar}) \left\| \begin{array}{c} Ce^{+++} \\ Ce^{++++} \end{array} \right| Pt \right.$$

$$E = E_1 - E_2$$

$$= (-0.285) - \left(-1.61 - \frac{0.0591}{1} \log \frac{[Ce^{++++}]}{[Ce^{+++}]} \right)$$

$$= 1.32 + 0.0591 \log \frac{[Ce^{++++}]}{[Ce^{+++}]}$$

The graph of a typical titration of this type is shown in Fig. 9. When dichromate is used for the titration of iron, the graph beyond the equivalence point depends on the hydrogen-ion concentration of the solution since in this case the predominating equilibrium is $2Cr^{+++} + 7H_2O = Cr_2O_7^= + 14H^+ + 6\epsilon$, and

$$E_1 = -1.36 - \frac{0.0591}{6} \log \frac{[Cr_2O_7^=][H^+]^{14}}{[Cr^{+++}]^2}$$

In all titrations of this kind when the potentials are plotted against volumes of titrating solution added, the equivalence point is found by bisecting the nearly vertical part of the curve. As a matter of fact, the change in e.m.f. is usually so great that it is often unnecessary to tabulate the values for the e.m.f. in order to determine the volume of titrating solution corresponding to the equivalence point. The titrating solution is added in small increments until the voltmeter shows a very sudden deflection, and the volume is read directly from the buret.

Potentiometric titrations can, of course, be applied to oxidation reactions other than the change from ferrous to ferric ions. The e.m.f. at the equivalence point is different for different reactions, but the sudden change in voltage is common to all.

EXAMPLE I.   Thirty milliliters of 0.10 N FeSO$_4$ are diluted to 100 ml. and are titrated with 0.10 N Ce(SO$_4$)$_2$.   A normal calomel half cell is used.   Calculate the e.m.f. of the cell when the following volumes of ceric sulfate have been added: (*a*) 20 ml.; (*b*) 30 ml.; (*c*) 50 ml.

SOLUTION: (*a*) Since the equivalence point is at the addition of 30 ml. of ceric sulfate, when 20 ml. have been added two-thirds of the ferrous

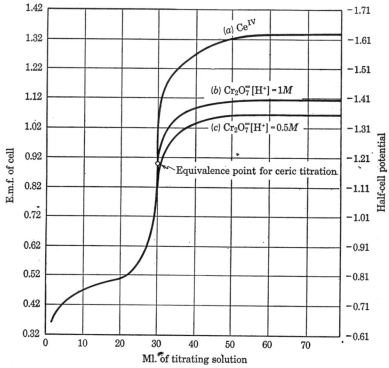

FIG. 9.   Curve for potentiometric titration of 30 ml. of 0.10 N FeSO$_4$ with (*a*) 0.10 N Ce(SO$_4$)$_2$; (*b*) 0.10 N K$_2$Cr$_2$O$_7$, [H$^+$] = 1 M; (*c*) 0.10 N K$_2$Cr$_2$O$_7$, [H$^+$] = 0.5 M.

ions have been oxidized (Fe^{++} + Ce^{++++} → Fe^{+++} + Ce^{+++}).   At that point the ratio of the concentration of the ferric ions formed to that of the ferrous ions remaining is therefore 2:1.

$$E_1 = -0.285 \text{ (calomel)}$$

$$E_2 = -0.771 - \frac{0.0591}{1} \log \frac{2}{1} = -0.789$$

$$E = E_1 - E_2 = 0.0504 \text{ volt.}   \textit{Ans.}$$

(*b*) At the point where 30 ml. of ceric sulfate have been added, the equivalence point has been reached.   Essentially all of the ferrous ions have been converted to ferric ions and an equivalent amount of cerous ions have been formed. Neglecting the possible formation of complex ions, the half-cell potential at the equivalence point in this case is the algebraic mean of the standard potential of ferrous-ferric and that of cerous-ceric (see Prob. 16.24):

$$E_2 = \frac{-0.771 + (-1.61)}{2} = -1.19$$

$$E = (-0.285) - (-1.19) = 0.90 \text{ volt.} \quad Ans.$$

(c) When 50 ml. of 0.10 N ceric sulfate (= 5.0 milliequivalents) have been added, there are 2.0 milliequivalents of ceric ions in the solution (since 3.0 milliequivalents have been reduced to cerous). The ratio of $[Ce^{++++}]$ to $[Ce^{+++}]$ is therefore $2:3$.

$$E_1 = -0.285 \text{ (calomel cell)}$$

$$E_2 = -1.61 - \frac{0.0591}{1} \log \frac{2}{3} = -1.60$$

$$E = E_1 - E_2 = 1.32 \text{ volts.} \quad Ans.$$

EXAMPLE II. In the titration in Example I above, calculate (a) the theoretical concentration of ceric ions at the point where 20 ml. of ceric sulfate have been added, and (b) the theoretical concentration of ferrous ions at the point where 50 ml. of ceric sulfate have been added.

SOLUTION: At all points in the titration the potential of the ferrous-ferric system is equal to that of the cerous-ceric system, since these four metal ions are all at equilibrium. Therefore,

$$\left(-0.771 - \frac{0.0591}{1} \log \frac{[Fe^{+++}]}{[Fe^{++}]}\right) = \left(-1.61 - \frac{0.0591}{1} \log \frac{[Ce^{++++}]}{[Ce^{+++}]}\right)$$

(a) At the point where 20 ml. of ceric sulfate have been added, the potential of the ferrous-ferric system is -0.789 volt [see solution to Example I(a)]. Since at this point the total volume of the solution is 120 ml., and $20 \times 0.10 = 2.0$ milliequivalents of cerous ions (= 2.0 millimoles) have been formed, the cerous-ion concentration is $2.0/120 = 0.0167$ molar.

$$-0.789 = \left(-1.61 - 0.0591 \log \frac{[Ce^{++++}]}{0.0167}\right)$$

$$[Ce^{++++}] = 2.1 \times 10^{-16} \text{ molar.} \quad Ans.$$

(b) At the point where 50 ml. of ceric sulfate have been added, the potential of the cerous-ceric system is -1.60 volts [see solution to Example I(c) above]. Since at this point the total volume of the solution is 150 ml. and $30 \times 0.10 = 3.0$ milliequivalents (= 3.0 millimoles) of ferric ions have been formed, the ferric-ion concentration is $3.0/150 = 0.020$ molar.

$$\left(-0.771 - 0.0591 \log \frac{0.020}{[Fe^{++}]}\right) = -1.60$$

$$[Fe^{++}] = 2.0 \times 10^{-16} \text{ molar.} \quad Ans.$$

114. Potentiometric Precipitation Titrations. The potentiometric principle can be applied to certain precipitation titrations. For example, in the titration of silver ions with halide ions, the concentration of silver ions changes during the progress of the titration. Using a silver electrode and a calomel half cell, we have the cell

$$Hg \mid \tfrac{1}{2}Hg_2Cl_2, Cl^- \text{ (1 molar) } \| Ag^+ \mid Ag$$
$$E_1 = -0.285 \text{ (calomel cell)}$$
$$E_2 = -0.800 - \frac{0.0591}{1} \log [Ag^+]$$
$$E = E_1 - E_2 = 0.515 + 0.0591 \log [Ag^+]$$

The graph of a titration of this type shows a sudden inflection at the equivalence point as in the case of acidimetric titrations and oxidation titrations. This titration is illustrated in Prob. 16.18.

Problems

(In the following problems it is assumed that a calomel half cell one molar in chloride ions is used.)

16.1. A cell made up of a certain basic solution and normal hydrogen-calomel electrodes gives at 25°C. an e.m.f. of 0.825 volt. What is the pH value and what is the hydroxyl-ion concentration of the solution?

Ans. 9.14, 1.38×10^{-5} molar.

16.2. A certain solution of sulfuric acid has a hydrogen-ion concentration of 3.60×10^{-3}. What is the pOH value? With regular hydrogen-calomel electrodes, what e.m.f. could be obtained at 25°C.?

Ans. 11.56. 0.429 volt.

16.3. With quinhydrone-calomel electrodes, approximately what e.m.f. could be obtained at 25°C. with a 0.0500 N solution of acetic acid (ionization constant 1.86×10^{-5})? What e.m.f. could be obtained from the same solution containing an additional mole of acetate ion per 500 ml.?

Ans. 0.237 volt. 0.041 volt.

16.4. With quinhydrone-calomel electrodes, a tenth-molar solution of a certain monobasic acid at 25°C. gives an e.m.f. of 275 mv. What is its approximate ionization constant?

Ans. 1.83×10^{-4}.

16.5. What is the hydroxyl-ion concentration of a solution which at 25°C. and with quinhydrone-calomel electrodes gives an e.m.f. of zero?

Ans. 1.07×10^{-7}.

16.6. In the titration of a weak base like NH_4OH with a strong acid like HCl, what relationship exists between the pH value of the solution and the ionization constant (Kb) of the base at that point in the titration which is halfway to the equivalence point?

Ans. pH $= 14 + \log$ Kb.

16.7. In the potentiometric titration of a solution of Sn^{++} with Ce^{++++}, what is the e.m.f. of the circuit at the equivalence point? Standard calomel cell is used. Assume no complex ions are formed.

Ans. 0.59 volt.

16.8. Calculate the potential at 25°C. obtainable from the cell made by connecting the half cell:

$$Pt \left| \begin{array}{l} Sn^{++} \text{ (0.0600 molar)} \\ Sn^{++++} \text{ (0.00100 molar)} \end{array} \right.$$

with a calomel half cell.

Ans. 0.188 volt.

16.9. Plot the following values of millivolts against milliliters of 0.100 N NaOH in the potentiometric titration of 2.50 grams of vinegar, hydrogen-calomel electrodes being used, and calculate the percentage of acetic acid in the vinegar. At what volume of NaOH is the solution neutral, and what volume corresponds to the equivalence point? What is the pH value at the equivalence point? 0.0 ml. = 420 mv.; 4.0 ml. = 475; 8.0 ml. = 540; 12.0 ml. = 588; 16.0 ml. = 620; 18.0 ml. = 638; 19.0 ml. = 650; 19.4 ml. = 670; 19.8 ml. = 790; 20.0 ml. = 830; 20.2 ml. = 856; 20.5 ml. = 875; 21.0 ml. = 900; 22.0 ml. = 930; 24.0 ml. = 948; 28.0 ml. = 970; 32.0 ml. = 985.

Ans. 4.75 per cent. 19.2 ml., 19.8 ml. 8.55.

16.10. A sample of sodium carbonate containing inert impurities weighs 1.10 grams. It is dissolved in water and titrated potentiometrically with 0.500 N HCl, hydrogen-calomel electrodes being used. Plot the following values of milliliters against corresponding millivolts, and calculate the approximate percentage of Na_2CO_3 in the sample. What are the pH values at the two equivalence points? 0.01 ml. = 928 mv.; 5.0 ml. = 922; 10.0 ml. = 912; 12.5 ml. = 900; 15.0 ml. = 880; 17.5 ml. = 838; 20.0 ml. = 762; 22.5 ml. = 710; 25.0 ml. = 696; 27.5 ml. = 682; 30.0 ml. = 669; 32.5 ml. = 650; 35.0 ml. = 607; 37.5 ml. = 484; 40.0 ml. = 452; 45.0 ml. = 427; 50.0 ml. = 416.

Ans. 87 per cent. 9.1, 4.5.

16.11. A sample of Na_2CO_3 is known to contain either NaOH or $NaHCO_3$, together with inert matter. A sample weighing 1.50 grams is titrated potentiometrically with 0.600 N HCl. Plot milliliters of acid against millivolts, and determine the approximate percentage composition of the sample. 0.10 ml. = 930 mv.; 5.0 ml. = 918; 10.0 ml. = 899; 12.5 ml. = 872; 15.0 ml. = 820; 17.5 ml. = 757; 20.0 ml. = 727; 22.5 ml. = 708; 25.0 ml. = 696; 27.5 ml. = 683; 30.0 ml. = 668; 32.5 ml. = 648; 35.0 ml. = 606; 37.5 ml. = 485; 40.0 ml. = 452; 45.0 ml. = 427; 50.0 ml. = 416.

Ans. 63.7 per cent Na_2CO_3, 20.1 per cent $NaHCO_3$.

16.12. A sample of formic acid (HCOOH) is dissolved in water and titrated potentiometrically with 0.400 N NaOH, quinhydrone-calomel electrodes being used. Plot the titration curve from the following data, and calculate the pH value at the equivalence point. Approximately how many grams of HCOOH are shown to be present in the solution?   0.0 ml. = 273 mv.; 10.0 ml. = 262; 25.0 ml. = 242; 35.0 ml. = 225; 45.0 ml. = 195; 55.0 ml. = 135; 60.0 ml. = 58; 62.5 ml. = 0; 65.0 ml. = −100; 70.0 ml. = −223; 80.0 ml. = −308.

Ans.   8.11.   1.2 grams.

16.13. In the potentiometric titration of 20 ml. of 0.10 N $Ce(SO_4)_2$ (diluted with water to 200 ml.) with 0.10 N $FeSO_4$, what is the e.m.f. of the circuit (*a*) at the point where 5 ml. of the $FeSO_4$ have been added; (*b*) at the point where 25 ml. of the $FeSO_4$ have been added?   (*c*) What is the concentration of ferrous ions at the former point, and (*d*) what is the concentration of ceric ions at the latter point?

Ans.   (*a*) 1.35 volts; (*b*) 0.522 volt.   (*c*) 4.9×10^{-18} molar; (*d*) 2.8×10^{-16} molar.

16.14. A cell is made up of a platinum wire, dipping into a solution of cerous and ceric ions, and a regular calomel cell.   At 25°C. an e.m.f. of 1,190 mv. is obtainable. Calculate the ratio of concentration of ceric ions to concentration of cerous ions in the solution.

Ans.   19.3.

16.15. A sample of limonite weighing 0.350 gram is dissolved in HCl, and the ferric ions are reduced by means of a slight excess of stannous chloride.   Without removal of the excess stannous ions the solution is titrated potentiometrically with 0.100 N ceric sulfate solution, platinum-calomel electrodes being used.   Plot the following values of milliliters of ceric sulfate against corresponding millivolts, and from the graph calculate the approximate percentage of Fe_2O_3 in the sample.   The stannous ions are oxidized by the ceric sulfate first.   0.0 ml. = 190 mv.; 1.00 ml. = 218; 2.00 ml. = 223; 3.00 ml. = 240; 4.00 ml. = 325; 5.00 ml. = 342; 6.00 ml. = 350; 9.00 ml. = 363; 15.0 ml. = 382; 20.0 ml. = 388; 25.0 ml. = 393; 30.0 ml. = 417; 32.0 ml. = 450; 34.0 ml. = 510; 35.0 ml. = 570; 36.0 ml. = 910; 37.0 ml. = 1,100; 39.0 ml. = 1,155; 45.0 ml. = 1,217; 50.0 ml. = 1,229.

Ans.   73 per cent.

16.16. In the potentiometric titration of a certain solution of $KMnO_4$ with $FeSO_4$, at the point halfway to the equivalence point the pH value of the solution is 1.00. What is the e.m.f. of the circuit at this point?   A calomel half cell is used.   What is the voltage of the circuit at the point 50 per cent beyond the equivalence point?

Ans.   1.14 volts.   0.497 volt.

16.17. What e.m.f. would be given by the circuit consisting of a calomel half cell and each of the following solutions?   (*a*) a 0.010-molar solution of a monobasic acid having an ionization constant of 1.0×10^{-4} (quinhydrone electrode); (*b*) 100 ml. of a 0.010-molar solution of the above acid in which has been dissolved 0.50 mole of NaOH (antimony electrode); (*c*) a 0.010-normal solution of ceric sulfate which has been titrated with ferrous sulfate to a point one-fifth of the way to the equivalence point (platinum electrode); (*d*) a saturated solution of AgBr (silver electrode); (*e*) a saturated solution of Ag_2CrO_4 (silver electrode).   Use solubility products given in the Appendix.

Ans.   (*a*) 0.238; (*b*) 0.037; (*c*) 1.36; (*d*) 0.151; (*e*) 0.303.

16.18. Twenty-five milliliters of 0.200 N $AgNO_3$ are diluted to 250 ml. and titrated potentiometrically with 0.200 N KBr, a silver electrode and a calomel electrode being used.   Assuming the solubility of silver bromide to be 5.9×10^{-7} mole per liter, calculate the theoretical value for E (*a*) when a fraction of a drop of bomide has been added, (*b*) at the equivalence point, (*c*) after 26 ml. of the bromide have been added.

(*Hint:* Find the silver-ion concentration in each case, and use the standard potential of Ag $=$ Ag$^+$ $+$ ϵ given in the Appendix.)

   Ans.   (*a*) $+0.414$ volt, (*b*) $+0.146$ volt, (*c*) -0.036 volt.

16.19. A certain solution of sodium hydroxide has a hydroxyl-ion concentration of 5.20×10^{-4}. With regular hydrogen-calomel electrodes, what e.m.f. could be obtained at 25°C.?

16.20. With quinhydrone-calomel electrodes, a certain solution at 25°C. gives an e.m.f. of 116 mv. What is the hydroxyl-ion concentration of the solution?

16.21. With regular hydrogen-calomel electrodes, a hundredth-molar solution of a certain monoacidic base gives at 25°C. an e.m.f. of 946 mv. What is the approximate ionization constant of the base? What e.m.f. would be obtained if 2.00 moles per liter of cation common to the base were introduced into the solution?

16.22. Plot values on graph paper showing the relationship between millivolts and pH values (*a*) when using normal hydrogen-calomel electrodes, (*b*) when using quinhydrone-calomel electrodes. Include the range between pH $=$ 14 and pH $=$ -2.

16.23. In the titration of a weak monobasic acid with a strong base, what is the relationship between the pH value of the solution and the ionization constant of the acid (K_a) at that point in the titration which is two-thirds of the way to the equivalence point?

16.24. Prove that in the potentiometric titration of ferrous ions with ceric ions the voltage at the equivalence point is given by the general expression $E_1 = (E_1{}^0 + E_2{}^0)/2$. (*Hint:* At the equivalence point, not only is the reaction Fe^{++} $+$ Ce^{++++} $=$ Fe^{+++} $+$ Ce^{+++} at equilibrium, and hence $E_1 = E_2$, but also [Fe^{++}] $=$ [Ce^{++++}] and [Fe^{+++}] $=$ [Ce^{+++}].)

16.25. In the potentiometric titration of 60.0 ml. of 0.100 N ferrous sulfate (diluted with water to 250 ml.) with 0.200 N ceric sulfate, what should be the voltage reading (*a*) after 10.0 ml. of ceric sulfate have been added, (*b*) after 30.0 ml. of ceric sulfate have been added, (*c*) after 45.0 ml. of ceric sulfate have been added? What is the ferrous-ion concentration at this last point?

16.26. In the potentiometric titration of a certain solution of dichromate ions with FeSO$_4$ (regular calomel half cell used) the hydrogen-ion concentration is 0.10 molar at the point one-third of the way to the equivalence point. What is the e.m.f. of the circuit at this point?

16.27. Fifty milliliters of 0.080 N Ce(SO$_4$)$_2$ are diluted to 100 ml. and titrated with 0.080 N FeSO$_4$. What is the concentration of ferrous ions at that point in the titration which is exactly halfway to the equivalence point?

16.28. The potentiometric titration of a 25-ml. pipetful of 0.268 N H$_2$SO$_4$ with NaOH solution gave the following values of millivolts for the corresponding volumes of NaOH: 0.0 ml. $=$ 369 mv.; 5.0 ml. $=$ 378; 10.0 ml. $=$ 388; 15.0 ml. $=$ 398; 20.0 ml. $=$ 406; 25.0 ml. $=$ 420; 28.0 ml. $=$ 460; 30.0 ml. $=$ 516; 30.5 ml. $=$ 690; 31.0 ml. $=$ 860; 35.0 ml. $=$ 949; 40.0 ml. $=$ 966; 45.0 ml. $=$ 982. Plot the millivolts of potential as ordinates against milliliters of NaOH as abscissas, and from the curve determine the pH value at the equivalence point and the normality of the NaOH solution.

16.29. Make a graph for the following potentiometric titration of 40.0 ml. of 0.213 M H$_3$PO$_4$ diluted with water to 200 ml. and titrated with 0.200 N NaOH at 25°C., hydrogen-calomel electrodes being used. Calculate the pH value at which the replacement of the first and second hydrogens of H$_3$PO$_4$ occurs. 0.0 ml. $=$ 300 mv.; 5.0 ml. $=$ 315; 10.0 ml. $=$ 350; 13.0 ml. $=$ 385; 13.5 ml. $=$ 398; 13.8 ml. $=$ 405; 14.0 ml.

= 415; 14.2 ml. = 450; 14.4 ml. = 525; 14.8 ml. = 555; 15.5 ml. = 566; 17.0 ml. = 580; 20.2 ml. = 603; 25.0 ml. = 640; 27.5 ml. = 658; 28.5 ml. = 675; 28.8 ml. = 685; 29.0 ml. = 740; 29.2 ml. = 760; 29.5 ml. = 795; 30.0 ml. = 815; 31.0 ml. = 835; 35.0 ml. = 870; 40.0 ml. = 890.

16.30. A cleaner is known to contain, in addition to inert material, either NaOH, Na_2CO_3, or mixtures of these. The potentiometric titration of a 1.00-gram sample in 100 ml. of water with 0.265 N HCl, regular hydrogen-calomel electrodes being used, give the following pH values: 0.0 ml. = 11.70; 5.50 ml. = 11.68; 10.0 ml. = 11.66; 20.0 ml. = 11.60; 30.0 ml. = 11.44; 45.0 ml. = 10.98; 55.0 ml. = 9.75; 60.0 ml. = 8.76; 62.0 ml. = 7.66; 64.0 ml. = 6.31; 66.0 ml. = 5.70; 68.0 ml. = 5.40; 70.0 ml. = 5.05; 72.0 ml. = 4.81; 73.0 ml. = 4.10; 74.0 ml. = 2.44; 76.0 ml. = 1.94; 78.0 ml. = 1.70; 85.0 ml. = 1.41; 95.0 ml. = 1.16.

Interpret the curve, stating which components are present and their approximate percentages. What voltage reading is obtained at the first point of inflection?

16.31. The chromium in 5.00 grams of steel is oxidized to dichromate and then titrated potentiometrically with 0.104 N FeSO$_4$ solution in the presence of acid. A normal calomel cell is used. Show the general appearance of the titration curve. If the point of maximum slope of the curve is at 8.80 ml. of ferrous sulfate, calculate the percentage of chromium in the steel. If at the point of adding 4.40 ml. of ferrous sulfate the hydrogen-ion concentration of the solution is 0.10 molar, calculate the voltage of the circuit at that point.

CHAPTER 17

CONDUCTOMETRIC TITRATIONS

115. Conductance. Strong acids, strong bases, and most salts, when dissolved in a relatively large volume of water, are practically completely dissociated into ions. These ions are capable of transporting electricity, and because of them the solutions are good conductors of the electric current. The *conductance* of a solution is the reciprocal of its electrical resistance and is expressed in *reciprocal ohms* or *mhos*.

The *specific conductance* of a solution is the conductance of a cube of the solution of 1-cm. edge. The specific conductance at 25°C. of 0.100 N HCl is 0.0394 mho; the specific conductance of 0.0100 N HCl is 0.00401 mho.

Equivalent conductance is the conductance of a solution containing one gram-equivalent weight of dissolved electrolyte between electrodes 1 cm. apart. It is therefore numerically equal to the product of the specific conductance of the solution and the number of milliliters containing one gram-equivalent weight of electrolyte.

$$Equivalent\ conductance = \frac{1,000 \times specific\ conductance}{normality}$$

The equivalent conductance of 0.100 N HCl is $0.0394 \times 10,000 = 394$ mhos; the equivalent conductance of 0.0100 N HCl is $0.00401 \times 100,000 = 401$ mhos. As a solution becomes more dilute, its equivalent conductance becomes somewhat greater owing to the fact that in more dilute solutions inter-ionic effects of electrolytes are lessened, which gives the apparent effect of increasing the degree of ionization of the dissolved substance.

By extrapolation it is possible to determine the equivalent conductance of a solution at infinite dilution. For hydrochloric acid this value at 25°C. is 425.8 reciprocal ohms. This is the theoretical conductance that would be given by a "perfect" solution containing 36.46 grams of HCl between electrodes 1 cm. apart.

116. Mobility of Ions. Different kinds of ions have different velocities, so that when an electric current is passed through a solution, the faster moving ions carry a relatively greater amount of the current. In the case of very dilute hydrochloric acid, the hydrogen ions, moving much faster than the chloride ions, carry about 82 per cent of the current; the chloride ions carry only about 18 per cent. The *mobility* of an ion is the equivalent conductance of that ion, and the equivalent conductance of an electrolyte is equal to the sum of the mobilities of its ions. Thus, the equivalent conductance at 25°C. of hydrochloric acid at infinite dilution (= 425.8) is equal to the sum of the mobility of the hydrogen ions (= 350) and the mobility of the chloride ions (= 75.8) at that temperature. If several electrolytes are present in a solution, all the ions contribute to the conductance of the solution. Mobilities increase by about 2 per cent for each degree centigrade increase in temperature.

Table III gives the equivalent conductances, or mobilities, at 25°C. of some of the common ions at infinite dilution. From it can be calculated the equivalent conductances of corresponding electrolytes at infinite dilution.

TABLE III. MOBILITIES OF SOME COMMON IONS (25°C)

Na^+	50.8	Cl^-	75.8
K^+	74.8	Br^-	77.7
Ag^+	63.4	I^-	76.0
H^+	350	OH^-	193
NH_4^+	74.9	$C_2H_3O_2^-$	40.8
Li^+	41.7	$\frac{1}{2}SO_4^=$	80.0
$\frac{1}{2}Mg^{++}$	55.0	ClO_3^-	63.3
$\frac{1}{2}Ba^{++}$	65.2	NO_3^-	70.9
$\frac{1}{2}Ca^{++}$	61	BrO_3^-	55.3
$\frac{1}{2}Pb^{++}$	71.0	IO_3^-	39.6
$\frac{1}{2}Ni^{++}$	53.6	$\frac{1}{2}C_2O_4^=$	73.5
$\frac{1}{2}Fe^{++}$	54	$\frac{1}{3}Fe(CN)_6^≡$	97.3
$\frac{1}{3}Fe^{+++}$	68.4	$\frac{1}{4}Fe(CN)_6^≣$	100.8

117. Conductometric Acidimetric Titrations. Consider the titration of a dilute solution of HCl with NaOH solution:

$$H^+Cl^- + (Na^+OH^-) \rightarrow Na^+Cl^- + H_2O$$

At the beginning of the titration, the HCl solution has a high conductance value, owing principally to the extremely high mobility of the hydrogen ions. As NaOH is added, the concentration of the hydrogen ions is decreased and, although hydrogen ions are replaced by sodium ions, the mobility of the latter is much less, so that the conductance of the solution decreases rapidly. At the equivalence point, the solution contains only NaCl, and the conductance is at a minimum for, on further addition of NaOH, the hydroxyl ions with their high mobility give a rapidly increasing conductance to the solution. If the titration is carried out under constant conditions of temperature, etc., and the volume of titrating solution is plotted against conductance, a curve of the appearance of line *ABC* in Fig. 10 is obtained.

In this figure, line *AH* represents that part of the conductance of the solution contributed by the HCl alone; *DBJ* represents that part of the conductance of the solution contributed by the NaCl alone.   Line *AB* is therefore the resultant of these two curves, the distance *GI* being equal to *FI + EI*.   Line *HK* represents the conductance of the excess NaOH alone; line *BJ* is the conductance of the NaCl present in the solution after the equivalence point has been reached; and *BC* is the resultant.

Ideal titration curves applying to perfect solutions can be calculated from the mobilities of the ions involved.   Thus, in the titration of a very

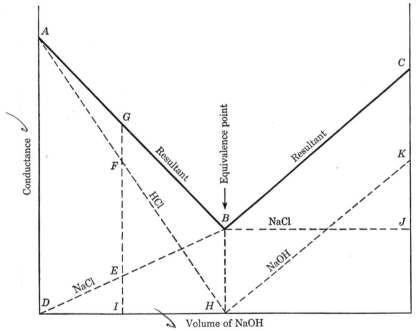

Fig. 10. Conductometric titration of dilute HCl with NaOH.

dilute solution containing a gram-equivalent weight of HCl with a relatively concentrated solution of sodium hydroxide (so as to give no appreciable change in the total volume of the solution being titrated), the theoretical conductance of the original solution is $350 (H^+) + 75.8 (Cl^-) =$ 425.8 mhos.   At the equivalence point the solution contains only NaCl and its conductance is $50.8 (Na^+) + 75.8 (Cl^-) = 126.6$ mhos.   An excess of one gram-equivalent weight of NaOH to the resulting solution would give a conductance of 50.8 $(Na^+) + 75.8$ $(Cl^-) + 50.8$ $(Na^+) +$ $193 (OH^-) = 370.4$ mhos.   Plotting these conductance values against corresponding relative volumes of NaOH gives a titration curve like that of the resultant line *ABC* in the figure.   The equivalence point is the intersection of two straight lines.

In an actual titration of this type the lines are likely to be slightly curved because of (1) variation in temperature, due, in part at least, to the heat of neutralization, (2) increase in the volume of the solution because of added reagent, and (3) interionic effects.   Foreign ions in the solution may distort the curve slightly, although their general effect is to increase the total conductance by a constant amount.   In spite of this, the inflection is sharp and three or four readings on each side of the

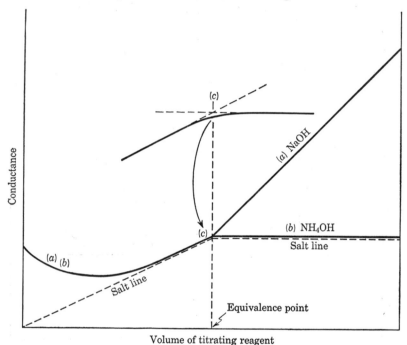

Fig. 11. Conductometric titration of 0.01 N $HC_2H_3O_2$ (*a*) with NaOH, (*b*) with NH₄OH.

equivalence point are usually sufficient to establish the point of intersection and hence the buret reading at the equivalence point.

The titration of a weak acid like acetic acid with a strong base like sodium hydroxide is shown in the curve (*a*) (*a*) of Fig. 11.   Here the first small amount of NaOH will, as before, cause a decrease in conductivity but, since the concentration of hydrogen ions in acetic acid is small, the conductance of the solution soon increases owing to the formation of sodium ions and acetate ions, the latter buffering the solution and thus cutting down the concentration of the highly mobile hydrogen ions.   The conductance values then follow closely those of the sodium acetate formed.   Beyond the equivalence point the formation of hydroxyl ions does not cause a sharp inflection in the titration curve.   If, on the other hand, NH_4OH is used to titrate the acetic acid, a curve (b) (b) is obtained with a sharper inflection at the equivalence point, for the excess NH_4OH, owing to its slight degree of ionization, has little effect on the conductance of the solution. In an actual titration of this type, the two parts of the conductance curve do not meet sharply at a point because of hydrolysis effects, but the equivalence point can be found by extending the straight parts of the titration graph to a common point [see part (c) of Fig. 11].

The titration of a mixture of a strong acid and a weak acid with a standard base can often be carried out conductometrically and the amount of each acid determined from the graph (see Prob. 17.6). A similar type of titration curve is obtained in the titration of certain dibasic acids (see Prob. 17.14).

118. Conductometric Precipitation Titrations. Many precipitation titrations are also possible by conductometric methods. Consider, for example, a very dilute solution containing a gram-equivalent weight of sodium sulfate being titrated with a concentrated solution of barium acetate. The theoretical conductance of the original solution is 50.8 (Na^+) + 80.0 ($\frac{1}{2}SO_4^=$) = 130.8 mhos. At the equivalence point the conductance is 50.8 (Na^+) + 40.8 ($C_2H_3O_2^-$) = 91.6 mhos. If an excess of a gram-equivalent weight of barium acetate is added, the conductance of the solution is 50.8 (Na^+) + 40.8 ($C_2H_3O_2^-$) + 65.2 ($\frac{1}{2}Ba^{++}$) + 40.8 ($C_2H_3O_2^-$) = 197.6 mhos. The titration curve is therefore a flat V-shaped one with the equivalence point at the intersection of two straight lines. Certain titration curves of this type are illustrated in the accompanying problems.

119. Other Conductometric Titrations. Certain redox titrations are possible by conductometric methods provided there is a change in the hydrogen-ion concentration during the progress of the titration (e.g., $6Fe^{++} + Cr_2O_7^= + 14H^+ \rightarrow 6Fe^{+++} + 2Cr^{+++} + 7H_2O$). Because of the high mobility of the hydrogen ion, a marked change in conductance can be expected during the initial part of the titration. The precision of such titrations is satisfactory only if the initial acidity is low.

A few titrations involving complex formations are possible.

Salts of strong bases and weak acids (e.g., $NaC_2H_3O_2$) can be conductometrically titrated with strong acids, and salts of weak bases and strong acids (e.g., NH_4Cl) can be titrated with strong bases.

Titration curves of some of these types are illustrated in the accompanying problems.

120. Conductometric Titration Apparatus. A simple hookup for determining the conductance of a solution is indicated in the diagram of Fig. 12, where MO is a slide-wire divided into 1,000 scale divisions, E is a pair of electrodes so fixed as to remain at a constant distance apart and dipping into the solution to be measured. S is a source of alternating current, stepped down by means of a transformer to about 6 volts, and R is a rheostat. G is a device for determining the point of bridge balance or null point on the slide wire. It can be (a) a galvanometer with rectifier to give a visible indication, (b) a telephone receiver to give an audible indication, or (c) an electronic device such as the familiar "magic eye" cathode-ray tube.

In measuring relative conductance values in a titration, the rheostat is first adjusted so that the null-point reading is obtained when the point of contact N is near the center of the slide-wire. From then on, the adjustment of the rheostat is not changed. The solution is then titrated, and

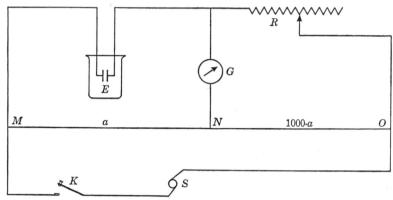

FIG. 12. Conductometric titration hookup.

bridge readings are taken between each increment of added solution by adjusting the slide-wire until the null-point indication is obtained. After any such adjustment,

$$\frac{a}{1,000 - a} = \frac{\text{resistance of cell}}{\text{resistance of rheostat}}$$

but, since the resistance of the rheostat is a constant (K) and the resistance of the cell is the reciprocal of its conductance,

$$aK = \frac{1,000 - a}{\text{conductance of cell}}$$

whence,

$$\text{Conductance of cell} = \left(\frac{1,000 - a}{a}\right)\frac{1}{K}$$

Since in an ordinary titration we are not interested in the actual conductance values but only in the relative changes in conductivity as a means of establishing a titration curve, it is only necessary to plot the volume of titrating solution against the values $(1,000 - a)/a$ as obtained from the bridge readings. Unlike the potentiometric graph, the conductometric titration curves are straight lines or nearly so, and they can therefore usually be fixed by a relatively few volume readings on each side of the equivalence point. In order for accurate values to be obtained and in order for the lines to be straight or nearly so, it is important to keep the temperature of the solution as nearly constant as possible, and it is also theoretically necessary that the volume of the solution shall not change during the titration. This last condition is fulfilled approximately enough for ordinary titrations if the total volume of reagent does not exceed 1 or 2 per cent of the solution titrated. The reagent should therefore be as concentrated, and the solution as dilute, as feasible. A solution $0.01 - 0.001$ normal titrated with a 1-normal solution of reagent would be a typical case.

Problems

17.1. If the specific conductance of $N/50$ HCl is 0.00792 mho, what is the equivalent conductance of $N/50$ HCl?

Ans. 396 mhos.

17.2. At 25°C, what is the equivalent conductance at infinite dilution of a solution of silver sulfate?

Ans. 143.4 mhos.

17.3. A solution containing a gram-equivalent weight of $BaCl_2$ at very high dilution is titrated at 25°C. with Li_2SO_4. From mobilities of the ions involved calculate the conductance of the solution (*a*) at the start of the titration, (*b*) at the equivalence point, and (*c*) at the point where a total of 2 gram-equivalents of Li_2SO_4 have been added. Plot these values to show the titration graph. Make similar calculations and graph for the titration of $BaCl_2$ with Na_2SO_4. Which gives the sharper inflection at the equivalence point?

Ans. (*a*) 141.0, (*b*) 117.5, (*c*) 239.2; (*a*) 141.0, (*b*) 126.6, (*c*) 257.4 mhos.

17.4. A very dilute solution of sodium hydroxide is titrated conductometrically with 1.00 N HCl. The following bridge readings of $(100 - a)/a$ were obtained at the indicated points in the titration. Plot the titration curve and from it determine the number of grams of NaOH present in the solution. 0.00 ml. $-$ 3.15; 1.00 ml. $-$ 2.60; 2.00 ml. $-$ 2.04; 3.00 ml. $-$ 1.40; 4.00 ml. $-$ 1.97; 5.00 ml. $-$ 2.86; 6.00 ml. $-$ 3.66.

Ans. 0.128 gram.

17.5. A solution approximately $N/100$ in sodium acetate is titrated conductometrically with 1.00 N HCl. From the following titration values showing relative conductivities plot the curve and calculate the number of grams of $NaC_2H_3O_2$ present in the solution. (*Hint:* Extend the nearly straight parts of the curve to a point of intersection.) 0.00 ml. $-$ 218; 4.00 ml. $-$ 230; 8.00 ml. $-$ 243; 9.00 ml. $-$ 247; 10.00 ml. $-$ 256; 11.00 ml. $-$ 269; 12.00 ml. $-$ 278; 14.00 ml. $-$ 325; 17.00 ml. $-$ 380. Show from mobilities and relative degrees of ionization why this form of curve is to be expected.

Ans. 0.820 gram.

17.6. A sample of vinegar has been adulterated with hydrochloric acid. It is titrated with 0.500 N NH₄OH and the following bridge readings of $(1,000 - a)/a$

were obtained at the indicated buret readings. Calculate the number of grams of HCl and of $HC_2H_3O_2$ in the sample. (*Hint:* Find the point of neutralization of the HCl by extending the nearly straight sides of the U-shaped part of the graph to a point of intersection.) 0.00 ml. − 2.87; 1.00 ml. − 2.50; 2.00 ml. − 2.10; 2.50 ml. − 1.85; 3.00 ml. − 1.70; 3.10 − 1.66; 3.20 − 1.70; 3.50 ml. − 1.76; 4.00 ml. − 2.00; 4.20 ml. − 2.10; 4.50 ml. − 2.15; 5.00 ml. − 2.15; 6.00 ml. − 2.14; 7.00 ml. − 2.16; 8.00 ml. − 2.18.

Ans. 0.057 gram HCl, 0.035 gram $HC_2H_3O_2$.

17.7. At 25°C. what is the equivalent conductance at infinite dilution of a solution of $BaCl_2$?

17.8. Sketch the general form of the titration curve you would expect to get in the conductometric titration of $N/100$ NH_4OH with (*a*) $N/1$ HCl, (*b*) $N/1$ $HC_2H_3O_2$.

17.9. Using the equivalent conductance values obtained from the mobilities of the ions, show the general form of the titration curve in each of the following cases: (*a*) titration of NaOH with HNO_3, (*b*) titration of $BaCl_2$ with K_2SO_4, (*c*) titration of $BaCl_2$ with H_2SO_4, (*d*) titration of $Ba(OH)_2$ with H_2SO_4, (*e*) titration of $MgSO_4$ with $Ba(OH)_2$, (*f*) titration of NH_4Cl with NaOH, (*g*) titration of $AgNO_3$ with LiCl.

17.10. In the titration of 80.0 ml. of a solution of HNO_3 with 4.85 N NaOH the following relative conductivities were obtained for the corresponding volumes of NaOH. Plot the curve and calculate the acid normality of the original acid solution. 0.00 ml. − 501; 1.00 ml. − 340; 2.00 ml. − 175; 3.00 ml. − 180; 4.00 ml. − 261; 5.00 ml. − 338.

17.11. A sample of vinegar weighing 5.00 grams is diluted to 500 ml. and titrated conductometrically with 0.500 N NH_4OH. The following relative conductivities were obtained from the bridge readings of $(1,000 − a)/a$ at the indicated buret readings: 0.00 ml. − 1.20; 0.50 ml. − 0.95; 1.00 ml. − 0.80; 1.50 ml. − 0.70; 2.00 ml. − 0.70; 3.00 ml. − 0.95; 4.00 ml. − 1.35; 5.00 ml. − 1.75; 6.00 ml. − 2.13; 7.00 ml. − 2.48; 7.50 ml. − 2.68; 8.00 ml. − 2.78; 9.00 ml. − 2.82; 10.00 ml. − 2.83; 14.00 ml. − 2.87. Plot these values and determine from the graph the buret reading at the equivalence point. From this calculate the acidity of the vinegar in terms of percentage of $HC_2H_3O_2$. Explain the chemistry involved to give the U-shaped appearance of the curve prior to reaching the equivalence point. What would be the general appearance of the graph if 0.500 N NaOH had been substituted for the NH_4OH in the titration? What is the advantage of using NH_4OH?

17.12. A solution approximately 0.01 N in sodium acetate is titrated conductometrically with 1.25 N HCl and the following relative conductivities were obtained at the corresponding buret readings: 0.00 ml. − 451; 1.00 ml. − 455; 2.00 ml. − 459; 2.50 ml. − 460; 2.75 ml. − 462; 3.00 ml. − 465; 3.25 ml. − 472; 3.50 ml. − 482; 3.75 ml. − 497; 4.00 ml. − 515; 4.50 ml. − 575; 5.00 ml. − 643; 6.00 ml. − 776. Plot the curve and calculate the number of grams of $NaC_2H_3O_2$ present in the solution.

17.13. A solution containing sodium bromide is titrated with 0.650 N silver nitrate. The following relative values were obtained for the conductances of the solution during the titration. Plot the curve on a large scale and calculate the number of grams of NaBr originally present in the solution. 0.00 ml. − 269; 0.50 ml. − 262; 1.00 ml. − 241; 1.50 ml. − 227; 2.00 ml. − 213; 2.50 ml. − 197; 3.00 ml. − 218; 3.50 ml. − 237; 4.00 ml. − 261; 4.50 ml. − 282; 5.00 ml. − 301.

17.14. Oxalic acid is a dibasic acid and can be considered as an equimolar mixture of a fairly strong acid ($H_2C_2O_4 \rightleftarrows H^+ + HC_2O_4^-$; $K' = 4 \times 10^{-2}$) and a weak acid

($HC_2O_4^- \rightleftarrows H^+ + C_2O_4^=$; $K'' = 5 \times 10^{-5}$). The following relative conductance values were obtained in the conductometric titration of a dilute solution of oxalic acid with $0.640 \, N$ NH_4OH. Plot the curve and calculate the number of grams of $H_2C_2O_4.$-$2H_2O$ present in the solution. 0.00 ml. − 285; 0.20 ml. − 235; 0.40 ml. − 188; 0.60 ml. − 141; 0.70 ml. − 118; 0.80 ml. − 109; 0.90 ml. − 115; 1.00 ml. − 123; 1.20 ml. − 147; 1.40 ml. − 173; 1.60 ml. − 184; 1.80 ml. − 183; 2.00 ml. − 181; 2.20 ml. − 181. What does the lowest point of the curve represent? Show how it would be possible in certain cases to analyze a mixture of oxalic acid and sodium binoxalate ($NaHC_2O_4$). What would be the general appearance of the curve in this case?

CHAPTER 18

AMPEROMETRIC TITRATIONS

121. Polarographic Principle. Suppose a solution containing a reducible substance is subjected to electrolytic reduction at an electrode consisting of metallic mercury dropping at a steady rate from a capillary tube, thus exposing a constantly fresh surface of the metal to the solution. If the applied e.m.f. is increased gradually, the amperage of the current remains near zero and increases only slightly until the decomposition potential of the substance is reached (see Sec. 66). At this point

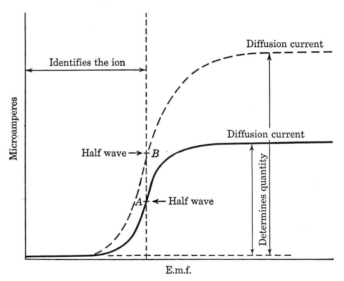

Fig. 13. Polarographic current-voltage relationship.

electrolytic reduction starts, and an increased e.m.f. causes a sharp increase in amperage in accordance with Ohm's law, $E = IR$. As electrolysis progresses, however, there is a depletion of the reducible substance at the electrode and the potential necessary for decomposition is increased. A point is reached where, because of nearly complete concentration polarization, an increasing e.m.f. causes practically no increase in amperage. The three steps are shown by the solid line in Fig. 13 where microamperes as ordinates are plotted against applied voltages as abscissas.

The nearly constant current corresponding to the upper right-hand part of the curve is called the *diffusion current*, and its magnitude is proportional to the concentration of the reducible substance remaining in the solution.

Point *A* on the curve is the potential at which the current is one-half of the diffusion current. It is called the *half-wave potential*, and its significance is seen from the broken-line curve in the same figure. This represents the curve applying to the electrodeposition of the same ion at a greater concentration. It is seen that the half-wave potential *B* in this case corresponds to the same point on the abscissa as the half-wave potential *A*. The half-wave potential of a reducible ion is therefore independent of the concentration and, with properly calibrated apparatus, serves as a means of identifying the substance being reduced.

The amperage of the diffusion current, on the other hand, is a measure of the quantity of the substance present in solution, so that

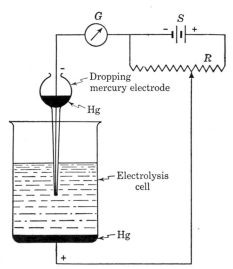

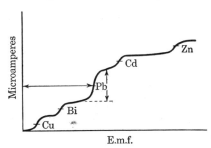

Fig. 14. Polarographic curve.   Fig. 15. Amperometric titration hookup.

a polarographic curve serves to identify an ion qualitatively and quantitatively. When several kinds of reducible ions are present in the same solution, and the respective half-wave potentials are not too close together, the nature and approximate quantities of the ions can be established by a single run. The polarographic curve in such a case is a series of diffusion current curves which are produced as the voltage is gradually increased and the ions are reduced in order. The general appearance of such a curve is shown in Fig. 14. In this figure, the value of the e.m.f. of the half wave at the end of the horizontal arrow identifies the lead. The quantity of lead is revealed by the number of microamperes spanned by the vertical arrow.

The bare essentials of a polarographic hookup are shown in Fig. 15. In this case, the cathode consists of a dropping mercury electrode from which the metal emerges from a capillary tube in a steady flow of small drops.   A fresh surface of mercury is thereby constantly exposed to the solution and there is therefore no effective change due to the formation of amalgams.   The anode in this case is a pool of mercury, and in most determinations an independent standard calomel cell is used as a reference electrode.

Actually, the current strengths vary between a minimum and a maximum for each drop of mercury as it forms, since there is a periodic change in the surface area of the drop.   Therefore the graph lines obtained are actually not the smooth lines shown in the accompanying figures, but are saw-toothed lines.   The amplitude of the fluctuations is small, however, and smooth lines can easily be drawn between them to represent average current strengths.   Current-voltage curves can be automatically recorded by means of a mechanism called a *polarograph*, but satisfactory curves can also be obtained manually.

122. Amperometric Titrations.   Quantitative results obtained from polarographic curves as indicated above are not of very high degree of precision.   However, polarographic principles can be applied to certain titrations with results of a precision comparable to that obtainable in potentiometric and conductometric titrations.

Suppose a reducible substance in a solution is subjected to an initial e.m.f. which is of such magnitude as to give the amperage corresponding to the diffusion current, and suppose the solution is subjected to a precipitation titration with a nonreducible reagent.   Such a case would be the titration of a solution of a lead salt with sulfate.   The concentration of the reducible substance (Pb^{++}) is steadily diminished as the sulfate is added.   The current, being proportional to the concentration of lead ions, likewise steadily diminishes as the titration proceeds and, if amperes are plotted (as ordinates) against volume of titrating solution added (as abscissas), a curve similar to that of Fig. 16 is obtained.   The equivalence point corresponds to the point of intersection of the two arms of the curve.   These arms are essentially straight lines, especially if the effect of dilution is corrected for.   In the above case, the nearly horizontal portion of the curve corresponds to the diffusion current of a saturated solution of lead sulfate.   Solubility effects may give a curved line in the close neighborhood of the equivalence point, but, as in certain conductometric titration curves [see Fig. 11(c)], extension of the two straight parts of the curve will give a point of intersection corresponding to the equivalence point.   As in conductometric titrations, it is advantageous to titrate a dilute solution with a relatively concentrated one.

An equally satisfactory titration curve is given in the amperometric titration of a nonreducible ion when it is titrated with a reagent capable of electrolytic reduction.   This type is illustrated in Prob. 18.3.

Certain titrations involving neutralization, oxidation, and reduction, and complex-ion formation are also possible by amperometric methods.

In general, although much work is still needed to bring about refinements of method and to extend the applications of the process, amperometric titrations are in many specific cases capable of giving very precise results. The method is satisfactory in many precipitation titrations where the solubility of the precipitate is too great for potentiometric or indicator methods to be used. Furthermore, foreign electrolytes which

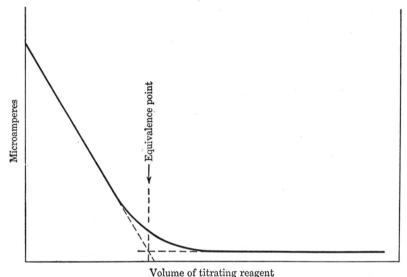

Volume of titrating reagent

FIG. 16. Amperometric titration curve ($Pb^{++} + SO_4^{=}$).

are often harmful in conductometric titrations do not usually interfere in amperometric titrations unless they are present at high concentrations and yield diffusion currents at the applied e.m.f.

Problems

18.1. It has been shown that fluoride ions in the presence of excess chloride ions can be titrated amperometrically with the formation of a precipitate of lead chlorofluoride (PbClF). In one such titration at pH 6.5 in which tenth-molar lead nitrate was used, the equivalence point was established from the graph as corresponding to a buret reading of 5.95 ml. How many milligrams of fluoride ions were shown to be present? Show the general appearance of the titration curve.

Ans. 11.3 mg. For titration curve see *Analytical Chemistry*, **22,** 1274 (1950).

18.2. What is the approximate ratio of the concentration of Pb^{++} to that of Cu^{++} in the solution giving the polarographic curve shown in Fig. 14?

Ans. 2:1.

18.3. In each of the following two titrations, plot the titration graph and determine the volume of titrating solution corresponding to the equivalence point. Calculate the number of grams of titrated constituent shown to be present in each case and explain the appearance of the curve.

(a) A certain volume of 0.0100 M K_2SO_4 is titrated amperometrically with 0.100 M $Pb(NO_3)_2$. The following values are the milliamperes obtained at the corresponding volumes of titrating solution. Dilution effects have been corrected for. 0.0 ml. = 0.8; 1.0 ml. = 0.8; 2.0 ml. = 0.8; 3.0 ml. = 0.8; 4.0 ml. = 0.9; 4.5 ml. = 1.3; 5.0 ml. = 4.2; 5.5 ml. = 11.3; 6.0 ml. = 20.0; 6.5 ml. = 28.9; 7.0 ml. = 37.5.

(b) A 50-ml. pipetful of dilute $Pb(NO_3)_2$ (in 0.10 M KNO_3) is titrated with 0.0500 M $K_2Cr_2O_7$. The following values are the milliamperes actually obtained at the corresponding volumes of titrating solution. Before plotting the titration curve, correct for dilution effect by multiplying each current reading by $(V + v)/V$ in which V = initial volume of solution, and v = total volume of reagent added. 0.0 ml. = 81.56; 1.0 ml. = 66.22; 2.0 ml. = 48.34; 3.0 ml. = 31.66; 4.0 ml. = 15.25; 4.8 ml. = 3.79; 4.9 ml. = 2.09; 5.0 ml. = 2.9; 5.1 ml. = 5.1; 5.3 ml. = 12.03; 5.5 ml. = 21.86; 6.0 ml. = 43.86. (*Note.* The large residual current at the equivalence point is due to the relatively high solubility of the precipitated $PbCrO_4$ in the acid formed by the titration: $2Pb^{++} + Cr_2O_7^{=} + H_2O \rightarrow \underline{2PbCrO_4} + 2H^+$.)

CHAPTER 19

COLORIMETRIC METHODS

123. Principles of Simple Colorimetric Methods. Colorimetric methods of analysis are ordinarily limited to determinations at relatively low concentrations (usually less than 2 per cent), and the underlying principle is the determination of the concentration of a solution by measuring the intensity of light transmitted by it as compared directly or indirectly to the intensity of light of the same wavelength transmitted through a solution or series of solutions of the same substance at known concentrations.

The following are commonly used symbols in colorimetric measurements:

I_o = intensity of incident light (*i.e.*, light entering a solution)

I = intensity of transmitted light (*i.e.*, light leaving a solution)

c = concentration of the solution

l = length of the absorbing layer

$T = \dfrac{I}{I_o}$ = transmittance of the solution

$100T$ = percentage transmittance of the solution

$A = \log_{10} \dfrac{I_o}{I}$ = optical density of the solution

Two laws are fundamental to optical methods. As applied to solutions, *Lambert's* (or *Bouguer's*) *law* states that, when monochromatic light passes through a solution, the intensity of the light decreases exponentially as the length of the absorbing layer increases arithmetically:

$$T = \frac{I}{I_o} = 10^{-k'l} \quad \text{or} \quad \log_{10} \frac{I_o}{I} = k'l$$

where k' is a constant the value of which depends on the nature of the medium, on the wavelength of the light, and on the concentration of the solution.

Beer's law states that, when monochromatic light passes through a solution, the intensity of the light decreases exponentially as the concentration of the solution increases arithmetically:

$$T = \frac{I}{I_o} = 10^{-k''c} \quad \text{or} \quad \log_{10} \frac{I_o}{I} = k''c$$

where k'' is a constant the value of which depends on the nature of the medium, on the wavelength of the light, and on the length of the absorbing layer.

Combination of these two laws gives us the so-called *Lambert-Beer law* which is expressed as follows:

$$T = \frac{I}{I_o} = 10^{-kcl} \quad \text{or} \quad \log_{10} \frac{I_o}{I} = kcl$$

Beer's law, and therefore the Lambert-Beer law, applies strictly only to solutions in which the structure of the colored solute does not change with concentration; that is, where changes in concentration are not accompanied by changes in degree of ionization, association, dissociation, or solvation of the solute. Conversely, the degree of divergence from the law offers a means of obtaining quantitative information regarding these phenomena.

124. Methods of Colorimetric Analysis. Most colorimetric determinations are made on true homogeneous solutions, and the color of the solution may be inherent in the constituent being determined, or it may be formed by the addition of an appropriate reagent. The methods can, however, be extended under certain conditions to cover the determination of quantities of substance in suspension (*turbidimetry* and *nephelometry*).

It is beyond the scope of this book to describe all the types of optical methods of analysis and the many forms of apparatus available for such methods. Suffice it to say that most of the simpler methods fall into the following classes:

(*A*) The concentration of the unknown is determined by matching visually its color with a series of solutions of the same depth containing the solute at known concentrations. The solutions are usually contained in long cylindrical tubes (*Nessler tubes*) and are viewed lengthwise against reflected white light. The standard solution which the unknown solution matches obviously has the same concentration of solute.

(*B*) The solution to be measured is compared with a single standard solution of known concentration. The more concentrated solution is diluted with water until the colors match when viewed transversely through equal thickness of solution. The concentration of the unknown can be determined from the volume relationships and the concentration of the standard.

(*C*) The solution to be measured is compared with a single standard solution of known concentration (preferably approximately the same as that of the unknown) by varying the relative viewing depths of the two solutions until a matching of colors is obtained. The most commonly used mechanical device for that purpose is the *Duboscq colorimeter* which permits the matching of colors of the transmitted light from the two solutions by projecting them simultaneously on a split-field eyepiece. From the Lambert-Beer law it follows that the concentrations of the matched solutions are inversely proportional to their depths:

$$\frac{c_1}{c_2} = \frac{l_2}{l_1}$$

(D) The concentration of the unknown is determined directly by measuring the intensity of light passing through a known depth of the solution and impinging on a photoelectric cell. The relative intensity is read directly from a graduated scale. The instrument used for this purpose is called a *photoelectric colorimeter*. An appropriate filter is used to give a source of light within a limited range of wavelength, and the instrument is previously calibrated against solutions of the constituent at known concentrations.

A *spectrophotometer* is even more precise and flexible in that it uses a source of light within any desired narrow range of wavelength.

Problems

19.1. What per cent of the incident light at a given wavelength is transmitted by a medium which at that wavelength has an optical density of 1.3?

Ans. 5 per cent.

19.2. A 250-ml. sample of drinking water is to be analyzed for its percentage of NH_3. It is diluted with 250 ml. of NH_3-free water, Na_2CO_3 is added, and the mixture is distilled. Three separate fractions of 50 ml. each are caught in 50-ml. Nessler tubes containing Nessler's reagent, which gives a yellow-orange color with small amounts of free NH_3.

A stock solution is prepared by dissolving 3.82 grams of NH_4Cl in 1 liter of NH_3-free water, taking 10 ml. of this solution and again diluting to 1 liter. A series of standards is prepared by placing varying volumes of the stock solution in 50-ml. Nessler tubes,' adding Nessler's reagent, and diluting to 50 ml.

The first fraction of the distillate from the sample is found to match in color with the standard containing 1.7 ml. of the stock solution; the second fraction matches with the standard containing 0.3 ml. of the stock solution; the third fraction is found to contain no appreciable NH_3.

Calculate the amount in parts per million of nitrogen (present as NH_3) in the original drinking water.

Ans. 0.08 p.p.m.

19.3. A sample of Bureau of Standards steel containing 0.410 per cent Mn and weighing 1.00 gram and a sample of similar steel of unknown manganese content weighing 1.10 grams are separately dissolved in HNO_3, and the manganese is oxidized to permanganate with KIO_4. The two solutions are diluted to the same volume and are compared in a Duboscq colorimeter. The match of color intensities is at a point where the depth of the standard sample solution is 10 per cent less than that of the other solution. Calculate the percentage of Mn in the unknown, assuming Beer's law to hold over the small range of concentration involved. Write an equation for the oxidation by the periodate.

Ans. 0.335 per cent.

19.4. It has been shown that, in the colorimetric determination of silica in the form of blue silicomolybdate, the transmittance values of solutions of the compound conform closely to Beer's law when light of an appropriate wavelength is used. As determined by a spectrophotometer, the percentage transmittance of a solution containing 0.020 mg. of SiO_2 was found to be 77.3; that of the same volume of solution containing 0.10 mg. of SiO_2 was 36.7. What is the calculated value of the percentage transmittance of a solution containing 0.060 mg. of SiO_2?

Ans.   53.3 per cent.

———————

19.5. Manganese is determined colorimetrically as permanganate by measuring the absorption of monochromatic green light. A standard solution in an absorption cell 5.000 cm. long absorbs 10.0 per cent of the light, while an unknown sample in a cell 1.000 cm. long absorbs 50.0 per cent of the light. The standard solution contains 2.000 mg. of Mn per liter. What is the concentration of the manganese in the unknown?

CHAPTER 20

GAS ANALYSIS

125. Fundamental Laws of Gases. Problems involving the determination of the proportional amounts of the components of a gaseous mixture and the determination of the amount of a given substance by measuring the quantity of gas which that substance may be made to evolve in chemical reaction are the only phases of gas analysis considered in this book.

Calculations of gas analyses make use of the following gas, laws, most of which apply strictly only to the so-called "perfect" gases, but which may be applied to ordinary analyses with results that are usually in keeping with the precision of analytical manipulation. These laws should already be more or less familiar to the student.

Boyle's Law. The volume of a fixed mass of a gas at constant temperature is inversely proportional to the pressure to which it is subjected. That is,

$$pv = p'v' = k$$

where pv and $p'v'$ are pairs of simultaneous values of pressure and volume of a given mass of gas and k is a constant.

EXAMPLE I. If a sample of gas occupies a volume of 500 ml. at a barometric pressure of 755 mm. of mercury, what volume would it occupy at a pressure of 760 mm.?

SOLUTION: An increase in pressure must cause a decrease in volume. In this case, the new volume will be

$$500 \times \frac{755}{760} = 496.7 \text{ ml.} \quad Ans.$$

Or, by substitution in the formula above,

$$755 \times 500 = 760 \times x$$

whence,

$$x = 496.7 \text{ ml.} \quad Ans.$$

Charles's Law. The volume of a fixed mass of a gas at constant pressure is directly proportional to the absolute temperature to which it is subjected; that is,

$$\frac{v}{v'} = \frac{T}{T'}$$

where vT and $v'T'$ are pairs of simultaneous values of volume and temperature expressed on the absolute scale. Zero on the absolute scale is at $-273°$C.; hence, the temperature in absolute units may be found by adding 273 to the temperature in centigrade units. Charles's law may therefore be written

$$\frac{v}{v'} = \frac{273 + t}{273 + t'}$$

where t and t' represent the respective temperatures in degrees centigrade.

EXAMPLE II.   If a gas occupies a volume of 500 ml. at 20°C. and the temperature is raised to 30°C. at constant pressure, what is the new volume of the gas?

SOLUTION: The temperatures on the absolute scale are 293 and 303°C., respectively.   If the temperature is raised, the gas must expand and the new volume becomes

$$500 \times \frac{303}{293} = 517 \text{ ml.}   Ans.$$

Or, by substitution,

$$\frac{500}{x} = \frac{273 + 20}{273 + 30}$$

whence,

$$x = 517 \text{ ml.}   Ans.$$

The formulas expressing the two gas laws mentioned above may be combined to give

$$\frac{pv}{T} = \frac{p'v'}{T'}$$

Dalton's Law.   The pressure exerted by a mixture of gases is equal to the sum of the pressures of the individual components, and the pressure exerted by a single component is the same as the pressure that component would exert if existing alone in the same volume.

EXAMPLE III.   Moist hydrogen gas is confined over water under a pressure of 760 mm. of mercury and a temperature of 26°C. What is the actual pressure of the hydrogen?

SOLUTION: At 26°C., the vapor pressure of water is equal to 25 mm. of mercury (see Table V, Appendix).   The partial pressure of the hydrogen is therefore $760 - 25 = 735$ mm.   *Ans.*

Gay-Lussac's Law.   Whenever gases unite or gaseous products are formed, the proportions by volume measured at the same temperature and pressure of all the gaseous products concerned can be represented by ratios of small integers.   Thus, in the reaction

$$2H_2 + O_2 \rightarrow 2H_2O$$

two parts by volume of hydrogen unite with *one* part by volume of oxygen to give *two* parts by volume of water vapor.

Avogadro's Law. Equal volumes of all gases under identical conditions of temperature and pressure contain the same number of molecules.

126. Gas-volumetric Methods. For convenience, gas analysis may be divided into the following groups:

(a) Gas-volumetric methods
(b) Absorption methods
(c) Combustion methods

Under gas-volumetric methods may be included those methods in which a gas is evolved by means of a chemical reaction, and from the volume of the gas the weight of the substance producing it is calculated.

From Avogadro's law it is evident that the weights of equal volumes of gases will be in direct proportion to the respective molecular weights. The weight in grams of 22.4 liters of any gas, when measured under standard conditions, *i.e.*, at 0°C. and under a pressure of 760 mm. of mercury, represents the molecular weight of the gas. If the molecular weight of a gas and the volume that a certain quantity of it occupies under standard conditions are known, the weight of that quantity can be readily determined. This is the principle underlying gas-volumetric analysis. Since it is usually inconvenient actually to measure the volume of a gas at 0°C. and under 760 mm. pressure, it is customary to measure the gas at any convenient temperature and pressure and by means of Boyle's and Charles's laws to calculate the volume that the gas would occupy under standard conditions.

EXAMPLE. A gas occupies a volume of 42.06 ml. under 765.0 mm. pressure and at 20.0°C. What is its volume under standard conditions?

SOLUTION: According to Boyle's law, if the pressure of the gas at a constant temperature is reduced from 765 to 760 mm., the volume would be increased in the same ratio, and, were the temperature the same, the new volume would be

$$42.06 \times \frac{765.0}{760.0} = 42.34 \text{ ml.}$$

The temperature, however, is to be reduced from 20.0°C. (293° Absolute) to 0°C. (273° Absolute), and, according to Charles's law, this change alone serves to decrease the volume of the gas by the ratio of 293:273. If both the pressure and temperature are changed to standard conditions, the volume of the gas becomes

$$42.06 \times \frac{765.0}{760.0} \times \frac{273.0}{293.0} = 39.45 \text{ ml.} \quad Ans.$$

Expressed according to the symbols used above,

$$v \times \frac{p}{p'} \times \frac{273 + t'}{273 + t} = v'$$

which is identical to the general expression

$$\frac{pv}{T} = \frac{p'v'}{T'}$$

127. Correction for Water Vapor. Evolved gases are frequently collected and measured over liquids which exert an appreciable vapor pressure, and in such cases the barometric pressure does not represent the pressure of the pure gas. It may be assumed that the gas will be saturated with the vapor of the liquid over which it is measured, and in such cases the vapor pressure of the liquid depends only upon the temperature. According to Dalton's law, the pressure of the pure gas may be found simply by subtracting the vapor pressure of the liquid at the given temperature from the barometric pressure. The values of the vapor pressure of water at different temperatures are given in Table V (Appendix).

128. Calculations of Gas-volumetric Analyses. These considerations may be applied to determine the percentage of a constituent of a given substance by gas-volumetric measurements.

EXAMPLE. A 0.500-gram sample of limestone on treatment with acid liberates 98.7 ml. of carbon dioxide when measured over water at 23°C. and 761 mm. pressure. What is the percentage of CO_2 in the sample?

SOLUTION:

Vapor pressure of water at 23°C. = 20.9 mm.
Pressure of the pure CO_2 = 761 − 20.9 = 740 mm.
Volume of CO_2 under standard conditions =

$$98.7 \times \frac{740}{760} \times \frac{273}{273 + 23} = 88.6 \text{ ml. } Ans.$$

The gram-molecular weight (44 grams) of CO_2 would occupy under standard conditions a volume of 22.4 liters = 22,400 ml. The weight of CO_2 evolved is, therefore,

$$44.0 \times \frac{88.6}{22,400} = 0.174 \text{ gram}$$

Percentage of CO_2 in the sample is

$$\frac{0.174}{0.500} \times 100 = 34.8 \text{ per cent. } Ans.$$

Alternative Method. Some chemists prefer to solve problems involving molar relationships of gases by means of the following general formula:

$$pv = NRT$$

where p = pressure of the gas, atmospheres

$$= \frac{\text{pressure in millimeters}}{760}$$

v = volume, milliliters

N = number of moles of gas

$$= \frac{\text{weight of gas}}{\text{molecular weight}}$$

R = "gas constant" = 82.07

T = temperature on the absolute scale

Applying this formula to the problem under consideration,

$$\frac{740}{760} \times 98.7 = \frac{\text{wt. of gas}}{44.0} \times 82.07 \times 296$$

Weight of CO_2 = 0.174 gram

$$\text{Percentage} = \frac{0.174}{0.500} \times 100 = 34.8 \text{ per cent.} \quad Ans.$$

Problems

20.1. If 500 ml. of hydrogen gas are cooled at constant pressure from 26 to $-10°C.$, what is the volume at the lower temperature?

Ans. 440 ml.

20.2. The pressure on a gas that at 758 mm. occupies a volume of 600 ml. is increased to 774 mm. at constant temperature. What is the resulting volume?

Ans. 588 ml.

20.3. Three hundred and sixty volumes of hydrogen are measured dry at $-13°C.$ and 760 mm. pressure. By heating at constant pressure, the volume is increased 10 per cent. What is the increase in temperature?

Ans. 26°C.

20.4. One hundred grams of pure calcium carbonate are dissolved in hydrochloric acid. Calculate the volume of gas evolved (*a*) measured dry at 0°C. and 760 mm. pressure, (*b*) measured dry at 15°C. and 780 mm. pressure, (*c*) measured over water at 30°C. and 748 mm. barometric pressure.

Ans. (*a*) 22.4 liters, (*b*) 23.0 liters, (*c*) 26.4 liters.

20.5. How many liters of oxygen gas measured over water at 17°C. and 777 mm. pressure can be obtained from 1.00 kilogram of pure $KClO_3$ by ignition to KCl?

Ans. 290 liters.

20.6. What weight of $CaCO_3$ must be treated with acid to produce 138.6 ml. of CO_2, measured over water (saturated with CO_2) at 10°C. and 773 mm. pressure?

Ans. 0.599 gram.

20.7. In the analysis of dolomite, 0.0500 gram of ferric oxide, 0.6080 gram of CaO, and 0.1505 gram of magnesium pyrophosphate were obtained. If these were originally present a ^{oo} $FeCO_3$, $CaCO_3$, and $MgCO_3$, how many milliliters of CO_2 measured dry at 20°C. and 780 mm. pressure could have been obtained from the same weight of sample?

Ans.   300.3 ml.

20.8. What weight of limestone should be taken for analysis so that the volume in milliliters of CO_2 measured dry at 20°C. and 780 mm. equals the percentage of CO_2 present?

Ans.   0.1880 gram.

20.9. A sample of pyrite (FeS_2) weighing 0.2000 gram yields 0.7783 gram of $BaSO_4$. How many cubic feet of air measured at 130°F. and 27 in. of mercury pressure would theoretically be required to burn 1.00 pound of the pyrite? What would be the volume of the gaseous residue (sulfur dioxide and residual nitrogen) measured at the same temperature and pressure?   ($4FeS_2 + 11O_2 \rightarrow 2Fe_2O_3 + 8SO_2$.   Air = 20.9 per cent O_2 by volume.   1 cu. in. = 16.39 ml.   1 lb. = 0.4536 kg.)

Ans.   52.4 cubic feet.   49.5 cubic feet.

20.10. Compute the volume of H_2O that can be obtained from 8.0 grams of $H_4Ca_{12}Al_6Si_{10}O_{43}$ measured at (*a*) 20°C. and 750 mm. pressure, (*b*) 750 mm. pressure and 900°C.   (Two significant figures.)

Ans.   (*a*) 0.18 ml., (*b*) 970 ml.

20.11. If a gas measured dry at 27°C. and 758 mm. pressure occupies a volume of 500 ml., calculate its volume if the temperature is increased to 87°C. and the pressure is kept constant.

20.12. If hydrogen gas when measured over water at 23°C. and 772 mm. pressure occupies 97.3 ml., what would be the volume under standard conditions?

20.13. A gas occupies a volume of 222 ml. over water at 12°C. and 751 mm. pressure.   What volume would it occupy over water at 31°C. and 770 mm. pressure?

20.14. $BaCO_3$ and $MgCO_3$ are mixed in the proportions by weights of 2:1.   Calculate the volume of 6.00 *N* HCl to decompose a 5.00-gram sample.   Calculate the volume of CO_2 gas formed when measured dry at 22.4°C. and 758 mm. pressure. What would the volume of the gas be if it were collected under the same conditions over water (saturated with CO_2)?

20.15. What weight of impure calcite ($CaCO_3$) should be taken for analysis so that the volume in milliliters of CO_2 obtained by treating the sample with acid and measuring the CO_2 dry at 18°C. and 763 mm. pressure will equal the percentage of CaO in the sample?

20.16. What volumes of nitrogen and carbon dioxide, each measured dry at 20°C. and 755 mm. pressure, could be obtained by the combustion of 0.2010 gram of urea $[CO(NH_2)_2]$?

20.17. What volume of nitrogen measured over water at 30°C. and 760 mm. pressure could be obtained from 0.1860 gram of tetraethyltetrazone $[(C_2H_5)_2:N.N:N.N:-(C_2H_5)_2]$?

20.18. If, in the analysis of a 1.00-gram sample of a carbonate, 18.0 ml. of CO_2 measured over water at 18°C. and 763 mm. pressure were obtained, find the percentage of carbon in the sample.

20.19. What weight of limestone should be taken for analysis so that the volume of CO_2 evolved measured over water at 15°C. and 749 mm. pressure will be three-fifths the percentage of CO_2 in the sample?

20.20. Compute the volume of oxygen required to oxidize a sample of pure Fe weighing 0.9000 gram, assuming that the product of combustion is composed of 60 per cent Fe_2O_3 and 40 per cent Fe_3O_4 and that the gas is measured dry at 21°C. and 756 mm. pressure.

20.21. A compound of C, N, and H yields a volume of nitrogen which when measured in milliliters over water at 22°C. and 767 mm. pressure is equal to 155.5 times the number of grams of sample taken. The carbon and hydrogen are present in the molar ratio of 1:1. What is the empirical formula of the compound?

20.22. Decomposition of a compound of carbon, hydrogen, nitrogen, oxygen, and bromine weighing 0.2000 gram yielded 8.70 ml. of nitrogen, measured over water at 18°C. and 758 mm. pressure. Combustion in oxygen of the same weight of sample gave 0.1880 gram CO_2 and 0.01924 gram H_2O. After decomposition of 0.2000 gram with HNO_3, a precipitate of AgBr weighing 0.2674 gram was obtained. The molecular weight was found to be about 275. What is the formula of the compound?

20.23. Decomposition of 0.1500 gram of indole gave 16.42 ml. of nitrogen when measured over water at 27°C. and 758 mm. pressure. Combustion in oxygen of 0.2000 gram of the sample increased the weight of a potash bulb by 0.6026 gram and of a calcium chloride tube by 0.1078 gram. Calculate the empirical formula of indole.

129. Absorption Methods.

Absorption methods of gas analysis apply to the determination of the proportionate amounts of the components of a gaseous mixture. The mixture of gases is treated with a series of absorbents, and the temperature and pressure are usually kept constant throughout the entire determination. In cases where these are allowed to vary, corrections for their effect may be made by applying the principles outlined in Sec. 125. The difference in the volume of the gas before and after it has been acted upon by each absorbing agent represents the amount of gas absorbed, and the amount is usually expressed on a percentage-by-volume basis. The many forms of apparatus used for carrying out gas absorptions are described in the textbooks on the subject, but the fundamental principles are identical. The reagents commonly employed are shown below.

GAS	REAGENT
Carbon dioxide	Sodium hydroxide
	Potassium hydroxide
Unsaturated hydrocarbons ("illuminants")	Bromine water
	Fuming sulfuric acid
Oxygen	Alkaline pyrogallol solution
	Yellow phosphorus
Carbon monoxide	Ammoniacal cuprous chloride
Hydrogen	Palladium sponge
	Palladous chloride solution
	Colloidal palladium solution.

EXAMPLE.   A sample of illuminating gas occupying a volume of 80.0 ml. is treated in succession with potassium hydroxide solution, fuming sulfuric acid, alkaline pyrogallol solution, and ammoniacal cuprous chloride solution.   After each treatment, the volume of the residual gas at constant temperature and pressure is measured as 78.7, 75.5, 75.1, and 68.3 ml., respectively.   What is the percentage composition of the gas as shown by these results?

SOLUTION:

$$\text{Volume of } CO_2 = 80.0 - 78.7 = 1.3 \text{ ml.}$$
$$\text{Volume of illuminants} = 78.7 - 75.5 = 3.2 \text{ ml.}$$
$$\text{Volume of } O_2 = 75.5 - 75.1 = 0.4 \text{ ml.}$$
$$\text{Volume of } CO = 75.1 - 68.3 = 6.8 \text{ ml.}$$

The percentages of the various components are therefore

$$\frac{1.3}{80.0} \times 100 = 1.6 \text{ per cent } CO_2$$

$$\frac{3.2}{80.0} \times 100 = 4.0 \text{ per cent illuminants}$$

$$\frac{0.4}{80.0} \times 100 = 0.5 \text{ per cent } O_2 \qquad \Big\} \quad Ans.$$

$$\frac{6.8}{80.0} \times 100 = 8.5 \text{ per cent } CO$$

$$\frac{68.3}{80.0} \times 100 = 85.4 \text{ per cent inert gases}$$

130. Combustion Methods.   If a gas mixture contains one or more components capable of combustion with oxygen, it is usually possible to determine the percentages of these components by allowing combustion to take place and measuring the contraction in volume, the amount of carbon dioxide formed, the volume of oxygen used, or combinations of these measurements, depending upon the number and character of the combustible components present.   Gay-Lussac's law underlies calculations involving contractions in volume.   Thus, in the combustion of carbon monoxide with oxygen

$$2CO + O_2 \rightarrow 2CO_2$$

two volumes of carbon monoxide unite with *one* volume of oxygen to form *two* volumes of carbon dioxide.   The combustion is therefore accompanied by a contraction equal to one-half the volume of the carbon monoxide present and produces a volume of carbon dioxide equal to the original volume of carbon monoxide.

Assume a gas mixture with hydrogen and methane as the only com-

bustible components.   Hydrogen reacts with oxygen according to the
equation

$$2H_2 + O_2 \rightarrow 2H_2O$$

in which *two* volumes of hydrogen unite with *one* volume of oxygen to
form water vapor, condensing at ordinary temperatures to liquid water.
Methane reacts with oxygen according to the equation

$$CH_4 + 2O_2 \rightarrow CO_2 + 2H_2O$$

in which *one* volume of methane reacts with *two* volumes of oxygen to
form *one* volume of carbon dioxide.   Let x represent the volume of hydrogen and y the volume of methane present in the gas mixture.   The volume of oxygen required for the hydrogen is $\frac{1}{2}x$, and the volume of oxygen
required for the methane is $2y$.   The total volume of oxygen required
B is therefore given by the expression

$$(1) \quad B = \tfrac{1}{2}x + 2y$$

The contraction in volume caused by the hydrogen reaction is $\frac{3}{2}x$, and
that by the methane reaction is $2y$.   The total contraction in volume C
is given by the expression

$$(2) \quad C = \tfrac{3}{2}x + 2y$$

whence

$$x = C - B = \text{volume of hydrogen}$$
$$y = \frac{3B - C}{4} = \text{volume of methane}$$

It is evident that by allowing this gas mixture to react with a determina-
ble volume of oxygen and measuring the resulting contraction which the
gas undergoes it is possible to determine the volume of hydrogen and
methane present.

Since carbon dioxide is appreciably soluble in water, it is customary in
accurate analyses to measure the contraction in volume after the carbon
dioxide has been entirely absorbed.   Under such conditions, in the combustion of a mixture of hydrogen and methane the volume of oxygen
required would be represented as before by the equation

$$(1) \quad B = \tfrac{1}{2}x + 2y$$

but the total decrease in volume due to *combustion and absorption* would be

$$(2) \quad C' = \tfrac{3}{2}x + 3y$$

whence

$$x = \tfrac{4}{3}C' - 2B = \text{volume of hydrogen}$$
$$y = B - \tfrac{1}{3}C' = \text{volume of methane}$$

Instead of measuring the contraction in volume and the oxygen consumed, the amounts of hydrogen and methane present in a mixture in which they are the only combustible components may be determined from the contraction in volume and the volume of carbon dioxide produced by combustion. Combustion of hydrogen of volume x causes a contraction in volume of $\frac{3}{2}x$ and produces no carbon dioxide; combustion of methane of volume y causes a contraction of $2y$ and produces a volume of carbon dioxide equal to y. The total contraction in volume C is therefore given by the equation

$$C = \tfrac{3}{2}x + 2y$$

and the total volume of carbon dioxide produced D is given by

$$D = y$$

Hence,

$$x = \frac{2C - 4D}{3} = \text{volume of hydrogen}$$

$$y = D = \text{volume of methane}$$

In a similar way, the percentage composition of other mixtures of gases may usually be calculated, provided that as many independent equations can be formulated as there are unknown components in the mixture.

The equations in the following table represent combustion reactions more commonly encountered in gas analysis, and the accompanying columns show the volume relationships in each case.

	Vol. gas	O_2 con-sumed	Con-trac-tion	CO_2 pro-duced
Hydrogen $2H_2 + O_2 \rightarrow 2H_2O$	1	$\frac{1}{2}$	$1\frac{1}{2}$	0
Carbon monoxide $2CO + O_2 \rightarrow 2CO_2$	1	$\frac{1}{2}$	$\frac{1}{2}$	1
Methane $CH_4 + 2O_2 \rightarrow CO_2 + 2H_2O$	1	2	2	1
Acetylene $2C_2H_2 + 5O_2 \rightarrow 4CO_2 + 2H_2O$	1	$2\frac{1}{2}$	$1\frac{1}{2}$	2
Ethylene $C_2H_4 + 3O_2 \rightarrow 2CO_2 + 2H_2O$	1	3	2	2
Ethane $2C_2H_6 + 7O_2 \rightarrow 4CO_2 + 6H_2O$	1	$3\frac{1}{2}$	$2\frac{1}{2}$	2
Propylene $2C_3H_6 + 9O_2 \rightarrow 6CO_2 + 6H_2O$	1	$4\frac{1}{2}$	$2\frac{1}{2}$	3
Propane $C_3H_8 + 5O_2 \rightarrow 3CO_2 + 4H_2O$	1	5	3	3
Butane $2C_4H_{10} + 13O_2 \rightarrow 8CO_2 + 10H_2O$	1	$6\frac{1}{2}$	$3\frac{1}{2}$	4

With this table, little difficulty should be experienced in formulating the necessary equations for the determination by combustion of any mixture of the gases.

In case air is used for combustion, it may be assumed to consist of 20.9 per cent of oxygen by volume.

EXAMPLE I. A mixture of carbon monoxide and nitrogen occupies a volume of 100 ml. and on combustion with oxygen produces 40 ml. of carbon dioxide. Calculate the percentage of nitrogen in the mixture.

SOLUTION: Let x represent the volume of carbon monoxide and y the volume of nitrogen. Since 1 volume of carbon monoxide on combustion gives 1 volume of carbon dioxide, the volume of carbon dioxide produced is equal to x. This volume is stated to be 40 ml., and the volume of nitrogen is therefore 60 ml. $N_2 = 60$ per cent. *Ans.*

EXAMPLE II. A mixture of carbon monoxide, methane, and nitrogen occupies a volume of 20 ml. On combustion with an excess of oxygen, a contraction of 21 ml. takes place, and 18 ml. of carbon dioxide are formed. What is the volume of each component in the mixture?

SOLUTION:

$$\text{Let } x = \text{volume of CO}$$
$$y = \text{volume of CH}_4$$
$$z = \text{volume of } N_2$$

Total contraction in volume, $C = \frac{1}{2}x + 2y$

Total volume of CO_2 produced, $D = x + y$

$$x = \frac{4D - 2C}{3} = \frac{72 - 42}{3} = 10 \text{ ml.}$$

$$y = \frac{2C - D}{3} = \frac{42 - 18}{3} = 8 \text{ ml.}$$

$$z = \text{volume original gas} - (x + y) = 2 \text{ ml.}$$

Ans.

EXAMPLE III. The residual gas mentioned in the example in Sec. 129 is assumed to consist entirely of hydrogen, methane, and nitrogen. To a 20.0-ml. sample are added exactly 100.0 ml. of air, and the mixture is exploded. After the carbon dioxide is absorbed in potassium hydroxide, the volume of the gas is found to be 88.0 ml.; and after the excess oxygen is absorbed in pyrogallol, the volume of the gas is 82.1 ml. What is the percentage of each component in the gas mixture and in the original illuminating gas?

SOLUTION:

Volume after adding air = 120 ml.

Contraction after explosion and absorption = 120 − 88.0 = 32.0 ml. = C'

Volume of oxygen taken = 100.0 × 0.209 = 20.9 ml.

Volume of residual oxygen = 88.0 − 82.1 = 5.9 ml.

Oxygen actually required = 20.9 − 5.9 = 15.0 ml. = B

On substitution of these values of B and C' in the equations derived above, *viz.*,

$$x = \frac{4}{3}C' - 2B$$
$$y = B - \frac{1}{3}C'$$

the results obtained are

$$x = (\tfrac{4}{3} \times 32.0) - (2 \times 15.0) = 12.7 \text{ ml.} = \text{volume of } H_2$$
$$y = 15.0 - (\tfrac{1}{3} \times 32.0) = 4.3 \text{ ml.} = \text{volume of } CH_4$$
$$20.0 - (12.7 + 4.3) = 3.0 \text{ ml.} = \text{volume of } N_2$$

The percentages by volume of these components are found by dividing these volumes by 20.0 and multiplying by 100.

$$\left.\begin{array}{l}63.5 \text{ per cent } H_2 \\ 21.5 \text{ per cent } CH_4 \\ 15.0 \text{ per cent } N_2\end{array}\right\} \quad Ans.$$

In the original illuminating gas (Example, Sec. 129) the percentages of these components are

$$\left.\begin{array}{l}12.7 \times \dfrac{68.3}{20.0} \times \dfrac{100}{80.0} = 54.2 \text{ per cent } H_2 \\[2mm] 4.3 \times \dfrac{68.3}{20.0} \times \dfrac{100}{80.0} = 18.3 \text{ per cent } CH_4 \\[2mm] 3.0 \times \dfrac{68.3}{20.0} \times \dfrac{100}{80.0} = 12.8 \text{ per cent } N_2\end{array}\right\} \quad Ans.$$

Problems

20.24. The following measurements are made under identical conditions. Calculate the percentages of CO_2, O_2, CO, and N_2 in a sample of gas containing no other components.

Sample taken	= 100.0 ml.
Volume after KOH treatment	= 91.5 ml.
Volume after pyrogallol treatment	= 81.4 ml.
Volume after cuprous chloride treatment =	81.1 ml.

Ans. $CO_2 = 8.5$ per cent, $O_2 = 10.1$ per cent, $CO = 0.3$ per cent, $N_2 = 81.1$ per cent.

20.25. A flue gas is known to contain 3.8 per cent O_2, 0.6 per cent CO, 15.0 per cent CO_2, and the rest N_2. A 95.0-ml. sample is drawn into an Orsat apparatus. What would be the volume reading after absorption in the following absorbents in the order stated: (*a*) potassium hydroxide, (*b*) pyrogallol, (*c*) ammoniacal cuprous chloride?

Ans.   (*a*) 80.7 ml., (*b*) 77.1 ml., (*c*) 76.5 ml.

20.26. How many liters of oxygen are necessary for the complete combustion of 5.0 liters of (*a*) methane, (*b*) acetylene, (*c*) hydrogen sulfide?

Ans.   (*a*) 10 liters, (*b*) 12.5 liters, (*c*) 7.5 liters.

20.27. The following measurements are made under identical conditions. Calculate the percentage composition of a mixture of hydrogen and nitrogen.

Volume of gas taken	= 58.2 ml.
Volume of oxygen added	= 32.0 ml.
Volume of oxygen consumed by combustion =	6.1 ml.

Ans. $H_2 = 21.0$ per cent, $N_2 = 79.0$ per cent.

20.28. The following measurements are taken under identical conditions. Calculate the percentage composition of a mixture of hydrogen and nitrogen.

$$
\begin{aligned}
\text{Volume of gas taken} &= 95.3 \text{ ml.} \\
\text{Volume of oxygen added} &= 40.8 \text{ ml.} \\
\text{Volume of gas after combustion} &= 40.1 \text{ ml.}
\end{aligned}
$$

Ans. $H_2 = 67.2$ per cent, $N_2 = 32.8$ per cent.

20.29. What is the percentage composition of a mixture of hydrogen and nitrogen if the contraction in volume due to combustion with oxygen is the same as the volume of the sample taken?

Ans. $H_2 = 66\frac{2}{3}$ per cent, $N_2 = 33\frac{1}{3}$ per cent.

20.30. What is the percentage of methane in a mixture of hydrogen, methane, and acetylene if 16.0 ml. of the mixture when exploded with an excess of air cause a contraction of 26.0 ml.?

Ans. 25.0 per cent.

20.31. The following measurements are made under identical conditions. Calculate the percentage composition of a mixture of hydrogen, carbon monoxide, and methane.

$$
\begin{aligned}
\text{Volume of gas taken} &= 10.5 \text{ ml.} \\
\text{Volume of air added} &= 137.4 \text{ ml.} \\
\text{Total volume after combustion} &= 136.1 \text{ ml.} \\
\text{Volume after removing } CO_2 &= 129.6 \text{ ml.}
\end{aligned}
$$

Ans. $H_2 = 38.1$ per cent, $CO = 45.7$ per cent, $CH_4 = 16.2$ per cent.

20.32. What is the percentage of propane in a mixture of propane, carbon monoxide, and methane if a 13.7-ml. sample on combustion produces 23.7 ml. of carbon dioxide?

Ans. 36.5 per cent.

20.33. What is the percentage composition of a mixture of carbon monoxide, ethane, and nitrogen, if, on combustion with oxygen, the contraction in volume and the volume of carbon dioxide produced are each numerically equal to the volume of the sample taken?

Ans. $CO = 33\frac{1}{3}$ per cent, $C_2H_6 = 33\frac{1}{3}$ per cent, $N_2 = 33\frac{1}{3}$ per cent.

20.34. To 40.8 ml. of a mixture of hydrogen, nitrogen, and carbon monoxide are added 150.0 ml. of air, and the mixture is exploded. If 4.8 ml. of CO_2 are produced and the residual oxygen requires 42.0 ml. of hydrogen for combustion, what is the percentage composition of the original mixture, and what was the total volume after the first combustion?

Ans. $H_2 = 39.0$ per cent, $N_2 = 49.3$ per cent, $CO = 11.7$ per cent. Volume $= 164.6$ ml.

20.35. A mixture of ethane (C_2H_6), hydrogen, carbon monoxide, and nitrogen has a volume of 28.0 ml. After combustion with 72.0 ml. of oxygen, the residual volume is 60.0 ml. and, after passing this into KOH solution, the residual gas occupies 34.0 ml. When this gas is passed over yellow phosphorous, only 4.0 ml. are left. Calculate the percentage composition of the original gas.

Ans. $C_2H_6 = 35.7$ per cent, $H_2 = 28.6$ per cent, $CO = 21.4$ per cent, $N_2 = 14.3$ per cent.

20.36. What is the percentage composition of a mixture of hydrogen, carbon monoxide, and methane if the volume of the oxygen consumed in combustion and the volume of the carbon dioxide produced are each equal to three-fourths of the volume of the original gas taken?

Ans. $H_2 = 25$ per cent, $CO = 58.3$ per cent, $CH_4 = 16.7$ per cent.

20.37. From the following data, calculate the percentage composition of a sample of illuminating gas:

Sample taken for analysis	$= 100.6$ ml.
Volume after KOH treatment	$= 98.4$ ml.
After Br_2 treatment	$= 94.2$ ml.
After pyrogallol treatment	$= 93.7$ ml.
After Cu_2Cl_2 treatment	$= 85.2$ ml.
Residual gas taken for analysis	$= 10.3$ ml.
Volume of air added	$= 87.3$ ml.
Volume after explosion	$= 80.1$ ml.
Carbon dioxide produced	$= 5.2$ ml.

Ans.

CO_2	$= 2.2$ per cent
Unsaturated compounds	$= 4.2$ per cent
O_2	$= 0.5$ per cent
CO	$= 8.5$ per cent
CH_4	$= 42.8$ per cent
H_2	$= 38.6$ per cent
N_2	$= 3.3$ per cent

20.38. The following measurements are made under identical conditions.   Calculate the percentages of carbon dioxide, oxygen, carbon monoxide, and nitrogen in a sample of gas containing no other components:

Sample taken	$= 79.5$ ml.
Volume after KOH treatment	$= 72.9$ ml.
Volume after O_2 absorption	$= 64.6$ ml.
Volume after CO absorption	$= 64.5$ ml.

Ans. $CO_2 = 8.3$ per cent, $O_2 = 10.4$ per cent, $CO = 0.1$ per cent, $N_2 = 81.2$ per cent.

20.39. A water gas is of the following composition: 33.4 per cent CO, 8.9 per cent unsaturated hydrocarbons, 3.9 per cent CO_2, 7.9 per cent N_2, 10.4 per cent saturated hydrocarbons, 34.6 per cent H_2, 0.9 per cent O_2. If a sample of 100 ml. is passed through the following absorbents in the order stated until constant volume is reached in each case, what is the volume reading following each treatment: (*a*) potassium hydroxide, (*b*) bromine water, (*c*) alkaline pyrogallol, (*d*) ammoniacal cuprous chloride?

20.40. A mixture of methane, air, and hydrogen having a volume of 130 ml. is conducted over gently ignited palladium asbestos, after which the volume of the gas is 105 ml.   Both measurements are made at 20°C. and 750 mm. pressure, a Hempel pipet filled with water being used.   Compute the percentage (by volume) of hydrogen in the original gas mixture and the weight of H_2O that could be formed from it.

20.41. If 12.0 grams of pure carbon undergo combustion in 31.3 liters of pure oxygen, what is the percentage-by-volume composition of the mixture after combustion?

20.42. Assume air to contain 20.9 volumes O_2 and 79.1 volumes of nitrogen.   If 100 volumes of air are mixed with 95 volumes of hydrogen and the mixture exploded, what is the composition of the gas remaining and what are the volumes of the various components after cooling to 20°C. and 760 mm. pressure?

20.43. A known volume of a mixture of methane, carbon monoxide, and nitrogen is exploded with an excess of air. Show by equations that the percentage composition of the mixture cannot be determined by measuring the contraction in volume and the volume of oxygen consumed.

20.44. A certain illuminating gas is known to contain the following components: H_2, CH_4, CO_2, N_2, O_2, CO, and unsaturated hydrocarbons. Calculate the percentage composition of the gas from the following data:

Sample taken for analysis	= 99.5 ml.
Volume after KOH treatment	= 97.6 ml.
After Br_2 treatment	= 94.4 ml.
After pyrogallol treatment	= 93.8 ml.
After Cu_2Cl_2 treatment	= 85.1 ml.
Residual gas taken for analysis	= 12.0 ml.
Volume of O_2 added	= 20.2 ml.
Volume after explosion	= 11.8 ml.
Combined $CO_2 + O_2$ remaining	= 11.4 ml.
(*i.e.*, absorbed in alkaline pyrogallol)	

20.45. A certain natural gas is known to contain methane, nitrogen, and carbon dioxide. A 50.0-ml. sample is passed into potassium hydroxide, and the volume of the residual gas is found to be 49.6 ml. Of this residual gas, 20.0 ml. are taken and an excess of air is added. Combustion causes a shrinkage in the total volume of 38.4 ml. Calculate the percentage composition of the original gas.

20.46. A blast-furnace gas is of the following composition: CO_2 = 12.5 per cent, CO = 26.8 per cent, H_2 = 3.6 per cent, N_2 = 57.1 per cent. If a 100-ml. sample were passed through a solution of potassium hydroxide, what would be the volume of the residual gas? If to 50.0 ml. of this residue were added 25.0 ml. of pure oxygen and the mixture exploded, what would be the new volume of the gas and what would be its percentage composition?

Part V

COMMON ANALYTICAL DETERMINATIONS

The following methods are those in common use in the gravimetric and volumetric determinations of the more common elements and radicals. They are given here in barest outline principally to serve as a reference in solving problems in this book. Colorimetric methods and other special methods involving little if any stoichiometry are omitted.

Aluminum

Precipitated with NH_4OH as $Al(OH)_3$, ignited, and weighed as Al_2O_3.

Precipitated with 8-hydroxyquinoline (oxine) as $Al(C_9H_6NO)_3$ and weighed as such, or ignited and weighed as Al_2O_3.

Precipitated with oxine as in the preceding case and the precipitate dissolved in HCl. KBr added and the oxine titrated with standard $KBrO_3$ to disappearance of color of methyl red or other suitable dye indicator. The indicator is oxidized by the excess bromate + bromide to a colorless product. Net equation for the oxine titration: $3C_9H_6NOH + 2BrO_3^- + 4Br^- + 6H^+ \rightarrow 3C_9H_4NBr_2OH + 6H_2O$. See Sec. 105.

Ammonium

(See under Nitrogen.)

Antimony

Precipitated as Sb_2S_3 or Sb_2S_5, ignited in an inert atmosphere, and weighed as Sb_2S_3.

Precipitated as Sb_2S_3 or Sb_2S_5, heated with $NH_4OH + H_2O_2$, ignited in air, and weighed as Sb_2O_4.

(*In alloys*) Left as a residue of hydrated Sb_2O_5 on treating alloy with HNO_3 ($6Sb + 10NO_3^- + 10H^+ \rightarrow 3Sb_2O_5 + 10NO + 5H_2O$). Residue ignited in air to Sb_2O_4. Tin must be removed.

Titrated in ice-cold HCl solution from 3 to 5 with standard $KMnO_4$ ($5SbCl_4^- + 2MnO_4^- + 12H_2O \rightarrow 5H_3SbO_4 + 2Mn^{++} + 20Cl^- + 9H^+$).

Titrated from 3 to 5 with standard $KBrO_3$ ($+KBr$) in HCl solution to disappearance of color of methyl red or other suitable dye indicator. The dye is oxidized by the excess $KBrO_3 + KBr$ to a colorless product. Net titration equation: $3SbCl_4^- + BrO_3^- + 9H_2O \rightarrow 3H_3SbO_4 + Br^- + 12Cl^- + 9H^+$. See Sec. 105.

Titrated from 3 to 5 with I_2 in a solution kept nearly neutral with excess $NaHCO_3$ ($SbO_3^= + I_2 + 2HCO_3^- \rightarrow SbO_4^= + 2I^- + 2CO_2 + H_2O$). The antimony is often held as a tartrate complex in this titration.

Titrated in strong HCl solution from 3 to 5 with standard KIO_3 ($2SbCl_4^- + IO_3^- + 5H_2O \rightarrow 2H_3SbO_4 + ICl + 7Cl^- + 4H^+$). Free I_2 is formed as an intermediate product and gives a violet color with chloroform. Titration is to disappearance of this color. See Sec. 104.

Brought to 5-valent form and the HCl solution treated with KI. The liberated I_2 titrated with standard $Na_2S_2O_3$ ($H_3SbO_4 + 2I^- + 4Cl^- + 5H^+ \rightarrow SbCl_4^- + I_2 + 4H_2O$).

Arsenic

Precipitated as As_2S_3 from 9 N HCl solution with H_2S and weighed as such.

Arsenate precipitated from ammoniacal solution as $MgNH_4AsO_4.6H_2O$, ignited, and weighed as $Mg_2As_2O_7$.

Precipitated with uranyl ions as $UO_2NH_4AsO_4.xH_2O$ which is ignited to U_3O_8 and weighed.

Arsenate precipitated from neutral solution as Ag_3AsO_4. Precipitate dissolved in HNO_3 and the Ag^+ titrated with standard KCNS with ferric alum indicator ($Ag^+ + CNS^- \rightarrow \underline{AgCNS}$).

Titrated from 3 to 5 with standard I_2 in a solution kept nearly neutral by excess $NaHCO_3$ ($AsO_3^= + I_2 + 2HCO_3^- \rightarrow AsO_4^= + 2I^- + 2CO_2 + H_2O$).

Titrated in strong HCl solution with standard KIO_3 ($2As^{+++} + IO_3^- + Cl^- + 5H_2O \rightarrow 2H_3AsO_4 + ICl + 4H^+$). Free I_2 is formed as an intermediate product and gives violet color with chloroform indicator. Titration is to disappearance of this color. See Sec. 104.

Titrated from 3 to 5 with standard $KBrO_3$ ($+KBr$) in HCl solution to disappearance of color of methyl red or other suitable dye indicator. The dye is oxidized by the excess $KBrO_3 + KBr$ to a colorless product. Net titration equation: $3As^{+++} + BrO_3^- + 9H_2O \rightarrow 3H_3AsO_4 + Br^- + 9H^+$. See Sec. 105.

(*Small amounts*) Reduced in acid solution with Zn and evolved as AsH_3 gas. The arsine oxidized to As and color compared to standards. Or AsH_3 absorbed in measured volume of I_2 solution. Excess I_2 titrated with standard $Na_2S_2O_3$ ($AsH_3 + 4I_2 + 4H_2O \rightarrow H_3AsO_4 + 8I^- + 8H^+$).

Barium

Precipitated as $BaSO_4$, ignited, and weighed as such.

Precipitated as $BaCrO_4$ and weighed as such.

Precipitated with $(NH_4)_2CO_3$ as $BaCO_3$, ignited, and weighed as such.

Precipitated as $BaCrO_4$. Precipitate dissolved in excess standard $FeSO_4$ ($+H_2SO_4$) and excess Fe^{++} titrated with standard $KMnO_4$ ($\underline{BaCrO_4} + 3Fe^{++} + 8H^+ + SO_4^= \rightarrow 3Fe^{+++} + Cr^{+++} + \underline{BaSO_4} + 4H_2O$).

Precipitated as $BaCrO_4$ and precipitate dissolved in KI + dilute HCl. Liberated I_2 titrated with standard $Na_2S_2O_3$ ($2BaCrO_4 + 6I^- + 16H^+ \rightarrow 2Ba^{++} + 3I_2 + 8H_2O$).

Beryllium

Precipitated with NH_4OH as $Be(OH)_2$, ignited, and weighed as BeO.

Precipitated from ammoniacal solution with 8-hydroxyquinoline, as $Be(C_9H_6NO)_2$, ignited, and weighed as BeO.

Precipitated as $BeNH_4PO_4$, ignited, and weighed as $Be_2P_2O_7$.

Bismuth

Precipitated with H_2S as Bi_2S_3 and weighed as such.

Precipitated as basic carbonate, ignited, and weighed as Bi_2O_3.

Precipitated as BiOI with KI from hot, very weakly acid solution and weighed as such.

Precipitated with cupferron ignited and weighed as Bi_2O_3.

Precipitated as $BiPO_4$ and weighed as such.

Electrolyzed and weighed as Bi.

Precipitated as oxalate, $(BiO)_2C_2O_4$, the precipitate dissolved in dilute H_2SO_4, and the oxalate titrated with standard $KMnO_4$.

Boron

Borate heated with methyl alcohol and the volatile methyl borate passed through a weighed amount of ignited lime: $2B(OCH_3)_3 + \underline{CaO} + 3H_2O \rightarrow 6CH_3OH + \underline{Ca(BO_2)_2}$. The material is reignited and weighed.   Gain in weight $= B_2O_3$.

Borate treated with methyl alcohol as above and the methyl borate hydrolyzed: $B(OCH_3)_3 + 3H_2O \rightarrow H_3BO_3 + 3CH_3OH$.   The CH_3OH is removed by evaporation and the H_3BO_3 titrated with standard NaOH in the presence of glycerol (or other polyhydric alcohol).   Only one hydrogen of H_3BO_3 reacts.

Bromine

(*Bromide*)   Precipitated as AgBr and weighed as such.

(*Bromide*) (*Volhard method*)   Precipitated as AgBr with measured amount of $AgNO_3$ and the excess Ag^+ titrated with standard KCNS using ferric alum indicator ($Ag^+ + CNS^- \rightarrow \underline{AgCNS}$).

(*Bromide*)   Titrated with standard $AgNO_3$ using eosin or other adsorption indicator.

(*Free bromine*)   Excess KI added and the liberated I_2 titrated with standard $Na_2S_2O_3 (Br_2 + 2I^- \rightarrow I_2 + 2Br^-)$.

(*Bromate*)   Excess KI added in the presence of acid and the liberated I_2 titrated with standard $Na_2S_2O_3$ ($BrO_3^- + 6I^- + 6H^{\scriptscriptstyle\textsf{I}} \rightarrow 3I_2 + Br^- + 3H_2O$).

(*Bromate*)   Measured amount of As_2O_3 (dissolved in $NaHCO_3$) added.   The solution is acidified, boiled, neutralized with $NaHCO_3$, and the excess arsenite titrated with standard I_2 ($BrO_3^- + 3H_3AsO_3 \rightarrow 3H_3AsO_4 + Br^-$; $AsO_3^{\equiv} + I_2 + 2HCO_3^- \rightarrow AsO_4^{\equiv} + 2I^- + 2CO_2 + H_2O$).

(*Bromate*)   Reduced with H_2SO_3 to bromide, which is determined by precipitating with $AgNO_3$ and weighing as AgBr.

Cadmium

Precipitated as CdS and weighed as such.

Electrolytically deposited as Cd and weighed as such.

Precipitated as CdS and the precipitate titrated with standard I_2 in the presence of HCl ($\underline{CdS} + I_2 \rightarrow Cd^{++} + S + 2I^-$).

Precipitated as $CdNH_4PO_4.H_2O$ and weighed as such or ignited and weighed as $Cd_2P_2O_7$.

Precipitated with 8-hydroxyquinoline (oxine) as $Cd(C_9H_6NO)_2.2H_2O$ and the precipitate dissolved in HCl.   KBr is added and the oxine titrated with $KBrO_3$ as in the case of magnesium (*q.v.*).

Calcium

Precipitated as $CaC_2O_4.H_2O$, ignited at low heat, and weighed as $CaCO_3$.

Precipitated as $CaC_2O_4.H_2O$, ignited strongly, and weighed as CaO.

Precipitated as $CaC_2O_4.H_2O$, ignited, moistened with H_2SO_4, reignited, and weighed as $CaSO_4$.

Precipitated as $CaWO_4$ and weighed as such.

Precipitated as $CaC_2O_4.H_2O$, the precipitate dissolved in dilute H_2SO_4, and the oxalate titrated with standard $KMnO_4$.

Precipitated as $CaC_2O_4.H_2O$ with a measured amount of oxalate.   The precipitate is filtered and the excess oxalate in the filtrate is titrated with standard $KMnO_4$.

Precipitated as $CaC_2O_4.H_2O$, and the ignited material (CaO, or $CaCO_3$, or CaO + $CaCO_3$) titrated with standard acid.

Carbon

(*In organic compounds*)   Substance is burned in O_2 and the CO_2 caught in an absorbing agent (*e.g.*, "ascarite") and weighed.

(*In iron and steel*)   Alloy is burned in O_2. The CO_2 is caught in absorbing agent (*e.g.*, "ascarite," = NaOH + asbestos) and weighed.   Or the CO_2 is caught in a measured volume of standard $Ba(OH)_2$ solution and (1) the $Ba(OH)_2$ filtrate or supernatant liquid is titrated with standard acid or (2) the change in conductivity of the $Ba(OH)_2$ is measured.

(*CO_2 in carbonates*) (*Alkalimeter method*)   Sample is treated with acid in a weighed alkalimeter and the loss in weight measured.

(*CO_2 in carbonates*)   Sample is treated with acid and the evolved CO_2 caught in an absorbing agent (*e.g.*, "ascarite") and weighed.

(*CO_2 in gas mixture*) CO_2 absorbed in KOH solution and the decrease in volume of gas mixture measured.

(*CO in gas mixture*)   CO absorbed in ammoniacal cuprous chloride solution and the decrease in volume of gas mixture measured.   Or volume change measured before and after combustion with O_2.

(*Oxalate*)   Precipitated as CaC_2O_4, ignited to CaO, or $CaCO_3$, or $CaSO_4$ (see under Calcium), and weighed.

(*Oxalate*)   Titrated with standard $KMnO_4$ ($5C_2O_4^- + 2MnO_4^- + 16H^+ \rightarrow 10CO_2 + 2Mn^{++} + 8H_2O$).

(*Formate*)   Titrated in essentially neutral solution with $KMnO_4(3CHO_2^- + 2MnO_4^- + H_2O \rightarrow 3CO_2 + 2\underline{MnO_2} + 5OH^-)$.

Cerium

Precipitated as $Ce(OH)_4$ or $Ce(OH)_3$ or $Ce_2(C_2O_4)_3$, ignited, and weighed as CeO_2.

Precipitated as $Ce(IO_3)_4$, converted to $Ce_2(C_2O_4)_3$, ignited, and weighed as CeO_2 ($2Ce(IO_3)_4 + 24H_2C_2O_4 \rightarrow \underline{Ce_2(C_2O_4)_3} + 4I_2 + 42CO_2 + 24H_2O$; $2\underline{Ce_2(C_2O_4)_3} + 4O_2 \rightarrow 4CeO_2 + 12CO_2$).

Cerous oxidized to ceric with $NaBiO_3$ or $(NH_4)_2S_2O_8$ and excess oxidizing agent removed.   Measured amount of $FeSO_4$ added and the excess ferrous titrated with standard $KMnO_4(2Ce^{+++} + NaBiO_3 + 6H^+ \rightarrow 2Ce^{++++} + Bi^{+++} + Na^+ + 3H_2O$; $Ce^{++++} + Fe^{++} \rightarrow Ce^{+++} + \underline{Fe^{+++}})$.

Chlorine

(*Chloride*)   Precipitated as AgCl and weighed as such.

(*Chloride*) (*Volhard method*)   Precipitated as AgCl with measured amount of $AgNO_3$ and the excess Ag^+ titrated with standard KCNS using ferric alum indicator ($Ag^+ + CNS^- \rightarrow \underline{AgCNS}$).

(*Chloride*)   Titrated with standard $AgNO_3$ using dichlorofluorescein or other adsorption indicator.

(*Chloride*) (*Mohr method, for small amounts*)   Titrated in neutral solution with standard $AgNO_3$ using K_2CrO_4 indicator.

(*Free chlorine*)   Excess KI added and the liberated I_2 titrated with standard $Na_2S_2O_3$ ($Cl_2 + 2I^- \rightarrow I_2 + 2Cl^-$).

(*Hypochlorite*)   Excess KI added in the presence of acid and the liberated I_2 titrated with standard $Na_2S_2O_3$ ($OCl^- + 2I^- + 2H^+ \rightarrow I_2 + Cl^- + H_2O$).

(*Hypochlorite*)   Titrated with standard Na_3AsO_3 using KI + starch as outside indicator ($OCl^- + AsO_3^= \rightarrow Cl^- + AsO_4^=$).

(*Chlorate*)   Reduced to chloride with Zn, $FeSO_4$, or H_2SO_3 and chloride determined gravimetrically as AgCl.

(*Hypochlorite*)   Reduced to Cl^- with $FeSO_4$ and the chloride determined gravimetrically as AgCl.

(*Chlorate*)   Excess KI added in the presence of acid and the liberated I_2 titrated with standard $Na_2S_2O_3$ ($ClO_3^- + 6I^- + 6H^+ \rightarrow Cl^- + 3I_2 + 3H_2O$).

(*Perchlorate*)   Precipitated as $KClO_4$ and weighed as such.

Chromium

Chromic ions precipitated with NH_4OH as $Cr(OH)_3$, ignited, and weighed as Cr_2O_3.

Chromate precipitated as $BaCrO_4$ from neutral or buffered acid solution, ignited gently, and weighed as such.

Dichromate reduced with measured amount of $FeSO_4$ and the excess ferrous titrated with standard $KMnO_4$, $K_2Cr_2O_7$, or $Ce(SO_4)_2$.

Dichromate reduced with excess KI and the liberated I_2 titrated with standard $Na_2S_2O_3$ ($Cr_2O_7^- + 6I^- + 14H^+ \rightarrow 2Cr^{+++} + 3I_2 + 7H_2O$).

Cobalt

Electrolytically deposited as Co from ammoniacal solution.

Precipitated with alpha-nitroso-beta-naphthol as $Co[C_{10}H_6O(NO)]_3$ and the precipitate (1) ignited in O_2 to Co_3O_4 and weighed, or (2) ignited in H_2 to Co and weighed.

The naphthol precipitate is digested with $HNO_3 + H_2SO_4$, evaporated, and the cobalt weighed as $CoSO_4$.

Precipitated with 8-hydroxyquinoline (oxine) as $Co(C_9H_6NO)_2.2H_2O$ and the precipitate dissolved in HCl.   KBr is added and the oxine titrated with $KBrO_3$ as in the case of magnesium (*q.v.*).

Measured amount of NH_4CNS and some pyridine added.   Precipitate of $Co(C_5H_5N)_4(CNS)_2$ filtered and the excess CNS^- titrated with standard $AgNO_3$ using ferric indicator.

Copper

Electrolytically deposited as Cu.

Precipitated with $H_2SO_3 + KCNS$ and weighed as CuCNS ($2Cu^{++} + H_2SO_3 + 2CNS^- + H_2O \rightarrow 2\overline{CuCNS} + SO_4^- + 4H^+$).

Precipitated with alpha-benzoinoxime (cupron) and weighed as $Cu(C_{14}H_{11}O_2N)$.

HCl solution passed through silver reductor ($CuCl_4^- + Ag \rightarrow CuCl_2^- + \overline{AgCl} + Cl^-$) into unmeasured amount of ferric alum ($Fe^{+++} + CuCl_2^- + 2Cl^- \rightarrow \overline{CuCl_4^-} + Fe^{++}$) and the reduced iron titrated with standard ceric sulfate using ferroin indicator.

Excess KI added and the liberated I_2 titrated with standard $Na_2S_2O_3$ ($2Cu^{++} + 4I^- \rightarrow \overline{Cu_2I_2} + I_2$).

Ammoniacal solution titrated with standard KCN to the point of decolorization ($2Cu(NH_3)_4^{++} + 7CN^- + H_2O \rightarrow 2Cu(CN)_3^- + CNO^- + 6NH_3 + 2NH_4^+$).

Precipitated as CuCNS (see above) and the precipitate titrated with standard KIO_3 forming I_2 which gives a violet color with chloroform ($10\overline{CuCNS} + 14IO_3^- + 14H^+ \rightarrow 10Cu^{++} + 10SO_4^- + 7I_2 + 10HCN + 2H_2O$).   Titration continued to disappearance of this color ($2I_2 + IO_3^- + 5Cl^- + 6H^+ \rightarrow 5ICl + 3H_2O$).   Net reaction: $4\overline{CuCNS} + 7IO_3^- + 14H^+ + 7Cl^- \rightarrow 4Cu^{++} + 4SO_4^- + 7ICl + 4HCN + 5H_2O$.

Cyanide

(See under Nitrogen.)

Fluorine

Precipitated as CaF_2, ignited, and weighed as such.

Precipitated as PbFCl from acid solution and weighed as such.

Precipitated PbClF dissolved in HNO_3 and the chloride determined by the Volhard method (see under Chlorine).

Titrated with standard $Th(NO_3)_4$ using zirconium-alizarin indicator ($4F^- + Th^{++++} \rightarrow \underline{ThF_4}$).

Evolved as SiF_4 by action with quartz and concentrated H_2SO_4, the gas absorbed in water and the solution titrated with standard NaOH using phenolphthalein ($4HF + SiO_2 \rightarrow SiF_4 + 2H_2O$; $3SiF_4 + 3H_2O \rightarrow 2H_2SiF_6 + \underline{H_2SiO_3}$; $H_2SiF_6 + 6OH^- \rightarrow 6F^- + \underline{H_2SiO_3} + 3H_2O$).

Gold

Chemically or electrolytically reduced to Au and weighed as such.

Reduced to metal by measured amount of reducing agent (*e.g.*, oxalate) and excess titrated with standard $KMnO_4$.

Hydrogen

Volatilized as water and loss in weight of sample determined.

Volatilized as water and measured by gain in weight of absorbing agent (*e.g.*, $CaCl_2$).

(*Gas analysis*) Absorbed on Pd sponge and loss in volume of gas mixture determined. Or volume change measured before and after combustion with O_2.

(*Hydrogen peroxide*) Titrated directly with standard $KMnO_4$($5H_2O_2 + 2MnO_4^- + 6H^+ \rightarrow 5O_2 + 2Mn^{++} + 8H_2O$) or with standard ceric sulfate.

(*Hydrogen peroxide*) Measured amount of standard Na_3AsO_3 added in presence of NaOH ($HO_2^- + AsO_3^\equiv \rightarrow OH^- + AsO_4^\equiv$) and the excess arsenite titrated with KIO_3 using chloroform indicator (see under Arsenic).

Iodine

(*Iodide*) Precipitated as AgI and weighed as such.

(*Iodide*) Precipitated as PdI_2 and weighed as such (Br^- and Cl^- not precipitated).

(*Iodide*) (*Volhard method*) Measured amount of $AgNO_3$ added and the excess Ag^+ titrated with standard KCNS ($Ag^+ + CNS^- \rightarrow \underline{AgCNS}$).

(*Iodide*) Excess $Fe_2(SO_4)_3$ added, liberated I_2 caught in KI solution and titrated with standard $Na_2S_2O_3$ ($2I^- + 2Fe^{+++} \rightarrow I_2 + 2Fe^{++}$) ($Br^-$ and Cl^- not affected).

(*Iodide*) Excess KIO_3 added in presence of acid and liberated I_2 boiled out. Excess IO_3^- determined in cooled solution by adding KI and titrating the liberated I_2 with standard $Na_2S_2O_3$ ($5I^- + IO_3^- + 6H^+ \rightarrow 3I_2 + 3H_2O$).

(*Iodide*) Titrated with standard KIO_3 in presence of concentrated HCl using chloroform as indicator. I_2 is first liberated and colors $CHCl_3$ violet. Color fades away at end point. Net reaction: $2I^- + IO_3^- + 3Cl^- + 6H^+ \rightarrow 3ICl + 3H_2O$.

(*Iodide*) Titrated directly with standard $AgNO_3$ using eosin adsorption indicator.

(*Iodate*) Excess KI added and the liberated I_2 titrated with standard $Na_2S_2O_3$ ($IO_3^- + 5I^- + 6H^+ \rightarrow 3I_2 + 3H_2O$).

(*Free iodine*) Titrated with standard $Na_2S_2O_3$ using starch indicator ($I_2 + 2S_2O_3^\equiv \rightarrow 2I^- + S_4O_6^\equiv$).

(*Free iodine*) Titrated with standard Na_3AsO_3 using starch indicator in solution kept nearly neutral with excess $NaHCO_3$ ($I_2 + AsO_3^\equiv + 2HCO_3^- \rightarrow AsO_4^\equiv + 2I^- + 2CO_2 + H_2O$).

(*Free iodine*) Titrated with standard KIO_3 in presence of concentrated HCl to formation of iodine chloride and disappearance of violet color of chloroform indicator $(2I_2 + IO_3^- + 6H^+ + 5Cl^- \rightarrow 5ICl + 3H_2O)$.

(*Iodate*) Reduced to iodide with H_2SO_3 and precipitated and weighed as AgI.

Iron

Precipitated as $Fe(OH)_3$ with NH_4OH or $NaOH$, ignited, and weighed as Fe_2O_3.

Precipitated with cupferron as $(C_6H_5NONO)_3Fe$ from acid solution, ignited, and weighed as Fe_2O_3.

Ferrous titrated with standard $KMnO_4$, $K_2Cr_2O_7$, or $Ce(SO_4)_2$ (*e.g.*, $5Fe^{++} + MnO_4^- + 8H^+ \rightarrow 5Fe^{+++} + Mn^{++} + 4H_2O$).

Ferric treated with large excess KI and liberated I_2 titrated with standard $Na_2S_2O_3$ $(2Fe^{+++} + 2I^- \rightarrow I_2 + 2Fe^{++})$.

Ferric titrated with standard $TiCl_3$ solution using $KCNS$ indicator $(Fe^{+++} + Ti^{+++} \rightarrow Fe^{++} + Ti^{++++})$.

Lead

Precipitated as $PbSO_4$ or $PbCrO_4$ or $PbMoO_4$ and weighed as such.

Electrolytically oxidized and deposited as PbO_2, and weighed as such $(Pb^{++} + 2H_2O \rightarrow PbO_2 + 4H^+ + 2\epsilon)$.

Precipitated and weighed as $Pb(IO_3)_2$.

Titrated with standard $(NH_4)_2MoO_4$ using tannin as outside indicator $(Pb^{++} + MoO_4^- \rightarrow PbMoO_4)$.

Precipitated as $PbCrO_4$, the precipitate dissolved in acid and the $Cr_2O_7^-$ determined volumetrically as under Chromium above.

Magnesium

Precipitated from ammoniacal solution as $MgNH_4PO_4.6H_2O$ and weighed as such, or ignited and weighed as $Mg_2P_2O_7$.

Precipitated with 8-hydroxyquinoline, dried, and weighed as $Mg(C_9H_6NO)_2$.

Precipitated with 8-hydroxyquinoline (oxine) as $Mg(C_9H_6NO)_2.2H_2O$ and the precipitate dissolved in HCl. KBr is added and the oxine titrated with $KBrO_3$ to disappearance of color with methyl red or other suitable dye indicator. The dye is oxidized by the excess $KBrO_3 + KBr$ to a colorless product. Net equation for the oxine titration: $3C_9H_6NOH + 2BrO_3^- + 4Br^- + 6H^+ \rightarrow 3C_9H_4NBr_2OH + 6H_2O$. See Sec. 105.

Manganese

Manganous ions oxidized by $KClO_3$ or $KBrO_3$ to MnO_2. Precipitate ignited in air and weighed as Mn_3O_4.

Precipitated as $MnNH_4PO_4$, ignited, and weighed as $Mn_2P_2O_7$.

(*Bismuthate method*) Oxidized with $NaBiO_3$ or BiO_2 to permanganate. Measured amount of $FeSO_4$ added, and excess ferrous titrated with standard $KMnO_4$ $(2Mn^{++} + 5NaBiO_3 + 14H^+ \rightarrow 2MnO_4^- + 5Bi^{+++} + 5Na^+ + 7H_2O)$.

(*Ford-Williams method*) Oxidized with $KClO_3$ in presence of concentrated HNO_3 to MnO_2. Measured amount of $FeSO_4$ added, and the excess ferrous titrated with standard $KMnO_4$ $(MnO_2 + 2Fe^{++} + 4H^+ \rightarrow Mn^{++} + 2Fe^{+++} + 2H_2O)$.

(*Persulfate method*) Oxidized with $(NH_4)_2S_2O_8$ $(+AgNO_3)$ to permanganate, and then titrated with standard Na_3AsO_3 to indefinite valence of $3+$. Arsenite standardized against similar sample containing known Mn.

(*Volhard method*) Manganous ions titrated directly with standard $KMnO_4$ in solution kept neutral with ZnO $(3Mn^{++} + 2MnO_4^- + 2ZnO \rightarrow 5MnO_2 + 2Zn^{++} + 2H_2O)$.

Mercury

Precipitated as HgS and weighed as such.

Electrolytically precipitated as Hg and weighed as such.

Titrated with standard KCNS using ferric alum indicator [$Hg^{++} + 2CNS^- \rightarrow Hg(CNS)_2$].

Precipitated as $HgZn(CNS)_4$ with $ZnSO_4 + NH_4CNS$ and weighed as such.

Precipitated as $Hg_5(IO_6)_2$ with periodate and weighed as such, or the precipitate dissolved in KI + HCl (forming $HgI_4^- + I_2$) and the liberated iodine titrated with standard thiosulfate.

Precipitated as Hg_2Cl_2 and the precipitate titrated with standard KIO_3 in the presence of concentrated HCl ($2Hg_2Cl_2 + IO_3^- + 6H^+ + 5Cl^- \rightarrow 4HgCl_2 + ICl + 3H_2O$). Free I_2 is formed as an intermediate product and gives a violet color with chloroform indicator. Titration is to disappearance of this color. See Sec. 104.

Molybdenum

Precipitated as $PbMoO_4$ and weighed as such.

Precipitated as Hg_2MoO_4 or as MoS_3, ignited, and weighed as MoO_3.

Precipitated with alpha-benzoinoxime (cupron), ignited, and weighed as MoO_3.

Precipitated with 8-hydroxyquinoline and weighed as $MoO_2(C_9H_6NO)_2$.

Reduced from 6 to 5 with silver reductor and titrated with standard ceric sulfate, using ferroin indicator.

Reduced with Zn and passed directly into ferric alum. The solution is then titrated with standard $KMnO_4$. The molybdenum is reduced by the Zn to Mo(3). Ferric ions oxidize it to Mo(5), and the permanganate oxidizes the reduced iron to ferric and the Mo(5) to Mo(6).

Nickel

Precipitated with dimethylglyoxime as $[(CH_3)_2.CNOH.CNO]_2Ni$ and weighed as such.

Electrolytically precipitated as Ni and weighed as such.

Measured amount of KCN added to ammoniacal solution and the excess CN^- titrated with standard $AgNO_3$ using KI indicator [$Ni(NH_3)_6^{++} + 4CN^- \rightarrow Ni(CN)_4^- + 6NH_3$; $2CN^- + Ag^+ \rightarrow Ag(CN)_2^-$].

Measured amount of NH_4CNS and some pyridine added. Precipitate of Ni-$(C_5H_5N)_4(CNS)_2$ filtered, and the excess CNS^- titrated with standard $AgNO_3$, using ferric indicator.

Precipitated with 8-hydroxyquinoline (oxine) as $Ni(C_9H_6NO)_2.2H_2O$, and the precipitate dissolved in HCl. KBr is added and the oxine titrated with $KBrO_3$ as in the case of magnesium (*q.v.*).

Nitrogen

(*Organic nitrogen*) (*Kjeldahl method*) Converted by digestion with concentrated H_2SO_4 + catalyst to NH_4HSO_4. Excess NaOH is then added, the liberated NH_3 distilled into measured amount of acid, and the excess acid titrated with standard NaOH using methyl red indicator.

(*Ammonium*) Excess NaOH added, the liberated NH_3 distilled into measured amount of acid, and the excess acid titrated with standard NaOH using methyl red indicator.

(*Ammonium*) Precipitated as $(NH_4)_2PtCl_6$ and weighed as such, or ignited to Pt.

(*Nitrate, nitrite*) Reduced to NH_4^+ with Zn or with Devarda alloy; then by Kjeldahl method above.

(*Nitrite*) Titrated with standard $KMnO_4 (5NO_2^- + 2MnO_4^- + 6H^+ \rightarrow 5NO_3^- + 2Mn^{++} + 3H_2O)$.

(*Cyanide*) Precipitated with $AgNO_3$ as $Ag[Ag(CN)_2]$ and weighed as such.

(*Cyanide*) (*Volhard method*) Measured amount of $AgNO_3$ added and the excess Ag^+ titrated with standard KCNS using ferric alum indicator $(2CN^- + 2Ag^+ \rightarrow Ag_2(CN)_2)$.

(*Cyanide*) (*Liebig method*) Titrated with standard $AgNO_3$ to faint turbidity of $Ag_2(CN)_2$ $[2CN^- + Ag^+ \rightarrow Ag(CN)_2^-]$.

(*Gas analysis*) Volume of residual nitrogen measured after absorbing other gases.

Oxalate

(See under Carbon.)

Oxygen

(*Gas analysis*) Volume of gas mixture determined before and after absorbing in alkaline pyrogallol.

Phosphorus

(*Phosphate*) Precipitated as $MgNH_4PO_4.6H_2O$, ignited to $Mg_2P_2O_7$, and weighed.

(*Phosphite*) Treated with $HgCl_2$ and the precipitated Hg_2Cl_2 weighed $(H_3PO_3 + 2HgCl_2 + H_2O \rightarrow Hg_2Cl_2 + H_3PO_4 + 2Cl^- + 2H^+)$.

(*Phosphite*) Oxidized with HNO_3 and determined as in the case of phosphate.

(*Iron and steel*) Precipitated as $(NH_4)_3PO_4.12MoO_3$ and weighed as such, or ignited and weighed as $P_2O_5.24MoO_3$.

(*Iron and steel*) (*Ferric alum method*) Precipitated as $(NH_4)_3PO_4.12MoO_3$, dissolved, the Mo reduced with Zn in a reductor and passed directly into excess ferric alum. The solution is then titrated with standard $KMnO_4$. The molybdenum is reduced by the Zn to $Mo(3)$. Ferric ions oxidize it to $Mo(5)$, and the permanganate oxidizes the reduced iron to ferric and the $Mo(5)$ to $Mo(6)$.

(*Iron and steel*) (*Blair method*) As in the preceding method except that the reduced solution is caught in an open flask where slight oxidation by the air occurs. The Mo, now having an average valence corresponding to the oxide $Mo_{24}O_{37}$, is titrated to MoO_4^- with standard $KMnO_4$.

(*Iron and steel*) (*Alkalimetric method*) Precipitated as $(NH_4)_3PO_4.12MoO_3$, dissolved in a measured amount of standard NaOH and the excess alkali titrated with standard HNO_3 using phenolphthalein indicator. Net reaction: $(NH_4)_3PO_4.12MoO_3 + 23OH^- \rightarrow 12MoO_4^- + HPO_4^- + 3NH_4^+ + 11H_2O$.

Platinum

Precipitated as K_2PtCl_6 and weighed as such.

Precipitated as $(NH_4)_2PtCl_6$ and weighed as such, or ignited to Pt and weighed.

Electrolytically reduced to Pt and weighed as such.

Reduced by formic acid to Pt and weighed as such.

Potassium

Precipitated as K_2PtCl_6 and weighed as such, or the precipitate reduced to Pt and weighed.

Precipitated as $KClO_4$ and weighed as such.

Small amounts precipitated as $K_2Na[Co(NO_2)_6].H_2O$ and weighed in the anhydrous form or determined by adding measured amount of standard $KMnO_4$ and back-titrating with standard oxalate $(5K_2Na[Co(NO_2)_6] + 11MnO_4^- + 28H^+ \rightarrow 10K^+ + 5Na^+ + 5Co^{++} + 30NO_3^- + 11Mn^{++} + 14H_2O)$.

See also under Sodium.

Selenium

Reduced by H_2SO_3, KI, etc., to Se and weighed as such.

Selenious acid treated with measured amount of $KMnO_4$, and the excess permanganate titrated with standard $FeSO_4(5H_2SeO_3 + 2MnO_4^- \rightarrow 5SeO_4^- + 2Mn^{++} + 4H^+ + 3H_2O)$.

Selenious acid treated with KI, and the liberated I_2 titrated with standard thiosulfate $(H_2SeO_3 + 4I^- + 4H^+ \rightarrow \underline{Se} + 2I_2 + 3H_2O)$.

Silicon

Precipitated as H_2SiO_3, ignited to SiO_2 and weighed. The impure SiO_2 is then treated with HF, evaporated, reignited, and impurities are weighed. Loss in weight = SiO_2 ($\underline{SiO_2} + 4HF \rightarrow SiF_4 + 2H_2O$).

Silver

Precipitated as AgCl and weighed as such.

(*Volhard method*) Titrated with standard KCNS using ferric alum indicator $(Ag^+ + CNS^- \rightarrow \underline{AgCNS})$.

Titrated with standard NaCl using dichlorofluorescein as an adsorption indicator.

Sodium

(*Silicates*) (*J. Lawrence Smith method*) Silicate decomposed by heating with $CaCO_3 + NH_4Cl$. Leached with water, Ca^{++} removed, filtrate evaporated, and residue ignited. NaCl + KCl weighed. K then determined as $KClO_4$ or K_2PtCl_6. Na determined by difference.

(*Small amounts*) Precipitated as $NaZn(UO_2)_3(C_2H_3O_2)_9.6H_2O$ or as $NaMg(UO_2)_3$-$(C_2H_3O_2)_9.6\frac{1}{2}H_2O$ and weighed as such.

Strontium

Precipitated as $SrSO_4$ and weighed as such.

Precipitated as the oxalate, $SrC_2O_4.H_2O$, ignited to SrO, and weighed as such.

Sulfur

(*Sulfate*) Precipitated as $BaSO_4$ and weighed as such.

(*Sulfate*) (*Hinman method*) Excess acid solution of $BaCrO_4$ added ($SO_4^- + Ba^{++}CrO_4^- \rightarrow BaSO_4 + CrO_4^-$). Excess NH_4OH added to precipitate excess $BaCrO_4$. Combined $\overline{BaSO_4} + BaCrO_4$ filtered. Filtrate acidified, treated with excess KI, and liberated I_2 titrated with standard $Na_2S_2O_3$ ($Cr_2O_7^- + 6I^- + 14H^+ \rightarrow 2Cr^{+++} + 3I_2 + 7H_2O$). In the titration each $Cr_2O_7^-$ is equivalent to $2SO_4^-$.

(*Sulfate*) Precipitated with benzidine hydrochloride giving $C_{12}H_8(NH_2)_2.H_2SO_4$. Suspension of precipitate titrated with standard NaOH which acts only on the H_2SO_4.

(*Sulfide*) (*Evolution method for alloys*) Evolved as H_2S by action of HCl and caught in ammoniacal solution of $ZnSO_4$. The solution is acidified and the H_2S titrated with standard I_2 or standard $KIO_3 + KI$ using starch indicator ($H_2S + I_2 \rightarrow \underline{S} + 2H^+ + 2I^-$).

(*Sulfide*) Oxidized to sulfate, precipitated as $BaSO_4$ and weighed.

(*Sulfite*) Oxidized with Br_2 or with $H_2O_2 + NH_4OH$ and weighed as $BaSO_4$.

(*Sulfite*)   Titrated with standard I_2 using starch indicator. $(SO_3^- + H_2O + I_2 \rightarrow SO_4^- + 2I^- + 2H^+)$.

(*Persulfate*)   Measured amount of $FeSO_4$ added and excess ferrous titrated with standard $KMnO_4$ $(S_2O_8^- + 2Fe^{++} \rightarrow 2SO_4^- + 2Fe^{+++})$.

(*Thiosulfate*)   Titrated with standard I_2 $(2S_2O_3^- + I_2 \rightarrow S_4O_6^- + 2I^-)$.

(*Thiocyanate*)   Measured amount of $AgNO_3$ added and excess Ag^+ titrated with standard KCNS $(CNS^- + Ag^+ \rightarrow \underline{AgCNS})$.

(*Thiocyanate*)   Precipitated as $\underline{Cu_2(CNS)_2}$ with $H_2SO_3 + CuSO_4$ and weighed as such.

(*Thiocyanate*)   Titrated with standard $AgNO_3$ using adsorption indicator as in the case of chloride and bromide.

(*Hyposulfite*)   Ammoniacal $AgNO_3$ added $(S_2O_4^- + 2Ag(NH_3)_2^+ + 2H_2O \rightarrow \underline{2Ag} + 2SO_3^- + 4NH_4^+)$.   The precipitated silver is dissolved in HNO_3 and titrated with standard KCNS using ferric alum indicator.

Thorium

Precipitated as $Th(C_4H_8CO_2)_2$ with sebacic acid, ignited, and weighed as ThO_2.

Precipitated as $Th(IO_3)_4$, converted to oxalate, ignited to ThO_2, and weighed as such.

Precipitated as oxalate, $Th(C_2O_4)_2$, ignited, and weighed as ThO_2.

Tin

Precipitated as H_2SnO_3 by hydrolysis, ignited, and weighed as SnO_2.

Precipitated as SnS_2, ignited, and weighed as SnO_2.

(*In alloys*)   Alloy treated with HNO_3 leaving H_2SnO_3 as residue.   This is ignited to SnO_2 and weighed.   Antimony must be removed. $(3\underline{Sn} + 4NO_3^- + 4H^+ + H_2O \rightarrow 3H_2SnO_3 + 4NO)$.

Precipitated with cupferron, ignited, and weighed as SnO_2.

Titrated from 2 to 4 with standard $KBrO_3$ $(+KBr)$ in HCl solution to disappearance of color of methyl red or other suitable dye indicator.   The dye is oxidized by the excess $KBrO_3 + KBr$ to a colorless product.   Net titration equation: $3Sn^{++} + BrO_3^- + 6H^+ + 18Cl^- \rightarrow 3SnCl_6^- + Br^- + 3H_2O$.   See Sec. 105.

Titrated from 2 to 4 in cold HCl solution in current of CO_2 with standard I_2 $(Sn^{++} + I_2 + 6Cl^- \rightarrow SnCl_6^- + 2I^-)$.

Titrated to yellow color with standard $FeCl_3$ $(Sn^{++} + 2FeCl_4^- \rightarrow SnCl_6^- + 2Fe^{++} + 2Cl^-)$.

Titanium

Precipitated as $Ti(OH)_4$, ignited, and weighed as TiO_2.

Precipitated with cupferron, ignited, and weighed as TiO_2.

Reduced by Zn (but not reduced by $SnCl_2$) to Ti^{+++} and titrated with standard $KMnO_4$, or passed from zinc reductor into ferric alum and the reduced iron titrated with standard $KMnO_4$ $(2Ti^{++++} + \underline{Zn} \rightarrow 2Ti^{+++} + Zn^{++}; 5Ti^{+++} + MnO_4^- + 8H^+ \rightarrow 5Ti^{++++} + Mn^{++} + 4H_2O)$.

Reduced to Ti^{+++} and titrated with standard ferric alum using NH_4CNS indicator $(Ti^{+++} + Fe^{+++} \rightarrow Ti^{++++} + Fe^{++})$.

Precipitated with 8-hydroxyquinoline (oxine) as $TiO(C_9H_6NO)_2$ and weighed as such, or dissolved in HCl and the liberated oxine titrated in the presence of KBr with standard $KBrO_3$ as in the case of magnesium (*q.v.*).

Tungsten

Precipitated with acid as H_2WO_4 or with cinchonine as cinchonine tungstate, ignited, and weighed as WO_3.

Precipitated with 8-hydroxyquinoline (oxine) and weighed as $WO_2(C_9H_6NO)_2$, or the oxine in the precipitate liberated and determined volumetrically with standard $KBrO_3$ as with magnesium (q.v.).

Reduced from 6 to 3 with hot lead amalgam and titrated back to 6 with standard $KMnO_4$.

Uranium

Precipitated with NH_4OH as $(NH_4)_2U_2O_7$, ignited in air, and weighed as U_3O_8.

Reduced from 6 to 4 with Zn and precipitated with cupferron. The precipitate ignited in air to U_3O_8 and weighed as such.

Precipitated as $UO_2NH_4PO_4$, ignited, and weighed as $(UO_2)_2P_2O_7$.

Reduced with Zn and titrated back with standard $KMnO_4$ ($UO_2^{++} + Zn + 4H^+ \rightarrow U^{++++} + Zn^{++} + 2H_2O$; $5U^{++++} + 2MnO_4^- + 2H_2O \rightarrow 5UO_2^{++} + 2Mn^{++} + 4H^+$).

Vanadium

Precipitated as $HgVO_3$, ignited, and weighed as V_2O_5.

Precipitated as $Pb(VO_3)_2$, fumed with H_2SO_4, filtered, ignited, and weighed as V_2O_5.

Measured amount of KI added to HCl solution of vanadate ($2H_3VO_4 + 2I^- + 6H^+ \rightarrow 2VO^{++} + I_2 + 6H_2O$). The excess iodide plus the liberated iodine titrated with standard KIO_3 using chloroform indicator (see under Iodine). Equation for net reaction: $4H_3VO_4 + 4I^- + IO_3^- + 18H^+ + 5Cl^- \rightarrow 4VO^{++} + 5ICl + 15H_2O$.

Reduced from 5 to 4 by SO_2 or H_2S and titrated back with standard $KMnO_4$ ($2VO_3^- + SO_2 + 4H^+ \rightarrow 2VO^{++} + SO_4^= + 2H_2O$; $5VO^{++} + MnO_4^- + 6H_2O \rightarrow 5VO_3^- + Mn^{++} + 12H^+$).

Zinc

Precipitated as ZnS, ignited, and weighed as ZnO.

Precipitated as $ZnNH_4PO_4$ and weighed as such or ignited to $Zn_2P_2O_7$ and weighed.

Reduced electrolytically from NaOH solution to Zn and weighed as such.

Precipitated with 8-hydroxyquinoline (oxine) and the precipitate dissolved in HCl. The liberated oxine titrated with standard $KBrO_3$ as in the case of magnesium (q.v.).

Titrated with standard $K_4Fe(CN)_6$ using $FeSO_4$ as internal indicator or $UO_2(NO_3)_2$ as external indicator. The net equation is: $3Zn^{++} + 2Fe(CN)_6^= + 2K^+ \rightarrow K_2Zn_3[Fe(CN)_6]_2$.

Zirconium

Precipitated as $Zr(OH)_4$, ignited, and weighed as ZrO_2.

Precipitated with cupferron or phenyl-arsonic acid, ignited, and weighed as ZrO_2.

Precipitated with H_2SeO_3 as $ZrOSeO_3$, ignited, and weighed as ZrO_2.

Precipitated as $Zr(HPO_4)_2$, ignited, and weighed as ZrP_2O_7.

Part VI

PROBLEMS ON SPECIFIC GROUPS AND DETERMINATIONS

A. QUALITATIVE ANALYSIS

Silver Group

(See also Probs. 5.23, 5.40, 5.69, 5.89.)

1. Silver chloride dissolves in NH_4OH according to the equation: $AgCl + 2NH_4OH \rightarrow Ag(NH_3)_2^+ + Cl^- + 2H_2O$. Calculate (a) number of gram-moles of NH_4OH equivalent to 1 F.W. of AgCl, (b) number of grams of NH_3 equivalent to 1 F.W. of AgCl, (c) number of gram-ions of Cl^- produced by dissolving 1 F.W. of AgCl.

2. Assuming 20 drops to equal a milliliter, how many drops of 2.0 formal NH_4Cl solution would be required to precipitate the silver from a solution containing 100 mg. of $AgNO_3$? How many millimoles and how many milligrams of NH_4Cl does each milliliter of the reagent contain? How many milliliters of 5.0 normal NH_4Cl should be taken in order to prepare 500 ml. of the 2.0 formal solution by dilution with water?

3. A neutral solution containing 0.0170 gram of dissolved $AgNO_3$ is treated with an aqueous solution of 0.600 millimole of HCl and the precipitated AgCl is filtered off. (a) How many gram-ions of Cl^- and how many grams of Cl^- are present in the filtrate? (b) How many milliliters of NH_4OH (sp. gr. 0.96 containing 9.9 per cent NH_3 by weight) would be required to neutralize the acid in the filtrate? (c) How many milliliters of 2.0 N NH_4OH would be required to dissolve the AgCl precipitate?

Ans. (a) 0.000500 gram-ions, 0.0177 gram, (b) 0.0894 ml., (c) 0.10 ml.

4. Complete and balance the following equation: $Hg_2Cl_2 + NH_4OH \rightarrow Hg + HgNH_2Cl + \ldots$. What oxidation numbers does mercury show in this reaction? How many grams of mercurous chloride would give 0.0100 F.W. of the amido compound by this reaction? How many gram-atoms of free mercury would be formed at the same time, and how many grams of ammonium chloride could be obtained by filtering and evaporating the filtrate to dryness? How many milliliters of ammonium hydroxide (sp. gr. 0.970, containing 7.31 per cent NH_3 by weight) would be required in the reaction?

5. What is the solubility product of lead chloride, $PbCl_2$, if 550 milligrams dissolve in 50.0 ml.? How many milligrams of chloride ions must be present in 3.00 ml. of a solution containing 0.100 millimole of $Pb(NO_3)_2$ in order to give a precipitate of lead chloride in the silver group?

6. To a solution containing 50.0 mg. of Ag^+ and 50.0 mg. of Pb^{++} are added sufficient NH_4Cl solution to give precipitates of AgCl and $PbCl_2$ and make the surrounding solution half normal in chloride ions. If the volume of the solution is 30.0 ml. and the solubility products of AgCl and $PbCl_2$ are 1.0×10^{-10} and 2.4×10^{-4}, respectively, how many milligrams of silver and of lead will remain unprecipitated?

How many milliliters of boiling water are required to dissolve the precipitated lead chloride if its solubility at 100°C. is 0.120 F.W. per liter of water?   How many milligrams of silver chloride would dissolve by this treatment if its solubility at 100°C. is 0.150 millimoles per liter of water?

Hydrogen Sulfide Group

(See also Probs. 3.14, 5.20, 5.22, 5.24, 5.37, 5.42, 5.77, 5.78, 5.82, 5.86, 5.87, 5.91.)

7. If precipitation of sulfides is carried out in a solution 0.30 N in hydrogen ions, what is the pH value of the solution?   What is the hydroxyl-ion concentration?

8. A solution contains dilute HNO_3 and 0.0485 gram of dissolved $Bi(NO_3)_3.5H_2O$. The bismuth is precipitated by H_2S as follows: $2Bi^{+++} + 3H_2S \rightarrow Bi_2S_3 + 6H^+$.   Calculate (a) number of formula weights of bismuth sulfide produced, (b) number of grams and number of milliliters (standard conditions) of H_2S theoretically required, (c) increase in the number of gram-ions of H^+ accompanying the precipitation.

9. The bismuth sulfide of the preceding problem is dissolved in HNO_3 according to the ionic equation: $Bi_2S_3 + 2NO_3^- + 8H^+ \rightarrow 2Bi^{+++} + 2NO + 3S + 4H_2O; 2NO + O_2 (air) \rightarrow 2NO_2$.   Calculate (a) number of formula weights of $Bi(NO_3)_3.5H_2O$ obtainable from the resulting solution, (b) number of formula weights of HNO_3 theoretically required; (c) number of milliliters of HNO_3 (sp. gr. 1.13, containing 21.8 per cent HNO_3 by weight) theoretically required, (d) number of gram-atoms of sulfur produced, (e) number of millimoles of NO gas formed; (f) number of grams of NO_2 subsequently produced, (g) percentage of nitrogen in the NO_2 gas.

10. How many milliliters of H_2SO_4 (sp. gr. 1.14, containing 19.6 per cent H_2SO_4 by weight) are theoretically required to precipitate 10.0 milligrams of Pb^{++}?   What is the normality of the above sulfuric acid and what is its composition in terms of percentage of combined SO_3?   How many formula weights of $NH_4C_2H_3O_2$ would be required to dissolve the resulting precipitate of lead sulfate?   If the latter solution were diluted to 50.0 ml., what would be its normality in terms of lead acetate and its molarity in terms of ammonium sulfate?

Ans.   0.0212 ml.   4.56 N, 16.0 per cent.   0.0000966 F.W.   0.00193 N, 0.000966 M.

11. When H_2S is passed into an acid solution containing 0.10 F.W. of $K_2Cr_2O_7$, the following reaction takes place: $K_2Cr_2O_7 + 3H_2S + 8HCl \rightarrow 2CrCl_3 + 2KCl + 3S + 7H_2O$.   (a) Write this equation in ionic form observing the usual conventions. (b) Express the reaction as the difference between two half-cell reactions.   (c) How many formula weights of chromic chloride and how many grams of potassium chloride could be obtained by evaporating the resulting solution to dryness?   (d) How many gram-atoms of sulfur are formed?   (e) How many millimoles of H_2S are oxidized? (f) How many milliliters (standard conditions) of H_2S are oxidized?   (g) If the initial solution has a volume of 100 ml. and is 0.30 N in HCl, what is the acid normality of the solution after the above reaction has taken place, assuming no appreciable change in volume?

12. In the precipitation of the copper-tin groups from acid solution with H_2S, oxidizing agents like permanganate ions and ferric ions are reduced by the H_2S and the latter is oxidized to free sulfur.   Write each of these two redox reactions as the difference between two half-cell reactions, and calculate the number of millimoles and the number of milligrams of $KMnO_4$ and of $FeCl_3$ thus reduced by 10.0 ml. of H_2S gas (measured under standard conditions).

13. Balance the following equation and express it as the difference between two half-cell reactions: $HgS + ClO_3^- + Cl^- \rightarrow HgCl_4^- + SO_4^-$. Assume that 0.233 gram of HgS is dissolved according to this equation and the solution diluted to 50.0 ml. If excess chloride ions are present in sufficient amount to make the chloride-ion concentration 0.510 molar, how many milligrams of mercury are present as simple Hg^{++} ions? (Dissociation constant of $HgCl_4^- = 1.0 \times 10^{-16}$.)

14. A solution containing 0.010 F.W. of $CdSO_4$ and 0.010 F.W. of $CuSO_4$ is made ammoniacal and treated with excess KCN, forming $Cd(CN)_4^-$ and $Cu(CN)_3^-$. The resulting solution is 0.80 molar in CN^- ions. What is the molar concentration of Cd^{++} and of Cu^+ in the solution if the dissociation constant of $Cd(CN)_4^-$ is 1.4×10^{-17} and that of $Cu(CN)_3^-$ is 5×10^{-28}? Are these values consistent with what happens when H_2S is passed into the complex cyanide solution?

15. Mercuric sulfide dissolves in a solution of $Na_2S + NaOH$ ($HgS + S^- \rightarrow HgS_2^-$) but not in a solution of $(NH_4)_2S + NH_4OH$. This is due to the difference in the degree of hydrolysis of the sulfide ion: $S^- + H_2O \rightarrow HS^- + OH^-$. Calculate the numerical value of the mass action hydrolysis constant $[HS^-][OH^-]/[S^-]$ by combining appropriate ionization constants given in Secs. 31 and 35.

Ans. 8.3.

16. A solution containing 30 milligram-atoms of bismuth as Bi^{+++} is treated with HCl in sufficient amount to make the hydrogen-ion concentration 2 molar and the chloride-ion concentration 2 molar. Most of the bismuth is converted to $BiCl_4^-$. The solution has a volume of 15 ml. and is made 0.10 molar in H_2S. From the ionization constant of H_2S calculate the concentration of S^- and, assuming the dissociation constant of $BiCl_4^-$ to be 1.0×10^{-20}, calculate the concentration of Bi^{+++}. Calculate the value of $[Bi^{+++}]^2[S^-]^3$ and predict from the solubility product of Bi_2S_3 whether a precipitation of the sulfide is to be expected.

Ammonium Sulfide Group

(See also Probs. 4.7, 4.8, 4.16, 5.34, 5.41, 5.54, 5.55, 5.68, 5.75, 5.76, 5.83, 5.84, 5.85, 5.88, 5.89.)

17. A solution contains 0.286 gram of dissolved $Fe_2(SO_4)_3.9H_2O$ in 500 ml. of solution. (*a*) What is the normality of the solution as a ferric salt? (*b*) What is its normality as a sulfate? (*c*) How many milliliters of 3.00 N NH_4OH are required to precipitate all the iron as $Fe(OH)_3$? (*d*) How many milliliters of barium chloride solution containing $\frac{1}{8}$ millimole of $BaCl_2.2H_2O$ per milliliter are required to precipitate the sulfate?

18. From the solubility products of $Mg(OH)_2$ and $Fe(OH)_3$ calculate the number of grams of ferric ions that can remain dissolved 100 ml. of a solution of such alkalinity that 243 mg. of Mg^{++} will just fail to precipitate as $Mg(OH)_2$.

19. What is the molarity of a solution of $CrCl_3$ which is 0.10 normal as a salt? How many milliequivalents of the salt are present in each milliliter? If the chromium is oxidized to dichromate and the volume is twice as great as before, what would be the normality as a sodium salt of the $Na_2Cr_2O_7$ present? How many milli-moles of $FeSO_4.7H_2O$ would be required to reduce this dichromate in one milliliter of the solution to chromic ions in the presence of acid? Write the ionic equation as the difference between two half-cell reactions.

Ans. 0.0333 M. 0.10. 0.0167 N. 0.050.

20. How many milliliters of H_2SO_4 (sp. gr. 1.20) are theoretically required to dissolve 0.010 F.W. of $Al(OH)_3$? What is the normality and what is the molarity of the acid?

21. Starting with 0.010 gram-ion of Zn^{++}, how many millimoles of NH_3 are theoretically required to form the complex ammonio ion? If three times this amount of ammonia are used and the total volume is 250 ml., what is the molar concentration of Zn^{++}?

Alkaline Earth and Alkali Groups

(See also Probs. 4.6, 5.38, 5.47, 5.56, 5.72, 5.92.)

22. A solution is 0.030 formal in Sr^{++} ions. What value must the chromate-ion concentration be in order for $SrCrO_4$ to start precipitating ($K_{S.P.}$ for $SrCrO_4$ = 3.0×10^{-5})? How many grams of Ba^{++} could remain dissolved in each milliliter of such a solution ($K_{S.P.}$ for $BaCrO_4$ = 3.0×10^{-10})? The mass-action constant for the equilibrium $2CrO_4^= + 2H^+ \rightleftarrows Cr_2O_7^= + H_2O$ is 4.2×10^{14}. If the above solution contains sufficient $HC_2H_3O_2$ and $NH_4C_2H_3O_2$ to give a pH value of 5.0, what would be the dichromate-ion concentration?

Ans. $1.0 \times 10^{-3} M$. 4.1×10^{-8} gram.   0.042 molar.

23. How many grams of $CaCl_2$ should be taken to prepare 100 ml. of 0.20 N solution? How many millimoles of $H_2C_2O_4.2H_2O$ would be required to precipitate all the calcium? How many gram atoms of magnesium could theoretically be held as $Mg(C_2O_4)_2^=$ by this amount of oxalic acid?

24. How many milliliters of a solution of $K_2Cr_2O_7$ which is 0.10 normal as a potassium salt would be required to precipitate 0.010 gram-atom of barium as $BaCrO_4$?

25. How many grams of NH_3 would be liberated from 1.00 gram-equivalent weight of $(NH_4)_2SO_4$ by the action of NaOH? If this NH_3 were absorbed in water and diluted to one liter, what would be the normality and the approximate specific gravity of the solution? How many milliliters of 3.40 M H_2SO_4 would it neutralize?

Anion Groups

(See also Probs. 3.19, 5.21, 5.39, 5.44, 5.50, 5.70, 5.71, 5.73, 5.80, 5.93, 5.94, 5.97.)

26. Complete and balance the following: $NO_3^- + Al + OH^- \rightarrow NH_3 + AlO_2^-$. Also write it as the difference between two half-cell reactions. If 250 mg. of $NaNO_3$ are reduced as above with excess aluminum in the presence of NaOH, how many milliliters of $N/2$ H_2SO_4 would be required to neutralize the NH_3 liberated? How many gram-atoms of aluminum are theoretically required for the reduction?

27. If 100 milligrams of sodium oxalate $Na_2C_2O_4$, are heated with concentrated H_2SO_4, what volume of mixed gases would be obtained when measured over water at 753 mm. pressure and 25°C.? ($Na_2C_2O_4 + H_2SO_4 \rightarrow Na_2SO_4 + CO + CO_2 + H_2O$.) What volume of gas would be obtained (under the same conditions of temperature and pressure as above) if the 100 mg. of sodium oxalate were treated with excess $KMnO_4$ in the presence of dilute H_2SO_4?

B. QUANTITATIVE ANALYSIS

Water.   Hydrogen Peroxide

(See also Probs. 8.19, 10.1, 10.2, 10.8, 10.9, 10.10, 10.13, 10.14, 10.15, 10.16, 10.18, 13.35, 13.98.)

28. A manufacturer purchased 130 tons of material at 0.20 cent per pound per cent A on a guarantee of 10.00 per cent A. The material was shipped in cars, and on arrival the manufacturer had it analyzed. The chemist reported 10.46 per cent A but neglected to state that he had dried the sample at 100°C. The manufacturer paid on a 10 per cent basis, figuring he had made money. In reality, he lost $520. What was the percentage of moisture in the material?

29. Ten tons of Na_2SO_3 containing 6.30 per cent moisture were purchased at the market price. During storage, 10.0 per cent of the sodium sulfite was oxidized to sodium sulfate. The salt when sold contained 3.20 per cent of its weight of water. The salt was sold as C.P. Na_2SO_3 at the same price as purchased. Calculate the gain or loss in the transaction figuring the market price as 3.25 cents per pound.

Sodium. Potassium

(See also Probs. 8.39, 8.73, 8.74, 8.80, 8.81, 8.89, 12.99, 12.101, 12.102, 12.103, 13.28, 14.11, 14.12, 14.17, 14.18, 14.20.)

30. In the J. Lawrence Smith method for potassium using a 0.5000-gram sample of mineral, the analyst fails to expel all the ammonium chloride from the $NaCl + KCl$. The insoluble precipitate with chloroplatinic acid weighs 0.08921 gram. On ignition the weight is changed to 0.05969 gram. What would be the weight if the ignited precipitate were washed with water and dried, and what is the percentage of K_2O in the mineral?

31. Caustic potash is to be produced by the electrolysis of a solution of potassium chloride. A solution containing 100 grams of KOH per liter is required. An average current of 900 amperes is used; and, at the end of 5.00 hours, 102 liters of caustic potash, 1.520 N as an alkali, have been produced. How much longer must the electrolysis be continued in order to produce the desired concentration, and what is the current efficiency at the cathode?

Ans. 52.3 minutes, 92.3 per cent.

32. How many grams of Pt (dissolved in aqua regia) and how many milliliters of $HClO_4$ (3.000 N as an acid) would theoretically be required to precipitate the potassium from 0.5000 gram of K_3PO_4 without allowing for the customary excess of reagent? How much would the former precipitate weigh after ignition?

Ammonium. Ammonia. Nitrogen

(See also Probs. 8.10, 8.18, 12.80, 12.83, 12.84, 12.85, 12.92, 12.104, 12.144, 19.2, 147.)

33. Ten milliliters of ammonium hydroxide (sp. gr. 0.960) are diluted to exactly 100 ml. in a calibrated flask; 10.00 ml. are withdrawn in a pipet, made acid with hydrochloric acid, and an excess of chloroplatinic acid is added. After evaporation and dilution with alcohol, the insoluble residue is dried and found to weigh 1.240 grams. Calculate the percentage of NH_3 by weight in the original ammonia sample.

34. The nitrogen in a half-gram sample of urea, $CO(NH_2)_2$, is determined by the Kjeldahl method. The evolved ammonia is passed into 150 ml. of 0.1200 N H_2SO_4. How many ml. of NaOH solution would be required for the excess acid if 1.000 ml. NaOH $\approx$ 0.00700 gram of hydrated oxalic acid?

35. Nitrogen, existing as nitride in a crucible steel, is determined by decomposing a 5.00-gram sample with HCl. The resulting NH_4Cl is decomposed with NaOH, and the liberated NH_3 is absorbed in 10.05 ml. of H_2SO_4 which is exactly 0.00990 N as an acid.   After absorption, the concentration of the H_2SO_4 is determined by adding an excess of KI and of KIO_3 and titrating with standard $Na_2S_2O_3$ the I_2 liberated.   The $Na_2S_2O_3$ is of such strength that 42.0 ml. are equivalent to the I_2 liberated from an excess of KI by 20.0 ml. of 0.0258 N $KMnO_4$, and in the above titration 5.14 ml. are used.   Calculate the percentage of nitrogen in the steel.

Ans.   0.0102 per cent.

36. A sample of impure ammonium chloride is dissolved in water, and the solution is divided into two equal portions.   One portion is made alkaline with NaOH, and the liberated ammonia is distilled into 100 ml. of 0.1000 N sulfuric acid which is then found to require 43.90 ml. of 0.1320 N NaOH for neutralization.   The other portion is treated with sodium hypobromite solution ($2NH_3 + 3OBr^- \rightarrow 3Br^- + N_2 + 3H_2O$), and the liberated nitrogen is found to occupy 51.30 ml. when measured over water at 20°C. and 753 mm. pressure.   If the first method gives correct results, what is the percentage error of the gas-volumetric method?

Silver.   Mercury.   Gold.   Platinum

(See also Probs. 9.2, 9.4, 9.7, 9.10, 9.15, 9.18, 13.100, 14.6.)

37. If a sample of silver coin weighing 0.2500 gram gives a precipitate of AgCl weighing 0.2991 gram, what is the percentage of silver in the coin and what volume of 0.05000 N KCNS solution would have been used if the silver in the same weight of sample had been determined volumetrically by the Volhard method?

38. Mercury, like silver, forms an insoluble thiocyanate [$Hg^{++} + 2CNS^- \rightarrow Hg(CNS)_2$] and can be determined by titration with standard KCNS.   How many milliliters of 0.08333 N KCNS would be required to titrate the solution of 0.6000 gram of an amalgam consisting of 70.00 per cent Hg and 30.00 per cent Ag?

Halogens.   Cyanide.   Thiocyanate.   Halogen Acids

(See also Probs. 8.9, 8.17, 8.27, 8.42, 8.44, 8.61, 8.75, 8.80, 8.83, 8.91, 8.92, 8.93, 8.94, 8.95, 8.96, 8.97, 13.81, 13.97, 14.1, 14.8, 14.9, 14.10, 14.13, 15.1, 15.2, 15.3, 15.4, 15.6, 15.7, 15.10, 15.11, 15.12, 15.13, 15.14, 18.1, 145.)

39. In the determination of fluoride in a given sample of a salt mixture, if 20.00 ml. of NaOH (1.000 ml. $\backsim$ 0.01021 gram potassium acid phthalate) were required, what weight of precipitate would be obtained if the same weight of sample were analyzed for fluoride gravimetrically by precipitating as lead chlorofluoride?

Barium.   Strontium.   Calcium.   Magnesium

(See also Probs. 8.36, 8.38, 8.41, 8.42, 8.58, 8.79, 8.82, 8.84, 8.85, 8.86, 8.90, 10.3, 12.88, 12.97, 12.100; 12.105, 13.30, 13.52, 13.99, 14.3, 14.5, 14.19, 20.29.)

40. A sample of calcite (impure $CaCO_3$) weighing 1.402 grams is titrated with HCl and requires 25.02 ml.   What is the alkaline strength of the sample in terms of per cent CaO if 20.00 ml. of the HCl will just neutralize the NH_3 that can be liberated from four millimoles of $(NH_4)_3PO_4.2H_2O$?

41. Given the following data: 35.27 ml. I_2 solution $\backsim$ 0.02991 gram As_2O_3; 30.00 ml. I_2 solution $\backsim$ 45.03 ml. $Na_2S_2O_3$ solution; 25.82 ml. $Na_2S_2O_3$ will reduce the iodine liberated from an excess of KI by 31.05 ml. $KMnO_4$ solution; 15.42 ml. $KMnO_4$ $\backsim$ 16.97 ml. $KHC_2O_4.H_2C_2O_4.2H_2O$ solution; 1.000 ml. $KHC_2O_4.H_2C_2O_4.2H_2O$ solution $\backsim$ 1.074 ml. NaOH solution; 10.00 ml. NaOH solution $\backsim$ 12.00 ml. HCl solution. How many grams of $CaCO_3$ will be reacted upon by 29.83 ml. of this HCl solution?

42. A sample of Epsom salts is supposedly C.P. $MgSO_4.7H_2O$. On analysis of a sample weighing 0.8000 gram, the magnesium precipitated as $MgNH_4PO_4$ and ignited to $Mg_2P_2O_7$ was found to weigh 0.3900 gram.

The sulfate precipitated as $BaSO_4$ weighed 0.8179 gram.

Does the material conform to the given formula? If not, in what way and to what degree does it differ?

43. Basic magnesium carbonate corresponds approximately to the formula $4MgCO_3.Mg(OH)_2.6H_2O$ (F.W. = 503.7). The substance is sometimes roughly analyzed by determining its loss on ignition, but more generally by titration.

A sample weighing 1.000 gram is dissolved in a 25-ml. pipetful of 1.000 N HCl and the excess acid requires 5.01 ml. of 1.010 N NaOH. Calculate the percentage purity of the sample in terms of the above theoretical formula. What would be the loss on ignition of a 1.000-gram sample of the pure substance?

44. A sample of limestone containing 34.75 per cent Ca is given to a student for analysis. Using a 1.000-gram sample the student reports 35.26 per cent Ca. If the error was due to insufficient ignition of the calcium oxalate precipitate causing contamination of the CaO by $CaCO_3$, what was the percentage of $CaCO_3$ in the ignited product? What was the percentage error? What volume of sulfuric acid (sp. gr. 1.06, containing 8.77 per cent H_2SO_4 by weight) should be added to this product to convert all the Ca into $CaSO_4$? What would be the new weight of the ignited product?

Limestone. Lime. Cement

(See also Probs. 8.6, 10.4, 10.8, 10.17, 10.19.)

45. A sample of magnesia limestone has the following composition:

Silica	= 3.00 per cent
Ferric oxide and alumina	= 0.20 per cent
Calcium oxide	= 33.10 per cent
Magnesium oxide	= 20.70 per cent
Carbon dioxide	= 43.00 per cent

In the manufacture of lime from the above, the carbon dioxide is reduced to 3.00 per cent. How many milliliters of 0.2500 N $KMnO_4$ will be required to determine the calcium volumetrically in a 1.000-gram sample of the lime?

46. From the following data, compute the percentage of SiO_2, Al_2O_3, MgO, and CaO in a sample of cement weighing 0.6005 gram: Weight of SiO_2 = 0.1380 gram. Weight of Fe_2O_3 + Al_2O_3 = 0.1201 gram. Weight of $Mg_2P_2O_7$ = 0.0540 gram. Volume of 0.1429 N $KMnO_4$ for the Fe in the above ignited precipitate = 2.05 ml. Volume of this $KMnO_4$ required to titrate the precipitated calcium oxalate = 45.12 ml.

47. A limestone contains only SiO_2, $CaCO_3$, $FeCO_3$, $MgCO_3$, $MnCO_3$. Calculate the percentage of CO_2 from the following data: Sample = 0.800 gram. Fe_2O_3 + Mn_3O_4 = 0.0521 gram and requires 5.00 ml. of 0.1112 N $KMnO_4$ for the iron $CaSO_4$ = 0.7250 gram. $Mg_2P_2O_7$ = 0.0221 gram.

48. A sample of limestone contains only silica, ferrous carbonate, calcium carbonate, and magnesium carbonate. From a sample weighing 1.200 grams there were obtained 0.0400 gram of ignited ferric oxide, 0.5003 gram of CO_2, and 0.5007 gram of magnesium pyrophosphate. Find the volume of ammonium oxalate solution [containing 35.00 grams of $(NH_4)_2C_2O_4.H_2O$ per liter] required to precipitate the calcium as oxalate. Also calculate the normality of $KMnO_4$ if 38.00 ml. are required to titrate the oxalate precipitate.

Iron.   Aluminum.   Titanium

(See also Probs. 4.8, 4.16, 8.5, 8.11, 8.30, 8.37, 8.40, 8.45, 8.49, 8.57, 8.64, 8.65, 8.66, 8.67, 8.72, 8.76, 8.87, 10.7, 10.16, 13.23, 13.25, 13.31, 13.36, 13.42, 13.53, 13.57, 13.58, 13.60, 13.62, 13.89, 16.15, 20.20.)

49. How many milliliters of ammonium hydroxide (sp. gr. 0.946, containing 13.88 per cent NH_3 by weight) are required to precipitate the iron as $Fe(OH)_3$ from a sample of pure $FeSO_4.(NH_4)_2SO_4.6H_2O$ which requires 0.34 ml. of hot HNO_3 (sp. gr. 1.350, containing 55.79 per cent HNO_3 by weight) for oxidation?   Assume reduction of HNO_3 to NO.

50. A 1.000-gram sample of limonite containing inactive impurities is dissolved in acid, and the solution is divided into two equal portions.   One portion is reduced and titrated with $KMnO_4$ (1.000 ml. $\backsimeq$ 0.008193 gram $H_2C_2O_4.2H_2O$).   The other portion is just neutralized, and 40.00 ml. of 1.500 N ammonia are added to precipitate the iron.   This is in excess of the necessary amount, and the number of milliliters in excess is equal to the number of milliliters of $KMnO_4$ required in the volumetric process.   What is the percentage of Fe in the sample?

Ans.   46.10 per cent.

51. If 60.00 ml. of $BaCl_2$ (0.1000 N as a precipitating agent) are required just to precipitate all the sulfate from a sample of pure ferric alum, $Fe_2(SO_4)_3.(NH_4)_2SO_4.-24H_2O$, how many milliliters of NH_4OH (sp. gr. 0.900, containing 28.33 per cent NH_3 by weight) would be required just to precipitate all the iron from the same weight of sample?

52. What is the percentage purity of a sample of ferrous sulfate $FeSO_4.7H_2O$ weighing 1.000 gram, if, after it has been dissolved in water, 10.00 ml. of 0.1100 N hydrochloric acid have been added to it, and it has been oxidized with bromine, 11.73 ml. of N NH_4OH are required to neutralize the acid and precipitate the iron as $Fe(OH)_3$?

53. How many milliliters of 0.1250 N $KMnO_4$ are needed to titrate a solution containing ferrous iron if by a gravimetric method 3.50 ml. of 6.00 N ammonia water are required to precipitate the iron after oxidation to the ferric condition?

54. After decomposition of a half-gram sample of a certain mineral and the removal of silica, the addition of bromine and NH_4OH precipitates $Fe(OH)_3 + Al(OH)_3$.   On ignition, these weigh 0.1205 gram.   They are then fused with $KHSO_4$, dissolved in dilute H_2SO_4, passed through a column of amalgamated zinc, and the iron titrated with $KMnO_4$ (1.000 ml. $\backsimeq$ 0.02500 millimole $Na_2C_2O_4$), requiring 22.46 ml.   What is the percentage of Al_2O_3 and of FeO in the original sample?   How many milliliters of NH_4OH (sp. gr. 0.970, containing 7.31 per cent NH_3 by weight) were required just to precipitate all of the ferric iron and aluminum from the solution after neutralizing the acid?

Ans.   6.16 per cent, 16.14 per cent.   1.24 ml.

55. "Iron by hydrogen" is obtained by reducing pure Fe_2O_3 with hydrogen.   It is a fine gray powder used analytically as a reagent for the determination of nitrates by reduction to ammonia.   The material should contain at least 90 per cent metallic iron and is generally contaminated with an oxide assumed to be Fe_3O_4, as the reduction is not complete.   The metallic iron in the sample is soluble in a neutral solution of $FeCl_3$, according to the equation $Fe + 2Fe^{+++} \rightarrow 3Fe^{++}$, and the ferrous chloride formed is determined by titration with $KMnO_4$.

In an actual analysis, 0.5000 gram is weighed into a 100-ml. measuring flask, the air displaced with CO_2, and water added, 2.500 grams (an excess) of anhydrous $FeCl_3$ (free from Fe^{++}) are added, and the flask stoppered and shaken for 15 minutes. The solution is diluted to the mark, mixed, and filtered. Twenty milliliters of the filtrate are titrated with 44.16 ml. of 0.1094 N $KMnO_4$ after the addition of sulfuric acid and manganese sulfate titrating solution and proper dilution. Calculate the percentage of metallic iron in the sample.

56. A sample of aluminum sulfate is known to be contaminated with iron and manganese. A sample weighing 3.362 gram is dissolved in dilute acid, and bromine and ammonia are added to precipitate $Al(OH)_3$, $Fe(OH)_3$ and MnO_2. Treating the precipitate with concentrated HNO_3 dissolves the iron and aluminum hydroxides and leaves the MnO_2. This MnO_2 is ignited in air (forming Mn_3O_4) and the product is found to weigh 0.0363 gram. The HNO_3 solution is evaporated with H_2SO_4 and the iron eventually reduced and titrated with 4.90 ml. of 0.1020 N $KMnO_4$. An acid solution of 3.829 grams of the original salt gives with bromine and ammonia a precipitate that on ignition in air weighs 0.5792 gram. What is the percentage of Al_2O_3 and of Mn and Fe in the original material?

57. A volumetric method for aluminum has been found useful in certain cases. The aluminum is precipitated with 8-hydroxyquinoline ("oxine") and the precipitate is dissolved in acid and titrated with standard $KBrO_3$ (+KBr). If an excess of KBr is used and the titration requires 48.0 ml. of $KBrO_3$ (of which 1.00 ml. will liberate from excess KI in the presence of acid sufficient I_2 to require 1.00 ml. of 0.100 N $Na_2S_2O_3$), what weight of residue would have been obtained if the oxine precipitate had been ignited in air?

Ans. 0.0204 gram.

58. A solution of ferric chloride is prepared by dissolving 10.03 grams of pure iron in HCl, oxidizing, and diluting to a liter. If 50.0 ml. of this solution react with 40.0 ml. of a $TiCl_3$ solution, what is the normality of the latter as a reducing agent?

59. A sample of titanium ore is treated in such a way that all the iron is present in the 2-valent condition and all the titanium in the 3-valent condition. The solution is then titrated with ferric alum solution of which 50.00 ml. yield 0.4000 gram of Fe_2O_3. If the original sample weighed 0.6000 gram and 15.00 ml. of ferric alum solution were used, find the percentage of TiO_2 in the ore.

60. The iron in a solution of a 0.800-gram sample of titanium ore was reduced with stannous chloride and then reacted with 26.0 ml. of $KMnO_4$ (1.00 ml. $\approx$ 0.800 ml. of potassium tetroxalate solution which is 0.08000 N as an acid). The sulfuric acid solution of the same weight of sample was reduced with zinc, and the reduced solution was caught in an acid solution of ferric alum which then reacted with 48.0 ml. of the above $KMnO_4$. Compute the analysis on the basis that the original sample contained only Fe_3O_4, TiO_2, and SiO_2. (Zinc reduces Ti from valence 4 to 3; $SnCl_2$ does not.)

61. A silicate rock is shown to contain ferrous iron, aluminum, and titanium. A sample weighing 0.6050 gram is decomposed by an oxidizing flux, the silica removed, and the precipitate obtained by NH_4OH filtered off, this precipitate consisting of the hydroxides of ferric iron, aluminum, and titanium. The ignited precipitate weighs 0.5120 gram. It is fused with $K_2S_2O_7$, and brought into solution, and the solution divided into two equal portions. One portion is poured through a Jones reductor containing amalgamated zinc and the solution caught directly in excess ferric alum solution. This solution is then titrated with 0.08333 N $KMnO_4$, of which 19.56 ml. are required. The other portion is reduced with $SnCl_2$, the excess stannous is destroyed, and the solution titrated with 0.08333 N $KMnO_4$, of which 11.94 ml. are required. Calculate the percentages of FeO, Al_2O_3, and TiO_2 in the original silicate.

Cerium. Thorium. Zirconium. Uranium. Beryllium. Bismuth. Boron

(See also Probs. 8.32, 10.12.)

62. From the methods given for the determination of cerium in Part V, outline a possible iodimetric method for that element and indicate the correct milliequivalent weight to be used.

63. A solution of uranyl nitrate is divided into two equal parts. One portion is evaporated to fumes with H_2SO_4, diluted, and passed through a Jones reductor. The uranium forms uranous ions (U^{++++}). The solution is titrated with 0.1200 N $KMnO_4$, requiring 20.50 ml. The uranium in the other portion is precipitated with NH_4OH as $(NH_4)_2U_2O_7$ and the precipitate is ignited and weighed (see Part V). Write equation for the titration and for the ignition (NH_3 and N_2 are among the products in the latter case) and calculate the weight of residue obtained in the ignition.

64. An iodimetric method for determining zirconium has been suggested. The element is precipitated with selenious acid (H_2SeO_3) as $ZrOSeO_3$. The precipitate is dissolved, treated with KI ($SeO_3^- + 4I^- \rightarrow Se + 2I_2 + 3H_2O$) and the liberated iodine subsequently titrated with standard $Na_2S_2O_3$. If 5.00 ml. of 0.0833 N $Na_2S_2O_3$ were required for a given weight of sample by this method, how many grams of residue would be obtained by igniting the $ZrOSeO_3$ obtained from another sample of the same weight?

Ans. 0.01283 gram.

65. Anhydrous sodium tetraborate reacts with water according to the following equation:

$$B_4O_7^- + 5H_2O \rightarrow 2H_2BO_3^- + 2H_3BO_3$$

The anhydrous salt may be dissolved in water and titrated directly by means of hydrochloric acid, with methyl orange as indicator, as represented by the following equation:

$$H_2BO_3^- + H^+ \rightarrow H_3BO_3$$

After conversion of the sodium tetraborate to boric acid by careful titration with HCl, methyl orange indicator being employed, a suitable polyhydric alcohol (inverted sugar, glycerin, mannitol, etc.) is added and the first hydrogen of the boric acid is titrated by means of standard sodium hydroxide, with phenolphthalein indicator.

The following data were obtained on a sample of tetraborate:

Sample = 0.3000 gram
Volume of HCl required, with methyl orange indicator = 26.35 ml.
Volume of NaOH required to titrate the boric acid = 58.10 ml.
Normality NaOH = 0.1030
40.00 ml. NaOH $\backsimeq$ 36.35 ml. HCl

Calculate the percentage of $Na_2B_4O_7$ present in the sample (*a*) using the data from the acid titration, (*b*) using the data from the alkali titration.

66. Barium can be determined volumetrically (after precipitating as $BaCrO_4$) either by a permanganate process or by an iodimetric process (see Part V, under Barium). If in the permanganate process 25.00 ml. of 0.1000 N ferrous ammonium sulfate were used ánd the excess ferrous required 10.50 ml. of 0.06667 N KMnO$_4$, what weight of BaSO$_4$ would be precipitated during the titration reactions? If the iodimetric method had been used on the same weight of sample, how many milliliters of 0.06667 N Na$_2$S$_2$O$_3$ would have been required?

Ans. 0.1400 gram. 27.00 ml.

67. Beryllium can be determined volumetrically by precipitating with oxine and titrating with KBrO$_3$ as in the case of aluminum (see Part V, under Aluminum). Write the corresponding equations for the behavior of beryllium and calculate the weight of the ignited residue (of BeO) using the same numerical data as given in Prob. 57.

68. If bismuth is determined by precipitating as bismuthyl oxalate and titrating with standard KMnO$_4$, what is the value of each milliliter of 0.1000 N KMnO$_4$ in terms of grams of Bi$_2$O$_3$?

69. In the volumetric method for boron (see Part V), what is the milliequivalent weight of B$_2$O$_3$? Look up the ionization constant for boric acid and plot the titration curve to show its general appearance. Show how it compares in appearance with the curve for the titration of HCl under similar conditions of concentration.

Copper. Lead. Zinc. Cadmium. Brass

(See also Probs. 8.8, 8.21, 8.24, 9.1, 9.5, 9.6, 9.8, 9.11, 9.13, 9.14, 9.17, 9.19, 9.21, 9.22, 9.24, 9.27, 9.28, 9.29, 9.30, 9.31, 9.32, 10.1, 12.82, 13.24, 13.66, 13.83, 13.90, 13.95, 13.101, 14.15, 15.5, 15.17, 18.3.)

70. How many milliliters of HNO$_3$ (sp. gr. 1.130, containing 21.77 per cent HNO$_3$ by weight) are theoretically required to dissolve 5.00 grams of brass containing 0.61 per cent Pb, 24.39 per cent Zn, and 75.00 per cent Cu? Assume reduction of the HNO$_3$ to NO by each constituent. What fraction of this volume of acid is used for oxidation?

71. What volume of sulfuric acid (sp. gr. 1.420) is required to displace the nitrate radical from the mixture of salts obtained by dissolving 25.00 grams of brass (68.29 per cent Cu, 31.50 per cent Zn, 0.21 per cent Pb) in nitric acid and evaporating to dryness?

72. What is the percentage of copper in a steel if with a 5.00-gram sample the volume of H$_2$S gas (measured under standard conditions) required to precipitate the copper as CuS is 2.00 ml. more than the volume of 0.100 N Na$_2$S$_2$O$_3$ solution subsequently required for the copper by the iodimetric method?

73. If 0.800 gram of a lead ore yields a precipitate of chromate that contains chromium sufficient to yield on treatment with an excess of KI in acid solution an amount of iodine to react with 48.0 ml. of 0.1000 N thiosulfate solution, find the percentage of Pb in the ore.

74. What weight of zinc ore should be taken for analysis so that the number of milliliters of 0.1000 molar ferrocyanide solution used will equal the percentage of Zn in the ore?

75. If a copper ore on being analyzed yields 0.235 gram of Cu$_2$S after being heated with sulfur in a stream of hydrogen, how many grams of KIO$_3$ would react in the iodate method with the same weight of ore?

76. If 0.5000 gram of a copper alloy containing 25.00 per cent Cu requires 20.00 ml. of KCN for titration, what is the equivalent of 1.000 ml. of the KCN (a) in terms of

Ag (using KI as indicator) and (b) in terms of Ni?   How many milliliters of KIO_3 solution would have been required by the iodate method if with an excess of KI, 15.00 ml. of the KIO_3 would have liberated I_2 enough to react with a volume of 0.1000 N thiosulfate equivalent to 0.1000 gram of $K_2Cr_2O_7$?

77. A brass weighing 0.800 gram contains 75.02 per cent Cu, 23.03 per cent Zn, and 1.95 per cent Pb.   What volume of 0.1000 N $Na_2S_2O_3$ would be used in the determination of copper by adding KI and titrating the liberated iodine?   What volume of 0.05000 N $KMnO_4$ would be required for the lead if it is precipitated as chromate, dissolved, reduced with 25.00 ml. of 0.04000 N $FeSO_4$, and the excess ferrous ions titrated with the $KMnO_4$?   What weight of zinc pyrophosphate would be obtained in the determination of zinc?

78. In a certain volumetric method for determining copper, the element is precipitated as CuCNS and the precipitate is titrated with standard KIO_3 according to the net equation: $4CuCNS + 7KIO_3 + 14HCl \rightarrow 4CuSO_4 + 7ICl + 4HCN + 7KCl + 5H_2O$.   If the KIO_3 is of such concentration that 1.000 ml. will liberate from excess KI in the presence of acid sufficient iodine to react with 1.000 ml. of 0.1000 N $Na_2S_2O_3$, what is the value of 1.000 ml. of the KIO_3 in terms of grams of Cu in the above method?

Ans.   0.0006054 gram.

79. If a solution contains that amount of Cu^{++} requiring 10.0 ml. of a $Na_2S_2O_3$ solution in the common iodimetric method for copper, how many milliliters of KIO_3 solution (1.00 ml. $\backsim$ 2.00 ml. of the above $Na_2S_2O_3$) would be required to reach that point in the titration by the iodate method (see Part V, under Copper) corresponding to the maximum intensity of color of the $CHCl_3$ indicator?

Ans.   42.0 ml.

80. Red lead (Pb_3O_4) is made by the direct oxidation of metallic lead.   Chemically it may be regarded as $2PbO.PbO_2$, but owing to uneven heating in the manufacturing process commercial samples vary somewhat from the theoretical composition and are likely to contain excess PbO_2.   When such samples are treated with dilute HNO_3, the monoxide dissolves, leaving a brown residue H_2PbO_3, which can be reduced by the addition of a measured excess of oxalate ion and the excess titrated with standard permanganate.

A sample weighing 0.7000 gram is treated with dilute HNO_3 and subsequently with a weighed amount of pure sodium oxalate (5.000 milliequivalents).   After complete reaction, the solution is diluted with boiling water, manganous sulfate solution added, and the excess oxalate ion titrated with 28.56 ml. of 0.09987 N permanganate.   Calculate: (a) the total percentage of PbO_2 (free and combined) in the sample; (b) the oxidizing power to percentage of Pb_3O_4; (c) on the assumption that the sample is composed only of $2PbO.PbO_2$ and excess PbO_2, the percentage of each.

Ans.   (a) 36.70 per cent total PbO_2; (b) 105.2 per cent Pb_3O_4; (c) 97.18 per cent Pb_3O_4, 2.82 per cent free PbO_2.

81. If in the analysis of a brass containing 28.0 per cent Zn an error is made in weighing a 2.500-gram portion by which 0.001 gram too much is weighed out, what percentage error in the zinc determination would be made?   What volume of a solution of diammonium phosphate, containing 90.0 grams of $(NH_4)_2HPO_4$ per liter, would be required to precipitate the zinc as $ZnNH_4PO_4$, and what weight of precipitate would be obtained?

82. In the electrolysis of a sample of brass weighing 0.8000 gram, there are obtained

0.0030 gram of PbO_2, and a deposit of copper exactly equal in weight to the ignited precipitate of $Zn_2P_2O_7$ subsequently obtained from the solution. What is the percentage composition of the brass?

Tin. Antimony. Arsenic. Bronze

(See also Probs. 8.23, 8.29, 8.43, 8.60, 8.77, 8.88, 9.20, 13.77, 13.79, 13.80, 13.84, 13.85, 13.93, 13.94, 14.7, 16.7.)

83. A sample of type metal weighing 1.100 grams is dissolved in concentrated H_2SO_4. Concentrated HCl is added to the cooled solution, and the solution is boiled. At this point antimony is in the 3-valent state; tin is in the 4-valent state. The antimony in the cold solution is then titrated rapidly with $KMnO_4$ (1 ml. $\approx$ 0.00558 gram Fe), requiring 32.80 ml. More HCl is added, and the solution is boiled with powdered lead which reduces the antimony from valence 5 to valence 3 and the tin from valence 4 to valence 2. The tin is then quickly titrated in cold acid solution with I_2 (1 ml. $\approx$ 0.0500 millimole As_2O_3), requiring 9.27 ml. What are the percentages of Sb and Sn in the alloy? If the same weight of alloy had been treated with 6 N HNO_3 and the residual metastannic and antimonic acids had been ignited, what weight of product would have been obtained?

Ans. 18.2 per cent Sb, 10.0 per cent Sn. 0.392 gram.

84. A sample weighing 0.250 gram and containing arsenic is dissolved, and the solution containing the trivalent element is electrolyzed (method of Hefti). Arsine is liberated and is conducted into 50.0 ml. of 0.125 N iodine solution. The excess of the latter reacts with 20.0 ml. of $Na_2S_2O_3$ solution, of which 1.00 ml. = 0.00500 gram of copper. Find (*a*) percentage of As_2O_3 in the sample and (*b*) the time required for electrolysis if a current of 3.00 amperes is used and only 40.0 per cent of the current is used in reducing the arsenic.

Ans. (*a*) 23.2 per cent, (*b*) 282 seconds.

85. An alloy containing arsenic weighs 5.10 grams. The arsenic is distilled as $AsCl_3$ from a strong HCl solution of the alloy and eventually titrated in nearly neutral bicarbonate solution with standard iodine (1.00 ml. $\approx$ 1.00 ml. $Na_2S_2O_3$ $\approx$ 0.0024 gram Cu). Calculate the percentage of arsenic in the alloy if 5.00 ml. are required. If the arsenic were evolved as arsine and the arsine absorbed in excess 0.100 N iodine (which oxidizes the arsenic to arsenate), how many milliliters of 0.0833 N $Na_2S_2O_3$ would be equivalent to the iodine used up?

86. A mixture of As_2O_3 + As_2O_5 + inert matter is dissolved and titrated in neutral solution with I_2 [1.00 ml. $\approx$ 1.00 ml. $KMnO_4$ $\approx$ 0.0500 millimole $FeSO_4.(NH_4)_2SO_4.$-$6H_2O$] requiring 20.00 ml. The resulting solution is acidified and an excess of KI is added. The liberated I_2 requires 30.50 ml. of $Na_2S_2O_3$ [1.00 ml. $\approx$ 0.0100 millimole of $KH(IO_3)_2$]. Calculate the weight in grams of combined As_2O_3 + As_2O_5 in the sample.

Ans. 0.2023 gram.

Carbon. Carbon Dioxide. Silicon. Tungsten. Molybdenum

(See also Probs. 8.31, 8.34, 8.35, 12.75, 19.4, 20.4, 20.6, 20.7, 20.8, 20.14, 20.15, 20.18, 47.)

87. If a 1.30-gram sample of iron containing 1.15 per cent carbon is analyzed by direct combustion, what would be the gain in weight of the absorption tube? If the gas is passed through 100 ml. of 0.0833 N $Ba(OH)_2$, how many milliliters of 0.100 N HCl would be required to titrate the supernatant liquid?

88. A sample of steel weighing 1.00 gram is burned in oxygen. The CO_2 is caught in a 100-ml. pipetful of $Ba(OH)_2$ solution. The supernatant liquid requires 96.50 ml. of 0.100 N HCl. If the steel contains 0.57 per cent carbon, what is the normality of the barium solution used and how many grams of $Ba(OH)_2.8H_2O$ are contained in each milliliter?

89. A 2-gram sample of steel is burned in oxygen, and the evolved CO_2 after passing through appropriate purifying trains is caught in 100 ml. of $Ba(OH)_2$ solution. The supernatant liquid requires 75.0 ml. of HCl [1.00 ml. $\backsimeq$ 0.00626 gram Na_2CO_3; 1.00 ml. $\backsimeq$ 1.12 ml. of the $Ba(OH)_2$ solution]. What is the percentage of carbon in the steel and what would have been the gain of an ascarite bulb if a similar sample had been analyzed by the absorption method?

Ans. 0.51 per cent. 37.2 mg.

90. What volume of 6.00 N hydrofluoric acid is theoretically required to volatilize the silica from 0.5000 gram of $KAlSi_3O_8$? What volume of SiF_4 at 29°C. and 765 mm. pressure is produced?

91. A 3.00-gram sample of steel contains 3.00 per cent Fe_2Si. After it has been dissolved in HNO_3 and evaporated, what weight of SiO_2 will be obtained? What volume of SiF_4 under standard conditions will be evolved by the action of HF $+$ H_2SO_4 on the SiO_2?

92. A 3.00-gram sample of steel containing 1.21 per cent Si and 0.23 per cent W is dissolved in concentrated HNO_3 and evaporated to dryness. What should be the weight of the ignited acid-insoluble residue before and after treatment with HF?

93. On the assumption that $Mo_{24}O_{37}$ is a mixture of MoO_3 and Mo_2O_3, what percentage of the total Mo is in the 3-valent state and what percentage is in the 6-valent state?

Ans. 97.33 per cent, 2.67 per cent.

Chromium. Vanadium

(See also Probs. 3.16, 4.7, 8.59, 13.39, 13.41, 13.51, 13.51, 13.63, 13.102, 16.31.)

94. From the following data compute the percentage of Cr in a sample of steel. Weight of sample = 1.850 grams. After the chromium has been oxidized to dichromate with $KMnO_4$ and the excess reagent removed, 150 ml. of 0.0800 N ferrous solution are added and the solution then reacts with 14.00 ml. of 0.0900 N $KMnO_4$.

95. It is desired to prepare a solution of chromium acetate to contain 8.00 per cent Cr_2O_3 by weight for use as a mordant. A batch of the material is made up to the approximate concentration and is found to have a specific gravity of 1.195. A 2.000-ml. sample is taken, and the chromium is oxidized to dichromate. To one-half the solution are added 50.00 ml. of ferrous sulfate solution, and the excess ferrous iron requires exactly 17.32 ml. of 0.1334 N $KMnO_4$ for oxidation (25.00 ml. $FeSO_4$ solution $\backsimeq$ 21.73 ml. $KMnO_4$ solution). How many pounds of water must be evaporated from one ton of the liquor to give the desired concentration?

96. A steel containing 0.90 per cent Cr weighs 2.000 grams. The chromium is oxidized to chromate, and to the acidified solution is added an excess of KI. The liberated iodine requires 10.00 ml. of thiosulfate solution. What is the normality of the thiosulfate solution?

97. Assuming that vanadium like nitrogen forms five oxides and that any other oxide is a mixture of two or more of these, compute the oxidation number of the vanadium in the reduced condition and show what combination of oxides could give this. Use the following data: 0.08500 gram of $Na_2V_4O_9$ after an abnormal reduction was oxidized to the 5-valent condition by 43.14 ml. of $KMnO_4$ of which 40.00 ml. reacted with 30.00 ml. of potassium tetroxalate solution which was 0.08000 N as an acid.

98. If 0.394 gram of $Na_2V_4O_9$ is reduced and requires 10.00 ml. of permanganate (1.000 ml. $\backsim$ 0.0536 gram $Na_2C_2O_4$) to oxidize the vanadium back to vanadic acid, find the oxidation number of the reduced vanadium.

99. A sample of chrome-vanadium steel weighing 2.00 grams is dissolved in $H_2SO_4 + H_3PO_4$, and HNO_3 is added to oxidize the iron and carbides. In the presence of silver ions (catalyst), ammonium persulfate is added to oxidize chromic ions to dichromate, vanadyl ions to metavanadate, and manganous ions to permanganate. Excess persulfate is destroyed by boiling, and the permanganate is reduced with a small quantity of HCl. The addition of 25.0 ml. of 0.1010 N $FeSO_4$ causes reduction of vanadate and dichromate, and the excess ferrous and the reduced vanadium are titrated with 0.1120 N $KMnO_4$, of which 12.6 ml. are required. A small amount of $FeSO_4$ is added to reduce the vanadium again and the excess ferrous ions destroyed with persulfate. The vanadium alone is then titrated with the above-mentioned $KMnO_4$, of which 0.86 ml. are required. Write ionic equations for all chemical changes involving the above-mentioned elements, and calculate the percentage of Cr and of V in the sample.

Ans. Cr = 0.967 per cent, V = 0.245 per cent.

100. The determination of vanadic acid (HVO_3) in the presence of molybdic acid (H_2MoO_4) depends upon the fact that vanadic acid alone is reduced to VO^{++} by sulfur dioxide in dilute sulfuric acid and can be reoxidized by standard permanganate solution. Both vanadic acid and molybdic acid are reduced by amalgamated zinc, the former to V^{++} and the latter to Mo^{+++}. These reactions are carried out in a Jones reductor and the reduced constituents oxidized by being passed into an excess of ferric salt and phosphoric acid. An equivalent reduction of the ferric iron to ferrous takes place. The ferrous iron is then titrated with standard permanganate.

REDUCTION WITH SO_2		REDUCTION WITH Zn	
Grams of sample	= 0.4500	Grams of sample	= 0.4500
Normality of $KMnO_4$	= 0.1092	Normality of $KMnO_4$	= 0.1092
Ml. $KMnO_4$	= 8.23	Ml. $KMnO_4$	= 41.74

a. Complete and balance all the equations in this process.

b. Express the amount of vanadate as percentage of V and the amount of molybdate as percentage of Mo.

101. Calculate the percentage of chromium and of vanadium in a chrome-vanadium steel from the following data:

Chromium. A sample weighing 2.00 grams is dissolved in an acid mixture. Subsequent treatments convert iron to Fe^{+++}, manganese to Mn^{++}, chromium to $Cr_2O_7^-$ and vanadium to VO_3^-. A 25-ml. pipetful of standard ferrous solution [39.2 grams of $FeSO_4.(NH_4)_2SO_4.6H_2O$ per liter] is added. Chromium is thus reduced to Cr^{+++}, vanadium to VO^{++}. The solution is titrated with $KMnO_4$ (1.00 ml. $\backsim$ 0.92 ml. of the ferrous solution) requiring 14.28 ml. to give a permanent pink color. Only vanadium and the excess ferrous iron are oxidized in this step. To correct for overtitration and color interferences, the solution is boiled until the permanganate color is destroyed, and the solution is brought to the same shade of color as before with the standard permanganate, requiring 0.08 ml.

Vanadium. The vanadium in the above solution is now reduced to VO^{++} with dilute $FeSO_4$ solution and the excess ferrous oxidized with a small amount of persulfate. The vanadium is then titrated back to VO_3^- with the above $KMnO_4$, requiring 1.10 ml. It may be assumed that the solution is overtitrated to the same degree as in the first titration.

Manganese

(See also Probs. 8.28, 9.23, 10.11, 10.20, 13.26, 13.27, 13.33, 13.37, 13.38, 13.40, 13.49, 13.56, 13.67, 13.76, 13.87, 19.3.)

102. What weight of pyrolusite containing 75.0 per cent MnO_2 will oxidize the same amount of oxalic acid as 35.0 ml. of a $KMnO_4$ solution of which 1.00 ml. will liberate 0.0175 gram of iodine from an excess of potassium iodide?

103. An oxide of Mn weighing 0.4580 gram is treated with dilute H_2SO_4 and 50.00 ml. of 0.1000 N ferrous ammonium sulfate solution. After the reduction of the manganese to the manganous condition is complete, the excess of ferrous solution reacts with 30.00 ml. of 0.03333 N $KMnO_4$. Find the symbol of the original oxide of Mn.

104. Given the following data in the analysis of pyrolusite by the iodimetric process, find the volume of disodium phosphate solution (90.0 grams of $Na_2HPO_4.12H_2O$ per liter) that would be necessary to precipitate the Mn as $MnNH_4PO_4$ from 0.5000 gram of the sample.

$$\text{Weight of sample} = 1.000 \text{ gram}$$
$$Na_2S_2O_3 \text{ solution} = 40.40 \text{ ml.}$$

The thiosulfate solution is equivalent in reducing power to a stannous chloride solution that contains 29.75 grams of tin per liter.

105. What volume of bromine water (30.0 grams Br_2 per liter) would theoretically be required to precipitate the manganese from an acetic acid solution of its salt, if the resulting precipitate of MnO_2 gives on ignition 0.1060 gram of Mn_3O_4? How many milliliters of sulfurous acid (sp. gr. 1.028, containing 5.00 per cent SO_2 by weight) would be required to dissolve the MnO_2 precipitate, and what weight of $Mn_2P_2O_7$ would be obtained from the resulting solution?

106. If the manganese in 50.0 ml. of 0.0833 N $KMnO_4$ solution were reduced to the manganous condition, how many milliliters of 0.0833 N $KMnO_4$ would be equivalent to the Mn in the reduced solution by the (*a*) Volhard method, (*b*) bismuthate method, and (*c*) chlorate method?

107. It has been shown that manganous ions can be titrated potentiometrically with standard $KMnO_4$ in nearly neutral pyrophosphate solution according to the equation: $4Mn^{++} + MnO_4^- + 8H^+ + 15H_2P_2O_7^= \rightarrow 5Mn(H_2P_2O_7)_3^\equiv + 4H_2O$. What is the value of each milliliter of $KMnO_4$ in terms of Mn by this method if each milliliter of the $KMnO_4$ is equivalent to 0.002040 gram of sodium formate ($NaCHO_2$) when titrated according to the equation: $3CHO_2^- + 2MnO_4^- + H_2O \rightarrow \underline{2MnO_2} + 3CO_2 + 5OH^-$?

Ans. 0.004394 gram.

108. When a constituent is to be determined with extreme accuracy, *e.g.*, in a case where the manganese content of a sample of steel may be in dispute, it is best to analyze for the constituent by two different methods. It is also best to standardize the solutions used against a sample of like material of known composition rather than in the usual way. This procedure gives a direct comparison under identical conditions with a standard.

The purchaser of a quantity of steel has reserved the right to reject the lot, which is to be used for a special purpose, if the manganese content is less than 0.350 per cent. The sample must therefore be prepared and the analysis made with extreme accuracy. On the basis of a representative sample, the method and results of an analysis follow. Calculate to three significant figures (a) the percentage of manganese in the steel by both methods, (b) the normality of the permanganate.

Persulfate Process. A 0.1000-gram sample of Bureau of Standards steel containing 0.660 per cent Mn required 7.03 ml. of arsenite solution. A similar-weight sample of the steel under investigation required 4.36 ml.

Bismuthate Process. A one-gram sample of the above-mentioned Bureau of Standards steel was used. A pipetful of $FeSO_4$ was used, and the excess ferrous salt required 16.96 ml. of standard $KMnO_4$. A one-gram sample of the steel under investigation, treated the same way, required 19.63 ml. of the $KMnO_4$. One pipetful of $FeSO_4 \backsimeq$ 23.97 ml. of $KMnO_4$.

109. A carefully prepared steel is to be used as a standard in subsequent analyses of other steels for manganese by the persulfate method. To determine the correct percentage of manganese in the standard steel a sample weighing 1.05 grams is analyzed by the bismuthate method. A 25-ml. pipetful of ferrous ammonium sulfate is used, and the titration requires 13.2 ml. $KMnO_4$ (1 ml. $\backsimeq$ 0.00201 gram $Na_2C_2O_4$; 1 ml. $\backsimeq$ 1.02 ml. of the ferrous solution). What is the percentage of manganese in the steel?

In the routine analysis of a certain plain carbon steel by the persulfate method, the analysis is run in parallel with a corresponding analysis of the above standard steel. The same weights of sample are used in the two cases. The above standard steel requires 10.4 ml. of arsenite solution; the unknown steel requires 17.1 ml. What is the percentage of manganese in the latter steel? If in the persulfate method a one-gram sample was used and the arsenite solution contained 1.10 grams of As_2O_3 per liter, to what average oxidation number was the manganese reduced in the titration?

Ans. 0.355 per cent. 0.584 per cent. 3.4.

Cobalt. Nickel

(See also Probs. 9.3, 9.16, 15.8, 15.9, 15.15, 15.16.)

110. A sample of ore weighing 0.8900 gram yields by electrolysis 0.2670 gram of Ni and Co, and from the deposited metal a precipitate weighing 0.9405 gram is obtained with dimethyglyoxime. Find the percentages of Ni and Co in the ore.

111. A nickel ore was analyzed by the volumetric method. The nickel solution was treated with KI solution and exactly 0.50 ml. of $AgNO_3$ solution containing 0.0125 gram of $AgNO_3$ per milliliter. The solution then reacted with 48.00 ml. of KCN solution containing 0.0140 gram of KCN per milliliter. What was the percentage of Ni in the ore if the sample taken weighed 0.900 gram?

112. What weight of dried glyoxime precipitate would be obtained from 5.00 grams of steel containing 1.48 per cent Ni?

Phosphorus

(See also Probs. 8.16, 8.17.)

113. How many milliliters of magnesia mixture (1.00 N with respect to $MgCl_2$) are required to precipitate the phosphorus from 0.2000 gram of pure apatite. Assume the formula of the latter to be $3Ca_3(PO_4)_2.CaCl_2$? How many grams of $(NH_4)_3PO_4.-12MoO_3$ could theoretically be obtained from this weight of apatite?

114. Calculate the percentage of phosphorus in a steel from the following data:

Two grams of steel furnished a yellow precipitate which was dissolved in 20.0 ml. of 0.500 N sodium hydroxide solution, and the excess of the latter reacted with 27.0 ml. of 0.333 N nitric acid.

Calculate the weight of a sample of steel to be taken for analysis so that every 100 ml. of 0.100 N $KMnO_4$ used in the titration by the Blair method (see Part V, under Phosphorus) will represent directly the percentage of P.

Calculate in this process the equivalent weight of (a) P, (b) P_2O_5, (c) Mo, (d) MoO_3, (e) $Mo_{24}O_{37}$.

115. A normal yellow precipitate of ammonium phosphomolybdate from a sample of bronze weighing 1.00 gram is reduced with zinc. The reduced solution requires 21.13 ml. of 0.100 N permanganate to oxidize the molybdenum to the hexavalent condition. If the alloy contains exactly 0.20 per cent of phosphorus, to what hypothetical oxide was the molybdenum reduced by the zinc?

116. What weight of steel should be taken for analysis so that the number of milliliters of 0.125 N permanganate required in the ferric alum method (see Part V) will be two hundred times the percentage of P in the steel?

117. A 2.00-gram sample of steel is dissolved in HNO_3 and the phosphorus is precipitated with molybdate as the normal yellow precipitate. The molybdenum in the precipitate is reduced to a form corresponding to the oxide $Mo_{16}O_{27}$ and requires 10.0 ml. of 0.100 N $KMnO_4$ for reoxidation to the oxidation number of 6. Calculate the percentage of P in the steel.

118. A sample is prepared for student analysis by mixing pure apatite [$3Ca_3(PO_4)_2.$-$CaCl_2$] with an inert material. If 1.000 gram of the sample gives 0.4013 gram of $Mg_2P_2O_7$, how many milliliters ammonium oxalate solution [40.00 grams of $(NH_4)_2$-$C_2O_4.H_2O$ per liter] would be required to precipitate the calcium from the same weight of sample?

119. Calculate the percentage of phosphorus in a sample of steel from the following data: 2.00 grams of steel furnished a normal yellow precipitate which when dissolved and passed through a Jones reductor reacted with 7.00 ml. of 0.0833 N $KMnO_4$.

120. In the analysis of a sample of steel weighing 1.881 grams, the phosphorus was precipitated with ammonium molybdate and the yellow precipitate was dissolved, reduced, and titrated with permanganate. If the sample contained 0.025 per cent P and 6.01 ml. of $KMnO_4$ were used, to what oxide was the molybdenum reduced? One milliliter of $KMnO_4$ was equivalent to 0.007188 gram of sodium oxalate.

121. The Pincus method for determining phosphate is to titrate it in acetic acid solution in the presence of ammonium ions with standard uranyl acetate solution according to the equation: $PO_4^{\equiv} + UO_2^{++} + NH_4^+ \rightarrow \underline{UO_2NH_4PO_4}$. The indicator is ferrocyanide which gives a brown color on a spot plate with excess UO_2^{++}. If the uranyl acetate solution is 0.100 N as an ordinary acetate salt and 10.0 ml. are used in the titration, how many grams of P_2O_5 are shown to be present?

122. A solution containing phosphoric acid was treated with ammonium molybdate, and an abnormal yellow precipitate was obtained, which after drying may be assumed to have consisted of [$(NH_4)_3PO_4]_x(MoO_3)_y$. This precipitate was dried, weighed, and dissolved in ammonia water, and the solution was made up to 500 ml. Of this, 50.0 ml. were taken, made acid with H_2SO_4, reduced with amalgamated Zn, and passed directly into an excess of ferric alum which served to oxidize the trivalent molybdenum to the 5-valent state. To oxidize the iron reduced by the molybdenum and to bring the molybdenum to the oxidation number of 6 required a number of milliliters of 0.125 N KMnO$_4$ equal to 15.39 times the weight in grams of the original yellow precipitate. What values of x and y may be taken in the formula of the yellow precipitate?

123. A carefully prepared steel is to be used as a standard for phosphorus determinations. It is analyzed by an accurate ("umpire") method in which, from a sample weighing 3.00 grams, a phosphomolybdate precipitate is obtained. This is dissolved and the phosphorus is subsequently precipitated as MgNH$_4$PO$_4$. On ignition this precipitate yields a pyrophosphate residue weighing 0.0109 gram.

In the routine analysis of a plain carbon steel by the alkalimetric method, the analysis is run in parallel with a corresponding analysis of the above standard steel. The same weights of sample are used in the two cases, and a 25-ml. pipetful of standard NaOH is used in each case. Back titration with HNO$_3$ using phenolphthalein indicator requires 10.2 ml. of the acid in the case of the standard steel and 8.6 ml. in the case of the unknown steel. If 1.00 ml. NaOH $\backsimeq$ 1.08 ml. HNO$_3$, what is the percentage of phosphorus in the plain carbon steel? If the concentration of the HNO$_3$ were 0.105 N, what weight of sample must have been taken in each case?

Ans. 0.0868 per cent. 3.0 grams.

Sulfur. Selenium

(See also Probs. 8.3, 8.4, 8.7, 8.11, 8.12, 8.25, 8.57, 10.14, 13.75, 13.82, 13.96, 14.2, 14.16, 18.3 20.9, 146.)

124. A sample of ferrous ammonium sulfate is prepared for student analysis by intimately mixing pure crystals of FeSO$_4$.(NH$_4$)$_2$SO$_4$.6H$_2$O with an inert substance. Using a 0.7650-gram sample a student correctly obtains 0.1263 gram of Fe$_2$O$_3$. What volume of barium chloride solution containing 25.00 grams of BaCl$_2$.2H$_2$O per liter would be necessary to precipitate the sulfur from the filtrate? What is the percentage of inert material in the sample?

125. A sample of pure ferric alum, Fe$_2$(SO$_4$)$_3$.(NH$_4$)$_2$SO$_4$.24H$_2$O, is dissolved in water and the iron is precipitated with NH$_4$OH. If the ignited precipitate weighs 0.1597 gram, (*a*) what volume of the NH$_4$OH (sp. gr. 0.900, containing 28.33 per cent NH$_3$ by weight) is theoretically required for the precipitation of Fe(OH)$_3$, (*b*) how many milliliters of 0.1000 N BaCl$_2$ would be required to precipitate the sulfate from the iron filtrate, and (*c*) how many milliliters of 0.1000 N Na$_2$S$_2$O$_3$ would be required in the determination of this amount of sulfate by the iodimetric (Hinman) method?

126. If nitrogen is reduced to the 4-valent state, compute the volume of fuming nitric acid actually required to oxidize 5.000 grams of pyritic ore containing 70.10 per cent FeS$_2$. Neglect the quantity of acid required for the remainder of the ore. Assume the acid to be of 1.500 specific gravity and to contain 94.10 per cent HNO$_3$ by weight. Also assume complete oxidation of sulfide to sulfate. Compute the weight of dry sodium peroxide required to carry out the same oxidation assuming the oxidation products to be Na$_2$FeO$_4$ and Na$_2$SO$_4$.

127. A sample of pure FeS$_2$ is analyzed by fusing a 0.5000-gram sample and precipitating the sulfur as BaSO$_4$. How large an error in the weight of the precipitate must be made to produce an error amounting to 0.10 per cent of the apparent amount of S in the mineral?

128. A soluble sulfate weighing 0.9261 gram is analyzed. The precipitate of BaSO$_4$ on ignition is found to weigh 1.3724 grams. On further ignition the weight increases to 1.3903 grams, owing to the fact that the precipitate as first weighed had been partly reduced to BaS which on further ignition was reoxidized to $BaSO_4$. Calculate the true percentage of S in the original sample. Calculate the percentage of S present as sulfide and the percentage of S present as sulfate in the first ignition product.

129. In the determination of sulfur by the evolution method, a notebook contains the following data:

$$\begin{aligned}
\text{Weight of sample} &= 5.0275 \text{ grams} \\
\text{Iodine used} &= 15.59 \text{ ml.} \\
Na_2S_2O_3 \text{ used} &= 12.68 \text{ ml.} \\
1.000 \text{ ml. iodine} &\eqsim 1.086 \text{ ml. } Na_2S_2O_3 \\
1.000 \text{ ml. } Na_2S_2O_3 &\eqsim 0.005044 \text{ gram Cu}
\end{aligned}$$

Find the percentage of sulfur.

Ans. 0.107 per cent.

130. A steel weighing 5.00 grams is treated with HCl, and the evolved H_2S is eventually titrated with a solution containing 0.0100 mole of KIO_3 and 0.4 mole of KI per liter. What is the normality of the $KIO_3 + $ KI solution as an oxidizing agent? If 3.00 ml. are used in the titration, what is the percentage of sulfur in the steel?

131. A sample of $Al_2(SO_4)_3.18H_2O$ which has lost a part of its water of crystallization and is therefore specified as $Al_2(SO_4)_3.XH_2O$, is analyzed to determine its approximate composition. The calculation in this particular instance is based upon a determination of total sulfur as follows: A 0.5000-gram sample is dissolved in dilute hydrochloric acid and diluted, and the sulfate ion precipitated as $BaSO_4$, yielding 0.5602 gram of ignited $BaSO_4$. Calculate to three significant figures the value of X.

132. It is desired to prepare a standard solution of iodine of such concentration that each milliliter will be equivalent to 0.010 per cent sulfur when the latter is determined on a 5.00-gram sample by the evolution method. The iodine solution is to be prepared in the following way. A certain volume of 0.105 N $KMnO_4$ is to be run from a buret into an aqueous solution containing an excess of KI, the solution is to be acidified with H_2SO_4 and diluted to exactly 1 liter. What volume of the $KMnO_4$ should be used?

Ans. 297 ml.

133. A carefully prepared steel is to be used as a standard in the evolution method for sulfur. A sample is dissolved in HNO_3 and the sulfur subsequently precipitated and weighed as $BaSO_4$. The sample weighs 4.57 grams and the $BaSO_4$ weighs 0.0110 gram.

In the routine analysis of a certain sample of Bessemer steel for sulfur by the evolution method the analysis is run in parallel with a corresponding analysis of the above standard steel. The same weights (5.00 grams) of sample are used. The above standard steel requires 3.3 ml. of $KIO_3 + $ KI solution; the Bessemer steel requires 8.3 ml. What is the percentage of sulfur in the Bessemer steel and how many grams of KIO_3 does each liter of the titrating solution theoretically contain?

Ans. 0.083 per cent, 1.12 grams.

134. What volume (two significant figures) of 15.0 N HNO_3 would be used in dissolving the Cu_2S precipitate from a 5.00-gram sample of steel containing 0.25 per cent Cu, if the precipitate were contaminated with 5 per cent of its weight of FeS (assume sulfur completely oxidized to sulfate and the HNO_3 reduced to NO_2)?

135. In the analysis of 0.8000 gram of a substance for sulfur by the barium chromate method, 25.00 ml. of 0.1110 N sodium thiosulfate solution were used. Compute the percentage of sulfur.

136. The H_2S in a sample of illuminating gas is determined by passing 10.0 cubic feet of the gas through an absorbing agent and oxidizing the sulfur to sulfate. By the Hinman method, there are used 12.00 ml. of thiosulfate solution having two-thirds the normality as a reducing agent as a certain potassium tetroxalate solution. 6.00 milliliters of the tetroxalate will reduce in acid solution 3.00 ml. of a $KMnO_4$ solution containing 0.00632 gram of $KMnO_4$ per milliliter. What is the H_2S content of the gas in parts per thousand (by volume)?

137. Sulfite liquor, used in the manufacture of sulfite paper pulp, consists essentially of a solution of $Ca(HSO_3)_2$, $Mg(HSO_3)_2$, and H_2SO_3. Titration with alkali converts all of these to normal sulfites (*i.e.*, to $SO_3^=$). Titration with iodine converts all sulfites and bisulfites to bisulfates. "Available SO_2" is the actual free H_2SO_3 plus one-half the SO_2 in the bisulfites of calcium and magnesium, and is given by the alkali titration (using phenolphthalein). "Combined SO_2" is one-half the SO_2 in the bisulfites of calcium and magnesium and is given by subtracting the "available SO_2" from the "total SO_2" (as given by the iodine titration).

A 10-ml. pipetful of sulfite liquor (sp. gr. = 1.028) is introduced into a 100-ml. measuring flask and diluted to the mark. A 10-ml. pipetful of the diluted solution is titrated with 0.03312 N NaOH, requiring 30.11 ml. to change the color of phenolphthalein. At this point starch is added, and the solution then requires 13.82 ml. of 0.1050 N iodine to give a blue coloration.

(*a*) Calculate the percentage of "available SO_2," and of "combined SO_2." (*b*) Calculate the percentage of "free SO_2" (*i.e.*, in the form of uncombined H_2SO_3). (*c*) Show by an equation why the pink color produced at the first end point disappears at the beginning of the second titration.

138. A solution of a mixture of H_2S and NaHS is acidified with a ml. of $N/10$ HCl, and the total H_2S then present is determined by adding b ml. of $N/10$ I_2 and titrating back with c ml. of $N/10$ $Na_2S_2O_3$. The acidity at the end of the titration is measured by d ml. of $N/10$ NaOH. Show that the number of grams of H_2S present in the original solution is given by the formula

$$[c + 2d - (b + 2a)]0.001704$$

139. The Norris and Fay method for determining selenium is to titrate with standard $Na_2S_2O_3$ according to the equation: $H_2SeO_3 + 4Na_2S_2O_3 + 4HCl \rightarrow Na_2S_4SeO_6 + Na_2S_4O_6 + 4NaCl + 3H_2O$.

The Jamieson method for determining arsenic is to titrate with standard KIO_3 according to the equation: $2AsCl_3 + KIO_3 + 5H_2O \rightarrow 2H_3AsO_4 + KCl + ICl + 4HCl$.

If the above KIO_3 is of such concentration that 3.00 ml. will liberate from excess KI in the presence of acid that amount of I_2 which reacts with 3.00 ml. of the above $Na_2S_2O_3$, and 3.00 ml. of the $Na_2S_2O_3$ will react with 3.00 ml. of 0.100 N I_2, (*a*) what is the value of 1.00 ml. of the KIO_3 in terms of grams of As and (*b*) what is the value of 1.00 ml. of the $Na_2S_2O_3$ in terms of grams of Se?

Ans. (*a*) 0.0025 gram, (*b*) 0.00197 gram.

General and Miscellaneous Analyses

140. A sample of pyrolusite analyzes as follows: MnO_2 = 75.00 per cent; CaO = 5.60 per cent; MgO = 4.00 per cent; SiO_2 = 15.40 per cent. A one-gram sample is dissolved in HCl ($MnO_2 + 4HCl \rightarrow MnCl_2 + Cl_2 + 2H_2O$), and the silica is removed in the regular way. The solution is neutralized and the manganese is precipitated with NH_4OH + bromine water: $MnCl_2 + Br_2 + 4NH_4OH \rightarrow \underline{MnO_2} + 2NH_4Cl + 2NH_4Br + 2H_2O$. From the filtrate the calcium is precipitated as oxalate, and the precipitate is dissolved and titrated with $KMnO_4$. The magnesium is precipitated with ammonium phosphate in the regular way, and the precipitate is ignited and weighed. Calculate to 3 significant figures: (a) the number of milliliters of 3.00 N NH_4OH and (b) the number of milliliters of 3.00 per cent Br_2 solution (sp. gr. 1.10) to precipitate the manganese according to the above equation, (c) the total number of milliliters of 1.00 N $Na_2C_2O_4$ solution to form $Mg(C_2O_4)_2^=$ and precipitate all the calcium, (d) the number of milliliters of 0.100 *molar* $KMnO_4$ to titrate the precipitated calcium, (e) the weight of the ignited magnesium precipitate, (f) the percentage of Mn in the material obtained by strongly igniting a sample of the original pyrolusite in air, assuming conversion of MnO_2 to Mn_3O_4 and no other changes.

Ans.   (a) 11.5 ml., (b) 41.8 ml., (c) 5.97 ml., (d) 4.00 ml., (e) 0.111 gram, (f) 52.2 per cent.

141. A certain mineral has the following composition:

$$
\begin{aligned}
FeO &= 14.41 \text{ per cent} \\
MnO &= 7.12 \text{ per cent} \\
CaO &= 28.00 \text{ per cent} \\
MgO &= 3.89 \text{ per cent} \\
SiO_2 &= 2.98 \text{ per cent} \\
CO_2 &= 43.60 \text{ per cent}
\end{aligned}
$$

A one-gram sample is decomposed without oxidizing the iron and put through a regular systematic analysis. Calculate to 3 significant figures: (a) number of milliliters of 6.00 N HF theoretically required to volatilize the silica, (b) total number of milliliters of bromine water (sp. gr. 1.100, containing 3.00 per cent Br_2 by weight) and (c) total number of milliliters of 3.00 N NH_4OH to precipitate the iron and manganese together according to the equations: $2Fe^{++} + Br_2 + 6NH_4OH \rightarrow 2Fe(OH)_3 + 2Br^- + 6NH_4^+$; $Mn^{++} + Br_2 + 4NH_4OH \rightarrow \underline{MnO_2} + 2Br^- + 4NH_4^+ + \underline{2H_2O}$, (d) weight of this precipitate after ignition, (e) total number of milliliters of 0.100 N $H_2C_2O_4$ solution to form the soluble complex $Mg(C_2O_4)_2^=$ and completely precipitate the calcium, (f) weight of the material obtained by precipitating the magnesium with $(NH_4)_2HPO_4$ in the regular way and igniting the precipitate, (g) number of milliliters of $KMnO_4$ required to titrate the iron in a one-gram sample of the original mineral after decomposition without oxidation. Each milliliter of the $KMnO_4$ is equivalent to 0.006802 gram of $NaCHO_2$ in the following titration: $3CHO_2^- + 2MnO_4^- + H_2O \rightarrow \underline{2MnO_2} + 3CO_2 + 5OH^-$.

Ans.   (a) 0.333 ml., (b) 9.70 ml., (c) 3.33 ml., (d) 0.236 gram, (e) 140 ml., (f) 0.113 gram, (g) 6.00 ml.

142. Ankerite is essentially a calcium-magnesium-ferrous carbonate occurring in nature as a vein mineral. A chemical analysis of a specimen of this mineral gave the following data:

a. Moisture. A well-mixed sample was dried at 105°C. to constant weight.

$$
\begin{aligned}
\text{Weight of sample} &= 10.000 \text{ grams} \\
\text{Weight after drying} &= 9.988 \text{ grams}
\end{aligned}
$$

b. Silica. A sample was dissolved in HCl, evaporated to dryness, heated at 105°C. for one hour, and dissolved in HCl, and the residue filtered, ignited, weighed, treated with HF, and reweighed. The small residue was fused with Na_2CO_3 acidified and was added to the main solution.

> Weight of sample = 5.000 grams
> Weight of residue = 0.0417 gram
> Weight of residue after HF = 0.0117 gram

c, d. Iron and Alumina. One-fifth of the filtrate from the silica determination was treated with bromine and made ammoniacal, and the precipitate of ferric and aluminum hydroxides ignited and weighed. The ignited oxides were then fused with Na_2CO_3 and dissolved in acid, and the iron reduced with Zn and titrated with $KMnO_4$. Weight of oxides = 0.2845 gram; volume of 0.1990 N $KMnO_4$ used = 17.33 ml.

e. The filtrate from the combined oxides was treated with ammonium oxalate and the precipitated calcium filtered, dissolved in H_2SO_4, and titrated with the above-mentioned $KMnO_4$. Volume required = 47.50 ml.

f. The filtrate from the calcium was treated with phosphate and the magnesium precipitate ignited. Weight ignited precipitate = 0.1430 gram.

g. A 0.1000-gram sample of the original mineral was treated with HCl and the evolved CO_2 purified and caught in a special apparatus and measured over water previously saturated with CO_2.

> Volume of CO_2 = 23.78 ml.
> Temperature = 20°C.
> Barometric pressure = 747 mm.
> Vapor pressure of H_2O at 20°C. = 17 mm.

Calculate percentage of: (1) H_2O, (2) SiO_2, (3) FeO, (4) Al_2O_3, (5) CaO, (6) MgO, (7) CO_2.

h. Neglecting the small percentages of H_2O, SiO_2, and Al_2O_3, calculate an empirical formula for the mineral.

i. How many milliliters of NH_4OH (sp. gr. 0.96, containing 10.0 per cent NH_3 by weight) would be required in step *c* above to precipitate the iron and alumina after neutralization of the acid and boiling out of the excess bromine?

j. If a sample of the mineral were ignited in the absence of air so that all the H_2O and CO_2 were lost, what would be the percentage of Fe in the resulting material?

143. The analysis of a sample of coal ashes produced by the combustion of a soft coal in a power station of a public-utility company was carried on by the following procedure with results of duplicate determinations as indicated. The analysis is similar to that of any undecomposable silicate.

Loss of Ignition. The loss was taken at 800 to 900°C., representing approximately the unburned fuel. Each sample weighed 20.000 grams.

Loss: 3.0951, 3.0960 grams.

Subsequent determinations were made on portions of the ignited material.

Silica. One-gram samples were fused with sodium carbonate, the entire fusion dissolved in hydrochloric acid, and the silica determined by the usual method of dehydration. No correction was made with hydrofluoric acid, as the sample was not considered to be representative enough to warrant such a procedure.

Weight of ignited SiO_2: 0.5284, 0.5302 gram.

Combined Oxides. The filtrate from the silica determination was used for the precipitation of combined oxides, assumed to be entirely ferric oxide and alumina.

Weight of ignited oxides: 0.3927, 0.3920 gram.

Calcium Oxide. The filtrate from the precipitation of the combined hydroxides was used for the precipitation of calcium as calcium oxalate, followed by the volumetric determination of the equivalent oxalate with 0.1020 N $KMnO_4$.

Volume of $KMnO_4$: 18.10, 18.05 ml.

Magnesium Oxide. The filtrate from the precipitation of calcium oxalate was used to determine magnesia as $MgNH_4PO_4.6H_2O$, ignited to $Mg_2P_2O_7$.

Weight of $Mg_2P_2O_7$: 0.0257, 0.0256 gram.

Total Iron. Two-gram samples were fused with sodium carbonate and dissolved in HCl, the silica was removed and the total iron determined volumetrically with 0.1020 N $KMnO_4$, after reduction with stannous chloride.

Volume of $KMnO_4$: 13.21, 13.21 ml.

Total Sulfur. Two-gram samples were fused with sodium carbonate and dissolved in HCl, and silica and combined oxides were removed and the sulfate content was determined by precipitation as $BaSO_4$.

Weight of $BaSO_4$: 0.0020, 0.0025 gram.

Calculate: loss on ignition, SiO_2, Fe_2O_3, Al_2O_3, CaO, MgO, SO_3 *on the original sample.* Report alkalies by difference.

144. A sample of meat scrap is submitted for analysis. The material consists principally of a mixture of beef and bone that has been processed by heating, and the sample has been ground in a Wiley mill to a fairly fine consistency. Material of this type is used commercially as an important component of poultry food, dog biscuit, and similar products.

The scrap from which the sample was taken was sold under the following specifications:

> Protein: not less than 45 per cent
> Ash: not greater than 35 per cent
> Bone phosphate: within the limits of 25 to 33 per cent
> Fat: not greater than 10 per cent
> Free fatty acid: not greater than 10 per cent of the fat
> Moisture: not greater than 9 per cent
> Crude fiber: not greater than 2 per cent

The following numerical data represent the averages of duplicate determinations in each case. Calculate the analysis of the material as indicated. Does it conform to specifications?

Protein. A 2.000-gram sample was analyzed by the Kjeldahl method (see Part V, under Nitrogen). The evolved NH_3 was caught in a 5 per cent solution of boric acid and titrated with standard HCl, requiring 19.40 ml. The HCl was standardized against the NH_3 liberated from pure $(NH_4)_2SO_4$ [1.000 ml. $\approx$ 0.03490 gram $(NH_4)_2SO_4$]. Arbitrary factor for converting percentage of nitrogen to percentage of protein = 6.25.

Moisture. A sample weighing 5.000 grams was dried to constant weight at 105°C. Weight of dried material = 4.638 grams.

Ash. The material from the moisture determination was ignited at dull red heat. Weight of residue = 1.611 grams.

Bone phosphate. This means phosphate expressed as $Ca_3(PO_4)_2$. The ash obtained above was dissolved in HNO_3, the solution evaporated dry, and the residue taken up in dilute HNO_3. The solution was filtered and a $\frac{1}{40}$ aliquot portion was treated with $(NH_4)_2MoO_4$. The yellow phosphomolybdate precipitate was filtered and dissolved in NH_4OH, and the phosphate was then precipitated as $MgNH_4PO_4$ and ignited. Weight of $Mg_2P_2O_7 = 0.0250$ gram.

Fat. A 3.000-gram sample of the original material was dried and extracted with anhydrous ether for 8 hours. The ether extract was evaporated. Weight of residue = 0.2700 gram.

Crude Fiber. The fat-free material was digested with dilute H_2SO_4 and then with dilute NaOH according to exact specifications of procedure. The residue was filtered off on an alundum crucible and dried at 105°C. Weight of residue (= fiber + inorganic material) plus crucible = 11.8366 grams. The crucible plus residue was then ignited at dull red heat. Weight of residue (inorganic material) plus crucible = 11.8016 grams.

Free Fatty Acid. The fat from the above ether extraction was heated with alcohol and titrated with standard NaOH, using phenolphthalein indicator. Volume of 0.05050 N NaOH required = 2.16 ml. Free fatty acid is usually expressed as percentage of oleic acid (milliequivalent weight = 0.282) present in the fat rather than in the original material.

Ans. Protein = 44.85 per cent. Moisture = 7.24 per cent. Ash = 32.22 per cent. Bone phosphate = 27.87 per cent. Fat = 9.00 per cent. Crude fiber = 1.17 per cent. Free fatty acid = 11.40 per cent.

145. It is proposed to discharge the spent dye liquor from a dyehouse, amounting at times to 126 gallons per minute, into a neighbouring stream. Laboratory tests indicate this may be done satisfactorily if the volume of the stream is sufficient to dilute the dye liquor one thousand times. Tests of the stream flow are made by adding to the stream a solution of sodium chloride at the rate of one gallon in 24 seconds. The chloride in the stream above the point of dosing is found by titrating 100 ml. with 0.01156 N $AgNO_3$, 1.10 ml. of the silver solution being required. A 100-ml. sample taken below the point of dosing required 1.22 ml. of the same solution. Each milliliter of the dosing solution required 73.17 ml. of $AgNO_3$. (*a*) What is the stream flow in gallons per minute? (*b*) What is the normal chloride content of the stream in parts per million? (*c*) What dilution would be obtained for the maximum discharge of dye liquor?

Ans. (*a*) 153,000 gallons per minute. (*b*) 4.51 parts Cl^- per million. (*c*) 1,214 times.

146. "Bisulfite liquor" is an aqueous solution of calcium and magnesium bisulfites [$Ca(HSO_3)_2$ and $Mg(HSO_3)_2$] and excess free sulfurous acid. It is made by passing SO_2 gas through a suspension of $Ca(OH)_2$ and $Mg(OH)_2$ and generally contains a small amount of sulfate because of the presence of SO_3 in the gas. The liquor is used in the sulfite digestion process for the production of paper pulp; it disintegrates the wood chips by rendering the noncellulose parts soluble.

For control tests in the mill, a volumetric method is usually sufficient. Gravimetric methods are used for a complete and more precise analysis.

Determination of Specific Gravity. By means of a Westphal balance determine the specific gravity of the liquor. Value obtained = 1.050.

Volumetric Control Analysis

Into a 100-ml. volumetric flask transfer a 10-ml. pipetful of the liquor, dilute to the mark, and mix.

Determination of Total SO_2. Titrate with standard iodine a 10-ml. pipetful of the above prepared solution. Volume of 0.1010 N I_2 required = 10.05 ml. (HSO_3^- + I_2 + $H_2O \rightarrow HSO_4^-$ + $2I^-$ + $2H^+$).

Determination of Available SO₂. Titrate with standard NaOH (using phenolphthalein) a 10-ml. pipetful of the prepared solution. Volume of 0.1100 N NaOH required = 6.04 ml.   ($HSO_3^- + OH^- \rightarrow SO_3^- + H_2O$).

GRAVIMETRIC ANALYSIS

Determination of Silica. Evaporate a 25-ml. pipetful of the original liquor with HCl to dryness. Dehydrate, dissolve in HCl, filter, and ignite residue in the regular way. Weight of residue = 0.0027 gram.

Determination of $Fe_2O_3 + Al_2O_3$. Use the filtrate from the silica determination and precipitate with NH₄OH. Filter and ignite in the regular way. Weight of ignited precipitate = 0.0051 gram.

Determination of CaO and of MgO. Evaporate a 25-ml. pipetful of the original liquor with H₂SO₄ to dryness. Weight of $CaSO_4 + MgSO_4$ = 0.5875 gram. Dissolve in HCl, add NH₄OH and $(NH_4)_2C_2O_4$. Filter the precipitated CaC_2O_4 and ignite. Weight of CaO = 0.2225 gram.

Determination of SO₃. Pipet 100 ml. of the original liquor into a flask, add HCl, and boil out the SO₂ in a current of CO₂ to exclude air. Precipitate the sulfate with BaCl₂. Weight of BaSO₄ = 0.0330 gram.

DISCUSSION AND CALCULATIONS

"Available SO₂" is the free H₂SO₃ plus one-half the SO₂ in the calcium and magnesium bisulfites and indicates the SO₂ in excess of the amount necessary to form neutral sulfites. It is given by the titration with NaOH. "Total SO₂" is given by the iodine titration. "Combined SO₂" is represented by one-half the SO₂ in the bisulfites of calcium and magnesium and is found by subtracting "available SO₂" from "total SO₂."

(a) From the volumetric analysis calculate the percentages of "available SO₂," "total SO₂" and "combined SO₂." (b) From these values find the percentage of "free SO₂" (*i.e.*, as free H₂SO₃). (c) From the gravimetric analysis calculate the percentages of SiO₂, $Fe_2O_3 + Al_2O_3$, and SO₃. (d) From the gravimetric analysis of calcium and magnesium calculate the weight of SO₂ combined as $Ca(HSO_3)_2$ and $Mg(HSO_3)_2$. One-half of this is "combined SO₂." Calculate this percentage and compare with the value obtained volumetrically.

Ans. (a) 2.03 per cent, 3.10 per cent, 1.07 per cent; (b) 0.96 per cent; (c) 0.010 per cent, 0.019 per cent, 0.011 per cent; (d) 0.5581 gram, 1.063 per cent.

147. Potassium biiodate [$KH(IO_3)_2$] can be obtained pure and serves as an excellent primary standard both in acidimetry and in iodimetry. A micro-Kjeldahl method has been proposed in which potassium biiodate serves in both capacities.

An organic nitrogenous material is digested as in the regular Kjeldahl method, the nitrogen being converted to ammonium bisulfate. The addition of excess sodium hydroxide to the solution liberates ammonia which is caught in a 10.0-pipetful of potassium biiodate solution made by dissolving 0.0100 mole of $KH(IO_3)_2$ in water and diluting to one liter. The iodate solution is therefore 0.0100 normal as an acid. Excess KI is added, and the liberated iodine is titrated with thiosulfate solution, requiring 3.10 ml. A separate 10.0-ml. portion of the biiodate when treated with KI liberates sufficient iodine to require 8.65 ml. of the thiosulfate. Remembering that the liberation of iodine from iodate ($IO_3^- + 5I^- + 6H^+ \rightarrow 3I_2 + 3H_2O$) takes place only so long as acid is present, calculate the number of milligrams of nitrogen shown to be present in the nitrogenous material. (*Note:* The concentration of the thiosulfate is not needed in the calculation.)

Ans. 0.898 mg.

APPENDIX

TABLE IV. DENSITY OF WATER AT TEMPERATURES 15 TO 30°C.

Temp., °C.	Density (unit = weight in vacuo of 1 ml. water at 4°C.)	Weight in grams of 1 ml. water, in glass container, in air against brass weights
15°	0.99913	0.99793
16°	0.99897	0.99780
17°	0.99880	0.99766
18°	0.99862	0.99751
19°	0.99843	0.99735
20°	0.99823	0.99718
21°	0.99802	0.99700
22°	0.99780	0.99680
23°	0.99757	0.99660
24°	0.99732	0.99638
25°	0.99707	0.99615
26°	0.99681	0.99593
27°	0.99654	0.99569
28°	0.99626	0.99544
29°	0.99597	0.99518
30°	0.99567	0.99491

TABLE V. VAPOR PRESSURE OF WATER

Temperature, °C.	Pressure, mm.	Temperature, °C.	Pressure, mm.
0	4.6	21	18.5
1	4.9	22	19.7
2	5.3	23	20.9
3	5.7	24	22.2
4	6.1	25	23.6
5	6.5	26	25.0
6	7.0	27	26.5
7	7.5	28	28.1
8	8.0	29	29.8
9	8.6	30	31.6
10	9.2	31	33.4
11	9.8	32	35.4
12	10.5	33	37.4
13	11.2	34	39.6
14	11.9	35	41.9
15	12.7	40	55.0
16	13.5	50	92.2
17	14.4	60	149.2
18	15.4	70	233.8
19	16.4	80	355.5
20	17.4	90	526.0

TABLE VI. SPECIFIC GRAVITY OF STRONG ACIDS AT $\frac{15°}{4°}$ IN VACUO

(According to G. Lunge)

(From Treadwell and Hall's "Analytical Chemistry," Vol. II, published by John Wiley & Sons, Inc., by permission)

Specific gravity at $\frac{15°}{4°}$ (vacuo)	Per cent by weight			Specific gravity at $\frac{15°}{4°}$ (vacuo)	Per cent by weight	
	HCl	HNO₃	H₂SO₄		HNO₃	H₂SO₄
1.000	0.16	0.10	0.09	1.235	37.53	31.70
1.005	1.15	1.00	0.95	1.240	38.29	32.28
1.010	2.14	1.90	1.57	1.245	39.05	32.86
1.015	3.12	2.80	2.30	1.250	39.82	33.43
1.020	4.13	3.70	3.03	1.255	40.58	34.00
1.025	5.15	4.60	3.76	1.260	41.34	34.57
1.030	6.15	5.50	4.49	1.265	42.10	35.14
1.035	7.15	6.38	5.23	1.270	42.87	35.71
1.040	8.16	7.26	5.96	1.275	43.64	36.29
1.045	9.16	8.13	6.67	1.280	44.41	36.87
1.050	10.17	8.99	7.37	1.285	45.18	37.45
1.055	11.18	9.84	8.07	1.290	45.95	38.03
1.060	12.19	10.68	8.77	1.295	46.72	38.61
1.065	13.19	11.51	9.47	1.300	47.49	39.19
1.070	14.17	12.33	10.19	1.305	48.26	39.77
1.075	15.16	13.15	10.90	1.310	49.07	40.35
1.080	16.15	13.95	11.60	1.315	49.89	40.93
1.085	17.13	14.74	12.30	1.320	50.71	41.50
1.090	18.11	15.53	12.99	1.325	51.53	42.08
1.095	19.06	16.32	13.67	1.330	52.37	42.66
1.100	20.01	17.11	14.35	1.335	53.22	43.20
1.105	20.97	17.89	15.03	1.340	54.07	43.74
1.110	21.92	18.67	15.71	1.345	54.93	44.28
1.115	22.86	19.45	16.36	1.350	55.79	44.82
1.120	23.82	20.23	17.01	1.355	56.66	45.35
1.125	24.78	21.00	17.66	1.360	57.57	45.88
1.130	25.75	21.77	18.31	1.365	58.48	46.41
1.135	26.70	22.54	18.96	1.370	59.39	46.94
1.140	27.66	23.31	19.61	1.375	60.30	47.47
1.145	28.61	24.08	20.26	1.380	61.27	48.00
1.150	29.57	24.84	20.91	1.385	62.24	48.53
1.155	30.55	25.60	21.55	1.390	63.23	49.06
1.160	31.52	26.36	22.19	1.395	64.25	49.59
1.165	32.49	27.12	22.83	1.400	65.30	50.11
1.170	33.46	27.88	23.47	1.405	66.40	50.63
1.175	34.42	28.63	24.12	1.410	67.50	51.15
1.180	35.39	29.38	24.76	1.415	68.63	51.66
1.185	36.31	30.13	25.40	1.420	69.80	52.15
1.190	37.23	30.88	26.04	1.425	70.98	52.63
1.195	38.16	31.62	26.68	1.430	72.17	53.11
1.200	39.11	32.36	27.32	1.435	73.39	53.59
1.205	.....	33.09	27.95	1.440	74.68	54.07
1.210	.....	33.82	28.58	1.445	75.98	54.55
1.215	.....	34.55	29.21	1.450	77.28	55.03
1.220	.....	35.28	29.84	1.455	78.60	55.50
1.225	.....	36.03	30.48	1.460	79.98	55.97
1.230	.....	36.78	31.11	1.465	81.42	56.43

SPECIFIC GRAVITY OF STRONG ACIDS AT $\frac{15°}{4°}$ IN VACUO. (*Continued*)

(According to G. Lunge)

Specific gravity at $\frac{15°}{4°}$ (vacuo)	Per cent by weight		Specific gravity at $\frac{15°}{4°}$ (vacuo)	Per cent by weight	Specific gravity at $\frac{15°}{4°}$ (vacuo)	Per cent by weight
	HNO_3	H_2SO_4		H_2SO_4		H_2SO_4
1.470	82.90	56.90	1.610	69.56	1.750	81.56
1.475	84.45	57.37	1.615	70.00	1.755	82.00
1.480	86.05	57.83	1.620	70.42	1.760	82.44
1.485	87.70	58.28	1.625	70.85	1.765	83.01
1.490	89.90	58.74	1.630	71.27	1.770	83.51
1.495	91.60	59.22	1.635	71.70	1.775	84.02
1.500	94.09	59.70	1.640	72.12	1.780	84.50
1.505	96.39	60.18	1.645	72.55	1.785	85.10
1.510	98.10	60.65	1.650	72.96	1.790	85.70
1.515	99.07	61.12	1.655	73.40	1.795	86.30
1.520	99.67	61.59	1.660	73.81	1.800	86.92
1.525	.....	62.06	1.665	74.24	1.805	87.60
1.530	.....	62.53	1.670	74.66	1.810	88.30
1.535	.....	63.00	1.675	75.08	1.815	89.16
1.540	.....	63.43	1.680	75.50	1.820	90.05
1.545	.....	63.85	1.685	75.94	1.825	91.00
1.550	.....	64.26	1.690	76.38	1.830	92.10
1.555	.....	64.67	1.695	76.76	1.835	93.56
1.560	.....	65.20	1.700	77.17	1.840	95.60
1.565	.....	65.65	1.705	77.60	1.8405	95.95
1.570	.....	66.09	1.710	78.04	1.8410	96.38
1.575	.....	66.53	1.715	78.48	1.8415	97.35
1.580	.....	66.95	1.720	78.92	1.8410	98.20
1.585	.....	67.40	1.725	79.36	1.8405	98.52
1.590	.....	67.83	1.730	79.80	1.8400	98.72
1.595	.....	68.26	1.735	80.24	1.8395	98.77
1.600	.....	68.70	1.740	80.68	1.8390	99.12
1.605	.....	69.13	1.745	81.12	1.8385	99.31

TABLE VII. SPECIFIC GRAVITY OF POTASSIUM AND SODIUM HYDROXIDE
SOLUTIONS AT 15°C.

(From Treadwell and Hall's "Analytical Chemistry," Vol. II, published by John Wiley
& Sons, Inc., by permission)

Specific gravity	Per cent KOH	Per cent NaOH	Specific gravity	Per cent KOH	Per cent NaOH
1.007	0.9	0.61	1.252	27.0	22.64
1.014	1.7	1.20	1.263	28.2	23.67
1.022	2.6	2.00	1.274	28.9	24.81
1.029	3.5	2.71	1.285	29.8	25.80
1.037	4.5	3.35	1.297	30.7	26.83
1.045	5.6	4.00	1.308	31.8	27.80
1.052	6.4	4.64	1.320	32.7	28.83
1.060	7.4	5.29	1.332	33.7	29.93
1.067	8.2	5.87	1.345	34.9	31.22
1.075	9.2	6.55	1.357	35.9	32.47
1.083	10.1	7.31	1.370	36.9	33.69
1.091	10.9	8.00	1.383	37.8	34.96
1.100	12.0	8.68	1.397	38.9	36.25
1.108	12.9	9.42	1.410	39.9	37.47
1.116	13.8	10.06	1.424	40.9	38.80
1.125	14.8	10.97	1.438	42.1	39.99
1.134	15.7	11.84	1.453	43.4	41.41
1.142	16.5	12.64	1.468	44.6	42.83
1.152	17.6	13.55	1.483	45.8	44.38
1.162	18.6	14.37	1.498	47.1	46.15
1.171	19.5	15.13	1.514	48.3	47.60
1.180	20.5	15.91	1.530	49.4	49.02
1.190	21.4	16.77	1.546	50.6	
1.200	22.4	17.67	1.563	51.9	
1.210	23.3	18.58	1.580	53.2	
1.220	24.2	19.58	1.597	54.5	
1.231	25.1	20.59	1.615	55.9	
1.241	26.1	21.42	1.634	57.5	

TABLE VIII. SPECIFIC GRAVITY OF AMMONIA SOLUTIONS AT 15°C.

(According to Lunge and Wiernik)

(From Treadwell & Hall's "Analytical Chemistry," Vol. II, published by John Wiley & Sons, Inc., by permission)

Specific gravity	Per cent NH_3	Specific gravity	Per cent NH_3
1.000	0.00	0.940	15.63
0.998	0.45	0.938	16.22
0.996	0.91	0.936	16.82
0.994	1.37	0.934	17.42
0.992	1.84	0.932	18.03
0.990	2.31	0.930	18.64
0.988	2.80	0.928	19.25
0.986	3.30	0.926	19.87
0.984	3.80	0.924	20.49
0.982	4.30	0.922	21.12
0.980	4.80	0.920	21.75
0.978	5.30	0.918	22.39
0.976	5.80	0.916	23.03
0.974	6.30	0.914	23.68
0.972	6.80	0.912	24.33
0.970	7.31	0.910	24.99
0.968	7.82	0.908	25.65
0.966	8.33	0.906	26.31
0.964	8.84	0.904	26.98
0.962	9.35	0.902	27.65
0.960	9.91	0.900	28.33
0.958	10.47	0.898	29.01
0.956	11.03	0.896	29.69
0.954	11.60	0.894	30.37
0.952	12.17	0.892	31.05
0.950	12.74	0.890	31.75
0.948	13.31	0.888	32.50
0.946	13.88	0.886	33.25
0.944	14.46	0.884	34.10
0.942	15.04	0.882	34.95

TABLE IX. IONIZATION CONSTANTS, 25°C.

Acids

	Constant for 1st hydrogen	Constant for 2d hydrogen	Constant for 3d hydrogen
Acetic acid, $HC_2H_3O_2$..........	1.86×10^{-5}		
Arsenic acid, H_3AsO_4............	$5 \quad \times 10^{-3}$	$4 \quad \times 10^{-5}$	$6 \quad \times 10^{-10}$
Benzoic acid, $HC_7H_5O_2$.........	6.6×10^{-5}		
Boric acid, H_3BO_3..............	5.5×10^{-10}		
Carbonic acid, H_2CO_3..........	3.3×10^{-7}	$5 \quad \times 10^{-11}$	
Chloracetic acid, $HC_2H_2O_2Cl$.....	1.6×10^{-3}		
Citric acid, $H_3C_6H_5O_7$...........	$8 \quad \times 10^{-4}$		
Formic acid, $HCHO_2$............	2.1×10^{-4}		
Hydrocyanic acid, HCN.........	7.2×10^{-10}		
Hydrogen sulfide, H_2S...........	9.1×10^{-8}	1.2×10^{-15}	
Hypochlorous acid, $HClO$.......	4.0×10^{-8}		
Lactic acid, $HC_3H_5O_2$..........	1.6×10^{-4}		
Nitrous acid, HNO_2............	4.5×10^{-4}		
Oxalic acid, $H_2C_2O_4$............	3.8×10^{-2}	4.9×10^{-5}	
Phosphoric acid, H_3PO_4.........	1.1×10^{-2}	2.0×10^{-7}	3.6×10^{-13}
Phosphorous acid, H_3PO_3........	$5 \quad \times 10^{-2}$	$2 \quad \times 10^{-5}$	
Selenious acid, H_2SeO_3..........	$3 \quad \times 10^{-3}$	$5 \quad \times 10^{-8}$	
Sulfurous acid, H_2SO_3...........	1.7×10^{-2}	$5 \quad \times 10^{-6}$	
Tartaric acid, $H_2C_4H_4O_6$.........	1.1×10^{-3}	6.9×10^{-5}	

Bases

Ammonium hydroxide, NH_4OH	1.75×10^{-5}
Aniline, $C_6H_5NH_2$............	$4 \quad \times 10^{-10}$
Diethyl amine, $(C_2H_5)_2NH$....	1.3×10^{-3}
Dimethyl amine, $(CH_3)_2NH$...	7.4×10^{-4}
Ethyl amine, $C_2H_5NH_2$........	5.6×10^{-4}
Methyl amine, CH_3NH_2.......	4.4×10^{-4}
Pyridine, C_5H_5N.............	2.3×10^{-9}

Complex Ions

$Ag(NH_3)_2^+$..	6.8×10^{-8}
$Cd(NH_3)_4^{++}$.	2.5×10^{-7}
$Co(NH_3)_6^{+++}$	$2 \quad \times 10^{-34}$
$Cu(NH_3)_4^{++}$.	4.6×10^{-14}
$Ni(NH_3)_4^{++}$.	$5 \quad \times 10^{-8}$
$Zn(NH_3)_4^{++}$.	$3 \quad \times 10^{-10}$
$Ag(CN)_2^-$...	1.0×10^{-21}
$Cd(CN)_4^=$...	1.4×10^{-17}
$Cu(CN)_3^=$...	5.0×10^{-28}
$Fe(CN)_6^\equiv$...	1.0×10^{-36}
$Hg(CN)_4^=$...	4.0×10^{-42}
$Ni(CN)_4^=$...	1.0×10^{-22}
HgI_4^-......	5.0×10^{-31}
$HgS_2^=$......	2.0×10^{-55}
$Ag(S_2O_3)_2^\equiv$..	4.0×10^{-14}

TABLE X. SOLUBILITY PRODUCTS, *Approximately* 25°C.

Compound	K_{sp}	Compound	K_{sp}
Aluminum hydroxide, $Al(OH)_3$	3.7×10^{-15}	Magnesium carbonate, $MgCO_3$..	2.6×10^{-5}
Barium carbonate, $BaCO_3$....	8.1×10^{-9}	fluoride, MgF_2.....	6.4×10^{-9}
chromate, $BaCrO_4$....	3.0×10^{-10}	hydroxide, $Mg(OH)_2$	3.4×10^{-11}
fluoride, BaF_2	1.7×10^{-6}	oxalate, MgC_2O_4....	8.6×10^{-5}
iodate, $Ba(IO_3)_2$......	6.0×10^{-10}	Manganese hydroxide, $Mn(OH)_2$	4.0×10^{-14}
oxalate, BaC_2O_4......	1.7×10^{-7}	sulfide, MnS.......	1.4×10^{-15}
sulfate, $BaSO_4$......	1.1×10^{-10}	Mercurous chloride, Hg_2Cl_2.....	1.1×10^{-18}
Bismuth sulfide, Bi_2S_3........	1.6×10^{-72}	bromide, Hg_2Br_2....	1.4×10^{-21}
Cadmium sulfide, CdS	3.6×10^{-29}	iodide, Hg_2I_2........	1.2×10^{-28}
Calcium carbonate, $CaCO_3$...	1.6×10^{-8}	Nickel sulfide, NiS...........	1.4×10^{-24}
chromate, $CaCrO_4$...	2.3×10^{-2}	Silver bromate, $AgBrO_3$........	5.0×10^{-5}
fluoride, CaF_2......	3.2×10^{-11}	bromide, $AgBr$	5.0×10^{-13}
iodate, $Ca(IO_3)_2$...	6.4×10^{-9}	carbonate, Ag_2CO_3.......	6.2×10^{-12}
oxalate, CaC_2O_4.....	2.6×10^{-9}	chloride, $AgCl$..........	1.0×10^{-10}
sulfate, $CaSO_4$	6.4×10^{-5}	chromate, Ag_2CrO_4.......	9.0×10^{-12}
Cobalt sulfide, CoS..........	3.0×10^{-26}	cyanide, $Ag_2(CN)_2$.......	1.2×10^{-12}
Cupric sulfide, CuS..........	8.0×10^{-45}	hydroxide, $AgOH$........	1.5×10^{-8}
Cuprous chloride, $CuCl$......	1.0×10^{-6}	iodate, $AgIO_3$..........	2.0×10^{-8}
bromide, $CuBr$......	4.1×10^{-8}	iodide, AgI.............	1.0×10^{-16}
iodide, CuI........	5.0×10^{-12}	nitrite, $AgNO_2$..........	7.0×10^{-4}
sulfide, Cu_2S.......	1.0×10^{-46}	oxalate, $Ag_2C_2O_4$.........	1.3×10^{-11}
thiocyanate, $CuCNS$.	1.6×10^{-11}	phosphate, Ag_3PO_4.......	1.8×10^{-18}
Ferric hydroxide, $Fe(OH)_3$....	1.1×10^{-36}	sulfate, Ag_2SO_4..........	7.0×10^{-5}
Ferrous hydroxide, $Fe(OH)_2$..	1.6×10^{-14}	sulfide, Ag_2S	1.6×10^{-49}
sulfide, FeS	1.5×10^{-19}	thiocyanate, $AgCNS$.....	1.0×10^{-12}
Lead carbonate, $PbCO_3$......	5.6×10^{-14}	Strontium carbonate, $SrCO_3$....	1.6×10^{-9}
chloride, $PbCl_2$.........	2.4×10^{-4}	chromate, $SrCrO_4$....	3.0×10^{-5}
chromate, $PbCrO_4$......	1.8×10^{-14}	fluoride, SrF_2........	2.8×10^{-9}
fluoride, PbF_2..........	3.7×10^{-8}	oxalate, SrC_2O_4......	5.6×10^{-8}
iodate, $Pb(IO_3)_2$........	9.8×10^{-14}	sulfate, $SrSO_4$.......	2.8×10^{-7}
iodide, PbI_2.........	2.4×10^{-8}	Zinc carbonate, $ZnCO_3$........	3.0×10^{-6}
oxalate, PbC_2O_4........	3.3×10^{-11}	hydroxide, $Zn(OH)_2$.......	1.8×10^{-14}
phosphate, $Pb_3(PO_4)_2$...	1.5×10^{-32}	sulfide, ZnS..............	1.2×10^{-23}
sulfate, $PbSO_4$........	1.1×10^{-8}		
sulfide, PbS	4.2×10^{-28}		

TABLE XI. STANDARD POTENTIALS

(Temperature = 25°C. Solution concentrations are 1 molar unless otherwise specified. Gases are at 1 atmosphere pressure)

HALF-CELL REACTION	$E°$
$K = K^+ + \epsilon$	$+2.922$
$Ba = Ba^{++} + 2\epsilon$	$+2.90$
$Sr = Sr^{++} + 2\epsilon$	$+2.89$
$Ca = Ca^{++} + 2\epsilon$	$+2.87$
$Na = Na^+ + \epsilon$	$+2.712$
$Al + 4OH^- = H_2AlO_3^- + H_2O + 3\epsilon$	$+2.35$
$Mg = Mg^{++} + 2\epsilon$	$+2.34$
$Al = Al^{+++} + 3\epsilon$	$+1.67$
$Mn = Mn^{++} + 2\epsilon$	$+1.05$
$Zn = Zn^{++} + 2\epsilon$	$+0.762$
$S^- = S + 2\epsilon$	$+0.51$
$H_2C_2O_4 = 2CO_2 + 2H^+ + 2\epsilon$	$+0.49$
$Fe = Fe^{++} + 2\epsilon$	$+0.440$
$H_2 = 2H^+(10^{-7} M) + 2\epsilon$	$+0.414$
$Cd = Cd^{++} + 2\epsilon$	$+0.402$
$Co = Co^{++} + 2\epsilon$	$+0.277$
$Ni = Ni^{++} + 2\epsilon$	$+0.250$
$Sn = Sn^{++} + 2\epsilon$	$+0.136$
$Pb = Pb^{++} + 2\epsilon$	$+0.126$
$Fe = Fe^{+++} + 3\epsilon$	$+0.036$
$H_2 = 2H^+ + 2\epsilon$	0.000
$Ti^{+++} = TiO^{++} + 2H^+ + \epsilon$	-0.04
$SO_2 + 2H_2O = HSO_4^- + 3H^+ + 2\epsilon$	-0.14
$H_2S \text{ (aq.)} = S + 2H^+ + 2\epsilon$	-0.141
$Sn^{++} = Sn^{++++} + 2\epsilon$	-0.15
$Cu^+ = Cu^{++} + \epsilon$	-0.167
$2S_2O_3^- = S_2O_6^- + 2\epsilon$	-0.17
$Sb + H_2O = SbO^+ + 2H^+ + 3\epsilon$	-0.212
$Ag + Cl^- = AgCl + \epsilon$	-0.224
$As + 3H_2O = H_3AsO_3 + 3H^+ + 3\epsilon$	-0.24
$Bi + H_2O = BiO^+ + 2H^+ + 3\epsilon$	-0.32
$Cu = Cu^{++} + 2\epsilon$	-0.344
$2I^- = I_2(I_3^-) + 2\epsilon$	-0.535
$H_3AsO_3 + H_2O = H_3AsO_4 + 2H^+ + 2\epsilon$	-0.56
$MnO_2 + 4OH^- = MnO_4^- + 2H_2O + 3\epsilon$	-0.58
$Hg_2Cl_2 + 2Cl^- = 2HgCl_2 + 2\epsilon$	-0.63
$H_2O_2 = O_2 + 2H^+ + 2\epsilon$	-0.682
$C_6H_4(OH)_2 = C_6H_4O_2 + 2H^+ + 2\epsilon$ (quinhydrone electrode)	-0.700
$Fe^{++} = Fe^{+++} + \epsilon$	-0.771
$2Hg = Hg_2^{++} + 2\epsilon$	-0.798
$Ag = Ag^+ + \epsilon$	-0.800
$H_2O = \frac{1}{2}O_2 + 2H^+(10^{-7} M) + 2\epsilon$	-0.815
$DS = DS' + \epsilon$ (diphenylamine sulfonate)	-0.84
$CuI = Cu^{++} + I^- + \epsilon$	-0.85
$Hg = Hg^{++} + 2\epsilon$	-0.86
$NO + 2H_2O = NO_3^- + 4H^+ + 3\epsilon$	-0.96
$2Br^- = Br_2 \text{ (aq. soln.)} + 2\epsilon$	-1.065

TABLE XI. STANDARD POTENTIALS. (*Continued*)

HALF-CELL REACTION	$E°$
$I^- + 3H_2O = IO_3^- + 6H^+ + 6\epsilon$	-1.085
$OP = OP' + \epsilon$ (ortho phenanthroline)	-1.14
$2H_2O = O_2 + 4H^+ + 4\epsilon$	-1.229
$Mn^{++} + 2H_2O = MnO_2 + 4H^+ + 2\epsilon$	-1.28
$2Cl^- = Cl_2 + 2\epsilon$	-1.358
$2Cr^{+++} + 7H_2O = Cr_2O_7^- + 14H^+ + 6\epsilon$	-1.36
$Au = Au^{+++} + 3\epsilon$	-1.42
$Br^- + 3H_2O = BrO_3^- + 6H^+ + 6\epsilon$	-1.45
$Pb^{++} + 2H_2O = PbO_2 + 4H^+ + 2\epsilon$	-1.456
$Mn^{++} + 4H_2O = MnO_4^- + 8H^+ + 5\epsilon$	-1.52
$Ce^{+++} = Ce^{++++} + \epsilon$	-1.61
$MnO_2 + 2H_2O = MnO_4^- + 4H^+ + 3\epsilon$	-1.67
$2H_2O = H_2O_2 + 2H^+ + 2\epsilon$	-1.77
$2SO_4^- = S_2O_8^- + 2\epsilon$	-2.05
$2F^- = F_2 + 2\epsilon$	-2.85

TABLE XII. FORMULA WEIGHTS

(These weights cover most of the compounds encountered in the problems of
this text)

Ag_3AsO_4	462.55	CeO_2	172.13
$AgBr$	187.80	$Ce(SO_4)_2.2(NH_4)_2SO_4.2H_2O$	632.56
$AgBrO_3$	235.80		
$AgCl$	143.34	CH_3COOH (acetic acid)	60.05
AgI	234.80	$(CH_3CO)_2O$	102.09
$AgNO_3$	169.89	C_6H_5COOH (benzoic acid)	122.12
Ag_3PO_4	418.65	CO_2	44.01
Ag_2SO_4	311.82	$CO(NH_2)_2$	60.06
		$CS(NH_2)_2$	76.12
$AlBr_3$	266.72		
Al_2O_3	101.94	$CrCl_3$	158.38
$Al(OH)_3$	77.99	Cr_2O_3	152.02
$Al_2(SO_4)_3$	342.12	$Cr_2(SO_4)_3$	389.20
$Al_2(SO_4)_3.18H_2O$	666.41		
		CuO	79.57
As_2O_3	197.82	$Cu_2(OH)_2CO_3$	221.17
As_2O_5	229.82	CuS	95.63
As_2S_3	246.00	Cu_2S	159.20
		$CuSO_4.5H_2O$	249.71
$Ba_3(AsO_4)_2$	689.90	$FeCl_3$	162.22
$BaBr_2$	297.19	$FeCl_3.6H_2O$	270.32
$BaCl_2$	208.27	$FeCO_3$	115.86
$BaCl_2.2H_2O$	244.31	$Fe(CrO_2)_2$	223.87
$BaCO_3$	197.37	$Fe(NO_3)_3.6H_2O$	349.97
BaC_2O_4	225.38	FeO	71.84
BaF_2	175.36	Fe_2O_3	159.70
BaI_2	391.20	Fe_3O_4	231.55
$Ba(IO_3)_2$	487.20	$Fe(OH)_3$	106.87
BaO	153.36	FeS_2	119.97
$Ba(OH)_2$	171.38	Fe_2Si	139.76
$Ba(OH)_2.8H_2O$	315.50	$FeSO_4.7H_2O$	278.02
$BaSO_4$	233.42	$Fe_2(SO_4)_3$	399.88
		$Fe_2(SO_4)_3.9H_2O$	562.02
BeO	25.02	$FeSO_4.(NH_4)_2SO_4.6H_2O$	392.15
		HBr	80.92
$Bi(NO_3)_3.5H_2O$	485.10	$HCHO_2$ (formic acid)	46.03
BiO_2	241.00	$HC_2H_3O_2$ (acetic acid)	60.05
Bi_2O_3	466.00	$HC_7H_5O_2$ (benzoic acid)	122.12
$BiOHCO_3$	286.02	HCl	36.47
Bi_2S_3	514.18	$HClO_4$	100.46
		$H_2C_2O_4.2H_2O$ (oxalic acid)	126.07
$CaCl_2$	110.99	$HCOOH$ (formic acid)	46.03
$CaCO_3$	100.09	HNO_3	63.02
CaF_2	78.08	H_2O	18.02
$Ca(NO_3)_2$	164.10	H_2O_2	34.02
CaO	56.08	H_3PO_3	82.00
$Ca(OH)_2$	74.10	H_3PO_4	98.00
$Ca_3(PO_4)_2$	310.20	H_2S	34.08
$3Ca_3(PO_4)_2.CaCl_2$	1041.59	H_2SO_3	82.06
$CaSO_4$	136.14	H_2SO_4	98.08

FORMULA WEIGHTS.   *(Continued)*

Hg_2Br_2	561.06		Mn_2O_3	157.86
Hg_2Cl_2	472.14		Mn_3O_4	228.79
Hg_2I_2	655.06		$Mn_2P_2O_7$	283.82
$KAl(SO_4)_2.12H_2O$	474.38		MoO_3	143.95
K_3AsO_4	256.20		$Mo_{24}O_{37}$	2894.80
$KBrO_3$	167.01		MoS_3	192.13
KCl	74.56			
$KClO_3$	122.56		Na_3AsO_3	191.91
$KClO_4$	138.55		$Na_2B_4O_7$	201.27
KCN	65.11		$Na_2B_4O_7.10H_2O$	381.43
$KCNS$	97.17		$NaBr$	102.91
K_2CO_3	138.20		$NaBrO_3$	150.91
K_2CrO_4	194.20		$NaCHO_2$ (formate)	68.01
$K_2Cr_2O_7$	294.21		$NaC_2H_3O_2$ (acetate)	82.04
$K_3Fe(CN)_6$	329.25		$NaCl$	58.45
$K_4Fe(CN)_6.3H_2O$	422.39		$NaCN$	49.02
$KHC_4H_4O_6$ (tartrate)	188.18		Na_2CO_3	106.00
$KHC_8H_4O_4$ (phthalate)	204.16		$Na_2C_2O_4$	134.01
$KHCO_3$	100.11		Na_2HAsO_3	169.91
KHC_2O_4	128.12		$NaHCO_3$	84.01
$KHC_2O_4.H_2O$	146.14		$NaHC_2O_4$	112.03
$KHC_2O_4.H_2C_2O_4.2H_2O$	254.19		Na_2HPO_4	141.98
$KH(IO_3)_2$	389.94		$Na_2HPO_4.12H_2O$	358.17
$KHSO_4$	136.16		$NaHS$	56.07
KI	166.02		NaH_2PO_4	119.99
KIO_3	214.02		$NaH_2PO_4.H_2O$	138.01
$KMnO_4$	158.03		NaI	149.92
$KNaC_4H_4O_6.4H_2O$	282.23		$NaKCO_3$	122.11
$KNaCO_3$	122.11		$NaNO_2$	69.01
KNO_2	85.10		$NaNO_3$	85.01
KNO_3	101.10		Na_2O	61.99
K_2O	94.19		Na_2O_2	77.99
KOH	56.10		$NaOH$	40.00
K_3PO_4	212.27		Na_3PO_4	163.97
K_2PtCl_6	486.16		$Na_3PO_4.12H_2O$	380.16
K_2SO_4	174.25		Na_2S	78.05
$K_2SO_4.Al_2(SO_4)_3.24H_2O$	948.76		Na_2SO_3	126.05
$K_2SO_4.Cr_2(SO_4)_3.24H_2O$	998.84		$Na_2SO_4.10H_2O$	322.21
			$Na_2S_2O_3$	158.11
$LiCl$	42.40		$Na_2S_2O_3.5H_2O$	248.19
Li_2CO_3	73.89			
Li_2O	29.88		NH_3	17.03
$LiOH$	23.95		NH_4Cl	53.50
			$(NH_4)_2C_2O_4.H_2O$	142.12
$MgCl_2$	95.23		$(NH_4)_2HPO_4$	132.07
$MgCO_3$	84.33		NH_4OH	35.05
$MgNH_4AsO_4$	181.27		$(NH_4)_3PO_4.12MoO_3$	1876.53
$MgNH_4PO_4$	137.33		$(NH_4)_2PtCl_6$	444.05
MgO	40.32		$(NH_4)_2SO_4$	132.14
$Mg(OH)_2$	58.34		NO	30.01
$Mg_2P_2O_7$	222.60		NO_2	46.01
$MgSO_4$	120.38		N_2O_3	76.02
$MgSO_4.7H_2O$	246.49			
MnO	70.93		$PbCl_2$	278.12
MnO_2	86.93		$PbClF$	261.67

Formula Weights. (*Continued*)

PbC_2O_4	295.23	$SnCl_2$	189.61
$PbCrO_4$	323.22	$SnCl_4$	260.53
PbI_2	461.05	SnO_2	150.70
$Pb(IO_3)_2$	557.05		
$Pb(NO_3)_2$	331.23	SO_2	64.06
PbO	223.21	SO_3	80.06
PbO_2	239.21		
Pb_2O_3	462.42	$SrCl_2.6H_2O$	266.64
Pb_3O_4	685.63	$SrCO_3$	147.64
$Pb_3(PO_4)_2$	811.59	SrO	103.63
$PbSO_4$	303.27		
		TiO_2	79.90
PdI_2	360.54		
		UO_3	286.14
P_2O_5	141.96	U_3O_8	842.21
Sb_2O_3	291.52	WO_3	231.92
Sb_2O_4	307.52		
Sb_2O_5	323.52	$ZnNH_4PO_4$	178.40
Sb_2S_3	339.70	ZnO	81.38
		$Zn_2P_2O_7$	304.72
$SiCl_4$	169.89	$ZnSO_4.7H_2O$	161.44
SiF_4	104.06		
SiO_2	60.06	ZrO_2	123.22

LOGARITHMS OF NUMBERS

Natural numbers	0	1	2	3	4	5	6	7	8	9	Proportional parts								
											1	2	3	4	5	6	7	8	9
10	0000	0043	0086	0128	0170	0212	0253	0294	0334	0374	4	8	12	17	21	25	29	33	37
11	0414	0453	0492	0531	0569	0607	0645	0682	0719	0755	4	8	11	15	19	23	26	30	34
12	0792	0828	0864	0899	0934	0969	1004	1038	1072	1106	3	7	10	14	17	21	24	28	31
13	1139	1173	1206	1239	1271	1303	1335	1367	1399	1430	3	6	10	13	16	19	23	26	29
14	1461	1492	1523	1553	1584	1614	1644	1673	1703	1732	3	6	9	12	15	18	21	24	27
15	1761	1790	1818	1847	1875	1903	1931	1959	1987	2014	3	6	8	11	14	17	20	22	25
16	2041	2068	2095	2122	2148	2175	2201	2227	2253	2279	3	5	8	11	13	16	18	21	24
17	2304	2330	2355	2380	2405	2430	2455	2480	2504	2529	2	5	7	10	12	15	17	20	22
18	2553	2577	2601	2625	2648	2672	2695	2718	2742	2765	2	5	7	9	12	14	16	19	21
19	2788	2810	2833	2856	2878	2900	2923	2945	2967	2989	2	4	7	9	11	13	16	18	20
20	3010	3032	3054	3075	3096	3118	3139	3160	3181	3201	2	4	6	8	11	13	15	17	19
21	3222	3243	3263	3284	3304	3324	3345	3365	3385	3404	2	4	6	8	10	12	14	16	18
22	3424	3444	3464	3483	3502	3522	3541	3560	3579	3598	2	4	6	8	10	12	14	15	17
23	3617	3636	3655	3674	3692	3711	3729	3747	3766	3784	2	4	6	7	9	11	13	15	17
24	3802	3820	3838	3856	3874	3892	3909	3927	3945	3962	2	4	5	7	9	11	12	14	16
25	3979	3997	4014	4031	4048	4065	4082	4099	4116	4133	2	3	5	7	9	10	12	14	15
26	4150	4166	4183	4200	4216	4232	4249	4265	4281	4298	2	3	5	7	8	10	11	13	15
27	4314	4330	4346	4362	4378	4393	4409	4425	4440	4456	2	3	5	6	8	9	11	13	14
28	4472	4487	4502	4518	4533	4548	4564	4579	4594	4609	2	3	5	6	8	9	11	12	14
29	4624	4639	4654	4669	4683	4698	4713	4728	4742	4757	1	3	4	6	7	9	10	12	13
30	4771	4786	4800	4814	4829	4843	4857	4871	4886	4900	1	3	4	6	7	9	10	11	13
31	4914	4928	4942	4955	4969	4983	4997	5011	5024	5038	1	3	4	6	7	8	10	11	12
32	5051	5065	5079	5092	5105	5119	5132	5145	5159	5172	1	3	4	5	7	8	9	11	12
33	5185	5198	5211	5224	5237	5250	5263	5276	5289	5302	1	3	4	5	6	8	9	10	12
34	5315	5328	5340	5353	5366	5378	5391	5403	5416	5428	1	3	4	5	6	8	9	10	11
35	5441	5453	5465	5478	5490	5502	5514	5527	5539	5551	1	2	4	5	6	7	9	10	11
36	5563	5575	5587	5599	5611	5623	5635	5647	5658	5670	1	2	4	5	6	7	8	10	11
37	5682	5694	5705	5717	5729	5740	5752	5763	5775	5786	1	2	3	5	6	7	8	9	10
38	5798	5809	5821	5832	5843	5855	5866	5877	5888	5899	1	2	3	5	6	7	8	9	10
39	5911	5922	5933	5944	5955	5966	5977	5988	5999	6010	1	2	3	4	5	7	8	9	10
40	6021	6031	6042	6053	6064	6075	6085	6096	6107	6117	1	2	3	4	5	6	8	9	10
41	6128	6138	6149	6160	6170	6180	6191	6201	6212	6222	1	2	3	4	5	6	7	8	9
42	6232	6243	6253	6263	6274	6284	6294	6304	6314	6325	1	2	3	4	5	6	7	8	9
43	6335	6345	6355	6365	6375	6385	6395	6405	6415	6425	1	2	3	4	5	6	7	8	9
44	6435	6444	6454	6464	6474	6484	6493	6503	6513	6522	1	2	3	4	5	6	7	8	9
45	6532	6542	6551	6561	6571	6580	6590	6599	6609	6618	1	2	3	4	5	6	7	8	9
46	6628	6637	6646	6656	6665	6675	6684	6693	6702	6712	1	2	3	4	5	6	7	7	8
47	6721	6730	6739	6749	6758	6767	6776	6785	6794	6803	1	2	3	4	5	5	6	7	8
48	6812	6821	6830	6839	6848	6857	6866	6875	6884	6893	1	2	3	4	4	5	6	7	8
49	6902	6911	6920	6928	6937	6946	6955	6964	6972	6981	1	2	3	4	4	5	6	7	8
50	6990	6998	7007	7016	7024	7033	7042	7050	7059	7067	1	2	3	3	4	5	6	7	8
51	7076	7084	7093	7101	7110	7118	7126	7135	7143	7152	1	2	3	3	4	5	6	7	8
52	7160	7168	7177	7185	7193	7202	7210	7218	7226	7235	1	2	2	3	4	5	6	7	7
53	7243	7251	7259	7267	7275	7284	7292	7300	7308	7316	1	2	2	3	4	5	6	6	7
54	7324	7332	7340	7348	7356	7364	7372	7380	7388	7396	1	2	2	3	4	5	6	6	7

LOGARITHMS. (*Continued*)

Natural numbers	0	1	2	3	4	5	6	7	8	9	Proportional parts								
											1	2	3	4	5	6	7	8	9
55	7404	7412	7419	7427	7435	7443	7451	7459	7466	7474	1	2	2	3	4	5	5	6	7
56	7482	7490	7497	7505	7513	7520	7528	7536	7543	7551	1	2	2	3	4	5	5	6	7
57	7559	7566	7574	7582	7589	7597	7604	7612	7619	7627	1	2	2	3	4	5	5	6	7
58	7634	7642	7649	7657	7664	7672	7679	7686	7694	7701	1	1	2	3	4	4	5	6	7
59	7709	7716	7723	7731	7738	7745	7752	7760	7767	7774	1	1	2	3	4	4	5	6	7
60	7782	7789	7796	7803	7810	7818	7825	7832	7839	7846	1	1	2	3	4	4	5	6	6
61	7853	7860	7868	7875	7882	7889	7896	7903	7910	7917	1	1	2	3	4	4	5	6	6
62	7924	7931	7938	7945	7952	7959	7966	7973	7980	7987	1	1	2	3	3	4	5	6	6
63	7993	8000	8007	8014	8021	8028	8035	8041	8048	8055	1	1	2	3	3	4	5	5	6
64	8062	8069	8075	8082	8089	8096	8102	8109	8116	8122	1	1	2	3	3	4	5	5	6
65	8129	8136	8142	8149	8156	8162	8169	8176	8182	8189	1	1	2	3	3	4	5	5	6
66	8195	8202	8209	8215	8222	8228	8235	8241	8248	8254	1	1	2	3	3	4	5	5	6
67	8261	8267	8274	8280	8287	8293	8299	8306	8312	8319	1	1	2	3	3	4	5	5	6
68	8325	8331	8338	8344	8351	8357	8363	8370	8376	8382	1	1	2	3	3	4	4	5	6
69	8388	8395	8401	8407	8414	8420	8426	8432	8439	8445	1	1	2	2	3	4	4	5	6
70	8451	8457	8463	8470	8476	8482	8488	8494	8500	8506	1	1	2	2	3	4	4	5	6
71	8513	8519	8525	8531	8537	8543	8549	8555	8561	8567	1	1	2	2	3	4	4	5	5
72	8573	8579	8585	8591	8597	8603	8609	8615	8621	8627	1	1	2	2	3	4	4	5	5
73	8633	8639	8645	8651	8657	8663	8669	8675	8681	8686	1	1	2	2	3	4	4	5	5
74	8692	8698	8704	8710	8716	8722	8727	8733	8739	8745	1	1	2	2	3	4	4	5	5
75	8751	8756	8762	8768	8774	8779	8785	8791	8797	8802	1	1	2	2	3	3	4	5	5
76	8808	8814	8820	8825	8831	8837	8842	8848	8854	8859	1	1	2	2	3	3	4	5	5
77	8865	8871	8876	8882	8887	8893	8899	8904	8910	8915	1	1	2	2	3	3	4	4	5
78	8921	8927	8932	8938	8943	8949	8954	8960	8965	8971	1	1	2	2	3	3	4	4	5
79	8976	8982	8987	8993	8998	9004	9009	9015	9020	9026	1	1	2	2	3	3	4	4	5
80	9031	9036	9042	9047	9053	9058	9063	9069	9074	9079	1	1	2	2	3	3	4	4	5
81	9085	9090	9096	9101	9106	9112	9117	9122	9128	9133	1	1	2	2	3	3	4	4	5
82	9138	9143	9149	9154	9159	9165	9170	9175	9180	9186	1	1	2	2	3	3	4	4	5
83	9191	9196	9201	9206	9212	9217	9222	9232	9232	9238	1	1	2	2	3	3	4	4	5
84	9243	9248	9253	9258	9263	9269	9274	9279	9284	9289	1	1	2	2	3	3	4	4	5
85	9294	9299	9304	9309	9315	9320	9325	9330	9335	9340	1	1	2	2	3	3	4	4	5
86	9345	9350	9355	9360	9365	9370	9375	9380	9385	9390	1	1	2	2	3	3	4	4	5
87	9395	9400	9405	9410	9415	9420	9425	9430	9435	9440	0	1	1	2	2	3	3	4	4
88	9445	9450	9455	9460	9465	9469	9474	9479	9484	9489	0	1	1	2	2	3	3	4	4
89	9494	9499	9504	9509	9513	9518	9523	9528	9533	9538	0	1	1	2	2	3	3	4	4
90	9542	9547	9552	9557	9562	9566	9571	9576	9581	9586	0	1	1	2	2	3	3	4	4
91	9590	9595	9600	9605	9609	9614	9619	9624	9628	9633	0	1	1	2	2	3	3	4	4
92	9638	9643	9647	9652	9657	9661	9666	9671	9675	9680	0	1	1	2	2	3	3	4	4
93	9685	9689	9694	9699	9703	9708	9713	9717	9722	9727	0	1	1	2	2	3	3	4	4
94	9731	9736	9741	9745	9750	9754	9759	9763	9768	9773	0	1	1	2	2	3	3	4	4
95	9777	9782	9786	9791	9795	9800	9805	9809	9814	9818	0	1	1	2	2	3	3	4	4
96	9823	9827	9832	9836	9841	9845	9850	9854	9859	9863	0	1	1	2	2	3	3	4	4
97	9868	9872	9877	9881	9886	9890	9894	9899	9903	9908	0	1	1	2	2	3	3	4	4
98	9912	9917	9921	9926	9930	9934	9939	9943	9948	9952	0	1	1	2	2	3	3	4	4
99	9956	9961	9965	9969	9974	9978	9983	9987	9991	9996	0	1	1	2	2	3	3	3	4

ANTILOGARITHMS

Logarithms	0	1	2	3	4	5	6	7	8	9	Proportional parts								
											1	2	3	4	5	6	7	8	9
.00	1000	1002	1005	1007	1009	1012	1014	1016	1019	1021	0	0	1	1	1	1	1	2	2
.01	1023	1026	1028	1030	1033	1035	1038	1040	1042	1045	0	0	1	1	1	1	2	2	2
.02	1047	1050	1052	1054	1057	1059	1062	1064	1067	1069	0	0	1	1	1	1	2	2	2
.03	1072	1074	1076	1079	1081	1084	1086	1089	1091	1094	0	0	1	1	1	1	2	2	2
.04	1096	1099	1102	1104	1107	1109	1112	1114	1117	1119	0	1	1	1	1	2	2	2	2
.05	1122	1125	1127	1130	1132	1135	1138	1140	1143	1146	0	1	1	1	1	2	2	2	2
.06	1148	1151	1153	1156	1159	1161	1164	1167	1169	1172	0	1	1	1	1	2	2	2	2
.07	1175	1178	1180	1183	1186	1189	1191	1194	1197	1199	0	1	1	1	1	2	2	2	2
.08	1202	1205	1208	1211	1213	1216	1219	1222	1225	1227	0	1	1	1	1	2	2	2	3
.09	1230	1233	1236	1239	1242	1245	1247	1250	1253	1256	0	1	1	1	1	2	2	2	3
.10	1259	1262	1265	1268	1271	1274	1276	1279	1282	1285	0	1	1	1	1	2	2	2	3
.11	1288	1291	1294	1297	1300	1303	1306	1309	1312	1315	0	1	1	1	2	2	2	2	3
.12	1318	1321	1324	1327	1330	1334	1337	1340	1343	1346	0	1	1	1	2	2	2	2	3
.13	1349	1352	1355	1358	1361	1365	1368	1371	1374	1377	0	1	1	1	2	2	2	3	3
.14	1380	1384	1387	1390	1393	1396	1400	1403	1406	1409	0	1	1	1	2	2	2	3	3
.15	1413	1416	1419	1422	1426	1429	1432	1435	1439	1442	0	1	1	1	2	2	2	3	3
.16	1445	1449	1452	1455	1459	1462	1466	1469	1472	1476	0	1	1	1	2	2	2	3	3
.17	1479	1483	1486	1489	1493	1496	1500	1503	1507	1510	0	1	1	1	2	2	2	3	3
.18	1514	1517	1521	1524	1528	1531	1535	1538	1542	1545	0	1	1	1	2	2	2	3	3
.19	1549	1552	1556	1560	1563	1567	1570	1574	1578	1581	0	1	1	1	2	2	3	3	3
.20	1585	1589	1592	1596	1600	1603	1607	1611	1614	1618	0	1	1	1	2	2	3	3	3
.21	1622	1626	1629	1633	1637	1641	1644	1648	1652	1656	0	1	1	2	2	2	3	3	3
.22	1660	1663	1667	1671	1675	1679	1683	1687	1690	1694	0	1	1	2	2	2	3	3	3
.23	1698	1702	1706	1710	1714	1718	1722	1726	1730	1734	0	1	1	2	2	2	3	3	4
.24	1738	1742	1746	1750	1754	1758	1762	1766	1770	1774	0	1	1	2	2	2	3	3	4
.25	1778	1782	1786	1791	1795	1799	1803	1807	1811	1816	0	1	1	2	2	2	3	3	4
.26	1820	1824	1828	1832	1837	1841	1845	1849	1854	1858	0	1	1	2	2	3	3	3	4
.27	1862	1866	1871	1875	1879	1884	1888	1892	1897	1901	0	1	1	2	2	3	3	3	4
.28	1905	1910	1914	1919	1923	1928	1932	1936	1941	1945	0	1	1	2	2	3	3	4	4
.29	1950	1954	1959	1963	1968	1972	1977	1982	1986	1991	0	1	1	2	2	3	3	4	4
.30	1995	2000	2004	2009	2014	2018	2023	2028	2032	2037	0	1	1	2	2	3	3	4	4
.31	2042	2046	2051	2056	2061	2065	2070	2075	2080	2084	0	1	1	2	2	3	3	4	4
.32	2089	2094	2099	2104	2109	2113	2118	2123	2128	2133	0	1	1	2	2	3	3	4	4
.33	2138	2143	2148	2153	2158	2163	2168	2173	2178	2183	0	1	1	2	2	3	3	4	4
.34	2188	2193	2198	2203	2208	2213	2218	2223	2228	2234	1	1	2	2	3	3	4	4	5
.35	2239	2244	2249	2254	2259	2265	2270	2275	2280	2286	1	1	2	2	3	3	4	4	5
.36	2291	2296	2301	2307	2312	2317	2323	2328	2333	2339	1	1	2	2	3	3	4	4	5
.37	2344	2350	2355	2360	2366	2371	2377	2382	2388	2393	1	1	2	2	3	3	4	4	5
.38	2399	2404	2410	2415	2421	2427	2432	2438	2443	2449	1	1	2	2	3	3	4	4	5
.39	2455	2460	2466	2472	2477	2483	2489	2495	2500	2506	1	1	2	2	3	3	4	5	5
.40	2512	2518	2523	2529	2535	2541	2547	2553	2559	2564	1	1	2	2	3	4	4	5	5
.41	2570	2576	2582	2588	2594	2600	2606	2612	2618	2624	1	1	2	2	3	4	4	5	5
.42	2630	2636	2642	2649	2655	2661	2667	2673	2679	2685	1	1	2	2	3	4	4	5	6
.43	2692	2698	2704	2710	2716	2723	2729	2735	2742	2748	1	1	2	3	3	4	4	5	6
.44	2754	2761	2767	2773	2780	2786	2793	2799	2805	2812	1	1	2	3	3	4	4	5	6
.45	2818	2825	2831	2838	2844	2851	2858	2864	2871	2877	1	1	2	3	3	4	5	5	6
.46	2884	2891	2897	2904	2911	2917	2924	2931	2938	2944	1	1	2	3	3	4	5	5	6
.47	2951	2958	2965	2972	2979	2985	2992	2999	3006	3013	1	1	2	3	3	4	5	5	6
.48	3020	3027	3034	3041	3048	3055	3062	3069	3076	3083	1	1	2	3	4	4	5	6	6
.49	3090	3097	3105	3112	3119	3126	3133	3141	3148	3155	1	1	2	3	4	4	5	6	6

ANTILOGARITHMS. (*Continued*)

Logarithms	0	1	2	3	4	5	6	7	8	9	Proportional parts								
											1	2	3	4	5	6	7	8	9
.50	3162	3170	3177	3184	3192	3199	3206	3214	3221	3228	1	1	2	3	4	4	5	6	7
.51	3236	3243	3251	3258	3266	3273	3281	3289	3296	3304	1	2	2	3	4	5	5	6	7
.52	3311	3319	3327	3334	3342	3350	3357	3365	3373	3381	1	2	2	3	4	5	5	6	7
.53	3388	3396	3404	3412	3420	3428	3436	3443	3451	3459	1	2	2	3	4	5	6	6	7
.54	3467	3475	3483	3491	3499	3508	3516	3524	3532	3540	1	2	2	3	4	5	6	6	7
.55	3548	3556	3565	3573	3581	3589	3597	3606	3614	3622	1	2	2	3	4	5	6	7	7
.56	3631	3639	3648	3656	3664	3673	3681	3690	3698	3707	1	2	3	3	4	5	6	7	8
.57	3715	3724	3733	3741	3750	3758	3767	3776	3784	3793	1	2	3	3	4	5	6	7	8
.58	3802	3811	3819	3828	3837	3846	3855	3864	3873	3882	1	2	3	4	4	5	6	7	8
.59	3890	3899	3908	3917	3926	3936	3945	3954	3963	3972	1	2	3	4	5	5	6	7	8
.60	3981	3990	3999	4009	4018	4027	4036	4046	4055	4064	1	2	3	4	5	6	6	7	8
.61	4074	4083	4093	4102	4111	4121	4130	4140	4150	4159	1	2	3	4	5	6	7	8	9
.62	4169	4178	4188	4198	4207	4217	4227	4236	4246	4256	1	2	3	4	5	6	7	8	9
.63	4266	4276	4285	4295	4305	4315	4325	4335	4345	4355	1	2	3	4	5	6	7	8	9
.64	4365	4375	4385	4395	4406	4416	4426	4436	4446	4457	1	2	3	4	5	6	7	8	9
.65	4467	4477	4487	4498	4508	4519	4529	4539	4550	4560	1	2	3	4	5	6	7	8	9
.66	4571	4581	4592	4603	4613	4624	4634	4645	4656	4667	1	2	3	4	5	6	7	9	10
.67	4677	4688	4699	4710	4721	4732	4742	4753	4764	4775	1	2	3	4	5	7	8	9	10
.68	4786	4797	4808	4819	4831	4842	4853	4864	4875	4887	1	2	3	4	6	7	8	9	10
.69	4898	4909	4920	4932	4943	4955	4966	4977	4989	5000	1	2	3	5	6	7	8	9	10
.70	5012	5023	5035	5047	5058	5070	5082	5093	5105	5117	1	2	4	5	6	7	8	9	11
.71	5129	5140	5152	5164	5176	5188	5200	5212	5224	5236	1	2	4	5	6	7	8	10	11
.72	5248	5260	5272	5284	5297	5309	5321	5333	5346	5358	1	2	4	5	6	7	9	10	11
.73	5370	5383	5395	5408	5420	5433	5445	5458	5470	5483	1	3	4	5	6	8	9	10	11
.74	5495	5508	5521	5534	5546	5559	5572	5585	5598	5610	1	3	4	5	6	8	9	10	12
.75	5623	5636	5649	5662	5675	5689	5702	5715	5728	5741	1	3	4	5	7	8	9	10	12
.76	5754	5768	5781	5794	5808	5821	5834	5848	5861	5875	1	3	4	5	7	8	9	11	12
.77	5888	5902	5916	5929	5943	5957	5970	5984	5998	6012	1	3	4	5	7	8	10	11	12
.78	6026	6039	6053	6067	6081	6095	6109	6124	6138	6152	1	3	4	6	7	8	10	11	13
.79	6166	6180	6194	6209	6223	6237	6252	6266	6281	6295	1	3	4	6	7	9	10	11	13
.80	6310	6324	6339	6353	6368	6383	6397	6412	6427	6442	1	3	4	6	7	9	10	12	13
.81	6457	6471	6486	6501	6516	6531	6546	6561	6577	6592	2	3	5	6	8	9	11	12	14
.82	6607	6622	6637	6653	6668	6683	6699	6714	6730	6745	2	3	5	6	8	9	11	12	14
.83	6761	6776	6792	6808	6823	6839	6855	6871	6887	6902	2	3	5	6	8	9	11	13	14
.84	6918	6934	6950	6966	6982	6998	7015	7031	7047	7063	2	3	5	6	8	10	11	13	15
.85	7079	7096	7112	7129	7145	7161	7178	7194	7211	7228	2	3	5	7	8	10	12	13	15
.86	7244	7261	7278	7295	7311	7328	7345	7362	7379	7396	2	3	5	7	8	10	12	13	15
.87	7413	7430	7447	7464	7482	7499	7516	7534	7551	7568	2	3	5	7	9	10	12	14	16
.88	7586	7603	7621	7638	7656	7674	7691	7709	7727	7745	2	4	5	7	9	11	12	14	16
.89	7762	7780	7798	7816	7834	7852	7870	7889	7907	7925	2	4	5	7	9	11	13	14	16
.90	7943	7962	7980	7998	8017	8035	8054	8072	8091	8110	2	4	6	7	9	11	13	15	17
.91	8128	8147	8166	8185	8204	8222	8241	8260	8279	8299	2	4	6	8	9	11	13	15	17
.92	8318	8337	8356	8375	8395	8414	8433	8453	8472	8492	2	4	6	8	10	12	14	15	17
.93	8511	8531	8551	8570	8590	8610	8630	8650	8670	8690	2	4	6	8	10	12	14	16	18
.94	8710	8730	8750	8770	8790	8810	8831	8851	8872	8892	2	4	6	8	10	12	14	16	18
.95	8913	8933	8954	8974	8995	9016	9036	9057	9078	9099	2	4	6	8	10	12	15	17	19
.96	9120	9141	9162	9183	9204	9226	9247	9268	9290	9311	2	4	6	8	11	13	15	17	19
.97	9333	9354	9376	9397	9419	9441	9462	9484	9506	9528	2	4	7	9	11	13	15	17	20
.98	9550	9572	9594	9616	9638	9661	9683	9705	9727	9750	2	4	7	9	11	13	16	18	20
.99	9772	9795	9817	9840	9863	9886	9908	9931	9954	9977	2	5	7	9	11	14	16	18	20

INTERNATIONAL ATOMIC WEIGHTS (1952)

(*Journal of the American Chemical Society*)

Element	Symbol	Atomic No.	Atomic weight*	Element	Symbol	Atomic No.	Atomic weight*
Actinium	Ac	89	227	Neodymium	Nd	60	144.27
Aluminum	Al	13	26.98	Neptunium	Np	93	[237]
Americium	Am	95	[243]	Neon	Ne	10	20.183
Antinomy	Sb	51	121.76	Nickel	Ni	28	58.69
Argon	A	18	39.944	Niobium			
Arsenic	As	33	74.91	(Columbium)	Nb	41	92.91
Astatine	At	85	[210]	Nitrogen	N	7	14.008
Barium	Ba	56	137.36	Osmium	Os	76	190.2
Berkelium	Bk	97	[245]	Oxygen	O	8	16.0000
Beryllium	Be	4	9.013	Palladium	Pd	46	106.7
Bismuth	Bi	83	209.00	Phosphorus	P	15	30.975
Boron	B	5	10.82	Platinum	Pt	78	195.23
Bromine	Br	35	79.916	Plutonium	Pu	94	[242]
Cadmium	Cd	48	112.41	Polonium	Po	84	210
Calcium	Ca	20	40.08	Potassium	K	19	39.100
Californium	Cf	98	[246]	Praseodymium	Pr	59	140.92
Carbon	C	6	12.010	Promethium	Pm	61	[145]
Cerium	Ce	58	140.13	Protactinium	Pa	91	231
Cesium	Cs	55	132.91	Radium	Ra	88	226.05
Chlorine	Cl	17	35.457	Radon	Rn	86	222
Chromium	Cr	24	52.01	Rhenium	Re	75	186.31
Cobalt	Co	27	58.94	Rhodium	Rh	45	102.91
Copper	Cu	29	63.54	Rubidium	Rb	37	85.48
Curium	Cm	96	[243]	Ruthenium	Ru	44	101.7
Dysprosium	Dy	66	162.46	Samarium	Sm	62	150.43
Erbium	Er	68	167.2	Scandium	Sc	21	44.96
Europium	Eu	63	152.0	Selenium	Se	34	78.96
Fluorine	F	9	19.00	Silicon	Si	14	28.09
Francium	Fr	87	[223]	Silver	Ag	47	107.880
Gadolinium	Gd	64	156.9	Sodium	Na	11	22.997
Gallium	Ga	31	69.72	Strontium	Sr	38	87.63
Germanium	Ge	32	72.60	Sulfur	S	16	32.066
Gold	Au	79	197.2	Tantalum	Ta	73	180.88
Hafnium	Hf	72	178.6	Technetium	Tc	43	[99]
Helium	He	2	4.003	Tellurium	Te	52	127.61
Holmium	Ho	67	164.94	Terbium	Tb	65	159.2
Hydrogen	H	1	1.0080	Thallum	Tl	81	204.39
Indium	In	49	114.76	Thorium	Th	90	232.12
Iodine	I	53	126.91	Thulium	Tm	69	169.4
Iridium	Ir	77	193.1	Tin	Sn	50	118.70
Iron	Fe	26	55.85	Titanium	Ti	22	47.90
Krypton	Kr	36	83.80	Tungsten			
Lanthanum	La	57	138.92	(Wolfram)	W	74	183.92
Lead	Pb	82	207.21	Uranium	U	92	238.07
Lithium	Li	3	6.940	Vanadium	V	23	50.95
Lutetium	Lu	71	174.99	Xenon	Xe	54	131.3
Magnesium	Mg	12	24.32	Ytterbium	Yb	70	173.04
Manganese	Mn	25	54.93	Yttrium	Y	39	88.92
Mercury	Hg	80	200.61	Zinc	Zn	30	65.38
Molybdenum	Mo	42	95.95	Zirconium	Zr	40	91.22

* A number in brackets is the mass number of the most stable known isotope.

INDEX

A

Absolute error, 2
Absorbing agents, 269
Absorption methods, 269
Accuracy of a value, 2
Acid mixtures, titration of, 167
Acidimetric titration curves, 175
Acidimetry, calculations of, 145
Acidity control in sulfide precipitations, 61
Activity, 49
Activity coefficient, 49
Adsorption indicators, 222
Alkali group, problems on, 294
Alkalimetry calculations, 145
Alkaline earth group, problems on, 294
Aluminum, problems on, 298
Ammonium, problems on, 295
Ammonium sulfide group, problems on, 293
Ampere, 114
Amperometric titration curve, 256
Amperometric titrations, 256
Analysis, gas (*see* Gas analysis)
  general, problems on, 311
  volumetric, divisions of, 145
Analytical chemistry, divisions of, 1
Anion group, problems on, 294
Antimony, problems on, 303
Antimony electrode, 236
Arsenic, problems on, 303
Arsenite-arsenate mixtures, titration of, 214
Atomic weights, calculation of, 96
  table of, 334
Average deviation, 3
Avogadro's law, 265

B

Back e.m.f., 119
Balance, sensitivity of, 83

Barium, problems on, 296
Beer's law, 259
Beryllium, problems on, 300
Bismuth, problems on, 300
Bismuthate method for manganese, 202
Boiling point, raising of, 131
Boron, problems on, 300
Boyle's law, 263
Brass, problems on, 301
Bromate process, 219
Bromine, problems on, 296
Bronze, problems on, 303
Buffered solutions, 46
  separations based on, 60

C

Cadmium, problems on, 301
Calcium, problems on, 296
Calibration of measuring instruments, 141
Calibration corrections, table of, 87
Calomel cell, 233
Carbon, problems on, 303
Carbon dioxide, problems on, 303
Carbonate mixtures, titration of, 183
Cement, problems on, 297
Cerate process, 205
Ceric sulfate process, 205
Cerium, problems on, 300
Charles's law, 263
Chemical balance, sensitivity of, 83
Chemical equations (*see* Equations)
Chemical factor, 93
Chemical formula, mathematical significance of, 27
Chlorate method for manganese, 202
Chlorine, problems on, 296
Chromium, problems on, 304
Cobalt, problems on, 307
Colorimetric analysis, methods of, 260
Colorimetric methods, 259

335